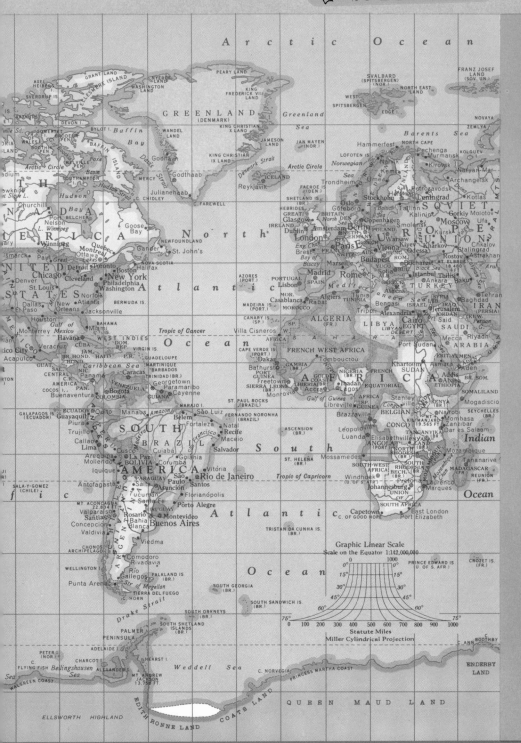

WORLD POLITICAL PATTERNS

Maps by WILLIS R. HEATH, *University of Washington*

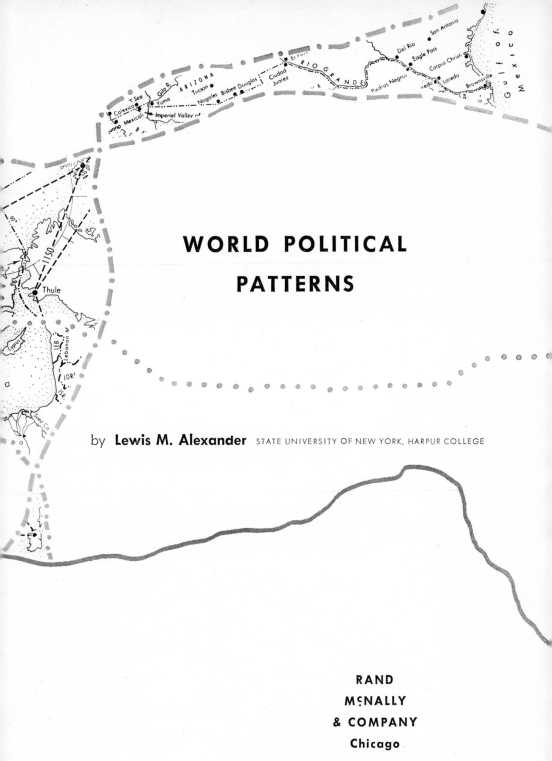

WORLD POLITICAL
PATTERNS

by **Lewis M. Alexander** STATE UNIVERSITY OF NEW YORK, HARPUR COLLEGE

RAND
McNALLY
& COMPANY
Chicago

JC
319
. A4

Rand McNally Geography Series

Edward B. Espenshade, Jr., CONSULTING EDITOR

THIS BOOK IS SET IN INTERTYPE BASKERVILLE
COMPOSITION, PRINTING, AND BINDING BY RAND McNALLY & COMPANY
BOOK DESIGN BY GORDON HARTSHORNE

To Jacqueline

CONTENTS

LIST OF MAPS

LIST OF TABLES

PREFACE

• This book is the product of several years of teaching regional political geography, and it represents an attempt to analyze the complex pattern of political units throughout the world. On the global or continental scale consideration is given to such forces as nationalism, imperialism, and economic competition, as they influence the political control of territory. On a more restricted scale national and local aspects of the political pattern are studied. At all levels of observation primary emphasis is placed on the nature of political control in a given region, on the effects of control on nonpolitical aspects of the landscape, and on the pressures which exist for change in the type and areal extent of this control. This approach has been selected with two objectives in mind. First, it offers an opportunity for the student to become acquainted with the existing pattern of political units on the earth's surface and with some of the territorial problems attendant upon this geographic distribution. Second, by means of generalizations and sample studies of particular situations it enables him to gain insight into the basic principles of the field of political geography, thereby equipping him to analyze in more detail the conditions of sovereignty throughout the world and to understand future problems of territorial control as they may arise.

The task of analyzing the world political pattern is complicated, first, by the great number and variety of political units and, second, by the constantly-changing nature of the pattern. In order to produce a concise book, suitable for teaching purposes, much material had to be sacrificed, but it is hoped that the lack of detail in many cases will be more than offset by the attempt at clearness of purpose and the adherence to a rigid definition of what the field of political geography encompasses. One of my principal reasons for writing this book was to answer those critics who claim that most college courses in political geography adhere to no clearly-defined area of study, and that as a result world political geography has become virtually indistinguishable from the general field of world regional geography. As for the changing nature of the world political pattern, I can only hope to outline some of the basic forces now in operation, and to suggest the types of changes in territorial control which are likely to occur in years to come.

The book is intended to serve two purposes: as an introduction to political geography and as a presentation of the geographic basis of international affairs. In any study of the political units of the world there are many elements of common interest to both fields, although the student of political geography approaches the material from the standpoint of the geography of political areas, while the student of international affairs is concerned primarily with the interactions which take place between states. It seems unnecessary to superimpose an artificial boundary through the area of study common to both disciplines. Since the purpose of this text is to consider the world distribution of political units, the relevancy of both political geography and international affairs is clearly acknowledged.

To my many colleagues who have helped in the preparation of this text I am deeply indebted. Among these special acknowledgement should be made to Dr. Joseph Van Riper, for his many comments and suggestions; to Mrs. Wilma Fairchild, editor of *The Geographical Review,* and Miss Alice Taylor, editor of *Focus,* for generously permitting the reproduction of considerable material from their respective publications; to Dr. G. Etzel Pearcy and Dr. Arthur R. Hall, who were particularly helpful in the early stages of preparation; and to Dr. Stephen B. Jones and Dr. George W. Hoffman, for their critical reading of the manuscript.

L. M. A.

1

THE NATURE AND DEVELOPMENT OF POLITICAL GEOGRAPHY

● The world political pattern—that is, the distribution of political regions
on a global scale—is a basic component of the field of political geography.
The differences in territorial control which exist from place to place are part
of the total environment of the earth's surface and are directly related to
such other factors as landforms, population distribution, and economic activities. Changes which take place in the sovereignty of a particular region may
be reflected in variations in other aspects of the region, such as the settlement pattern or the utilization of natural resources. The pattern of political
control of territory is likewise significant to the relationships which exist
within and between states. Thus political geography—the study of political
regions—is not only a part of the general field of regional geography; it also
has a definite bearing on national and international affairs.

A political region may be defined as a portion of the earth's surface,
throughout which a common type or types of political behavior takes place.
The behavior most frequently cited in the delimitation of political regions is
that of political control over territory by a particular government. In terms
of political control the land surface of the world is divided into many political regions, ranging in level of organization from national units down to
counties, townships, and villages.

An illustration of the basic characteristics of a political region may be
found in a typical county in the United States. The limits of the county are
defined on the map by political boundaries. Administration over the area
within these boundaries is carried on by the central government, located at
the county seat. The county is divided and subdivided into other political

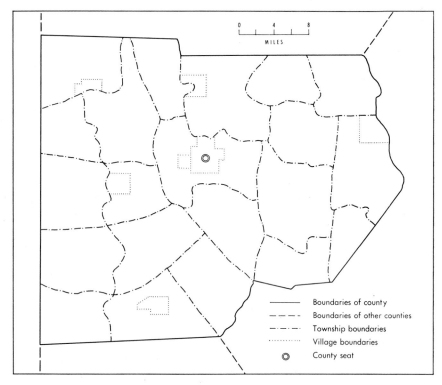

0   4   8
MILES

————— Boundaries of county
— — — Boundaries of other counties
—·—·— Township boundaries
·········· Village boundaries
◎ County seat

Figure 1. The County as a Political Region.

regions—townships, cities, and villages (Figure 1). Within the boundaries of the county are natural features, such as climate, landforms, soils, and water resources. Here also are population features, including size and distribution as well as composition according to race, religion, and language. There are the economic features of agriculture, industry, and commerce. Finally, there are political features, reflecting political behavior; these include the boundaries, the county seat, and administrative subdivisions.

Although the county boundaries cannot actually be seen unless there are special markers, they nevertheless represent sharp lines of political control separating one county from its neighbors. Various aspects of county life, such as voting districts, school laws, and police jurisdiction, change immediately as one crosses the boundary. On the other hand, nonpolitical features, such as climate, soils, race, or economic activities, may change very gradually as one passes from one county to another. Thus political boundaries may exist independently of physical or cultural boundaries, and the change represented is far more distinct than that of the other boundaries.

Within the county—as in all political regions—there exist five basic elements: (1) an expanse of territory delimited by boundaries; (2) a responsible government, which controls the area; (3) a resident population; (4) an economic structure; and (5) a circulatory system of transportation and communication networks. A discussion of these basic elements will be found in Chapter 2.

The political geographer not only describes and analyzes regions; he may also at times be called upon to apply his specialized training and experience to certain situations involving territorial control. In the case of a specific boundary dispute he may render an opinion as to the most equitable decision possible. He would also be able to contribute to studies involving such matters as the relocation of political boundaries within a state, a shift in the location of a capital, and the partitioning of a particular country or uniting it with a neighboring state. Even in situations where no disputes over territorial control are present, the political geographer has much to offer. For example, the pattern of political regions in western Europe has a decided influence on local commerce and industry. Canal construction in Belgium and the Netherlands, shipping restrictions on the Rhine, and the movement of iron ore in the Luxembourg-Lorraine area are economic activities which can be understood thoroughly only after the pattern of political control in the area has been carefully studied. On a different level, political geography can contribute much useful material to such problems as the changing status of world empires, the expansion of communist power, or the political and military significance of Gibraltar, Cyprus, Okinawa, and the Panama Canal in the Cold War.

The scale of study may vary from global analyses to "microgeographic" investigations. In the case of large areas, local differences are obscured and only broad generalizations can be drawn. On the other hand, local studies, such as those relating to specific boundary locations, may involve individual streets, houses, or plots of land. Generalizations on one scale of study may require modifications on another scale. For example, that the Andes Mountains form a good physical basis upon which to draw the boundary between Argentina and Chile is a valid generalization on a global scale; on a more local scale, however, various difficulties can be observed. The crest of the mountains and the drainage divide frequently do not coincide, the southern sector of the chain is low and the crests poorly marked, and there is the problem of control of passes through the mountains.

Political geography then is the study of the differences which exist between political regions. These differences result from variations in the nature and the functioning of political control within the respective regions. Boundaries, capitals, forces of unity and diversity, centers of political power, the effects of laws on resource utilization—these and similar phenomena represent the impress of political processes in the state, county, township, or other politically-organized area, an impress which is unique for each particular one. In order to describe and analyze political regions the political geographer must take into account the physical and cultural features within the geographic unit he is studying, since the impress of political processes varies under differing environmental conditions. He must also consider physical and cultural features existing outside the boundaries of his region, since no geographic area, whether it be defined politically, economically, climatically, or on any other basis, can exist independently of other areas. Like all branches of geography, the political approach is a comprehensive one. It includes those nonpolitical aspects within a region which affect the processes of political control, as well as those elements of interdependence which exist between this particular region and other regions of the earth's surface.

In this text emphasis will be placed on political control of territory on the local, national, and international levels. Basic forces in the current world political pattern will be dealt with, not only in their relationship to specific problems, but also as they illustrate fundamental principles of political geography itself. In this way attention may be given both to the regional treatment of political geography and to the systematic aspects of the field, which in turn may form the basis for more detailed investigation of political regions.

THE DEVELOPMENT OF POLITICAL GEOGRAPHY

The study of political geography began more than 2,000 years ago, although only since the late nineteenth century has the subject been recognized as a separate discipline. Prior to this time what is now known as political geography was included in the broad field of human geography, in which the relationship of the physical environment to all aspects of human behavior was studied. Some of the relationships which past scholars found to exist between physical features and political behavior have survived down to the present time to be incorporated as basic principles of political geography. Other relationships have been found to be scientifically false and have been discarded. Aristotle, for example, noted that in regions of diverse topography a number of political areas—instead of one political area— tended to develop. The validity of this idea has been borne out by history. On the other hand, the direct influence which climate was once thought to have on the abilities of certain groups to govern others is no longer considered to be a true relationship.

A brief survey of the historical development of political geography will be presented here in order to provide a basis for considering recent concepts in the field. For purposes of classification this survey will be divided into three phases: (1) the study of environmental relationships; (2) the study of national power; and (3) the study of political regions. Two points should be noted with respect to these politico-geographic concepts. The first is that they have kept pace with intellectual and technical developments. Thus Aristotle thought in terms of the city-state in a protected lowland, Ritter of an expanding Germanic culture, and Mackinder of sea power versus land power on a global scale. Seversky's recent theory of air supremacy is a response to the development of a new medium for transportation and for warfare.

A second point is that the three-way division presented here of the history of political geography does not imply that as new approaches to the subject were developed the old ones were quickly abandoned. The environmental relationships which the Greek and Roman scholars propounded still found acceptance among many political geographers during the first few decades of the twentieth century. Likewise, variations of the "National Power" approach of the late nineteenth and early twentieth centuries are still evident in the writings of political geographers and persons in allied fields today. Attempts to catalogue the various theories in any branch of knowledge involve the risk of oversimplification, both as to content and to time. The following survey is offered merely as a device for better understanding the over-all field of political geography.

The Study of Environmental Relationships

Elemental relationships between physical features and human behavior were clearly recognized by certain of the ancient scholars. Aristotle (384–322 B.C.) wrote in his *Politics* (Book VII, Chap. 7):

> The peoples of cold countries generally, and particularly those of Europe, are full of spirit, but deficient in skill and intelligence; and this is why they continue to remain comparatively free, but attain no political development and show no capacity for governing others. The peoples of Asia are endowed with skill and intelligence but are deficient in spirit: and this is why they continue to be peoples of subjects and slaves. The Greek stock, intermediate in geographical position, unites the qualities of both sets of peoples. It possesses both spirit and intelligence: the one quality makes it continue free; the other enables it to attain the highest political development, and to show a capacity for governing every other people—if only it could achieve political unity.[1]

Living in the city-state of Athens, Aristotle felt that a nation should be well protected by hills against possible attack and situated close to a good harbor in order to make use of overseas commerce. Through the wise utilization of physical resources such a nation could become powerful and eventually expand its territory.

---

[1] Ernest Barker (trans.), *The Politics of Aristotle* (Oxford: Clarendon Press, 1946), p. 296.

Other writers of ancient times also considered these relationships. Strabo, a Greek scholar (63 B.C.–A.D. 24) surveying the Roman Empire, concluded in his *Geography* that a large political unit required a strong central government with one ruling head in order to function properly. He also reasoned that because of its excellent location, climate, and resources Italy was the logical place for this state to be situated.

During the Dark Ages philosophical efforts were concentrated largely on religious questions and little was accomplished in the realm of geographic thought. Beginning in the sixteenth century, however, the study of relationships between physical and political phenomena was again pursued. Scholars like Bodin (1530–96) and Montesquieu (1689–1755) elaborated on such matters as the influence of climate on human aggressiveness and organizational ability or on the laws of various cultural groups. In time the study of environmental determinism gradually expanded into an elaborate science of relationships in which every aspect of man's political behavior was interpreted in terms of his physical surroundings.

It was during the nineteenth century that many of the environmentalist concepts of earlier scholars were brought together and systematically developed. In political geography much of the progress made at this time was due to the efforts of two Germans—Karl Ritter and Friedrich Ratzel. Ritter (1779–1859) was Professor of Geography at the University of Berlin. He was not only interested in the effects of environment on human development and behavior as his predecessors had been, but he also went on to study the influence of environment on cultures and civilizations as well. Borrowing from Darwin's laws of evolution, Ritter worked out an "organic" theory of cultures, in which he postulated that cultures, like plants and animals, are born, grow, mature, and eventually die. Darwin had written on the biological laws of natural selection, survival of the fittest, and the need a healthy species has for space in which to develop. In the writings of Ritter these laws were tailored to fit his political theories. Elements of strength within a culture were of major importance to its continued existence in a competitive world. He felt that in order to survive a culture or civilization must fight for space, crushing out weaker elements which compete with it.

The Study of National Power

The second major approach to political geography—that of the geographic basis of national and international power—was developed largely by Ratzel (1844–1904), who became Professor of Geography at the University of Leipzig about twenty years after Ritter's death. Aristotle, Strabo, and other scholars had written of broad general relationships existing between environment and power, but it was for Ratzel and those who followed him to evolve a systematic classification of environmental influences on the power of nations.

National Determinism.   In his writings on political geography Ratzel was particularly interested in the growth of states. According to him the state was an organic entity in itself, involved in an endless struggle for space or "living room" (*Lebensraum*). He reasoned that states, as well as living beings, were subject to the laws of natural selection, with only the strong surviving.

In 1897 Ratzel published *Politische Geographie,* the first book really to embody the principles of political geography as they had been developed up to that time. Throughout the book appears the theme that the land area of a state is the best indication of its political power and that citizens should become conscious of their country's "spatial requirements." Ratzel looked upon international boundaries as only temporary markers, indicating a particular condition in the spatial contest between states. He felt that eventually small political regions would be absorbed by larger units until there emerged only a few complex and powerful states. These states in time would themselves become involved in a titanic struggle for world domination. Such was the law of progress! During the 1930's the organic concept of states was used by Nazi leaders as an excuse for naked aggression. Germany, they claimed, was merely expanding according to "natural laws."

Actually Ratzel's spatial concepts are an oversimplification of historical processes. In his efforts to evolve a scientific set of laws governing national behavior he was faced with a seemingly impossible task, for the state is a complex phenomenon that seldom follows predetermined paths. The analogy between it and a living organism is an imperfect one. The laws of biology might well be applied to all manner of inanimate objects; the fact that an apparent correlation exists between these laws and the behavior pattern of the object does not prove that the object itself has the capacity to live.

A somewhat modified concept of the state as an organic being was offered by the Swedish writer, Rudolf Kjellén (1864–1922). Kjellén advanced a step beyond Ratzel's thinking in that he envisioned the state not only as a living organism, but also as a conscious being equipped with moral-intellectual capacities. He agreed with Ratzel that the final objective of a state's development was the attainment of power; however, Kjellén held that in its quest for power the state need not follow the simple organic laws of territorial expansion. Instead it might employ modern cultural advances and techniques in the achievement of its desired goals. The final objective of a state's power development was "to acquire good natural frontiers externally, and harmonious unity internally."[2] Kjellén was the

---

[2] Andrew Gyorgy, *Geopolitics: the New German Science* (Berkeley and Los Angeles: University of California Press, 1944), p. 166.

first writer to use the term "geopolitics," which he defined as the natural environment of the state. Later the Germans expanded geopolitics to denote a basic knowledge of the over-all physical, ethnic, and economic foundations of the state. During Hitler's regime the term came to include also a number of nongeographic concepts, such as the Nazi theories of racial supremacy. Because of its perversion in the 1930's, the word "geopolitics" has lost much of its former significance. In its present usage it generally refers to the study of national power, with particular emphasis on those policies best suited to a country's self-interest.

The French Possibilists. In contrast with the determinist doctrines of Ratzel, Kjellén, and their contemporaries were the possibilist theories of leading French geographers of the late nineteenth and early twentieth centuries, including Jean Brunhes, Jacques Ancel, Albert Demangeon, and Paul Vidal de la Blache. These writers held that the state is not an organic power-political entity but rather a cultural and national unit whose activities are directed by the collective consciousness of its citizens. The physical environment, rather than exerting a determining influence on human activities, as Ratzel and Kjellén had claimed, actually presented the citizens with a number of possible choices for development, leaving them free to select which course the state should pursue. The writers rejected the principle of national existence as a fight for space, and pointed out that throughout history many small states had survived for long periods of time and contributed significantly to human culture. This humanist philosophy laid great stress on moral and spiritual forces, such as liberty and patriotism, but it failed to offer such concise explanations of national behavior as did the theories of the determinists, with their ready answers to the complex relationships of physical, cultural, and political forces.

Global Relationships. The emphasis in political geography on national power led certain writers to broaden their scope of interests to include political patterns on a global scale. The growth of colonial empires during the nineteenth century focused attention on Africa and Asia and on the sea lanes which connected these continents with Europe and North America. In 1900 Ratzel published a book in which he conceived of the sea as the great unifying element in human culture. He wrote at length on the eventual struggle for world domination between continental and maritime peoples, and concluded that ultimate victory would go to the land-based power because of its superior resources. The Pacific was characterized as the "ocean of the future"; the nations bordering it would in time become world powers.

The role of the sea in human destiny was also treated by an American admiral, Alfred Thayer Mahan (1840–1914). Mahan emphasized the importance of maritime development in a state's history, and asserted that the most essential geographic factor of national power was not the number of square miles of land in a country but the length of its coast line and the character of the harbors. He was greatly impressed by the overseas expansion of Great Britain; the United States, he felt, should pay close attention to its own sea frontiers. Mahan advocated possession of the Hawaiian Islands, establishment of control in the Caribbean, and construction of a canal across Central America to link the Atlantic and Pacific oceans. Mahan's best-known work was *The Influence of Sea Power upon History, 1660–1783*. Throughout this and other writings runs the theme that future world power rests on control of the seas. His books were read and appreciated by Theodore Roosevelt, himself an advocate of naval supremacy. During Roosevelt's administration many of Mahan's ideas were adopted as basic tenets of American foreign policy.

One of the outstanding concepts of global power forces was the Heartland theory of the British scholar, Sir Halford Mackinder (1861–1947). Like Ratzel, Mackinder felt that in the eventual struggle for world domination victory would go to the continental rather than the maritime power. Borrowing from both geography and history, he set out to prove by a series of logical steps the truth of his contention.

Mackinder noted that three-fourths of the earth's surface is water while of the remaining land quarter two-thirds is occupied by the continents of Eurasia and Africa. He further noticed that seven-eighths of the world's population dwells on the Eurasian-African land mass while the remaining one-eighth lives in the offshore islands and the other continents. He reasoned that if one power could gain control of the Eurasian-African land mass or, as he termed it, the "World-Island," it would be in a position to conquer the world, since it would dominate two-thirds of the earth's land area and seven-eighths of its population. No maritime power could challenge it, for the land state would seize the naval bases around its margins (such as Gibraltar, Aden, Bombay, Singapore). With superior resources and population the land power could eventually build up overwhelming naval strength to invade and subdue any offshore islands and foreign continents.

Control over the Eurasian-African land mass could be achieved only by a power occupying the protected interior lowlands of Eurasia, stretching from the Baltic-Black Sea isthmus 2,500 miles eastward to the Yenisey, and from the Arctic Ocean south to the mountain barriers which extend from Turkey to Mongolia. Here lies an enormous plains area of 4¼ million square miles with great economic potentialities in terms of natural resources. The state occupying this interior lowland (or, as Mackinder termed it, the "Heartland") would be virtually invulnerable to attack, except from the west, and in turn would be able to utilize its resources for the development of a strong agricultural-industrial power. With this development would come also the opportunity to strike out from the central

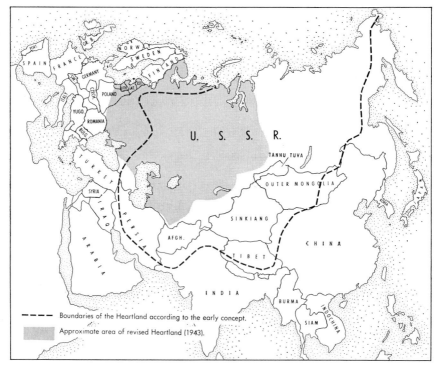

Figure 2. Mackinder's Heartland. (After Mackinder, *Democratic Ideals and Reality.* Used by permission of Henry Holt & Co., copyright 1919, 1942.)

lowland and conquer Europe, the Middle East, India, and the Orient, thereby gradually gaining control of the entire land mass. With this accomplished, subjugation of Australia and the Western Hemisphere would in time also be possible (Figure 2).

The invulnerability to attack of Mackinder's Heartland area is largely the result of its physical features. Its rivers drain to the Arctic or to inland bodies of water. Only through the Baltic and Black seas could hostile naval forces strike at the Heartland. The interior lowland is likewise protected from overland attack as a result of natural barriers. To the northeast is Lenaland, a rugged mountainous area of eastern Siberia, containing 3¾ million square miles of territory. To the east are the Altai and Tien Shan mountains, across which lie the arid wastes of Mongolia and Sinkiang. To the south are the Hindu Kush Mountains and the plateaus of Afghanistan and Iran, while between the Caspian and the Black seas lie the Caucasus Mountains and, beyond them, the plateau of Armenia. Even on the southwest the Carpathian Mountains form a natural defense barrier. On the northwest are the Baltic Sea and the wastes of Lapland, while to the north is the Arctic Ocean. Only on the west, between the Carpathian Mountains and the Baltic Sea, is there a direct lowland route into the Heartland.

In his writings Mackinder divided Europe into East and West, the dividing line between them running from the Adriatic to the Baltic Sea, or roughly from Trieste to Stettin. East Europe he characterized as an historic area of struggle between Teutonic and Slavic peoples, in which no balance of power has ever been successfully established. He pointed out, however, that eventually control of East Europe might one day pass to either the Teutonic peoples of Germany or the Slavs of Russia as a result of a decisive conflict between them, from which one group would emerge victorious.

Since the gateway to the Heartland lies in East Europe, and since the Heartland is a natural fortress capable of development and expansion, Mackinder formulated his famous hypothesis:

> Who rules East Europe commands the Heartland:
> Who rules the Heartland commands the World-Island:
> Who rules the World-Island commands the World.[3]

The logic of Mackinder's analysis was practically unnoticed by his contemporaries for many years. One of the few persons who appreciated his reasoning was Karl Haushofer (1869–1946), a German geographer and soldier of the early twentieth century. Haushofer was sent by the German General Staff to Japan as a military observer in 1908, when he was a young army officer. From this visit he acquired a firsthand knowledge of the Far East and the Pacific Ocean. He taught geography at Munich prior to World War I, and during the war he rose to the rank of major general in the German army. Following the armistice he returned to Munich to teach political geography and military science. In 1924 he helped to found the *Zeitschrift für Geopolitik,* a magazine devoted to the furthering of geopolitics.

Haushofer borrowed widely from other writers in forming his concepts. He agreed with Ratzel that the Pacific was a dominant power area and he accepted the doctrine of the organic state and its need for space. Unlike Ratzel, however, he was an outspoken nationalist and continually applied his concepts to the needs of his own country. Haushofer was intrigued with the potentialities of the Heartland and looked forward to the day when Germany would be in control of this vital area. He never advocated war with Russia, but rather concentrated on a "conquest by subversion," the first step of which was a German-Russian alliance. This alliance would be followed by a gradual German encroachment on Russia's military and economic systems. Haushofer was delighted with the signing of the Russo-German nonaggression pact in August, 1939; two years later,

---

[3] Sir Halford J. Mackinder, *Democratic Ideals and Reality: A Study in the Politics of Reconstruction* (New York: Henry Holt and Company, 1942), p. 150.

when Germany invaded the U.S.S.R., he had grave doubts about the outcome of the struggle.

To Haushofer and his contemporaries of the Munich Institute for Geopolitics, political geography was something to be twisted and perverted into a tool for nationalist dogma. It is difficult to separate the truth from the fiction in Haushofer's works and in the magazine which he edited. As a result, much of the material appearing in these publications has been discredited as far as scientific thought is concerned.

In the United States the question of global politics has received attention from a number of writers within recent years. One of the foremost analysts was Nicholas J. Spykman (1893–1943), onetime Professor of International Relations at Yale. Spykman's interest lay in the relationship between geography and foreign policy, and he published several works on the subject. "Geography is the most fundamental factor in the foreign policy of states because it is the most permanent," he once wrote. "Ministers come and ministers go, even dictators die, but mountain ranges stand unperturbed."[4]

His most outstanding work from a geopolitical point of view was *The Geography of the Peace,* published in 1944 shortly after his death. Several basic ideas concerning geopolitical thought were outlined in this book. The first was that national power is the final determinant of security for a state. The only way to achieve lasting peace is through a collective security system, such as an armed League of Nations or by means of an international balance-of-power arrangement. His second idea was in line with Mackinder's thesis, namely, that control of the World-Island could enable a nation to achieve eventual world domination. Spykman approached the problem from the American point of view, and remarked that the Western Hemisphere is "surrounded" by the Eastern Hemisphere, including the Eurasian land mass and the continents of Africa and Australia. The area of the Eastern Hemisphere is two and a half times that of the Western, and its population is ten times as great. In terms of 1937 output, the Old World produced over two-thirds of the earth's coal and iron ore. Spykman's conclusion was that the Western Hemisphere could scarcely stand up against the Eastern in a prolonged global struggle; therefore, one of the basic tenets of American foreign policy should be to prevent the consolidation of Eurasia under one power.

In his book Spykman considered Mackinder's analysis of global politics and concluded there were several fallacies in the Englishman's reasoning. The most important of these to Spykman's mind was Mackinder's overemphasis of the Heartland's potentialities. The American writer pointed out that much of the area between Poland and the Yenisey River is waste-

---

[4] Nicholas J. Spykman, *America's Strategy in World Politics: The United States and the Balance of Power* (New York: Harcourt, Brace & Company, 1942), p. 41.

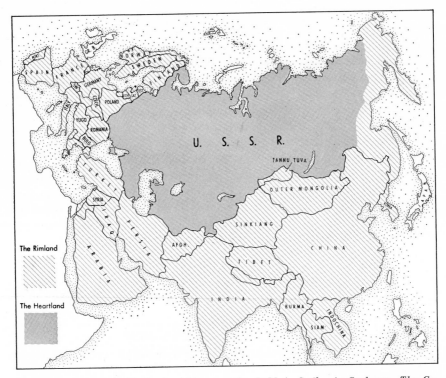

Figure 3. Spykman's Rimland. (After map by J. McA. Smiley in Spykman, *The Geography of the Peace*, copyright 1944 by Harcourt, Brace & Co. Used by permission.)

land, and that the real power potential of Eurasia lies not in the Heartland itself but in the belt of nations surrounding the Heartland. This belt Spykman called the "Rimland" (Figure 3). Within it are the majority of the world's population and much of its resources. History, he maintained, has never been a clear-cut struggle between land power and sea power, but rather a series of contests in which the Rimland has served as a buffer zone between the Heartland and the island empires of Britain and Japan. Spykman concluded that the geopolitical slogan of world power should read, "Who controls the Rimland rules Eurasia; who rules Eurasia controls the destinies of the world."[5]

Despite the apparent logic of the global predictions of Mahan, Mackinder, and Spykman, considerable criticism has been leveled against them on the grounds that they are oversimplifications of history. Each great political analysis was written for a particular era; regardless of how valid the conclusions may have been at the time they were first announced they could

---

[5] Nicholas J. Spykman, *The Geography of the Peace* (New York: Harcourt, Brace & Company, 1944), p. 43.

not apply over an indefinite period of time. Writing in the magazine *Foreign Affairs* in 1950, the British geographer W. Gordon East asserted that Mackinder's theory "contains generalizations and assumptions which scarcely withstand close analysis. In a world of rapid technological progress the geography of territory, since it is ever-changing, should be continually revalued."[6] Professor East was aware of similarities between Mackinder's Heartland idea and the present world-power alignment, yet he maintained, "It is surely both unwise and dangerous to accept as a predetermined end the prediction that world hegemony must, on certain assumptions, inevitably pass to the rulers of one specified portion of the earth."[7]

Perhaps the true value of these global studies lies in their brilliant analyses of long-term historical trends rather than in the ultimate validity of their forecasts. Scholars indeed may question the accuracy of these world-power formulae; but they can scarcely ignore the geopolitical developments which led men like Mahan and Mackinder and Spykman to evolve their now-famous doctrines.

In line with post-World War II technical developments new global theories have been evolved which hold that air is now the medium in which ultimate power resides. One of the most noted proponents of this type of theory is Major Alexander de Seversky, whose book *Air Power: Key to Survival*[8] has been widely read and discussed. In Seversky's reasoning global power reaches its ultimate form. He describes the bipolarization of power in North America and in Eurasia, and concludes that a great industrial nation should organize its military efforts toward the establishment of worldwide air supremacy. Seversky holds no brief for small wars, as in Korea and Indochina, since they sap the strength of the United States without seriously affecting the basic strength of the Soviet Union. He feels that the great deterrent to communist aggression should be the threat of massive air retaliation on so large a scale as to amount to virtual annihilation of the enemy. Under such conditions the United States has little need for military bases and alliances in the Eastern Hemisphere; rather it should confine itself to the defense of the Americas.

The Study of Political Regions

During the early years of the twentieth century not all the work done in the field of political geography was concerned with the differential power aspects of the world. A trend was developing among geographers toward more detailed studies of specific politico-geographic problems. By 1920, for example, several excellent books had appeared in Britain on the subject of international frontiers. During the deliberations of Allied statesmen at the

---

[6] W. Gordon East, "How Strong is the Heartland?" *Foreign Affairs*, XXIX, No. 1 (October, 1950), 80.
[7] *Ibid.*, p. 80.
[8] Alexander de Seversky, *Air Power: Key to Survival* (New York: Simon and Schuster, 1950).

Peace Conference following World War I, political geographers were able to be of particular service. When the time came to redraw the political map of Europe, President Woodrow Wilson sought the advice of geographic specialists, among them Dr. Isaiah Bowman, then Director of the American Geographical Society. Several of the experts' recommendations were used by the American delegation as bases for discussions with representatives of other Allied nations, thereby demonstrating a practical application of the political geographer's training and experience to international affairs.

In 1921 Dr. Bowman published *The New World,* in which he discussed most of the politico-geographic problem areas then in existence throughout the world. Although much of its factual material is no longer pertinent, the book is recognized as having been one of the most important works to appear in the field of political geography. For the first time a geographer had compiled a volume in which the major problem areas of the time were assembled and analyzed, not only as individual studies but also in their relationship to the over-all political pattern of the world. In this way emphasis was placed on the importance of regional studies within the framework of global political geography.

Since the publication of *The New World,* increased American participation in world affairs, together with major developments in the theory of political geography, have resulted in the appearance of a great many books and articles in the field. These writings may be divided roughly into two categories, systematic and regional. The systematic literature has dealt with the history and various broad concepts of political geography. Representative works in this group are Hartshorne, "Recent Developments in Political Geography"; Bowman, "Geography *vs.* Geopolitics"; and Jones, "A Unified Field Theory of Political Geography." (See bibliography for complete listings.) The regional literature has been concerned with specific areas or types of problems, such as boundaries or plebiscites. Among the writings of this type are Broek, "The Problem of Natural Frontiers"; Saucerman, *International Transfers of Territory in Europe;* and Wambaugh, *Plebiscites Since the World War.* Some works, such as Whittlesey, *The Earth and the State,* although regional in outline, succeed also in developing many of the important politico-geographic concepts.

The relationships which exist between the physical and cultural environment of an area on the one hand and the political aspects of the area on the other is an important component of the field of political geography. Rejecting environmental determinism and various power formulae as being scientifically unsound does not solve the basic problem of defining at least the general outlines of their relationships. Thus three fundamental aspects of this state-area association may be described as follows:

  1. The physical environment offers the possibility of choice to peo-

ples and to states. It does not determine the courses they will follow, but it places limits on the alternatives from which they may select. The ultimate selection will depend on the goals and abilities of the peoples involved.

2. The world has become a community of interdependent phenomena: any major event, whether it be political, economic, or of some other nature, will have reverberations well beyond the limits of the state or states in which it occurs. Likewise, all parts of the world have significance in terms of political, military, and economic affairs. Changing conditions may result in a rapid increase in the relative importance of a particular area. There is, however, no one pivotal center of world power, but rather a number of areas of critical importance.

3. Because of the great complexity of forces affecting the world political pattern it is impossible to evolve a set law or series of laws which can adequately account for the over-all developmental process of political regions. No two areas of the world are alike, and what holds true for one region may not be true for another. Political geographers can establish certain generalized criteria for describing and analyzing political regions and for comparing one region with another, but they have been unable to establish any simplified formulae for explaining and predicting the intricate ramifications of governmental control of territory throughout the world.

BIBLIOGRAPHY

Bowman, Isaiah. *The New World.* Yonkers-on-Hudson: The World Book Company, 1921.

A basic text on political regions throughout the world.

———. "Geography *vs.* Geopolitics," *The Geographical Review,* XXXII, No. 4 (October, 1942), 646–58.

A discussion of the differences between these two fields.

Broek, Jan O. M. "The Problem of Natural Frontiers," in *Frontiers of the Future.* Berkeley and Los Angeles: University of California Press, 1940, pp. 3–20.

A description, with illustrations, of the concept of "natural" frontiers.

Dorpalen, Andreas. *The World of General Haushofer: Geopolitics in Action.* New York: Farrar & Rinehart, Inc., 1942.

A well-documented history of German geopolitics between the two world wars.

Hartshorne, Richard. "Recent Developments in Political Geography,"

American Political Science Review, XXIX, No. 4 (Oct.-Dec., 1935), 758–804, 943–66.

A detailed discussion of various concepts of political geography, including a thorough bibliography.

————. "Political Geography," in *American Geography: Inventory and Prospect,* P. E. JAMES and C. F. JONES (eds.). Syracuse: Syracuse University Press, 1954, pp. 167–226.

The development and the conflicting concepts of political geography.

JONES, STEPHEN B. "A Unified Field Theory of Political Geography," *Annals of the Association of American Geographers,* XLIV, No. 2 (June, 1954), 111–24.

A proposed outline which can be applied to various studies of political phenomena.

KISH, GEORGE. "Political Geography into Geopolitics: Recent Trends in Germany," *The Geographical Review,* XXXII, No. 4 (October, 1942), 632–45.

A discussion of pre-World War II trends in geopolitics in Germany.

MACKINDER, SIR HALFORD J. "The Round World and the Winning of the Peace," *Foreign Affairs,* XXI, No. 4 (July, 1943), 595–606.

A restatement of Mackinder's theory of world power in the light of World War II developments.

RATZEL, FRIEDRICH. *Politische Geographie.* Munich: R. Oldenbourg Verlag, 1897.

A book of historical interest because of the early concepts of the field which it contains.

RITTER, KARL. *Comparative Geography.* Philadelphia: J. B. Lippincott & Co., 1864.

A treatment of the early organic theory of cultures.

SAUCERMAN, SOPHIE. *International Transfers of Territory in Europe.* Washington: U. S. Government Printing Office, 1937.

An extremely detailed summary of territorial transfers in Europe following World War I.

SPYKMAN, NICHOLAS J. *The Geography of the Peace.* New York: Harcourt, Brace & Company, 1944.

Spykman's major concepts of national power.

STRAUSZ-HUPÉ, ROBERT. *Geopolitics: The Struggle for Space and Power.* New York: G. P. Putnam's Sons, 1942.

A general treatment of the principles of geopolitics.

WAMBAUGH, SARAH. *Plebiscites Since the World War, with a Collection of Official Documents.* Washington: Carnegie Endowment for International Peace, 1933.

The basic work on this subject.

WEIGERT, HANS W. *Generals and Geographers: The Twilight of Geopolitics.* New York: Oxford University Press, 1942.

Like the writings of Dorpalen and Strausz-Hupé, this is a contemporary book on the German geopolitics.

WHITTLESEY, DERWENT. *The Earth and the State: A Study of Political Geography.* New York: Henry Holt and Company, 1944.

A world regional text which contains a great many fundamental concepts of political geography.

2

THE STATE AS A POLITICO-GEOGRAPHIC UNIT

● The state[1] is a fundamental component of the political pattern. As such it warrants detailed consideration in a political geography text. In Chapter 1 the five essential elements of political regions were noted: (1) an expanse of territory delimited by boundaries; (2) a responsible government, which controls the area; (3) a resident population; (4) an economic structure; and (5) a circulatory system of transportation and communication networks. Naturally there are many cases of overlap among these five categories: the distribution of population, for example, may be influenced by natural features such as climate and soils, by governmental policies, and by the state's economic structure, including the development of transportation systems. In this chapter, however, the five categories will be considered as separate entities, in order to provide a framework for analyzing the various political regions of the world.

AN EXPANSE OF TERRITORY DELIMITED BY BOUNDARIES

The entire land surface of the globe—with the exception of Antarctica —is divided into political regions. Some are dependent, some independent, yet each has a central governmental structure and each is separated from its neighbors by political boundaries. This first category actually consists

---

[1] The term *state* is used here in refering to a national political region which has *de jure* (legal) independence. A *country* is any political unit on the national level (in contrast to the provincial and local levels), regardless of whether the unit is dependent or independent. A *nation* is a state in which independence is *de facto* (actual) as well as *de jure,* and in which there is a general sense of national cohesion among all or most of the inhabitants.

of two concepts—territory and boundaries. The word *territory* implies not only areal extent but also the physical attributes which accrue to a region. The *boundaries* represent the outer limits of the territory, within which the central government exercises political control. In the discussion which follows this first element of a state will be described in terms of territory, then of boundaries.

Physical Attributes of Territory

The physical attributes of territory include location, size, shape, climate, surface configuration, soils, natural vegetation, water features, and mineral resources. These various elements, taken singly and in combination with one another, may be of great significance to political control within and between states. In certain situations some factors are obviously of greater importance than others. Thus, for example, Germany's coal deposits have aided the nation's industrial development and its military power potential. Panama's location at the isthmus connecting North and South America, Russia's tremendous size, and Greenland's inhospitable climate are other cases in which physical attributes have been of particular significance to a state's politico-geographic structure.

(1) **Location** is probably the most important single aspect of a state's physical make-up. It may be considered under three headings, namely, with respect to latitude, to land and water bodies, and to neighboring states.

In terms of latitude it is significant that no state lying wholly or primarily within the tropical or polar regions has succeeded as yet in modern times in developing into a strong, cohesive nation. There are various reasons for this fact. Climate is important, although in many areas its limiting influence is due more to human preference than to inherent qualities of "good" or "bad" in the climate itself (see page 24). Another reason is the general location of coal resources between 40 and 60 degrees of latitude, thereby providing the base for industrialization of states within this zone. However, if atomic power can be successfully harnessed for industry, the coal-poor tropical lands of the world will have greater opportunity for national development than has been the case in the past.

Location with respect to water bodies is important because of the tempering effect they have on climate and of the opportunities the seas and oceans offer for commercial activities and for political and economic expansion. Britain's maritime location illustrates these advantages. Access to the sea is a prize many states have sought at various times (Figure 4). Some, such as the United States and France, have access to several seas; others like Iraq and Belgium, have only limited coast lines; still others (Bolivia, Austria) have been completely cut off from the sea.

Proximity to land bodies, on the other hand, may entail climatic

Figure 4. Poland's Corridor to the Baltic Sea, 1920–39.

extremes, it may provide opportunities for trade and territorial expansion on the mainlands, and it may also be a source of danger because of potential invasion and occupation by states located on the mainland. Japan may be taken to illustrate all three points. Cold air masses in winter move eastward from Asia to Japan; nearness to the mainland provided opportunity for Japanese territorial expansion there in the first four decades of the twentieth century; finally, proximity to the Asian land mass since World War II has carried with it the danger of attack on Japan from a continental power.

Location with respect to neighboring states (vicinal location) is probably the most important of the three locational aspects. The boundaries which separate a state from its neighbors and the territorial disputes arising therefrom are of profound importance to the state's political development; the problems relating to invasion, defense, and economic dominance take on added significance. Thus, for example, Poland's territorial problems with its neighbors have been a major factor in that state's history as a national unit. Belgium—although its boundaries have remained fairly stable since 1839—has twice been the victim of German military aggression directed toward France. The history of territorial control in Korea has been strongly influenced by the peninsula's location with respect to Japan, China, and Russia.

(2) **Size** is important to a state in terms of both defense and political control. The more area a state has in which to fall back before invading forces, the better are its chances for survival. The position of the Soviet Union during World War II is an example of trading "space for time" in the face of the enemy. Large size also permits dispersion of population and industries as targets for bombing; on the other hand, it also means longer borders to defend against ground and air attack. With respect to internal control large size may be a disadvantage, for communications between the

capital and faraway regions may be difficult to maintain, leading to the possible development of separatist movements in peripheral areas. For example, distance has been an important factor in the weakening of China's control over Sinkiang and Outer Mongolia.

(3) Shape is also important for defense and internal control. A narrow country, no matter how great the area, is more difficult to defend than one which is compact. For internal political cohesion, a circular shape, with the capital in the center, would be advantageous, since distances from the capital to outlying areas are kept to a minimum.

Extremes of shape are found in the *enclave*, the *bridgehead*, the *glacis*, and the *projection* (Figures 5, 6, 7, 8). An *enclave* is a portion of one country's territory that is completely surrounded by another country. In most situations the terms *enclave* and *exclave* are used interchangeably.

Figure 5. Belgian Enclave in the Netherlands.

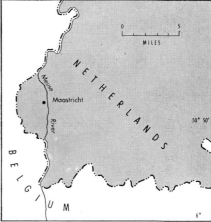

Figure 6. Dutch Bridgehead in Belgian Territory.

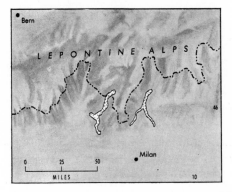

Figure 7. *Swiss Glacis Extending South Into Italy.*

Figure 8. Projection of Afghanistan Between U.S.S.R. and Pakistan.

West Berlin, for example, is an *enclave* within East Germany and an *exclave* of West Germany. The Portuguese territory of Goa is a coastal enclave within India, since it is surrounded on three sides by India and on the fourth by water. East Pakistan, also surrounded on its land borders by India, is too large to be considered an enclave; a better term for it might be *outlier*. An examination of the world political map will reveal several other examples of enclaves. Most are relics of historical political patterns, or of military compromises—such as the Hebrew University enclave in the Jordanian sector of Jerusalem.

A *bridgehead* is an extension of territorial control by one state across a river. Here again there are few examples left in the world. The Dutch bridgehead at Maastricht is shown in Figure 6. At Edirne (Adrianople) is a Turkish bridgehead across the Maritsa River into Greece.

A *glacis* is an extension of a country across a mountain divide. Switzerland has two: one across the Jura Mountains at Porrentruy into France and one across the Alps into Italy. The latter is interesting in that within this area Italian-speaking citizens of Switzerland live in the Po lowlands and carry on most of their economic activities with Italy. Another glacis —that of Austria in South Tyrol—was annexed by Italy after World War I.

A *projection* is a long narrow extension of territory separating two countries from one another (or one country from the sea). One of the most unique is "Caprivi's Finger" in southern Africa, a thin extension of Southwest Africa to the Zambezi River, thus separating Angola from Bechuanaland. Other projections are in Afghanistan between Russia and Pakistan, in Greece between Bulgaria and the Aegean Sea, and in the French Cameroons extending north to Lake Chad.

All of these extremes of shape represent somewhat anomalous situations, remnants for the most part of historical compromises of territorial control. The difficulties created by the existence of most of these extremes may be of relatively minor importance in international affairs, but these irregularities of shape provide opportunities for important microgeographic studies of the various complexities of the functioning of political regions.

(4) Climate, as it affects political development, may be difficult to assess, for it is often impossible to isolate the climatic influence from that of other physical and cultural forms. During past centuries there has been a spread of civilization from warmer to cooler climates, with a resultant strengthening of cultures in the cooler areas. Today the great world powers are located in the mid-latitudes where there are seasonal variations of temperature.

Much has been written about a climatic "optimum" in the mid-latitudes, but many of the conclusions stressed are debatable. The seasonal cold and the forests of the higher latitudes undoubtedly were effective obstacles to the northward spread of early civilizations from their subtropical locations. Toynbee writes that "the challenge of the northern seasonal cold . . . evoked a new creative response in such as did not succumb to it."[2] Only with the development of new tools and techniques were the people of early civilizations able to overcome the challenge of the cold and the forests. Certainly Western civilization, as we know it today, had its roots in the Roman-Hellenic world, but was nourished and developed first in the forest clearings of northwestern Europe and later in the pioneer lands of the New World. The development of a particular civilization is associated with the economic, military, and political strength of its political units, especially in relation to the units of other civilizations.

When Western civilization spread outwards from its center in northwestern and north central Europe, it became established for the most part in those places of the world that had humid, mid-latitude climates, similar to the climates left behind in Europe. Neither the humid tropics, the desert oases, the steppe grasslands, nor the northern lands held much attraction for settlement by the European peoples; to these areas they came primarily for exploitation rather than for permanent settlement. Even in the coloni-

[2] Arnold J. Toynbee, *A Study of History,* abridgement by D. C. Somervell (New York and London: Oxford University Press, 1947), p. 70.

zation of humid mid-latitude climates the initial goals of the Europeans were essentially exploitative, but this period lasted a relatively short time. In such areas as Canada, Australia, the United States, and New Zealand exploitation eventually gave way to permanent settlement.

The present location of Western industrial societies throughout the world is thus more the result of human preference than of inherent limitations of particular climates. The Europeans chose to transfer their culture to areas having mid-latitude climates; this culture, with its greater utilization of inanimate energy and its background of technical discoveries, has provided the basis for the development of the world's most powerful nations. During the past several decades there has been a process of diffusion —as opposed to the earlier displacement—of Western civilization into new areas in both the mid- and low-latitudes. The latter case—that is, the spread to subtropical areas of Western industrial cultures, and with it the potentialities for achievement of major-power status—refutes the theory of direct relationships between climate and the power position of nations.

In addition to climatic influences on the distribution of world power areas, there are relationships between climate and the political structure of individual states, particularly the effects of climatic diversity on forces of political unity and disunity. The pattern of climates within a state is related to population distribution. Regions of pronounced cold, aridity, or humid tropical climates are often sparsely populated, a factor contributing to the state's political complexity. Much of the economic and political power of the state is located in its *core area*, that is, the area in which there is a major concentration of population. If population is concentrated in only a small portion of the national territory (as in China) much of the state's area may not be effectively organized, and in time parts of it may become separated from the capital's control. On the other hand, there may be two or more core areas in a state (as in Bolivia) separated by sparsely-inhabited territory, resulting in the presence of strong centrifugal forces.

Climatic differences may also contribute to economic diversity in a state. The resultant conflict of interests may represent a strong centrifugal force, such as existed between North and South prior to the Civil War, where the South, because of its humid, subtropical climate, depended largely on a plantation economy and the use of slaves, while the North could not benefit from this type of economy. On the other hand, economic differences may contribute to national unity, as, for example, in Australia, where regional groups saw the advantages of combining into a single political unit.

(5) **Surface Configuration**—that is, mountains, plateaus, hills, and plains—may be of great importance to a state's politico-geographic structure. Mountain peoples may enjoy some semblance of isolation with resulting independence (Afghanistan, Andorra), while people in lowland areas, such as the Ukrainians, may often be subject to foreign interference and

thus have little opportunity for self-rule. The presence of mountain ranges along a boundary can help to defend a state against attack from its neighbors and therefore preserve its independence. The Pyrenees between France and Spain and the Alps separating Italy from Austria are examples of mountain areas which have figured prominently in military campaigns between the adjoining states.

There are various situations in which surface configuration affects the internal unity of a state. Upland and lowland areas—like climate—influence population distribution, and thus the location of a state's core area. The presence of mountain ranges may hamper communications between the capital and outlying regions, and as a consequence tend to weaken the state's political cohesion. Likewise, groups inhabiting upland areas may develop different attitudes and goals than those in lowland environments, again creating disruptive political forces within the state. Ecuador, with upland and lowland core areas (centered on Quito and Guayaquil, on the coast), illustrates the conflict of interests resulting in part from a mountain and lowland environment within the state (Figure 9).

(6) Soils and **(7) Natural vegetation** in themselves have little effect on the political development of states. They may, however, represent prizes over which territorial disputes and even warfare may develop. Timberland, at the end of World Wars I and II, formed one of the bases for claims by some of the Benelux countries to German territory. Similarly, the fertile soils of the Ukraine have represented one of the principal assets of this area over which so much disputed control has existed during past centuries.

(8) Water features may be of considerable significance to a state. Rivers are frequently cohesive factors within a country, as are the Tigris and Euphrates in Iraq or the Magdalena in central Colombia. Lakes may have a similar role. About the shores of Lake Malar was formed a political nucleus for the early development of southern Sweden, while a somewhat analogous

Figure 9. Diverse Topography. Peru also claims the territory from the present eastern boundary west to dotted line. See also Figure 27.

situation with respect to Switzerland took place about Lake Lucerne. The sea represents a unifying element in island states, such as Japan, the Philippines, and Indonesia.

On the other hand, water bodies may divide areas rather than unite them. Rivers—such as the Rio Grande and the Amur—and lakes—as Lake Erie and Lake Geneva—are often used to mark international boundaries. Some boundary rivers, like the Rhine, may be of considerable military importance to the defense of a state. Investigation of the political map of the world will reveal many other examples of water boundaries.

Water features may also be important for transportation and trade, or for hydroelectric power. Associated with this is the role water features play as avenues of a state's territorial expansion, such as occurred in Africa in the nineteenth century, when the limits of several colonies were defined as the basin areas of particular rivers.

(9) Mineral resources (including coal and petroleum) are significant not only as fundamental requirements of modern industrial society but also because they often figure prominently in territorial disputes. The existence of valuable mineral resources in border areas may result in armed conflict between neighboring states. For example, discovery of nitrate deposits in the Atacama Desert of western South America led to the violent War of the Pacific (1879–84), involving Chile, Peru, and Bolivia for possession of the area. Industrial nations, such as the United States, Britain, and the Soviet Union, are keenly interested in less powerful areas, such as Venezuela, Iran, and Bolivia, within whose boundaries are located valuable resources. To protect their access to these resources the industrial nations may at times establish "power spheres" over the weaker states.

This discussion of physical attributes does not imply that within each state all nine elements are of basic importance to matters of territorial control. Within each state all nine elements exist, but in each state only one or two attributes may be of political significance. The classification given here—as well as the discussions which follow in this chapter—should be thought of as something of a check list, to be used in analyzing a particular political region. By considering each of these elements in relation to the political region, one may gain considerable insight into its politico-geographic structure.

Boundaries

Boundaries are important components of a state since they limit the areas of territorial control. There are two principal classification systems for boundaries, one based on origin and one on cultural relationships. Both systems are presented here, since each, under certain conditions, can prove useful to an analysis of a political region.

The classification based on origin consists of four types of boundaries
—physical, ethnic, historical, and geometric. Actually many boundaries
represent combinations of two or more of these types.

Physical boundaries are those which follow some physical feature, such
as a mountain range, river, sea coast, lake, or swamp (Figures 10 and 11).
One of the chief advantages of physical boundaries is the relative ease of
establishing their location, both on a map and in the field. Many of the
boundaries which cross sparsely-inhabited territory, as in South America
or Africa, are of this type.

Numerous problems, however, arise in connection with physical boundaries if one examines them closely. In the case of rivers, should the boundary
follow the middle of the channel? What then of fishing and navigation
rights; maintenance of bridges, dams, and navigation channels; distribution
of water for irrigation? What if the river frequently shifts its course during
floodtime? River valleys are often ethnic and economic units; to divide them
politically may work hardship on the inhabitants. With mountain boundaries other problems are present. Should the boundary line follow the crest
itself, or the drainage divide? What nation should control the passes? What
of intermontane basins? Still other problems come up in the case of lakes
and swamps. Each type of physical feature has its distinctive problems with
respect to use as a political boundary.

Theoretically, the best type of physical boundary is the coast line of
a sea or ocean, since only one state is generally involved in the determination and maintenance of the boundary. Even here, however, difficulties may
arise. A foreign power may gain control of offshore islands—as Hong Kong
and Macao off the China coast. Another problem is that of offshore limits of
control. Since 1793 the United States has adhered to a three-mile limit of
territorial sovereignty, although recently this distance has been affected by
boundary claims of individual states (see page 72). In the case of other
countries the figure varies considerably, some (including the Soviet Union)
claiming sovereignty up to 12 miles from shore and some up to 200 miles.
Beyond these limits there are questions concerning the control of resources
(particularly petroleum) which lie beneath the ocean floor, as well as of
fishing rights in waters adjacent to a particular country.

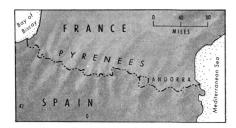

Figure 10. Physical Boundary.

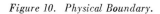

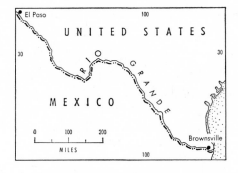

Figure 11. Physical-Ethnic Boundary.

Ethnic boundaries separate peoples of differing race, religion, or language (Figure 11). If accurately delimited[3] they may be successful in reducing friction between states, for each political region would then contain its own particular ethnic group or groups. Unfortunately, ethnic boundaries are often extremely difficult to delimit, particularly if the various groups have inhabited a boundary area for many years and their patterns of settlement are closely intermingled with one another. Following World War I many of the boundaries of central and eastern Europe were redrawn so as to separate dissimilar cultural groups wherever possible. Plebiscites were resorted to on several occasions in order to ascertain the desires of people in border areas. Despite the efforts of Allied statesmen at the Versailles Conference, 3,200,000 Germans, 700,000 Hungarians, and 80,000 Poles were included within Czechoslovakia; over 900,000 Germans were left within Poland's borders; 420,000 Albanians remained in Yugoslavia; and there were many parallel cases involving smaller numbers of peoples.

If they remain undisturbed for long periods of time, ethnic boundaries may come to achieve their primary purpose of reducing friction, for the peoples on both sides of the border will gradually adjust themselves to its presence. Such has been the case along the northern German-Dutch border. Demands by the Netherlands in 1945 for modifications of this border were justified on the basis of German aggression during World War II, but opposing this was the fact that the existing border had become a well-functioning division line. The peoples close to the border had come to accept it as a more or less permanent feature of the landscape; a new delimitation, many experts felt, would serve only to destroy a well-adapted boundary situation and lead to future friction between the Dutch and the Germans.

Ethnic boundaries are sometimes based on physical features, and as such may be considered a combined ethnic-physical type. In the central Pyrenees between France and Spain, for example, the physical feature has served to divide cultural groups as well as nations from one another. Ac-

---

[3] The term "delimit" refers to fixing the location of a boundary on the map. "Demarcate" means to locate a boundary line on the ground.

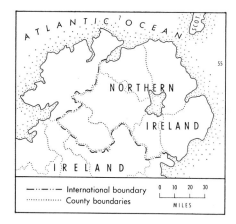

Figure 12. Historical Boundary.

tually, there are few international boundaries which succeed completely in separating unlike cultural groups from one another, unless considerable unoccupied area exists between population centers or there has been a mass deportation of minorities across the border.

Historical boundaries follow old political division lines, and as such may not coincide with either physical or ethnic patterns. The French-German boundary, for example, follows in part the historical boundaries of the duchy of Alsace; the border between Northern Ireland and the Republic of Ireland coincides with the boundaries of old counties (Figure 12). In both instances ethnic groups are divided from one another, although neither boundary is exact in its function of cultural delimitation. Thousands of Irish Catholics were left in Northern Ireland by the boundary location, while along the French-German border many persons on the French side speak German as their native tongue. Other examples of historical borders are those of Switzerland and some Latin American states.

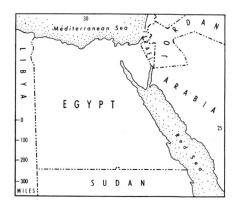

Figure 13. Geometric Boundary.

Geometric boundaries. A geometric boundary is one which follows a straight line, a meridian of longitude, or a parallel of latitude (Figure 13). Such boundaries exist primarily in regions of sparse population, as in Africa or the American Northwest, for if a considerable population is present in the boundary area demands for modifications of the boundary are likely to be made to conform to ethnic or economic needs. The principal asset of geometric boundaries lies in the simplicity of their delimitation on a map, and in the fact that they can be demarcated accurately by astronomical measurements.

Another classification of boundaries—that based on cultural relationships—considers boundary characteristics only with respect to human aspects of the landscape, that is, patterns of settlement and land utilization or the distribution of various population types. The three categories in this classification are *antecedent, superimposed,* and *consequent.*

Antecedent boundaries are those which predate the development of an area's cultural features, such as the arrangement of roads and villages or the pattern of economic activities. The United States-Canadian boundary west of Lake Superior is antecedent; so are many of the boundaries of Africa and Latin America.

In contrast with these are the boundaries which have been delimited after the development of an area has taken place. Such boundaries (sometimes termed *subsequent*) may cut across the cultural pattern of an area, and thus are *superimposed,* or they may conform to the distribution of population or of ethnic or economic regions, and thus are *consequent* in nature. The Israeli-Jordan border in the vicinity of Jerusalem is superimposed; the boundary between Norway and Sweden is consequent, since it has always effectively separated the peoples of the two nations from one another because of the nature of the terrain.

This classification has an advantage over the more detailed system based on origin in that it permits careful consideration of the effects of boundary location on human activities within an area. On the other hand, the classification according to origin may be of greater value to a study of the structure and functioning of a specific boundary, since it indicates the precise basis on which the boundary was delimited. In the following chapters use will be made of both systems.

One important point about boundaries is that their effectiveness often reflects relations between neighboring states. A boundary which has been delimited in the most "scientific" manner possible may still prove a source of friction, should there be general tension between the nations involved. On the other hand, boundaries, which by their manner of delimitation would seem to offer numerous sources for potential friction, will actually cause few problems if the respective states maintain cordial relations with one another.

A RESPONSIBLE GOVERNMENT

Political geographers are not concerned with the form or structure of government by itself, that is, the division of functions among executive, legislative, and judicial branches or whether it is democratic or totalitarian. These are matters for the political scientist. Political geography asks the question: Is there a central government exercising control over a certain portion of the earth's surface? Associated with this question are three topics: (a) the *type* of political control which is exercised over an area, (b) the *degree* of control, and (c) the *effectiveness* of control processes.

A. Type of Political Control

The differences in type of political control are reflected first in the existence of both dependent and independent states throughout the world, and, second, in the several variations of dependencies which have been developed. The present political pattern consists of about 85 independent states and over 120 dependent ones. Actually, the precise number of units within the "independent" and "dependent" categories will vary according to definition. Thus in this classification British dominions and republics are included as "independent states," while North Korea and the Soviet satellite states are listed as "dependent." The differentiation between dependent and independent areas is further complicated by the legal incorporation of certain overseas regions within the metropolitan area of the mother country, as the Azores within Portugal and Corsica within France.

Despite the great variety of political associations one state may have with another, there are certain broad categories of control which currently exist throughout the world. These are colonies, protectorates, satellites, trusteeship territories, and dominions and republics. In addition, there are special forms of sovereignty such as international zones and condominiums.

In a *colony* much of the political power is exercised by the mother country. It is presumed that the local inhabitants are not in a position to handle their own affairs except at local levels, and there is frequently little or no native representation on the governing bodies which make major decisions with regard to the colonial area. Nationals of the mother country often receive special privileges in the colony, and the economy of the region generally is geared for the benefit of the colonial power. Within the British and French empires there are also *dependencies* of the colonies, which are minor territorial areas governed by the colony's administration.

The dependent areas of the United States (with the exception of the Commonwealth of Puerto Rico) are termed territories and possessions rather than colonies. The degree of local autonomy varies among the several possessions, but in all of them the executive officers are appointed by the United States President and many of the important affairs relating to the possession are handled in Washington.

A *protectorate* is a colonial area in which there is a local ruler, but in which defense, foreign affairs, and various other matters are in the hands of the mother country. A governor general, or other administrative officer appointed by the controlling state, wields considerable power over the protectorate, including generally the right of veto over any legislation passed by the local governing councils.

The term *satellite* is used by noncommunist countries with reference to those communized states wherein independence is still officially maintained but which, in reality, are dependent areas of the U.S.S.R. or of China. Albania, Bulgaria, Czechoslovakia, East Germany, Hungary, Poland, and Romania are satellites of the Soviet Union, while North Korea has a somewhat similar position with regard to China. The satellite status of Outer Mongolia and of North Vietnam is impossible to determine accurately due to the lack of information which is available concerning the political relationships of these areas with Russia and China.

Trusteeship territories are an outgrowth of the former League of Nations Mandate System, set up in 1920, under which the colonial possessions of the defeated powers of World War I were apportioned among some of the victorious Allied states. The League undertook to guarantee certain civil liberties of the native populations, and annual reports on the administration of the territories were made to the international body by the Mandate Powers. If the situation in a given territory appeared to warrant it, there was a provision for an investigation by the League Mandates Commission, leading to a possible recall of the mandate and its reassignment to some other power. With the establishment of the United Nations in 1945, supervision over the former mandates passed to the United Nations Trusteeship Council. Accordingly, the former mandate powers (with the exception of Japan and the Union of South Africa) became trusteeship powers, while the mandates themselves became trusteeship (or trust) territories (see also page 344).

Dominions are self-governing states which retain certain political, economic, and other ties with the former mother country. The dominion system has been most highly developed within the British Commonwealth; the political tie between the dominions and Great Britain is their common allegiance to the British Crown. Membership of the dominions within the Commonwealth is entirely voluntary. In addition to political bonds, there are various economic and military matters in which the dominions cooperate with Great Britain and with one another. India and Pakistan, although still within the Commonwealth, have changed from dominion to republic status, thereby ending the legal sovereignty of the British Queen over these areas. The dominion system has served as the basis for political control by other powers as well. Puerto Rico is a self-governing territory of the United States, in a relationship which, in many respects, resembles the dominion organization. France is seeking to establish bonds of "interdependence" with some of its former colonial possessions, whereby these areas, although independent, will permit certain functions to continue to be administered by the former mother country.

Finally, there are special forms of territorial control, such as international areas, condominiums, occupation zones, and military bases. The concept of an *international area* was exemplified by the city of Tangier, on the North African coast just west of the Strait of Gibraltar. Because of the port's strategic location there were bitter disputes among European powers over control of the area, and an international commission was set up in 1925 to administer the city. The international status lasted until 1956, when the city was incorporated into the new state of Morocco. Another variety of international control was applied under the League of Nations between World Wars I and II, when League Commissions were established to administer the Saar and the city of Danzig (now a part of Poland). Since the founding of the United Nations two proposals for international control have been suggested, one for Trieste and the other for Jerusalem, but neither proposal was put into operation.

Where two or more powers share control of an area the resultant governmental structure is known as a *condominium*. The degree of control by each state may vary considerably. The Sudan—formerly the Anglo-Egyptian Sudan—was until 1955 the major condominium of the world; the New Hebrides Islands and Nauru Island in the Pacific are the only significant condominiums still in existence.[4]

Occupation zones are sectors of a state which remain occupied by foreign troops for a limited time following cessation of warfare. In 1945, for example, Germany and Austria were each temporarily divided into four occupation zones. In these zones government was carried on by the occupying power, although it was understood that such control was to be for a short time only. In addition, Berlin and Vienna were set up as special four-power occupation areas. Japan, Korea, Trieste, and various nations of eastern Europe were also under military occupation for several years after World War II.

In a somewhat different category are the *military zones* and *bases* which one country may control within the boundaries of another. In Panama, for example, the United States has rights "in perpetuity" over a ten-mile

---

[4] The United Nations trusteeship over Nauru Island is held jointly by Britain, Australia, and New Zealand, but the area is actually administered by Australia. Canton and Enderbury islands in the central Pacific are condominiums of Britain and the United States. The two so-called Neutral Zones on the Arabian Peninsula also have a condominium status.

wide strip of territory through which passes the Canal. The United States also has many military establishments on foreign soil; in each instance special agreements exist with regard to matters of sovereignty within the military area. Permission for the United States to operate these military establishments is granted voluntarily by sovereign states and may be withdrawn at any time if the foreign government so decides.

B. Degree of Control

The actual degree of control which central governments exercise over the territory within their states' boundaries varies widely from place to place. In some cases, such as remote areas of the Amazon basin, there exist groups of people who are untouched by the laws and requirements of the national government. Thus the capital exercises *de jure,* but not *de facto,* control over these areas.[5] More frequent, perhaps, are situations where the capital's authority over certain parts of the state may be effective only at certain times and under certain conditions. Invasion, or threat of invasion, for example, is a potent force for strengthening central authority within a state. Maps showing conditions of *de facto* political control by central governments throughout the world—although difficult to compile—might have more meaning than those showing the familiar *de jure* pattern of sovereignty.

Certain aspects of governmental control over a political region were described by Richard Hartshorne in an article, "The Functional Approach in Political Geography."[6] He uses the term "centripetal forces" to apply to those pressures which tend to unite regions together into a state. Among these forces is the state-idea, that is the *raison d'être,* or reason for the state's existence as a separate political region. If the state-idea is weak initially—or if in time it should disappear—then the existence of the state as a political entity may be seriously threatened. Another centripetal force is the "concept of nation," ". . . a feeling of kinship, of belonging together."[7] This sense of belonging to a certain state on the part of its citizens is an important element of the state's cohesiveness. Switzerland is cited as an example in which this concept of nation is strong, despite the existence of dissimilar languages and of other elements tending to divide the nation.

Against these forces are the "centrifugal forces" working to divide the political regions. Among these would be distance, the presence of physical features hindering communications between various sectors, the existence of ethnically diverse groups within a state, and regional differences in

---

[5] The term *de jure* is defined as "by right, according to law." *De facto* means "actually existing, whether with or without right." These terms are important to any consideration of the realities of territorial control throughout the world.
[6] *Annals of the Association of American Geographers,* XL, No. 2 (June, 1950), 95–131.
[7] *Ibid.,* p. 113.

attitudes. Thus, each political region has the two types of forces, the one working to unite the state and the other to divide it.

The *raison d'être* and the concept of nation, if applied to various political regions, often provide clues to the cohesion of states and to the possibilities for future change in the political pattern. In Africa and southeast Asia, for example, the boundaries of many of the colonial areas were delimited during the nineteenth century, often with little reference to physical, ethnic, or historical considerations. Such *raison d'être* as existed for these areas was based largely on administrative efficiency. By the mid-twentieth century centrifugal forces within a number of these countries had become strong, and pressures existed for partitioning the political regions. In India and Palestine the approach of independence resulted in considerable weakening of the former state-idea. Economic and religious factors outweighed any concept of nation which might have been developed among the majority of the peoples in these areas, and political partitioning was the eventual outcome. On the other hand, Burma and the Sudan have retained their preindependence borders, despite the various differences which exist in both states. In each of these two areas the *raison d'être* is a complex one; among the contributing factors is the determination of the dominant political and economic groups in both Burma and the Sudan to prevent any breakup of their country. Even though the borders remain intact, however, there is no common concept of nation throughout either of these states, with the result that powerful centrifugal forces still exist.

Capitals and Core Areas. The location and functioning of a state's capital and the position of the core area are important aspects of the degree of control exercised by the central government within a state. Each state forms originally about a particular nucleus; this nucleus is frequently the core area as well. In time, however, the core area may move away from this nucleus, or additional core areas may develop; in either situation strong centrifugal forces may come into being. Brazil is an example in which the core area moved away from the original nucleus along the northeast coast. Spain, on the other hand, represents a country in which there are two core areas, one centered at Madrid, the capital, and the other at Barcelona.

The capital city may remain at the original nucleus (London, Paris), it may shift to a relocated core area (Rio de Janeiro), or it may become located outside of both of them. Canberra, Australia, for example, lies midway between the two great cities of Sydney and Melbourne, and Ottawa was chosen as a neutral position with respect to both English- and French-speaking Canada. In analyzing the location and functioning of a national capital, historical forces must be taken into account, for the role played by the capital city in the early years of a state may change considerably in later times. Spate[8] classifies capital cities into three types according to

[8] O. H. K. Spate, "Factors in the Development of Capital Cities," *The Geographical Review,* XXXII, No. 4 (October, 1942), 622–32.

function: (1) as a unifying center in a federation, (2) as a link with external influences, and (3) as a "forward capital" close to an active frontier. Canberra represents a unifying center; London, in historical times, was a link with the Continent; while Berlin was once a "forward capital," facing the dynamic Eastern frontier. Regardless of their original function, most capitals, if their location remains fixed, will in time become economic and population centers, with the result that their original functions may become obscured. Spate terms this "historical inertia," and compares it with "historical imitation," in which the seat of government may be moved to a former capital city for prestige purposes. For example, the Italians in the early 1870's located the capital of the modern Italian state at Rome, and the Chinese Communists, once they had overrun the nation, moved the capital from Nanking back to Peking (Peiping).

C. The Effectiveness of Control Processes

In addition to type and degree of control is this third aspect, which is associated largely with internal politico-geographic situations. The effectiveness of a state's political and legal systems depends in part upon the adaptation of these systems to the physical and cultural environment. Laws relating to land ownership, or to mineral and fishing rights, for instance, should conform to the particular requirements of the political region in which they apply; otherwise unnecessary disputes may arise over the settlement of claims, resources may not be wisely used, and the cultural needs of the peoples involved will not be adequately served.

The transfer of political systems formulated in one type of environment to a totally different type may have significant effects on cultural adjustments to physical conditions. The techniques of boundary delimitation in Belgium, for example, obviously differ from those in the Belgian Congo, the Arabian desert, or the Arctic wastes; so, too, do the respective laws relating to border functioning, voting, taxation, and many other problems. One of the important aspects of the spread of European culture to overseas areas since 1500 has been the gradual evolution of new techniques of political control to conform to new environmental conditions. Political geographers have only begun to analyze the complex relationships which exist between processes of political control and the physical and cultural environment. Nevertheless, such relationships represent important components of the over-all problem of governmental control of territory.

A RESIDENT POPULATION

Population factors of a political region are of great importance in a politico-geographic study. Size, distribution, and type of population are the three major elements to consider.

The number of people resident within a national region is important not only in terms of a state's ability to provide for its own needs but also of its power potential. Certain states, such as Italy, Japan, the Netherlands, and Britain, are densely populated, particularly with respect to their arable land. Even with modern agricultural techniques, they are unable to raise sufficient food to feed their people and must build up exports or services to pay for the needed imports. The problems of "overcrowded" states are extremely complex; only a few aspects can be suggested here.

The normal method for obtaining exports in food-deficient countries is through industrial production. Industry provides employment for many of the people and will earn foreign credits. Along with production, however, must come markets for the manufactured goods. As more countries begin to industrialize, thereby producing goods to satisfy their own needs, markets become scarcer for the exports of densely-populated states. At the present time the greatest potential markets in the world for industrial goods lie in the communist countries; yet to send these countries the industrial goods they desire, such as machinery and locomotives, would increase their economic and military strength relative to the noncommunist world. On the other hand, failure of the crowded noncommunist states to secure markets for their exports may lead to economic instability, unemployment, and inability to assume important roles in the anticommunist movement.

In place of industrialization and exports a densely-populated country may (a) increase domestic food sources, (b) build up an overseas empire which will assist it in economic development, (c) reduce its population through large-scale emigration, or (d) substantially lower its general standard of living. An increase in domestic food supplies to a magnitude sufficient to feed the entire population may be impossible due to limitations of the physical environment. Even a lesser expansion of food production may be economically impractical due to the availability of inexpensive food imports.

The other three alternatives have strong political connotations. The days of colonial empires are gradually disappearing, as the Dutch, the British, and the French have discovered. Areas for emigration are generally restricted by quotas, as in the United States, Canada, and Australia, or by undesirable physical features, such as are found in parts of Latin America and Africa. Further, emigration may weaken the population structure of a state, for the young and ambitious are often the ones to leave. Finally, no democratic government can operate for long on a policy of continued reduction in the standard of living; eventually the voters will turn it out of office.

The relationship between population size and national power potential involves education and technological skills, as well as the ability of the central government to organize the population for the service of the state. Education and technological skills enable the people to utilize effectively the national resources. An example or organization was evidenced in Germany prior to and during World War II. Here were 65,000,000 persons, possessing considerable talent and skills, who were organized for the furtherance of national aims. Much of Germany's remarkable political and military power during those years must be attributed to the size and training of its population.

Allied with population size is the question of distribution, which is significant in terms of both internal unity and diversity, and of relations between one state and another. Many of the political effects of population distribution have already been alluded to. For instance, regions of dense population have a profound effect on the cohesive structure of a state; similarly, areas of sparsely-inhabited land lying between populated areas may be conducive to powerful centrifugal forces. Large-scale population movements may result in a shifting of the major power centers of an area. On the international scene, boundaries through regions of low population density frequently cause less friction than those through more crowded areas. Populous areas located close to a potentially-hostile neighbor may be detrimental to a state, for the capture of an area might seriously weaken the state's resistance. The location of Paris with respect to France's northeastern boundary is a case in point.

A third element of population—that of type—includes language, religion, and race. People possessing similar characteristics with respect to one or more of these features comprise what is known as an ethnic group. Differing language groups exist in Canada, Belgium, Czechoslovakia, and Yugoslavia, while religious cleavages are found in Canada, Yugoslavia, the Netherlands, Indonesia, and Northern Ireland. Dissimilar racial groups inhabit the Union of South Africa, Malaya, and the United States.

The presence of more than one ethnic group within a state may seriously weaken its political unity, for the groups may seek to change the existing pattern of control. In some instances there is a movement by one group to separate the territory it inhabits from the control of the national government and set up an independent state, as the Karens attempted in Burma. At other times the various ethnic groups vie for control of the central government itself, as the Walloons and the Flemings once did in Belgium. Some ethnic groups retain ties of national loyalty with foreign powers rather than with the state in which they reside. Czechoslovakia, prior to the Munich crisis of 1938, had Germans, Hungarians, and Poles within its borders whose loyalties were primarily with their respective "homelands." Such a situation can be of great potential danger, for these groups may seek the political partitioning of the state and annexation of the areas they inhabit by an adjoining country. There are some cases in which little or no friction develops as a result of ethnic complexity. The states of Latin America, for example, have few difficulties as a result of the intermixture of various racial groups within their borders.

AN ECONOMIC STRUCTURE

In society economic strength is a basic criterion for military and political power. American industrial and agricultural output have been major factors in the Allied victories of World Wars I and II. Likewise, near-autarky, or economic self-sufficiency, enabled the Germans to resist Allied blockades on imports of strategic commodities in both conflicts. In time of peace economic domination of one country by another often carries with it measures of political influence as well. Nazi Germany's economic dominance over Romania, Hungary, and Bulgaria prior to World War II is an illustration of this occurrence.

The relationships which may exist between economic and political diversity within a state were mentioned on page 25. Differences in economic interests may foster strong centrifugal forces. On the other hand, diverse economic regions within a state may complement one another and serve to unite the area for interregional trade, thus leading to close political ties between groups. Under these conditions people in differing economic regions would find it more to their mutual advantage to remain together within one political unit than to separate into two or more states. In addition to Australia, both the United States and Canada may be cited as examples in which the desire for economic unity on the part of various groups was an important stimulus to political unification.

Another factor is that of economic exploitation by one state over another, a situation which may or may not be accompanied by political domination as well. In the development of the great part of the overseas empires of modern times political annexation was carried out subsequent to —or in conjunction with—economic expansion of the mother country over the colonial area. Even after a colonial country receives political independence (as in the case of Iraq), it may not in reality be truly sovereign unless it achieves a measure of economic freedom from its former mother country as well. Whittlesey in *The Earth and the State* considers at some length what he terms "The Concept of the Exploitable World." He points out a number of important correlations between the political and economic relationships between states. For instance, he writes, "The real test of exploitability is economic subservience rather than political dependence. Cuba, politically independent, is exploitable, whereas British Canada is not."[9] Here, as in other situations, the relationships between economic and political control of territory may have many elements of interdependence with one another.

---

[9] Derwent Whittlesey, *The Earth and the State*, p. 81. Used by permission of Henry Holt and Company, copyright 1944.

A CIRCULATORY SYSTEM

The final essential element of a state involves the accessibility of its various areas—and of the state itself—to people and to ideas. Movement is essential to the political organization of space and to the maintenance of this organization. The term circulation is used here to denote "the flow of peoples, armies, material goods, capital, messages, and ideas across the space open to men's activities."[10] The various media through which this flow is made possible form the "circulatory system," and include such factors as transportation systems, radio, and the press.

The increase in the facilities for communication, particularly since the beginning of the twentieth century, has, of course, greatly improved the effectiveness of circulatory systems throughout the world. One result of this has been stronger political organization of space. The number of people who still remain untouched by the authority of their country's government is steadily declining, so that in only a relatively few areas of the world is the *de facto* control of the central government completely ineffective. Another indication of this improved effectiveness is that even uninhabited Antarctica is becoming politically organized.

The effects of circulation within states are of two general types. On the one hand, it tends to unite the political area in that it permits the central authority to be carried more effectively to outlying regions; on the other hand, it can be a source of instability and change, inasmuch as it exposes many people to new ideas and new wants, with the result that they may become dissatisfied with the conditions of political organization that currently exist. As illustration, the increased effectiveness of Canada's circulatory system after the mid-nineteenth century prevented a possible partitioning of the country and the creation of a separate political entity in the far west. In contrast with this, an expanded circulatory system in the new Sudan state could signify an attempt to strengthen Khartoum's authority over the Negroid peoples who inhabit the southern forest lands. Some of these peoples, already distrustful of the Arab majority in the central and northern parts of the country, might seek a partitioning of the Sudan, particularly if the Arabs attempt to force their own culture on them.

Circulatory systems function on the international level as well. Foreign travel and the beaming of propaganda, or, conversely, the imposition of "iron curtains" and the jamming of radio programs, are aspects of circulation which often have strong political overtones. Again, the net effect may

---

[10] Jean Gottman, "The Political Partitioning of our World: an Attempt at Analysis," *World Politics*, IV, No. 4 (July, 1952), 515.

be toward either political cohesion or political diversity. Within each state and between it and other states, is a complex series of circulation media, which, like the four elements covered earlier in this chapter, contribute to the basic structure of a political region.

The complex nature of territorial control throughout the world becomes evident when one considers all the possible variations which exist with respect to these five basic elements of a state. In a survey covering the entire globe only the most obvious features of each political region can be considered. Major power centers, significant changes in political status, territorial disputes which have (or once had) important international repercussions—items such as these represent the basic materials for a general study of world political geography. If time and interest permit, however, closer examination of any one of the various political regions of the world will reveal significant (if less world-shaking) aspects of governmental control of territory, which could form the basis for rewarding research and analysis.

BIBLIOGRAPHY

Boggs, S. Whittemore. *International Boundaries: A Study of Boundary Functions and Problems.* New York: Columbia University Press, 1940.

A basic text on the nature and function of international boundaries.

———. "National Claims in Adjacent Seas," *The Geographical Review,* XLI, No. 2 (April, 1951), 185–210.

A fully-documented description of this problem as it existed at the time of publication.

Bowman, Isaiah. "The Strategy of Territorial Decisions," *Foreign Affairs,* XXIV, No. 2 (January, 1946), 177–95.

Some of the fundamental problems involved in territorial claims and adjustments.

Carr-Saunders, A. M. *World Population: Past Growth and Trends.* Oxford: Clarendon Press, 1936.

Statistics and descriptions of trends by one of the recognized experts in this field.

Emeny, Brooks. *The Strategy of Raw Materials.* New York: The Macmillan Company, 1934.

Contains some thought-provoking ideas on control of important raw materials by major world powers.

FAWCETT, CHARLES B. *Frontiers: A Study in Political Geography.* Oxford: Clarendon Press, 1918.

One of the early works on this subject. Many of the conclusions are still pertinent to current conditions.

FISCHER, ERIC. "On Boundaries," *World Politics,* I, No. 2 (January, 1949), 196–222.

An interesting discussion of various aspects of boundaries, including a description of some boundary problems in central Africa.

HALL, H. DUNCAN. *Mandates, Dependencies, and Trusteeships.* Washington: Carnegie Endowment for International Peace, 1948.

A detailed handling of certain problems of colonial administration.

HARTSHORNE, RICHARD. "The Politico-Geographic Pattern of the World," *The Annals,* CCXVIII (1941), 45–57.

A discussion, with map, of actual degrees of political control throughout the world prior to World War II.

HOLDICH, THOMAS H. *Political Frontiers and Boundary Making.* London: Macmillan and Co., Ltd., 1916.

Like Fawcett's book, this is one of the early classics on boundaries, and is of interest particularly to serious students of this subject.

JONES, STEPHEN B. *Boundary Making: A Handbook for Statesmen, Treaty Editors and Boundary Commissioners.* New York: Columbia University Press, 1945.

A detailed discussion of the techniques of boundary delimitation.

MARKHAM, S. E. *Climate and the Energy of Nations.* New York: Oxford University Press, 1947.

Contains interesting, if sometimes controversial, material on climate and the activities of nations.

VAN VALKENBURG, SAMUEL, and STOTZ, CARL L. *Elements of Political Geography.* 2d ed. New York: Prentice-Hall, Inc., 1954.

A standard text on the basic principles of political geography.

WRIGHT, QUINCY. *Mandates Under the League of Nations.* Chicago: The University of Chicago Press, 1930.

Although much of the material is out of date, this is an important book to any understanding of the mandate system.

3

ANGLO-AMERICA

● The name Anglo-America refers to the predominantly English-speaking portion of the Western Hemisphere, including the United States, Canada, and Alaska.[1] With its rich resource base and its separation by water areas from the power centers of Europe and Asia, Anglo-America has become one of the principal economic, military, and political regions of the world. Centrifugal forces, such as distance, climatic differences, and variations in historical development, have had little effect on the political pattern here, for within and between the countries of this area there exist few problems of territorial control. On the world scene, Anglo-America also represents a force for territorial stability, for its elements of strength serve to counterbalance the threat of communist expansion into noncommunist areas, such as South Korea, Taiwan (Formosa), and Greece.

The United States

The United States with 2,974,726 square miles of land and 170,000,-000 persons (1957) ranks fifth in size and fourth in population among the nations of the world. In recent decades the United States has developed the world's most powerful economy, producing a little less than half of the world's steel and piling up a large surplus of agricultural commodities. This economic position has been made possible by the existence within con-

---

[1] Greenland, although generally not considered a part of Anglo-America, will be considered as a separate unit in this chapter after a discussion of the other three areas.

tinental United States of a wide variety of minerals and power fuels[2] as well as of large areas of arable land.

The tremendous wealth of the United States has placed the nation in a position of leadership throughout much of the noncommunist world. This status of leadership has, in turn, served to focus world attention on developments within the United States' borders; as a result, such problems as racial discrimination, the treatment of communists, and the policies of political parties toward labor, agriculture, and foreign aid become matters of common knowledge and interest to people of every continent of the globe. It is with some of the past and present aspects of America's development as a political unit that the following sections are concerned.

The Physical Environment

Location has been one of the dominant influences in the development of the United States. The protection afforded by 3,000 miles of ocean, the mid-latitude climates, and the vicinal location with respect to the rest of the Western Hemisphere have all contributed in many ways to the United States' power position. Although the barrier effect of the Atlantic has been diminishing since the advent of the Air Age, the presence of this water body, together with that of the Pacific Ocean and of the Arctic region, still represents an element of protection for Anglo-America from potential enemies in Eurasia. Location on two oceans means that the United States has long sea frontiers to defend, but it has facilitated the nation's maritime development and the establishment of overseas contacts with the other parts of the world.

Because of the mid-latitude location of the United States there are no areas of arctic climate, except for some of the high mountain regions, and the only tropical climate is in southernmost Florida. Thus Europeans were attracted to the country for settlement even as far back as the early seventeenth century. An additional climatic advantage of the nation is that there is a sufficiently wide variety of climates within its borders to permit many types of crops to be grown. On the other hand, the major climatic disadvantage is the fact that much of the western portion is arid, or semi-arid, a limiting factor of the nation's agricultural potential.

With respect to vicinal location, neither Canada nor Mexico represents a potential rival to the United States. Likewise, none of the Latin American states is, or has been, a threat to the nation's security. The unrivalled power position of the United States in the Western Hemisphere has been of great importance to economic and political growth.

The nation's size has been sufficiently great to permit considerable expansion of settlement and to offer the possibilities of a wide variety of

---

[2] The term "power fuels" is used here to refer to petroleum, natural gas, coal, and water.

natural resources within its borders. The shape is fairly compact, so that no portion of the nation is particularly isolated from any other sector. In terms of internal control, however, distance represents a strong centrifugal force, which has been partly overcome only by the development of an extensive circulatory system throughout the country.

Surface configuration in the United States is significant primarily in terms of the economy. The upland areas are important for water power and for timber; some of the mountains and hills are also rich in minerals and power fuels. Upland regions, however, often limit the agricultural potential of a particular area as a result of slope, of soil types, or of their effects on temperature and precipitation. In terms of internal political cohesion, surface configuration is important primarily because of its effect on population distribution. This, in turn, has influenced the distribution of political power within the United States, but its effect on national unity has been minimized with the development of modern communication media. Mountain groups may have certain cultural differences from the majority of the population, but here again there are no powerful centrifugal forces when measured on the national scale. Surface configuration also has little effect on the structure and functioning of the international borders. For only 175 miles, between Maine and Quebec does a portion of the United States boundary follow a landform—in this case an upland area, which is a northern extension of the White Mountains. Mountains, however, have provided the bases for the delimitation of some state borders, as between Idaho and Montana, and North Carolina and Tennessee.

Soils and natural vegetation contribute to the resource base of the United States, although in both cases human use—or misuse—has tended to lessen their value. Most of the virgin forests of the nation have disappeared, and the United States is now dependent on Canada for much of its wood requirements. The destruction of the forests has resulted in serious soil erosion; the tremendous quantities of alluvium which are carried downstream each year by the Mississippi River and its tributaries are in part the result of deforestation in the upper Mississippi basin. The ploughing up of natural grasslands in the semiarid parts of the nation has contributed to the great dust storms in that area, which have further depleted the natural resource base. Here then are two physical assets whose potential value has declined considerably within the past two centuries.

With regard to minerals and power resources, the United States is self-sufficient in many items, such as coal, copper, petroleum, and iron ore, although the gradual depletion of domestic sources of petroleum and iron ore is forcing the nation to look to other areas for supplies. The United States, however, is almost completely dependent on foreign sources for chromite, nickel, tin, manganese, platinum, asbestos, quartz crystals, and industrial diamonds; it is also partially dependent on foreign areas for over a dozen other items, including cobalt, lead, zinc, and tungsten. The nation has a large water-power potential, which is not completely utilized. Further developments on such rivers as the Niagara, the Colorado, and the Columbia will increase considerably the national hydroelectric power output.

Water features are a final physical asset. In terms of transportation the Mississippi and its tributaries (notably the Ohio, the Tennessee, and the Missouri) and the Great Lakes comprise two of the most valuable inland water systems of the world. Canalization, dredging, and the development of the St. Lawrence Seaway, connecting the Great Lakes with the Atlantic, are engineering improvements which have greatly enhanced the value of these waterways to the United States. The factor of hydroelectric power has already been mentioned. In addition, some of the water bodies have also been useful for irrigation and for water supplies to industrial areas.

Type, Size, and Distribution of Population

The population of the United States represents a complex mixture of cultural groups. Only one element, the 350,000 Indians, are descendants of the original inhabitants of the country. Generally speaking, the various groups composing the white population have become well assimilated. Little attention is paid to differences between Protestant, Catholic, or Jew, between descendants of particular European stocks, or between recent immigrants and those whose forefathers have been in America for many decades. Difficulties arise, however, in connection with the nonwhite population—Negroes, Indians, and Orientals—as well as with Latin American groups, such as Mexicans and Puerto Ricans. One of the major causes of discrimination against these groups is fear on the part of the American whites of a lowering of their social and economic levels, should full economic and political equality be granted to these lower-income groups. The proportions of this racial conflict are magnified in the United States because of the large number of nonwhite and of Mexicans and Puerto Ricans who reside in the nation. The percentage of white-Negro intermixture, for example, is greater in the United States than in any other country of the world, with the exception of South Africa and Brazil. This problem of minority groups tends to weaken the nation's over-all structure of political cohesion. There are over 15,000,000 Negroes in the United States, representing about nine per cent of the nation's population. In some Southern states the Negro population approaches that of the white, with resultant social, economic, and political repercussions (Figure 14).

Discrimination against specific minorities in the United States is stressed continually in anti-American propaganda. Two-thirds of the world's population is nonwhite, and American minority policies are often resented by peoples of other countries, particularly in Asia. Although in the United

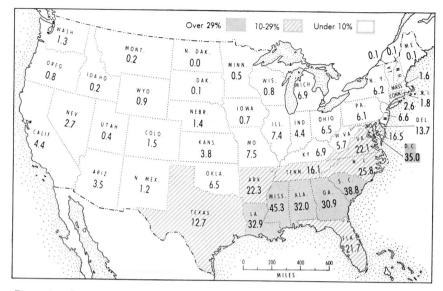

Figure 14. Percentage of Negroes in the United States by States, 1950. Note the correlation between the distribution of Negroes and the states of the Confederacy in the Civil War (Figure 16).

States itself there has been little association of the nonwhite peoples with the Communist Party, the political potentialities of this ethnic diversity are very real.

The growth of the nation's population from about 3,000,000 at the time of independence to over 170,000,000 in 1957 was occasioned not only by natural increase but also by large-scale immigration, particularly from Europe. Between 1860 and 1924 over 33,000,000 persons immigrated to the nation. In the years of an expanding agricultural frontier and of growing industrialization the United States could absorb a great number of foreigners to form a reservoir of cheap labor. By the beginning of the twentieth century, however, the era of unclaimed agricultural land was ending, and not long after this the industrial expansion of the nation was also slowed due to the lack of domestic and foreign markets. In the face of widespread unemployment following World War I, the United States government promulgated an immigration law (1921) which limited immigration from Europe and certain other areas to three per cent of the population of each country resident within the United States at the time of the 1910 census. Quotas for most Asiatic countries had already been fixed by separate agreements, while immigration from other parts of the Western Hemisphere continued without numerical restrictions as to numbers. In 1924 the quota was reduced from three to two per cent, where it now remains.

The existence of a large, unified population in the United States, with a high degree of education and training, is one of the important facets of the nation's power potential. The rate of annual population increase in 1956 was approximately 1.7 per cent, or close to 2.8 million persons. In the period of national prosperity which has followed the ending of World War II the birth rate at no time has dropped below 2 per cent per year. Thus, unlike some of the nations of western Europe, the United States has not yet approached the point of stability of national population total.

The distribution of population has been affected both by climate and by industrialization. Although the bulk of the nation's peoples in the past has been concentrated east of the Mississippi, the geographic center of population has been moving steadily westward, so that in 1950 it was in southern Illinois. The semiarid and mountain regions west of the Mississippi are still, for the most part, sparsely populated, but a great population growth has taken place in the Pacific coast states. Between 1940 and 1950 five Western states—California, Arizona, Nevada, Oregon, Washington—reported a population increase of more than thirty-five per cent. Accompanying this westward shift has been the movement of peoples to urban areas, so that, in 1950, 64 per cent of the nation's population was classed as urban. These population changes, of course, influence the distribution of political power in the nation, as evidenced by the increase in membership from the Far West in the House of Representatives and the corresponding decrease in membership from the northeastern states.

Economic Position of the United States

The tremendous economic strength of the United States is a potent factor in world affairs. War, or threat of war, in the past has often been the final arbiter in international disputes, and America's economic status, as a reflection of its military potential, has since 1917 been one of the basic components of world power relations. The economic power of the United States is based primarily upon the nation's possession of essential commodities, such as food, petroleum, and steel, its position as a market, and its control of funds and credits which are advanced to less wealthy countries.

Of the nearly 3,000,000 square miles of land area nearly one quarter is classed as arable. Actually the United States is one of the few nations of the world which has been systematically reducing its total amount of cultivated land; about three quarters of the area classified as arable is actually in crops. In normal times the nation produces surpluses of such commodities as wheat, corn, and other grains, and of cotton and tobacco, and is virtually self-sufficient in wool, meats, fruits, and vegetables.

In terms of industrial output the United States annually produces nearly 45 per cent of the world's steel. The miracle of American production has resulted in part from the tremendous market available to United States producers. The forty-eight states are in effect in an economic union with one another, since no trade barriers of any kind exist between them and production on a mass basis can thus be developed for the large national market. The flexibility of industrial production permits the United States to match the flexibility of military demands, and not only keep abreast of technical developments in the military field but also to expand or contract military or consumer output on short notice when the situation warrants the move.

From 1946 through 1956 the United States extended over 55 billion dollars worth of goods and credits to foreign countries in order to build up their economic strength and to aid them in arming against possible attack; this figure is part of a continuing program which represents large-scale American commitments to foreign areas. Despite this foreign aid, however, the nation's wealth has been in several respects a detriment to relations with other countries. For one thing, the existence of large agricultural surpluses has tended to create resentment on the part of the peoples in such countries as India, where a large segment of the population has insufficient food. Secondly, the great economic development within the United States tends to build psychological barriers between it and some of the less-developed states of the world, for the peoples in these areas feel that the American people cannot possibly understand or appreciate their problems of poverty. Finally, because of its market potential and its control of large-scale foreign aid, the United States occupies a position of great power and responsibility with respect to the economies of many other states. Consequently, the United States is frequently criticized for various situations which may adversely affect the economic conditions of individual nations, even though these matters (for instance, a drop in the price of copper or coffee) may be entirely beyond the power of United States officials to control.

Territorial Growth

The United States became an independent nation in 1783. At that time its area was just over 800,000 square miles, but almost immediately the new nation began to expand in a westward direction. Little resistance was encountered from other powers during this expansion. There was no political unit on the west coast of sufficient strength to expand eastward toward the Great Plains and challenge the supremacy of the eastern states. The center of power in Mexico lay nearly 1,000 miles to the south of America's path of westward progress, while to the north in Canada energies were being devoted for the most part to problems of development of the eastern regions, rather than to interference with American expansion to the west. Although territorial disputes with both the Mexicans and Canadians arose

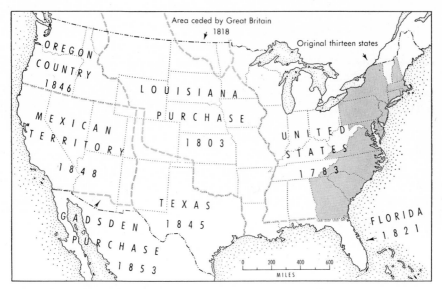

Figure 15. United States: Territorial Growth.

during the first half of the nineteenth century, they were eventually settled
with few lasting ill effects. By 1853 the United States had reached its present
size and shape (Figure 15).

The division of the nation into forty-eight states was not completed
until 1912, when New Mexico and Arizona were admitted. The process of
delimiting state boundaries was a complex politico-geographic one in certain areas, reflecting both the nature of the land itself and the interplay
of "pressure politics" in the United States Congress, where the decisions as
to the limits of new states were ultimately made.[3] The frequent use of
rivers, mountain crests, and straight lines, particularly west of the Mississippi,
reflects the fact that here, as in Latin America and Africa, political borders
are largely of the antecedent type, that is, laid down before the advent of
appreciable settlement in the border areas. As in the case of the external
boundaries of the country, the stability of the state boundaries stands out
in contrast to the more changeable internal political patterns in such nations
as the Soviet Union, India, or China.

The relative security from foreign aggression—occasioned both by location and by the preoccupation of European powers in Continental wars

---

[3] For accounts of disputes over state boundaries see Isaiah Bowman, "An American Boundary
Dispute: Decision of the Supreme Court of the United States with Respect to the Texas-Oklahoma
Boundary," *The Geographical Review*, XIII, No. 2 (April, 1923), 161–90; and Benjamin E.
Thomas, "Boundaries and Internal Problems of Idaho," *The Geographical Review*, XXXIX, No. 1
(January, 1949), 99–109.

—which America enjoyed during the early years of its development, was, of course, an asset of primary importance to the young nation. Since colonial times no other country of the Western Hemisphere has possessed power commensurate with that of the United States. This virtual immunity from attack enabled the United States to develop its considerable resources without the liabilities of extensive military expenditures, which most young independent countries are forced to assume.

Centrifugal and Centripetal Forces

The factors of distance and of diversity of physical elements, including surface configuration and climate, have represented important centrifugal forces in the United States. Population is distributed unevenly over a large area of land, and peoples in different parts of the nation have developed divergent opinions with regard to national and international issues. Evidence may be found in the general distribution of "segregationists," "isolationists," and "high-tariff men."

The most important of the centripetal forces have been the great mobility of the American population and the development of a strong circulatory system, including modern transportation facilities and the "standardization" of much of American culture as the result of a common language and mass communication media. The fact that there have been no nearby

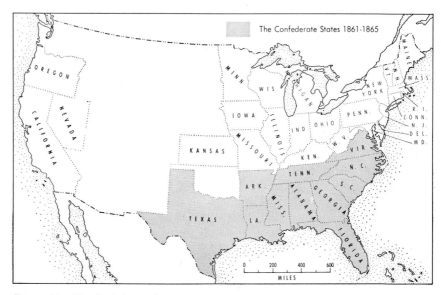

The Confederate States 1861-1865

Figure 16. The Confederate States, 1861–65.

powers tending to attract segments of the United States away from Washington's control has also contributed to the unity of the country.

There were times, of course, in the nation's development when strong divisive forces did appear. The territories of Kentucky and Tennessee, isolated from the east by the Appalachians, threatened for a time to withdraw from the nation, and the Republic of Texas existed for ten years as an independent state before becoming incorporated within the United States. The most serious threat to national unity occurred in 1861, when eleven Southern states, comprising one quarter of the nation's area and about eighteen per cent of its population, seceded from the Union and announced the formation of the new Confederacy (Figure 16). The Northern armies, however, succeeded in restoring the political cohesion of the nation.

Since the end of the Civil War the problems of reconciling regional interests with those of the nation as a whole have been reflected both in the patterns of voting in Congress and in the struggle for power between the state and federal governments. Interregional voting blocs, composing such diverse groups as, for example, Southern Democrats and Midwest Republicans, have succeeded in obtaining the passage of Congressional bills favoring the interests of particular geographic areas. The changing distribution of population in the United States has, of course, influenced the activities of regional groups, as evidenced in the relative decline in the political strength of the northeastern urban areas during recent decades. The struggle between the state and federal governments is shown in the conflicts over hydroelectric-power developments, taxation policies, and control of the submerged lands off the nation's coasts (see page 72). Such a struggle is endemic to any political system in which power is divided between the national and the state or provincial bodies, but it is particularly strong in the United States, due to the relative power of the individual states.

International Boundaries

Although the United States borders only two other nations, the length of its boundaries totals over 5,900 miles, of which 4,000 are with Canada and 1,900 with Mexico. Over half of the border with Canada follows water bodies, including the St. Lawrence River, the Great Lakes, Lake of the Woods, and the straits of Georgia and Juan de Fuca between Washington and British Columbia (Figures 17 and 18). West of Lake Superior the boundary trends in a general northwesterly direction to the northwestern corner of the Lake of the Woods. This is the northernmost position of the boundary; from here it runs due south for about twenty-five miles until it meets the 49th parallel. In so doing it cuts off from Canada a peninsula which extends into the lake from the western shore. This peninsula, surrounded on three sides by water and on the fourth by the province of

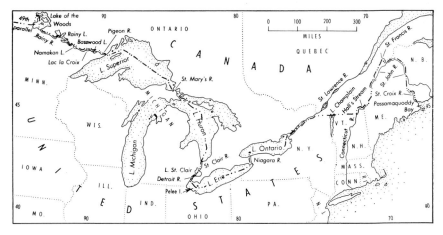

Figure 17. United States-Canadian Boundary—Eastern Sector.

Manitoba, is, in effect, an American enclave in Canada. After reaching the 49th parallel south of this peninsula, the boundary turns west and follows the parallel for nearly 900 miles until it reaches an arm of the Pacific.

The Mexican border, starting at the Gulf of Mexico, follows the Rio Grande for 1,210 miles to El Paso, Texas. From here it consists of a series of straight lines, except for twenty miles in the west where the Colorado River separates the two nations (Figure 19).

The boundaries between the United States and its two neighbors are somewhat unique; first, in that they are completely unfortified and, second, in the ease of border crossing. No passports are required of citizens of the adjoining countries, and millions of persons cross the borders each year

Figure 18. United States-Canadian Boundary—Northwestern Sector.

as commuters, tourists, and temporary inhabitants. No quotas are maintained on permanent immigration in either direction across the United States-Canadian or United States-Mexican borders, although there are restrictions as to the number who may cross as temporary laborers in the United States from Mexico. Along each border an International Boundary Commission, composed of representatives of the two adjoining nations, acts as a permanent body for inspection of the borders, repair or replacement of border markers, and determination of the exact border location in cases of dispute. Along the United States-Mexican border the International Boundary Commission, in addition to its other tasks, also handles water problems involving the two countries. An International Joint Commission maintains jurisdiction over the use, obstruction, diversion, and pollution of joint United States-Canadian waterways and of waters that cross the border from one nation to the other.

Several important disputes have arisen between the United States and its neighbors, most of them in connection with common water features. Chicago's diversion of the waters of Lake Michigan, for use in its navigation-sanitation canal running westward to the Illinois River, has brought protests from the Canadian government because of the lowering of the Great Lakes and St. Lawrence River and the resultant navigation hazards. Power development at Niagara Falls and navigation and power developments on the St. Lawrence are also matters which require joint United States-Canadian action.

The division of water for irrigation in both the Rio Grande and the Colorado River has created problems for the United States and Mexico. Although about half the water in the Rio Grande comes from Mexican tributaries, the United States normally takes about eighty per cent of the

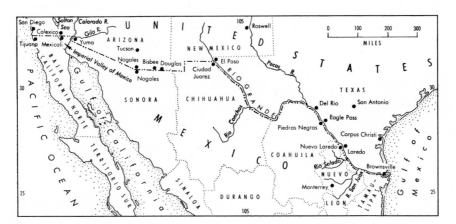

Figure 19. United States-Mexican Boundary.

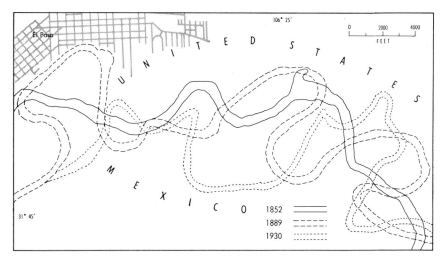

Figure 20. Fluctuations of the Rio Grande Between the United States and Mexico. (After map by International Boundary and Water Commission, United States and Mexico. Used by permission.)

water used for irrigation. On the other hand, all the water in the Colorado River comes from American sources, yet Mexico's Imperial Valley depends upon the Colorado for irrigation. Treaties were eventually evolved to regulate the quantities of water each country might take out of the Rio Grande and Colorado.

Two other United States-Mexican border problems involve the location of the Rio Grande and illegal immigration from Mexico. The Rio Grande below El Paso flows in part through a broad flood plain, with the river meandering considerably and often changing its course. Not only is the boundary lengthened by the meanders, but, with a shift of the main channel, areas formerly in one country become included in the other (Figure 20). In 1933 a program was undertaken for flood control and straightening the channel of the Rio Grande, and the middle of the deepest channel now serves to mark the international border.

The problem of the Mexican "wetbacks" (so called because many of them swim the Rio Grande to get to the United States) has been a frequent source of friction between the United States and Mexico. Each year the United States government officially contracts for the temporary services of a certain number of Mexicans as agricultural workers, particularly in the south central and southwestern states. By means of this contract system, smuggling, traffic in narcotics, and the spread of disease can be watched, and the interests of the laborers protected against exploitation by American farmers. By this means, too, the wage levels of contract Mexican laborers, as well as of American workers, are maintained, for the illegal immigrant will generally work for lower wages than will either of these other two groups. The lure of higher wages in the United States, however, attracts far more Mexicans than are handled by the contract system; as a result hundreds of thousands cross the border illegally, and, despite the efforts of immigration authorities, probably over half the "wetbacks" escape detection and remain for indefinite periods of time in the United States.

TERRITORIAL CONTROL OVERSEAS

United States Possessions

The growth of the American overseas empire began in the 1850's, when tiny Howland, Baker, and Jarvis islands in the mid-Pacific were acquired because of their guano deposits, which were being exploited by United States companies. In 1867 the Midway islands were also annexed, and in the same year the United States purchased Alaska from Russia for $7,200,000. Although at the time of the purchase the United States showed little interest in Alaska, the territory has since proved extremely valuable in terms of resources (gold, fish, furs, timber) and of strategic location. Five years later American Samoa was obtained as a naval base. In 1898, upon the petition of its government, Hawaii became a United States possession, and following the war with Spain (1898) Puerto Rico and the Philippines were also acquired. Construction of the Panama Canal in the early years of the twentieth century led to the granting by Panama of a perpetual lease over the Canal Zone. In 1917 the Virgin Islands, east of Puerto Rico, were purchased from Denmark to protect the eastern approaches to the canal. Thus by the end of World War I the American empire totalled nearly 700,000 square miles in area, placing it eighth in size among the empires of the world. With the exception of Alaska, virtually all the United States possessions were of particular naval significance, indicating the trend of thinking prevalent among statesmen during the years when the United States was taking its position among the leading political powers of the world.

Since 1920 two major developments have occurred in America's overseas territories. These are, first, the granting of independence to the Philippines in 1946 and, second, the acquisition of United Nations trusteeships over the former Japanese-mandated islands in the central and western Pacific following World War II. As a result of these changes the empire of the United States totals 598,000 square miles and slightly less than four million persons.

Overseas territories have several possible values to the mother country. They may serve as sites for bases, as sources for raw materials, or as areas for investments or marketing of the mother country's products. They may also be potential regions for emigration from the homeland, and the local inhabitants may provide cheap labor or be available for service in the armed forces. The United States possessions fulfill some but not all of these requirements. Political control of Alaska, the Canal Zone, and the island areas affords the United States sites for military bases. Raw materials are provided by Alaska, and both Hawaii and Puerto Rico are important markets and areas for investments. On the other hand, few Americans emigrate; rather, thousands of territorial residents, particularly from Puerto Rico, come each year to reside in the United States, most of them in the hope of obtaining better employment. Finally, the territorial population forms a small potential labor supply or military pool for use by the United States. The overseas possessions have never assumed as important a role in United States affairs as have, for example, the territories of Britain, France, and the Netherlands in those nation's activities.

Control of the United States over its various overseas possessions is in a state of gradual change. Puerto Rico has become a commonwealth, and both Hawaii and Alaska desire statehood. Some degree of internal autonomy may eventually be granted to American Samoa. Despite the variations in the political status of the overseas areas there is little pressure for independence on the part of the peoples of these regions. Consequently the American empire represents a stable political entity in size and in geographical distribution.

Political Problems of the North Atlantic Bases

The threat of Soviet territorial aggression in western Europe in the years following World War II led to the formation in 1949 of the North Atlantic Treaty Organization (NATO), which united the United States and Canada with ten European nations.[4] One major feature of this agreement has been that the United States has undertaken to assist in the military build-up of its European allies, in order to bolster western Europe against possible invasion from the east and to maintain air and naval supremacy over the North Atlantic Ocean itself.

Associated with NATO has been the development of United States military bases on foreign soil throughout the general North Atlantic area. These bases serve both the purpose of offense against a potential enemy and of defense for Anglo-America itself. The first group of bases is located in Europe and in Morocco; the second group stretches from Greenland through the central Atlantic; the third group is in Canada, Bermuda, and on some of the Caribbean islands (Figure 21).

All manner of political problems are associated with the development

---

[4] Belgium, Denmark, France, Great Britain, Iceland, Italy, Luxembourg, the Netherlands, Norway, and Portugal. West Germany, Greece, and Turkey have subsequently been added to the organization.

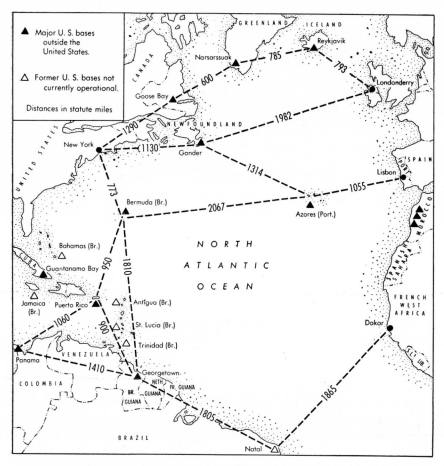

Figure 21. Major United States Bases in the North Atlantic, 1956. The two bases in Canada are actually Canadian-controlled, but a portion of each base is set aside for American military use.

of the network of United States bases: the conduct of military personnel on foreign soil, the continued granting of permission for the maintenance of foreign installations within a country, and the extent of United States sovereignty over the area granted to it. Morocco's achievement of independence has meant that the treaty between the United States and France, providing for the maintenance of American bases in Morocco, is no longer effective. Any treaty between the United States and Morocco concerning continued United States operation of the bases there must take into account Morocco's special interests, particularly its need for large-scale financial aid. In a somewhat different situation, the Icelandic government in 1956 requested that the United States abandon its base on the island. Although the government withdrew its request after the Soviet military action in Hungary in the fall of 1956, the event points up the extent to which "neutralism" may develop even among NATO members, particularly during times in which Cold War pressures are eased. The problem of maintaining United States bases on foreign soil involves not only NATO members but also such countries as Spain, Libya, Saudi Arabia, the Philippines, and Japan, where American military installations are also located.

Canada

The Dominion of Canada is the largest of the three political units in Anglo-America. Its more than 3,800,000 square miles of territory place it third in size among the nations of the world, yet most of this area has a population density of less than one person per square mile. Over one-half the dominion's population of 15,400,000 lives within 100 miles of the United States border, and most of the remaining within 200 miles of the border (Figure 22).

In Canada, as in the United States, distance and variations in the physical landscape are important centrifugal forces. The country measures over 3,000 miles from east to west, and consists of several major physiographic regions—the Eastern Mountains, the St. Lawrence Lowland, the Canadian Shield, the Interior Plains, the Western Upland, and the Arctic Islands. These regions are important not only because of economic diversity but also because of their effect on population distribution. The latter is particularly true with respect to the Canadian Shield, a 2,000,000 square-mile area of thin soils and generally poor agricultural potential. Because of the scarcity of population and transport facilities throughout much of Canada, the difficulties of effective organization of these northern regions represent an important problem confronting the Canadian government and people.

Canada's Economy

Agriculture, manufacturing, and the extractive industries (mining, lumbering, and fishing) are important aspects of the Canadian economy. In minerals and power fuels the nation is unbelievably rich. Canada leads the world in the production of nickel, platinum, asbestos, and radium; stands second in zinc; third in copper and gold; and fourth in lead. It is second or third in developed hydroelectric power, while its reserves of three other important commodities—iron ore, petroleum, and coal—are of vast and undetermined amounts. The nation has advanced to a position

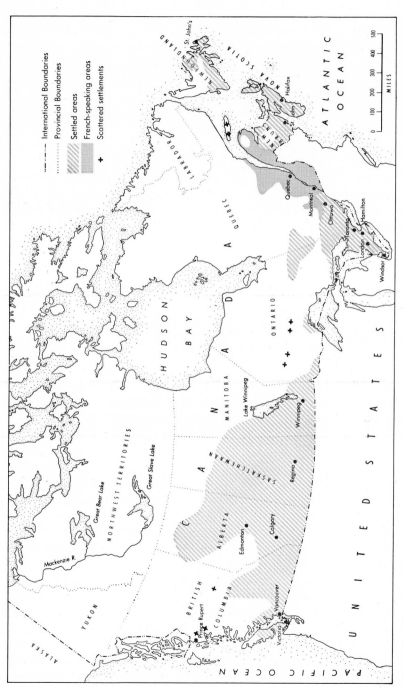

Figure 22. Canada.

International Boundaries
Provincial Boundaries
Settled areas
French-speaking areas
Scattered settlements

MILES
0 100 200 300 400 500

ATLANTIC OCEAN

NEWFOUNDLAND
St. John's
NOVA SCOTIA
Halifax
NEW BRUNSWICK
St. John
LABRADOR
QUEBEC
Quebec
Montreal
Ottawa
Hamilton
Toronto
London
Windsor
HUDSON BAY
ONTARIO
CANADA
MANITOBA
Lake Winnipeg
Winnipeg
SASKATCHEWAN
Regina
NORTHWEST TERRITORIES
Great Bear Lake
Great Slave Lake
ALBERTA
Edmonton
Calgary
Mackenzie R.
YUKON
BRITISH COLUMBIA
Prince Rupert
Vancouver
Victoria
ALASKA
UNITED STATES
PACIFIC OCEAN

of fifth among the industrial nations of the world in terms of steel output, and with its tremendous resource base it undoubtedly is destined to develop much further in the future. One of the principal facets of Canada's economy is that the nation is a major supplier to the United States of industrial raw materials, such as nickel, asbestos, and wood pulp; this trade represents a considerable source of income for the Canadians.

Agricultural land is limited by the short growing season, rough terrain, and infertile soils to about one-sixth of the nation's total area. Although these limitations are cited as obstacles to Canada's population growth, many experts agree that in the future the dominion could well support over 40,000,000 persons. Canada is one of the world's leading producers of grains; the wheat crop alone averages over 600,000,000 bushels a year. Like their American counterparts, Canadian farmers are often troubled by the existence of surplus crops, for which no markets can be found.

Territorial Development

The development of control by the Canadian government over the vast dominion may be studied from two approaches: the growth and unification of Canada itself, and the evolution of Canadian independence from Great Britain. Both processes are too long and complicated to be described in detail; hence only a few salient events will be noted. Canada was settled during the seventeenth and eighteenth centuries by both French and British colonists. The British were largely in Newfoundland and at settlements in the Hudson Bay area; the French settled in Nova Scotia and the lower St. Lawrence Valley. Warfare between France and Britain in Europe was reflected in the New World by frequent skirmishes between the colonists. In 1713 France yielded to Britain her claims to Hudson Bay, Newfoundland, and Nova Scotia. Fifty years later, as a result of the British victory in the French and Indian War, all of Canada, with the exception of the two small islands of St. Pierre and Miquelon just south of Newfoundland, became the possession of Great Britain.

In its early years as a British colony, Canada found it necessary to assimilate three diverse groups—Frenchmen, Scots, and American Tories. The 65,000 Catholic Frenchmen, proud of their language, religion, and customs, were determined to maintain their cultural indentity in the new political area. The descendants of the Scotch Highlanders had migrated to Canada in the early eighteenth century as a result of an oppressive policy on the part of the London government toward Scotland. In 1763 these persons considered themselves the logical "heirs" to the new British colony. The third group comprised the approximately 40,000 American Loyalists, who left the United States (particularly New England) at the close of the American Revolution and settled in Canada.

Canada's political unity and eventual self-rule were slow in coming. Not until 1867 did the area become a federated political region with a parliament of its own; at that time Ontario, Quebec, Nova Scotia, and New Brunswick were joined together. Two years later the Hudson's Bay Company relinquished control of the Prairie provinces to the colonial government, and in 1871, upon the promise by the Ottawa administration to link the two coasts with a transcontinental railroad, British Columbia on the Pacific coast joined the federation. Canada has been a self-governing dominion only since the end of World War I. At the Peace Conference of Paris in 1919 the various dominions of the British Empire were accorded representation in the League of Nations as though they were independent states, but not until the Imperial Conference of 1926 were the dominions officially recognized as equal partners with Britain in the British Commonwealth. Their status of equality was legally recognized in 1931 by the Statute of Westminster.

Together with political freedom, economic independence has also come gradually. In 1929 Britain accounted for 31 per cent of the dominion's exports and 15 per cent of her imports. By 1955 the same export and import percentages were 18 and 8 respectively. The tremendous contributions of Canada to Britain during World War II, both in military power and in economic assistance, helped to raise the status of the dominion closer to one of equality with the former mother country. Although Canada is a member of the Commonwealth trading bloc and thus enjoys special economic ties with Britain, it would be wrong to assume that it is in any position of political or economic subservience to the British. Close ties bind the two nations together, but as equals rather than as mother country and dependency. For all practical purposes British control in northern Anglo-America has disappeared.

Newfoundland. Newfoundland presents an interesting example of regional political geography. It illustrates the point that the expense of government operations may be a critical factor in a state's capacity to exist as a self-governing political unit.

During Canada's development Newfoundland—together with Labrador—remained a separate British governorship. In 1926 Newfoundland was awarded dominion status, but eight years later the area found itself economically unable to continue the responsibilities of self-government. The island dominion, with few natural resources, was not involved in the great economic expansion Canada was beginning to undergo. Consequently Newfoundland voluntarily accepted a temporary end to its dominion status and inclusion within the British Empire as a special category of colony. This return to colonialism was followed in 1948 by a general referendum among the peoples of Newfoundland to decide between three alternatives: continued colonial status for another five years, confederation with Canada, or return of dominion status as it existed prior to 1934. Proponents of confederation with Canada were successful in the ballotting, and in March, 1949, Newfoundland—along with Labrador—became Canada's tenth province. There are actually few parallel cases in modern history of voluntary renunciation of independence by a nation's citizens.

The Modern Canadian Nation

Canada is divided politically into two parts—the northern territories and the ten provinces. Most of the region north of the 60th parallel consists of two federal areas—Yukon and the Northwest Territories. Only a few thousand persons live within this area, which comprises 42 per cent of the dominion. South of 60° are the provinces, where the bulk of Canada's population is grouped in four main areas: the Maritime sector along the Atlantic coast, the upper St. Lawrence Valley and eastern Great Lakes region, the southern and central parts of the Prairie provinces, and the Pacific coast. These areas are shown quite prominently in Figure 22. The second of the areas (consisting of southern Quebec and Ontario provinces) is the political and economic heart of the country, possessing nearly half the total population. Ottawa, located in this core area, represents a compromise capital between English- and French-speaking Canada, since it lies on the linguistic border between the two.

Population

Canada's population has grown from 2,750,000 in 1851 to over 15,000,-000 in 1955, an increase of nearly 450 per cent in about a century. Since 1900 over 8,000,000 persons have immigrated to Canada, most of them from northern and eastern Europe. The structure of the population by national origin in 1955 was approximately as follows: British and American, 48 per cent; French, 31 per cent; German, 4 per cent; Ukrainian, 3 per cent; others, 14 per cent (including about 75,000 Asiatics and 170,000 Indians and Eskimos). Religiously the nation is divided into the following faiths: Protestant, 49 per cent; Roman Catholic, 43 per cent; others, 8 per cent. Since the majority of those of French descent retain their French speech and Catholic faith, there would seem to be a basis for national weakness. One Canadian writer has complained that the French-speaking peoples refer to themselves as "Canadien," to the rest as "les Anglais," while to the English-speaking majority *they* are the Canadians, and the French-speaking portion "French-Canadian."[5] The French outnumber the English-speaking population only in Quebec province; here the ratio is better than four to one. The birth rate of the French Canadians is higher

---

[5] Hugh MacLennan, "The Psychology of Canadian Nationalism," *Foreign Affairs*, XXVII, No. 3 (April, 1949), 417.

than that of the English-speaking groups, and as a result the ethnic composition of Canada is gradually changing. The distribution is also changing, for the French-speaking settlements are expanding into northern New Brunswick and into eastern and northern Ontario.

The fact that the French- and English-speaking peoples of Canada work together as well as they do is the result of several historical causes. In 1774 Britain's parliament passed the Quebec Act, guaranteeing to the French Canadians freedom of religion, freedom to preserve their own language, and to continue to practice civil law. This act still forms the basic framework within which the two linguistic groups exist side by side. There are actually few nations in the world in which the language and culture of a large minority group have been so carefully protected as in Canada.

A second reason is that the French nation has never tried to work through the French Canadians to undermine British (or Canadian) power, as, for example, the Germans worked through the Sudeten Czechs in 1938. Actually, there are few ties left between France and French Canada; France is in no way a champion of the French Canadians. Thus the French-speaking peoples of Canada represent one of the few minority groups which retain the culture of their former homeland but have severed most of the ties of sentiment and loyalty. Another cause for peaceful relations in Canada has been the remarkable tact and diplomacy displayed by Canadian leaders, among them the long-time Prime Minister, W. L. Mackenzie King, who skillfully managed to avoid head-on collisions between members of the two linguistic groups for over three decades. Finally, both French- and English-speaking Canadians are united in their determination to remain independent of foreign control. The concept of nation is thus quite a strong centripetal force in this country.

Canada's Military Position

The strategic importance of Canada's location in the Air Age can perhaps best be demonstrated by a polar projection map, illustrating great-circle routes between Anglo-America and the U.S.S.R. (Figure 23). Anglo-America and the Soviet Union face one another across the Arctic Ocean; from the northern coast of Canada it is about 2,500 miles in a direct line to the Soviet mainland. Two radar networks now exist across Canada as warning systems against the approach of hostile aircraft from the north. In addition, a 3,000 mile "Distant Early Warning" line—a radar project which will stretch from Baffin Island in the east to northwestern Alaska—is under construction 1,400 miles north of the United States-Canada border. Canadian airfields are scattered about the northern sectors of the nation, and five joint Canadian-American weather stations have been established in the islands north of the Canadian mainland. The United States

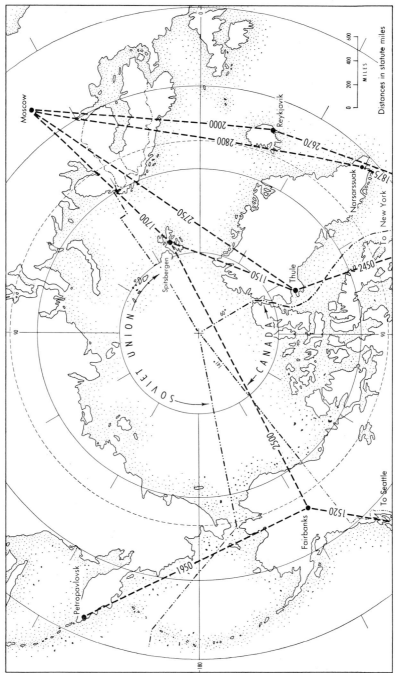

Figure 23. The Arctic Basin: Political Control and Major Air Bases.
Spitsbergen, although it has no military installations, is shown because of its strategic location. Distances in statute miles.

maintains large air installations in Newfoundland (Gander) and Labrador (Goose Bay), and is developing facilities on Baffin Island (Frobisher Bay). Air protection is further afforded from American bases in northern United States, Alaska, and Greenland.

Defense needs and the development of economic resources (uranium, petroleum, iron ore) in northern Canada are hastening the construction of transportation facilities in the former wilderness area, and are acquainting scientists and engineers with the climate and other physical handicaps of the region. Airlines are being expanded, often utilizing planes equipped with pontoons or skis in the absence of prepared landing strips. Waterways, such as the Mackenzie River, flowing north to the Arctic Ocean, now serve as important transportation routes, and there has been a marked increase in highway and railroad construction in sparsely-settled areas of Canada during the past two decades. Research groups are investigating the effects of arctic cold on new types of clothing, shelter, lubricants, and paving material, as a prelude to Canada's role as a major economic and military power.

As custodians of a rich, independent area, only beginning to be developed, the peoples of Canada occupy a vital position in the world political structure. Their national growth is of great concern to the United States, Britain, and the other members of the Atlantic community, as well as to the Soviet Union and countries of the Pacific basin. Already Canada must be considered as one of the major powers of the world.

Alaska

Alaska, the largest outlying territory of the United States, has an area of 571,000 square miles and a population of about 155,000 persons, of whom some 35,000, or about one-fifth, are Aleuts, Eskimos, or Indians. Purchased from Russia shortly after the end of the Civil War, it became a territory by Act of Congress in 1912, with its own legislative assembly and with one nonvoting delegate elected biennially to the United States House of Representatives. Increased development of resources and the expansion of military facilities in the strategic area have been responsible for the trebling of the territory's inhabitants since 1930. Accompanying this population increase have been growing pressures for Alaska's admittance to the United States as a state, thereby granting its peoples voting representation in Congress.

Within Alaska important population concentrations are few and widely separated from one another. The southern part of the territory—including the southeastern Panhandle—consists of a series of mountain ranges which tend to isolate the central lowland from the southern coast. The central region, drained by the Yukon, opens westward to the Bering Sea. North of this is the Brooks Range, and beyond it a broad plain which slopes north-ward to the Arctic Ocean.

The three areas of population concentration are (1) the southeast, including the Juneau-Skagway region, (2) the Seward-Anchorage district to the west along the southern coast, and (3) the Fairbanks region some 200 miles north of Anchorage in the Yukon lowland. Included within the second district is the Matanuska Valley, one of the most promising agricul-tural regions in Alaska. The Alaskan capital, Juneau, is located in the south-east, and was one of the early towns of the territory. It is outranked in population by both Anchorage and Fairbanks. In years to come pressure may develop in Alaska for a shift of the capital to a more centrally-located area.

Economy

Alaska's economy is based primarily upon the devolpment of three resources—fish, fur, and minerals—of which fishing (particularly salmon) represents about 70 per cent of the total income. Gold is the most important mineral produced, but the territory is known to have extensive coal deposits and there is the possibility of large-scale petroleum resources. The potential for water-power development is very good, particularly in southern Alaska. In the southeast permission of the Canadian government would be neces-sary before large-scale power projects could be undertaken, for most of the essential water is on the Canadian side of the border. The Canadians, already involved in hydroelectric developments of their own, have been re-luctant to grant United States concerns permission to utilize Canadian rivers for giant Alaskan power plants. Another Alaskan resource is lumber, but the cost of transportation to the United States is so high that Alaskan lumber has little chance of competing with American or Canadian lumber in the United States market.

A final economic value of Alaska to the United States is its potential role as a settlement area, but here again there has been relatively little activity. Only about eleven per cent of the territory is considered suitable for settlement, and the principal "pioneer" activity has taken place in the Matanuska Valley, north of Anchorage, where some 2,000 persons from the United States have undertaken to settle and farm the area since 1935.

The Federal government controls 99.86 per cent of Alaska, leaving only a small area for private ownership. Federal ownership was set up by Con-gress to protect the territory's natural resources against unwise commercial exploitation. Mining and timber rights on government-owned land are leased to private concerns; but throughout the greater part of Alaska little eco-nomic development has taken place. One drawback to economic develop-ment has been the lack of adequate transportation facilities. There are only two main railroads in Alaska—a 509-mile line connecting Fairbanks with

Seward, and the much shorter White Pass and Yukon Railroad connecting Skagway with White Horse, Canada. The Yakutat and Southern is a small line, serving the fishing area at the northern end of the Panhandle. Not until 1942 was a direct overland road completed between Alaska and the United States. The Alcan Highway, forming a major portion of this route, connects Fairbanks with Dawson Creek, British Columbia, a Canadian road and rail head. Ships, operating mostly from Seattle, still constitute the principal link and almost exclusive freight mover between the United States and its largest possession. Airlines now represent an additional means of communication.

Defense Position

Alaska is located close to the Soviet Union; Attu Island, at the western end of the Aleutians, is but 200 miles from the Soviet-controlled Komandorski Islands and 600 miles from the Kamchatka Peninsula, while to the north, the Alaskan and Siberian mainlands are 56 miles from one another across the Bering Strait.

The development of large-scale military operations in Alaska has been a recent phenomenon. The great-circle route between the American Northwest and the Japanese islands lies across southern Alaska, and during World War II defense installations were constructed in various parts of the territory. In 1942 Japanese forces occupied several islands in the western Aleutians, and enemy attacks were made on the Alaskan mainland. The conclusion of peace with Japan in 1945 was soon followed by an increase in tension between the United States and the Soviet Union, and again Alaska's military importance became evident. Eventually United States defense officials decided upon an Alaskan "Heartland" defense concept, which called for the maintenance of three large air bases—two in the vicinity of Fairbanks (Ladd and Eielson fields) and one in the neighborhood of Anchorage (Elmendorf Field). These are supplemented by several smaller fields, among them bases at Nome and on the Aleutians. The presence of radar screens, a strong antiaircraft defense, ground forces to protect the air bases, and, of course, naval support along the coasts, constitute the supplementary elements of this "air-defense" project. The locational significance of these bases may be illustrated by the fact that Fairbanks lies 2,900 miles from the Manchurian border, 1,500 miles from Seattle, and 3,200 miles from New York. In American hands these bases represent a menace to eastern Siberia; in Soviet hands they would be a far greater menace to the United States.

The Alaskan-Canadian Boundary

In 1898 a dispute arose between Great Britain and the United States over the location of the Alaskan-Canadian boundary in the Panhandle

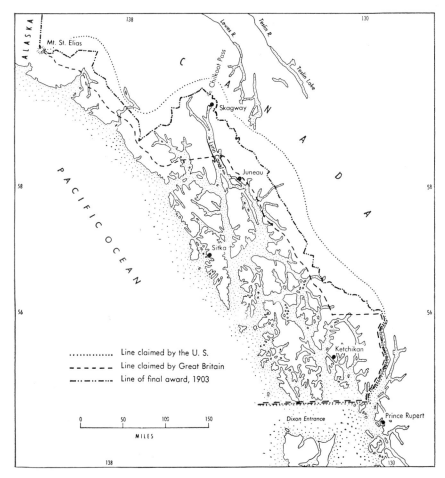

Figure 24. Southeast Alaska-Canadian Boundary: Controversy and Settlement. Note how the final award denied Canada access to the sea north of Prince Rupert. (After Bemis, *A Diplomatic History of the United States.* Used by permission of Henry Holt & Co., copyright 1936, 1942, 1950, 1955.)

section, southeast of Mount St. Elias. The Treaty of 1825 between Russia and Britain fixed the Panhandle boundary ". . . along the summit of the mountains parallel to the coast," leaving ambiguous the allocation of indentations which extended inland past the coastal ranges (Figure 24). When control of Alaska passed to the United States, the nation's statesmen assumed, as the Russians had, that the salt water indentations were part of Alaskan territory, but with the discovery of gold in the Klondike the route north from Skagway, at the head of the Lynn Canal, became one of great significance. British authorities in Canada then claimed that by the terms of the 1825 treaty Skagway and the upper Lynn Canal, as well as the upper portions of the other indentations, were Canadian territory. The dispute was eventually submitted to arbitration, and in 1903 a compromise line was agreed upon which retained the indentations within Alaskan territory.

The Alaskan-Canadian boundary dispute points up the unusual situation of one nation's possession controlling much of another nation's coast line. Were it not for the fact that Britain—and, more recently, Canada—had no particular need for access to the Pacific through northern British Columbia, it is probable that the Russian and American claims to control of this coast would have been more strenuously opposed than was actually the case. There has been some talk of a possible "swap" between Canadian and Alaskan interests here—the award to Canada of a corridor to the sea through the Alaskan Panhandle, in exchange for the use of Canadian rivers by Alaskan power plants.

Greenland

To the northeast of Canada lies Denmark's island possession of Greenland, with an area of 840,000 square miles and a population of about 25,000 persons. The country extends from 60° north latitude to nearly 84°, a point about 450 miles from the North Pole. Over three-fourths of the island is covered by a great mass of ice, in some places over 10,000 feet thick. Along the ice-free coast, particularly on the west, dwell the area's inhabitants, engaged for the most part in fishing.

The importance of Greenland to the world political pattern lies in its strategic location, both to trans-Arctic air routes and to the great-circle Atlantic route between Newfoundland and the British Isles (Cape Farewell at the southernmost tip of Greenland lies about 550 miles north of such a great-circle line). The new American air base at Thule in northwestern Greenland is 1,900 miles from New York and 2,800 miles from Moscow. Control of Greenland and its bases is an important element in global air strategy.

The island was settled by Icelanders shortly before A.D. 1000, and during the next two centuries a republic was maintained in southern Greenland. Norway gained control of the area in 1261 and maintained it until 1814, when Denmark was awarded possession. American interest in Greenland was not particularly strong until April, 1940, when German troops invaded and conquered Denmark. A year later the United States assumed responsibility for the defense of Greenland. The island was subsequently used both as an intermediate stop for air flights across the North Atlantic and as an area for the collection of valuable weather information. In the latitudes above about 30 degrees most of the weather moves in a general west-east direction, and much of the weather phenomena affecting Britain and northwest Europe have their origin on the Greenland icecaps. The port of Gronnedal was also used as a base by the U.S. Navy in its North Atlantic operations.

In April, 1951, the United States and Denmark signed an agreement providing for the joint defense of Greenland under the North Atlantic Treaty Organization. One of the key factors in Greenland's military position is the great American air base at Thule, nearly 700 miles north of the Arctic Circle. Greenland's economy has also been strengthened in the past few decades by new developments in the fishing industry. Instead of hunting for seals and walrus, many fishermen are now engaged in commercial fishing for mackerel, cod, and other species which have migrated northward in response to an apparent warming of the ocean waters. Political developments in Greenland have accompanied the growth of its economic and military importance. In June, 1953, the island became an integral part of the Kingdom of Denmark (an arrangement somewhat analogous to that of the proposed Alaskan statehood). For the first time Greenland has become something of an economic asset, and the Danes are now justly proud of their large overseas possession.

Problem Areas

1. The Submerged Lands Dispute

The controversy over submerged lands (sometimes incorrectly termed "tidelands") off the United States involves two issues of political control, one between the several states and the Federal government, and the other with respect to national offshore boundary claims. Several precedents have been established in the field of international law regarding submerged lands as a result of these disputes.

The impetus for the submerged lands controversy was provided initially by the discovery of petroleum beneath the floors of the Gulf of Mexico and Pacific Ocean and of methods of recovering such petroleum by drilling in water up to several hundred feet in depth. In September, 1945, President Truman issued a proclamation which asserted Federal control over mineral resources beneath the continental shelf[6] off the United States mainland, its territories, and possessions. The total area involved in this proclamation amounted to 760,000 square miles. Rough estimates of oil reserves beneath the continental shelf off the United States mainland alone run to 12–15 billion barrels, or as much as one-third of the present *proved* reserves in the United States. It was specifically stated in the proclamation that control of mineral resources did not affect navigation on the high seas above the shelf, nor did it extend the limits of the territorial waters of the United

---

[6] The continental shelf is that area extending seaward to a depth of about 600 feet, beyond which the ocean bottom drops off sharply.

States. In other words, the United States in 1945 claimed jurisdiction over resources alone, not sovereignty over the areas involved. Despite this clear distinction between types of jurisdiction, a number of Latin American states subsequently laid claim to sovereignty over large ocean areas off their coasts, in conformity with this "precedent" set by the United States.

At the time of the Truman proclamation, there already were conflicting claims to ownership of offshore areas within the national three-mile limit. Leases on the ocean floor for drilling purposes had been granted to oil companies by the coastal states since the early 1930's. The question of ownership of the ocean floor arose in connection with income received from the leases and the legality of these leases.

By 1937 officials of the Federal government had begun to question the rights of the various states (particularly Texas, California, and Louisiana) to issue leases on submerged coastal lands without the consent of Congress. Thus began a three-way political struggle, with Congress passing laws granting title to the states, the President vetoing the measures, and the Supreme Court acknowledging Federal ownership of offshore lands until such time as a law was enacted specifically granting title to the coastal states. Finally, in the spring of 1953 the Submerged Lands Act granting title to the various states was signed by President Eisenhower and became law.

Officials of certain of the coastal states maintained that their historic state boundaries exceeded the national three-mile offshore limit. Texas claimed control out to ten and one-half miles (three leagues) in the Gulf of Mexico, because prior to 1845 the legislature of the Lone Star Republic had proclaimed this limit as marking the country's seaward boundary. Florida likewise claimed ten and one-half miles as the boundary off its west coast in the Gulf of Mexico. The Submerged Lands Act grants the coastal states sovereignty over submerged lands within their "historic" boundaries— to a distance of three miles in the Atlantic and Pacific oceans, and to ten and one-half miles in the Gulf of Mexico.

Since 1793 the United States government has held the three-mile limit as marking the offshore boundary of United States sovereignty. The position was maintained at the International Congress at The Hague in 1930, and is used by the American delegates in their efforts to dissuade other powers from making unreasonable demands for offshore sovereignty in the case of their own coast lines. Extension of the control of Texas and west Florida to the ten and one-half mile limit carries with it the implication of United States control as well.

The presidential proclamation of 1945 and the passage of the Submerged Lands Act are of great significance to the political partitioning of previously unclaimed ocean areas. Will offshore control extend to ten and one-half miles only in the case of Texas and west Florida? What will be the American stand at future international conventions on limits to national sovereignty? The whole question of political control over the high seas has reached a critical stage: increased development of resources in ocean areas will eventually force a permanent decision on sovereignty to be made.

2. The Arctic Basin

The real political meaning of the Arctic Basin lies, first, in its strategic position between the two greatest power groups of the world and, second, in the gradual partitioning of the area among the states which are adjacent to it. Mention has already been made of the great-circle air routes between Eurasia and Anglo-America in terms of their paths across the Arctic areas. Since 1954 commercial airlines have maintained service via the Arctic between Europe and the west coasts of the United States and Canada. In defense against possible attack from Eurasia the United States and Canada cannot afford to have the Arctic too unexplored nor too empty of settlements, for without development it would represent a potential power vacuum close to the borders of the U.S.S.R. The creation of weapons for polar warfare, the pattern of bases and of warning systems, and the construction and maintenance of transportation facilities are matters which directly affect the security of both Anglo-America and of the Soviet Union. For this reason, the Arctic—despite its great expanses of empty areas—has become a vital theater for the interplay of global power forces, a region about which information on geography and military operations is only gradually being assembled. Here, then, is a clear example of the principle that, with changing conditions of technology and international affairs, new areas of the world come to have strategic importance in the pattern of power relations.

With respect to territorial control in the Arctic, the Dominion of Canada claims sovereignty over all land areas in a pie-shaped sector between longitudes 60° west and 141° west (the Canadian-Alaskan border) northward to the Pole (Figure 23).[7] Inclusion of Newfoundland as a Canadian province may prompt dominion authorities to expand their eastern limits to 53° west. In the Eastern Hemisphere the Soviet Union likewise claims sovereignty over the land areas in the Arctic northward from the U.S.S.R. to the Pole. To date the United States has made no such claims for the Arctic sector north of Alaska, although the presidential proclamation of 1945 would indicate United States control over mineral resources beneath the continental shelf off the Alaskan coast. Likewise, no claims to sovereignty have been made in the portion of the Arctic Basin which lies north of the Atlantic Ocean.

---

[7] The 60° border actually juts westward at one point where a portion of Greenland extends into this pie-shaped quadrant.

3. Statehood for Alaska

Since the end of World War II many of the people of Alaska have been agitating for admission of the territory into the United States as the 49th state (or 50th, if Hawaii should be admitted first). The rapid growth in Alaska's population since 1940, the area's military development, completion of overland connections between Alaska and the United States— these and other factors are cited as justification for statehood. Since Alaska's admission as a state would change the pattern of United States political control the factors for and against it will be treated briefly here.

Arguments against Alaskan statehood range from location and historical precedent to economics. On political grounds Alaskan statehood is opposed by some Republicans, who feel it would be normally a Democratic stronghold, and by certain "States' Rights" Democrats, who are concerned about the inclusion of two Alaskan senators and one representative in Congress. Because of its small population the new state would thus have a disproportionate power in Congress, as there would be one senator for less than 80,000 people and one representative for 155,000 as against, for example, New York, where there is one senator for 7,500,000 people and one representative for 350,000. This same contention of overrepresentation has been used against the admission of virtually every new state into the Union since 1783, but it still has political appeal. The noncontiguous nature of Alaska's location with respect to the United States is also cited (as also in the case of Hawaii) as cause for denying statehood. Each of the 48 states adjoins one or more of the others, while southeast Alaska is 400 miles north of the state of Washington.

Inability of the territory to meet the costs of state responsibilities is another point often mentioned. Some experts contend that the cost to Alaska of maintaining such services as public roads administration, fish and wildlife service, and public schools (all of which are now supported by the Federal government) will run as high as $14,000,000 per year. To raise the necessary funds the government would have to increase personal taxes considerably and/or levy heavy duties against the area's industries, particularly salmon fishing and mining establishments.

Arguments for Alaskan statehood are based first on popular demand. In 1946 a referendum was held in Alaska on the subject of statehood, and it was approved by a margin of three to two. Then there is the question of "taxation without representation." Unlike the Puerto Ricans, the residents of Alaska must pay Federal income taxes. Many persons also claim that Alaska's present population of nearly 155,000 persons justifies statehood, and they point to the fact that the territory now has more people than twenty-seven states did when they entered the Union.

Statehood for Alaska would give impetus to the territory's economic development. Most decisions concerning economic activities must be settled in Washington, rather than Juneau. Permission must be granted by Congress, for example, for any lumbering done on the over 99 per cent of Alaskan territory which is controlled by the Federal government. Some experts also disagree with the figure of $14,000,000 as the additional cost for public services, and hold $5,000,000 to $6,000,000 to be a more realistic estimate. This figure could easily be raised through taxation. Finally, proponents of statehood insist that the peoples of Alaska have earned the right to self-government through their economic, political, and cultural advances as a territory of the United States.

The factors pro and con concerning Alaskan statehood are of interest not only in this particular situation but also because they represent some of the arguments used in the advancement of self-government in other parts of the world. Particularly is it significant to note the problem of the economic ability of the government to carry out the responsibilities of independence or autonomy without undue taxation of the region's people and industries. Perhaps Alaska, with its resource base, can provide for the expense of self-government, while Newfoundland found this to be impossible.

BIBLIOGRAPHY

BEMIS, SAMUEL FLAGG. *A Diplomatic History of the United States.* New York: Henry Holt and Company, 1950.

An excellent treatise on U.S. territorial expansion, both domestic and overseas. Extremely good maps, prepared by S. Whittemore Boggs.

HARTSHORNE, RICHARD. "Racial Maps of the United States." *The Geographical Review,* XXVIII, No. 2 (April, 1938), 276–89.

Detailed maps and text (1930 census) showing distribution of Negroes, Mexicans, native Indians, Orientals, and foreign-born whites.

LAWRENCE, HENRY. "Waterway Problems on the Canadian Boundary," *Foreign Affairs,* IV, No. 4 (July, 1926), 556–74.

An excellent summary of background materials, particularly on the St. Lawrence Seaway and the Chicago Drainage Canal.

McGRATH, SIR PATRICK T. "The Labrador Boundary Decision," *The Geographical Review,* XVII, No. 4 (October, 1927), 643–61.

A comprehensive treatment of the Labrador-Quebec boundary dispute, including considerable historical data.

TEAL, JOHN J., JR. "Alaska, Fulcrum of Power," *Foreign Affairs,* XXVII, No. 1 (October, 1948), 86–96.

————. "Greenland and the World Around," *Foreign Affairs,* XXXI, No. 1 (October, 1952), 128–42.

These articles present well-balanced accounts of the strategic importance of the two areas.

TIMM, CHARLES A. "The International Boundary Commission—United States and Mexico." Austin: University of Texas Publication No. 4134, 1941.

A detailed summary of United States-Mexican border problems.

4

LATIN AMERICA

● Latin America is an area in transition. It includes that portion of the Western Hemisphere south of the United States,[1] a region roughly equal to Anglo-America in size and population, although differing from it in the complexity of its political pattern and in levels of economic development. The states of Latin America for nearly a century following the achievement of independence underwent relatively little economic, social, and political progress, and most of the area came under the dominant influence of the United States. In recent decades, however, new trends have appeared. Although legacies of the past still remain in many regions of Latin America, powerful forces for change have come into being in Mexico, Argentina, Brazil, and other of the republics. Because of the expanded circulatory systems many peoples have become aware of new ideas and of new wants. As a result, it is no longer possible to predict the pattern of relationships which will exist within and between the various states of this area or between Latin America and other parts of the world.

PHYSICAL FACTORS

Location. The area of Latin America stretches from 32° north latitude to 56° south latitude, but the bulk lies in, or adjacent to, the Tropics. Only in Chile, Argentina, and Uruguay does all or most of the national

---

[1] The area of Latin America is generally divided into two regions: *Middle America,* consisting of the mainland countries from the United States-Mexican border south through Panama, as well as the islands in the Gulf of Mexico and the Caribbean Sea, and *South America,* comprising the area south of Panama. *Central America* is the mainland area between Mexico and Colombia.

territory lie outside the tropical zone. Because of its location in the low latitudes much of Latin America experiences a climate which has failed to attract large-scale white immigration, yet one in which tropical and subtropical crops, such as coffee, sugar cane, cacao, bananas, and cotton, can be produced for consumption by the peoples of Anglo-America and Europe. As a result of this, large amounts of foreign capital have been invested in agricultural production in Latin American countries, and the economies of these states have been closely linked with those of the nations in the northern mid-latitudes.

The proximity of the United States to Latin America and the existence of ocean masses between the Western and Eastern Hemispheres have aided in the maintenance of the United States' position of dominance in the Latin American area. Within recent years expanded facilities for the interchange of goods, peoples, and ideas have brought the United States into even closer proximity with Latin America. These facilities, however, have also affected communications between the Western and Eastern Hemispheres; as a result the relative isolation of Latin America, particularly from Europe, is breaking down, with an accompanying decline in the predominant position of the United States in Latin American affairs.

The location of eastern South America with respect to Africa and the South Atlantic is of significance in terms of the over-all defense of the Western Hemisphere against possible attack from the Eastern Hemisphere. The 1,800-mile distance across the Atlantic from Cape São Roque, in eastern Brazil, to Dakar, French West Africa, represents the closest the Eastern and Western Hemispheres approach one another. Military control of the northeast coast of South America clearly is important to the maintenance of power in the North Atlantic Basin, and for this reason the United States and other major world powers have long been interested in the matter of political sovereignty over this vital coastal area. During World War II the United States maintained important military bases at Trinidad, Georgetown in British Guiana, and in the vicinity of Natal in easternmost Brazil. A major function of these bases was to forestall any possibility of an Axis foothold being secured in northeastern South America.

Surface Configuration. The surface configuration of Latin America is characterized by a series of young, rugged mountains, stretching from the United States through Mexico and Central America, then along the west coast of South America to the southern tip (Figure 25). Few low passes exist through this mountain barrier, particularly in South America, but there are numerous intermontane basins, some of which contain significant population concentrations. In addition to this mountain chain there are other important features, such as the plateaus and broad river basins in eastern South America, the coastal plains of Mexico and Central America, and the mountain arc which swings east from northern Central America to form most

Figure 25. Latin America: Physical Features.

of the islands of the Caribbean. These features have considerable political significance to the individual states, particularly in terms of their effect on communications and population distribution. River valleys and lowlands about inland water bodies often serve as nuclei for settlement or as transportation links between populated areas. Highland regions may separate sectors of a country, as in Colombia and the Dominican Republic, and thus act as centrifugal forces; on the other hand, because of special climatic advantages, they may serve as core areas for settlement, as in Guatemala and Costa Rica. Surface configuration is also important with respect to economic diversity. Ecuador was cited in Chapter 2 as a state in which the contrast between mountain and lowland areas has resulted in economic and political differences, a situation which also exists in most other western Latin American states, such as Bolivia and Guatemala.

Climate. The predominance of tropical climates in Latin America has already been noted. Like surface configuration, climate has influenced the distribution of population and has contributed to regional differences within individual states. In Chile, for example, the aridity of the Atacama and the cool, humid conditions in the southern part have contributed to the concentration of over 90 per cent of the population in middle Chile—a potent centripetal force in that 2,600-mile-long country. The wet tropical Amazon basin of Brazil, Argentina's semiarid Patagonian plateau, and the heat and humidity of the Caribbean coastal lowlands of Central America are other areas in which climate has been a dominant factor limiting settlement.

In Latin America, as in other parts of the world, economic diversity, reflecting climatic differences, can be either a centrifugal or a centripetal force within a country. Argentina may be cited as an example in which diverse economic areas are closely knit into a cohesive national unit.

POPULATION FACTORS

Size. The population of Latin America totals over 180,000,000 persons. Of these, nearly one-half live in the "ABC" countries—Argentina, Brazil, and Chile—and some 50,000,000 more inhabit Middle America. Birth rates are high; death rates are being drastically cut by the application of modern medical practices throughout much of the area. Latin America has one of the most rapidly growing populations in the world. One estimate places the population in the year 2000 at 373,000,000,[2] an increase of over 125 per cent in less than half a century. With the prospects of such a large population growth in coming decades, the countries of Latin America must prepare to expand greatly both their productivity and the means of distribution to satisfy a growing market, or else face mounting discontent, owing to a scarcity of food products and other consumer items.

Type. Three ethnic types have combined to produce the bulk of the Latin American population. These types are the whites, the Indians (indigenous at the time of European colonization), and the Negroes (brought to Latin America by the Europeans as slaves). Mixed racial groups include mestizos (white-Indian), mulattoes (white-Negro), and zambos (Indian-Negro). In addition, there are Orientals, particularly in Brazil and Peru, and East Indians in British Guiana and Trinidad. Of the total population, about one-third is mestizo, and about a quarter is white. Indians and Ne-

[2] Preston James, *Latin America* (New York: The Odyssey Press, 1950), p. 770.

groes each comprise slightly less than one-fifth. Whites predominate in Argentina, Uruguay, and Puerto Rico, and are in a slight majority in Brazil and Costa Rica. The Indians constitute majorities in many of the western Latin American states and in Paraguay. The Negroes are concentrated primarily in the Caribbean area.

Racial distinctions in Latin America have not resulted in the strong interracial frictions which are characteristic of the United States. Racial interbreeding has long been common, although some Europeans have consistently attempted to maintain as much "racial purity" as possible. Economic class distinctions appear to be more stringent than those based on race or color. Latin Americans, as a rule, have little sympathy with the racial practices in the United States. In their anti-American propaganda beamed at the Latin Americans the communists have often played up anti-Negro sentiment in the United States; at the same time they accuse the United States of being "anti-Indian," a theme which finds some reception among the Indian-mestizo peoples of Middle America and western South America.

Distribution. Distribution and density of population vary widely from place to place. Some of the general aspects of the settlement patterns were mentioned under the heading "Physical Factors." In addition to such limiting elements as steep slopes, cold, aridity, and poor soils, inaccessibility and the prevalence of disease (particularly in the tropical rain forest) have also contributed to low population densities in various regions. On the other hand, there are certain environmental conditions which have served to attract settlement, such as the volcanic soils in the Central American highlands, the mineral deposits of Bolivia and northern Chile, and the oases of the Peruvian coastal desert. Only in Uruguay, El Salvador, and some of the island areas can the total national territory be said to be effectively occupied.

In an article entitled "The Distribution of People in South America,"[3] Preston James points out several characteristics of population distribution, all of which are applicable to the mainland nations of Middle America as well. Of these, the most important to a study of political geography is the observation that "each [population] cluster forms the core of effective national or state territory, and the boundaries, with few exceptions, pass through scantily occupied areas which separate the clusters."[4] In discussing this phenomenon, James suggests that the failure of the populations of the various republics to spread out and occupy effectively their national territory may be due in part to the fact that ". . . throughout the four-hundred-odd years of European settlement . . . essentially the same modes have governed the process of living on the land."[5] In other words, the

---

[3] In *Geographic Aspects of International Relations,* ed. C. C. Colby (Chicago: The University of Chicago Press, 1938), pp. 217–43.
[4] *Ibid.,* p. 219.
[5] *Ibid.,* p. 231.

pattern of economic activities, established in the early agricultural and mining days, has not changed radically throughout most of Latin America, and the land which was not utilized in early colonial times, remains today largely undeveloped. Practically all of Latin America was settled by penetrations from the coastal areas, so that the majority of population clusters and lines of transportation extend inland from the coast rather than parallel to it. The factors of distance and ease of communication between settlements are, of course, important to the forces of political cohesion within countries.

The nature of Latin America's population pattern has influenced the history of territorial control here, in that border disputes generally involve larger areas of land than is the case in many of the microterritorial problem areas of Europe and Asia, where the cultural patterns in frontier zones are more complex. Invariably little attention is paid to the wishes of the indigenous peoples in the case of boundary changes; the only major plebiscite ever scheduled for contested territory in Latin America was never carried out (see discussion of the Atacama area on page 95).

ECONOMIC FACTORS

The characteristic economy of the Latin American states is based on the production and export of agricultural goods or of minerals and petroleum. Many of the republics are dependent upon one or two basic commodities for the bulk of their exports, tying their whole economic structure to fluctuating world prices. Venezuela's petroleum, Brazil's coffee, Bolivia's tin, Cuba's sugar, and the bananas of Guatemala and Honduras represent situations where the national economy is particularly sensitive to the export of a single commodity. The predominance of a single market for the exports of many of the countries is evidenced by the fact that the United States normally takes over three-fourths of the exports (by value) of Colombia, Costa Rica, El Salvador, Guatemala, Panama, and Venezuela, and over fifty per cent of the exports of eight other republics.

There are both direct and indirect political consequences of such economic dependence. For example, the United States has heavy investments in such areas as Cuba and Venezuela, and is in a position to exert influence upon these countries' governments.[6] Likewise, the United States may be expected to resist any outbreaks of violence within these and other exporting countries, either of the internal type (riots, revolutions, attempts to destroy the political unity of the state) or of an external type (invasions, territorial wars), for such violence might endanger investments and the nor-

---

[6] Conversely, Argentina, which carries on relatively little trade with the United States, has often pursued violently anti-American policies, one reason perhaps being that the economic system here has less to lose than in most other countries as a result of American antagonism.

mal flow of goods. Attempts by third powers to disrupt these economic bonds by "capturing" some of the exports or by influencing the political and economic policies of the exporting Latin American states are also apt to be resisted strongly by the United States.

Latin America is rich in agricultural and mineral resources. Over one-half the world's coffee and bananas are produced here, as well as between one-third and one-half of its cacao and sugar cane. These products form important items of export, along with beef, wool, hides, flaxseed, and citrus fruits. About fifteen per cent of the world's petroleum comes from the area. Important minerals include tin, copper, bauxite, lead, vanadium, tungsten, quartz crystals, and industrial diamonds. There are large known reserves of iron ore in Brazil and Venezuela and smaller ones in Chile, Cuba, and the Dominican Republic. Only small amounts of the petroleum and minerals produced in Latin America are used locally; most of them are free to enter the world market. Unfortunately there is little coal in Latin America and most of the water-power potential is undeveloped—one of the major handicaps to the region's economic development.

The process of industrialization has been slow and spotty. Brazil, Mexico, and Puerto Rico are the three areas in which greatest development has occurred, but even these countries lag by United States or western European standards. Lack of industry has meant three things: first, that no Latin American state is capable of initiating or supporting a major war, since aircraft and heavy armaments cannot be produced in quantity; second, that minerals such as iron ore, manganese, industrial diamonds, and tin, which are important for modern industry, are available for export; and third, that there has been little development of an industrial "middle class," an element which is generally important to the maintenance of stable, democratic governments. The Latin Americans are usually either quite rich (the numerically small upper class) or very poor. Average annual incomes per capita throughout most of the countries are less than twenty per cent of that in the United States.

With improved circulatory systems throughout the Latin American states this widespread poverty can have strong political repercussions. Dynamic political groups (particularly the communists) stand ready to capitalize on popular discontent—against the government, against major business concerns, or against the United States, which plays such an important role in the economic life of many of the republics. "Anti-Yankee" sentiments are quick to be aroused, and countermeasures, designed to reduce these sentiments, are difficult to carry out. Lack of economic diversity and industrialization, poor transportation facilities, unstable political conditions, shortage of capital—these are but a few of the long-term conditions which must be remedied if the annual income of the Latin American is to be substantially improved, and his resentment against continued poverty removed. In some areas, such as Puerto Rico and Mexico, strenuous efforts are being made to combat these evils and considerable progress has been made. The United States, through various inter-American agencies, has also contributed to the improvement of economic and social conditions. However, much more remains to be done. Until the average Latin American is assured that he can look forward to a substantially higher standard of living, he will remain prey to various utopian programs offered him as a means of attaining painlessly a more equitable distribution of wealth.

POLITICAL FACTORS

One of the outstanding characteristics of the political pattern of Latin America during the last century and a quarter has been its relative stability in terms of both national sovereignty and boundary locations. The large number of national political units and the ability of these units to maintain their independence over long periods of time are in sharp contrast with the turbulent conditions of political control which have existed in many other parts of the world since the early nineteenth century. This stability of the political pattern has persisted in spite of the revolutions and changes of administration which take place frequently within the national governments in many of the Latin American states. It also has existed in seeming defiance of internal centrifugal forces brought on by the ethnic differences and scattered population patterns in many of the countries.

Various external factors are responsible for the relative permanence in the political pattern of this area. The Monroe Doctrine has had the effect of excluding from Latin America since 1823 much of the same type of colonial activities as have been carried on by European powers in Africa, Asia, and the Pacific basin. As a result, during the past century and a quarter the extension of the intra-European wars to the Western Hemisphere has been largely prevented. Coupled with this has been the development by the United States, particularly since the beginning of the twentieth century, of a "Pax Americana" policy with respect to the nations of Latin America. Under this policy the United States has endeavored, wherever possible, to prevent conflicts from breaking out between the Latin American republics, primarily in order to protect foreign investments and to prevent the deterioration of United States influence in this area.

Some of the factors within Latin America which contribute to the stability of the political pattern have already been mentioned. Among these are the lack of population concentrations and of exploitable resources in the boundary areas, and the fact that in most of the Latin American states population totals are small and the national economies are at an early stage of development. Thus few of the countries possess the population and economic strength to wage sustained territorial war against their neighbors.

Further, there has been little urge for territorial expansion in order to secure additional "living space." The lack of adequate transportation facilities between many of the neighboring states of Latin America has also served to reduce the possibilities of aggression.

Political History

The Colonial Period. The early explorations and conquests of Latin America were carried out largely by the Spaniards during the sixteenth and seventeenth centuries, except for that portion of South America east of 50° west longitude, where, according to the Treaty of Tordesillas (1494), Portugal was accorded the right to be the dominant power. The conquerors came originally in search of precious metals and slaves, and many were accompanied by Catholic missionaries, intent upon converting the Indians to Christianity. The whole pattern of early colonial life was based on a "get-rich-quick" concept, and even today throughout much of Latin America an atmosphere of speculation and quick profits remains. From the sixteenth to the nineteenth centuries the Spanish and Portuguese empires were divided and subdivided into administrative districts, the local boundaries of which were in a state of frequent change. When the states of Latin America achieved their independence early in the nineteenth century many of the borders of these former administrative districts were taken to mark the international boundaries between the new nations. "The national idea . . . in Latin America got solidified into units whose size was determined by systems of communication and transportation that were available around 1800. By the next century, when methods of communication might have made a unified Spanish America possible the national idea had become so firmly implanted as to make any union seem utterly impractical despite its obvious advantages from every point of view except the maintenance of nationalism."[7] Thus the vestiges of early partitionings are of considerable importance to present political developments in this area.

Colonial efforts on the part of Britain, France, and the Netherlands in Latin America were confined largely to the Caribbean basin and the Guiana coast. Spain and Portugal remained important land powers down to the nineteenth century, but on the coast lands and islands of eastern Latin America the sea power of the more northerly European nations became increasingly important after 1588 in establishing colonial possessions. One of the principal attractions of this part of the world lay in the products which could be obtained from the area, including sugar, tobacco, indigo, cotton, and dyewoods. Following France's defeat by Britain in 1763 some British statesmen viewed the transfer of the French colony of Martinique

---

[7] Marsten Bates, *Where Winter Never Comes* (New York: Charles Scribner's Sons, 1952), p. 254. Used by permission.

to Britain as preferable to British control of French Canada; and at the time of the American Revolution the British island of Jamaica, with its sugar, rum, and molasses, was said to bring more revenue to the mother country than did the thirteen American colonies.

Independence Movements of the Early Nineteenth Century. Achievement of independence among the Latin American states took place almost entirely during a twenty-five year period at the beginning of the nineteenth century, when much of Europe was embroiled in the Napoleonic Wars. In 1804 the government of Haiti declared itself independent of French control. Revolts against European domination were already breaking out in other parts of Latin America, and in the years following Haiti's declaration of independence, many of the other colonies also won self-rule. In two cases political units were formed which lasted but a few years. The first was Gran Colombia, 1821–30, comprising Colombia, Venezuela, and Ecuador; the second was the Federation of Central America, 1824–38, consisting of the various Central American states (excluding Mexico). In each case centrifugal forces in the form of relief, differing histories, political leaders, and economic interests, were eventually strong enough to break up the political units into separate parts.

One of the problems confronting the newly-independent states of Latin America was the delimitation of their boundaries. The individual governments, at least in principle, agreed to accept the *uti possidetis* of 1810 as a basis for future negotiations on territorial disputes. *Uti possidetis* was a term which signified that the newly-independent states were the successors of the former provincial units of the Spanish Empire, within essentially the same territorial limits as existed at the time independence was established. The principle was also used to apply to the former Portuguese territory of Brazil. Because of the constantly changing pattern of the Spanish subdivisions during that country's period of control in Latin America, definite determination of boundaries affected by the principle of *uti possidetis* was often extremely difficult and led to numerous controversies between the new states.

Many of the boundaries of Latin America were based on physical features, such as rivers, mountain crests, and drainage divides. It is far easier to determine boundaries such as these on a map than in the field, for when and if the time comes to demarcate the line all manner of disagreements may arise. Such problems as location of drainage divides, relation of towns to markets or water supply, or of farmers to their fields may prove to be far more complex than was anticipated when delimiting the border on the map. Many Latin American boundaries have never been completely demarcated. Unless population pressure or the utilization of resources demands it, they may remain indefinitely as vague zones of delimitation. "So long as the potential wealth of an area is imperfectly known, the contestant countries hesitate to have boundaries precisely defined lest they later discover that they abandoned valuable resources to a rival neighbor."[8]

Political Patterns Since 1838. In the years since 1838 only five Latin American states have undergone a complete change in political status. In 1844 the Dominican Republic, at the eastern end of the island of Hispaniola, became independent of Haitian control. Fifty-four years later, at the conclusion of the Spanish-American War, Spanish sovereignty in Puerto Rico and Cuba was replaced by that of the United States. Puerto Rico remained a United States possession, while Cuba was eventually set up as an independent state, although with close ties to the United States (see page 92). In 1903 Panama, with assistance from the United States, broke away from Colombia and became the twentieth independent state in Latin America. Finally, in 1917 Denmark relinquished possession of the Virgin Islands to the United States for the sum of $25,000,000.

Territorial conflicts in Latin America since the early nineteenth century have been concentrated for the most part in a relatively few areas. Mexico, in the years from 1836 to 1854, lost over 700,000 square miles of territory to the United States. These losses were the result of both American territorial ambitions and centrifugal forces within Mexico itself, occasioned by the lack of contact between Mexico City and the nation's northern regions.

In South America Paraguay and Bolivia suffered major territorial losses. Paraguay, after a disastrous five-year war (1865–70) against Argentina, Brazil, and Uruguay—during which approximately four-fifths of the nation's population was killed—saw its territory reduced by 55,000 square miles. An inland country, Paraguay has remained since then one of the poorest nations in Latin America. Bolivia's territorial losses to Chile and to Paraguay are described later in this chapter. Because of these losses Bolivia has been cut off from both the Pacific and from the Paraguay-Paraná river system in eastern South America. In addition, Bolivia in 1903 was forced to cede the rubber-rich Acre territory in the Amazon basin to Brazil, thereby cutting off the nation's access to the Amazon. Thus Bolivia, like Paraguay, is a land-locked country, dependent upon the permission of neighboring states for its access to the sea.

There have also been a number of boundary disputes in Central America and northern South America and in the La Plata estuary between Argentina and Uruguay. These disputes generally have involved less territory than did the cases mentioned above, but some of them—for example, the controversy between Guatemala and Honduras over territory containing banana plantations—have never been settled to the mutual satisfaction of the interested states.

---

[8] Derwent Whittlesey, *The Earth and the State* (New York: Henry Holt and Company, 1944), p. 451.

Unity and Diversity Within the Latin American States

The location of the national capital and its relation to other centers of population are important aspects of centrifugal and centripetal forces in the individual states. By studying political and population maps, the effects of location and the relative concentrations of populations in capital areas can be ascertained. In each of the republics of Latin America, with the exception of Brazil and Ecuador, the national capital is also the dominant city in terms of population. In Brazil, Rio de Janeiro, the capital, and São Paulo, located 225 miles to the southwest, are both cities of over two million persons, while in Ecuador, Quito, the capital, and Guayaquil, the Pacific port, also approximate one another in population (over 200,000 each). In both states this bipolarity operates as a centrifugal force. In Bolivia there are actually two capitals, Sucre, the legal seat, located in the eastern mountains, and La Paz, Bolivia's largest city, the *de facto* capital on the Altiplano. In Nicaragua, the capital, Managua, was selected as a midway point between two rival cities, León and Granada. As all three centers are located within a sixty-five-mile zone in the populous southwestern uplands, there is little divisive force operating here between the urban centers.

Most of the Latin American republics have recognized the difficulties of maintaining political control over their national territories because of poor circulatory systems, and have attempted to remedy this by the construction of transportation routes leading out from the capital city. Ecuador has one railroad which travels over a tortuous route to link Quito with the Pacific coast. A second one from Quito to San Lorenzo on Ecuador's coast near the Colombian border is under construction. Bolivia has connected its population centers on the Altiplano at great expense, and has constructed two links eastward to serve agricultural communities in the eastern mountains. Peru and Colombia are especially handicapped by the presence of towering mountains and deep valleys. Recently Colombia has begun a railroad which eventually will greatly improve Bogotá's connections with population centers in the central and western parts of the nation. Buenos Aires has for many years been the hub of an extensive rail net spreading across the Pampas, with connections to many outlying sections of Argentina. The result has been a marked centralization of political and economic affairs in the Argentine capital.

Brazil. In terms of centrifugal forces the most complex of the South American republics is probably Brazil—over 3,000,000 square miles in area and stretching about 2,500 miles both in a north-south and an east-west direction. The distribution of population, the diverse relief, climate, and vegetation, the great distances and the lack of adequate transportation facilities, and finally the off-center location of the economic and political metropolises represent major forces of disunity. On the other hand, unifying factors include the use of a common language, a sparsely-inhabited interior, and the absence of populated areas across the borders from western and northern Brazil.

The Brazilian nation consists of several geographic regions. In the north is the Amazon basin, a lowland tropical rain-forest area which contains two-fifths of the country's area but only about six per cent of its population. To the south of this basin is an extensive grassland area, much of it rolling plateau, which stretches to the southern borders. This central interior area, like the Amazon basin, has attracted little settlement.

Northeast Brazil consists of a humid tropical coast and a dry interior upland. The Natal-Recife-Salvador area along the coast represents one of the core areas of the country; the population is slowly expanding into the dry interior as well. South of this region is the east central plateau area, averaging 1,000 to 3,000 feet in elevation. Within this area are located Brazil's two principal cities, as well as over half the nation's population. Here, in the main core area, are well-developed transportation nets, as well as coffee, cotton, iron ore, hydroelectric power, industries, and other facets of Brazil's economic development. The plateau continues into southern Brazil, although in the extreme south it gives way to a low grassland region. In the Curitiba-Pôrto Alegre sector of southern Brazil is the nation's third important population concentration.

The problem of tying such a large area together politically is handicapped by the great distances and by the lack of easy topographic routes of travel. The Amazon is the only major river navigable for a considerable distance upstream from the sea, and it drains an area whose climate has not attracted white settlement. Many other rivers rise near the coast, but flow inland away from the Atlantic, or, if they enter the ocean, their course is interrupted by rapids close to the mouth. Early settlement was naturally along the coastal area, but much of this sector (particularly in the southeast) is backed by mountains which hinder communications with the interior. James notes the lack of natural transportation hubs in Brazil,[9] a factor which has tended to restrict the development of population clusters in the nation. Railroads have been constructed at considerable expense to link various sectors of Brazil together, but the network is far from complete. Only the southeastern portion of the nation could be termed well-served; from here, rail lines fan out north and west for about 500 miles, but there is no through line to the northeast coastal area, and most of the interior has no rail service whatever. Air lines are now being developed to make up for some of this deficiency.

The nation's capital with its magnificent harbor easily dominates Bra-

---

[9] Preston James, *Latin America*, p. 356.

zil's foreign trade. Despite the existence of a mountain wall to the west, rail and highway transportation lines link Rio de Janeiro with a large hinterland to the south, west, and north. However, Brazilian leaders have recognized the need for the country to turn its attention inland in order to develop the interior, and a new federal district has been created 500 miles north-northwest of Rio, to serve as the site for the future capital of Brazil. Moving the capital away from the southeastern core area in order to centralize it more in relation to the interior and the northeast may in time prove beneficial, but if the bulk of Brazil's population and wealth remain in the Rio-São Paulo area there will be a strong force here pulling away from the new capital.

Foreign Control in Latin America

Although most of the Latin American area consists of independent states, foreign control is exercised here by the United States, Great Britain, France, and the Netherlands. The United States has sovereignty over Puerto Rico, the Virgin Islands, and the Panama Canal Zone. The three European powers have territories on the Guiana coast of northeastern South America, and Britain also has sovereignty over British Honduras in Central America and the Falkland Islands in the South Atlantic. In addition, all three European states exercise control over various Caribbean islands.

Within recent decades there has been a trend toward reorganization of dependent territories in Latin America. Movements toward federation have taken place among some of the British possessions in the Caribbean (see page 103) as well as in the Dutch territories, and in the dependent areas of all four controlling powers increasing measures of self-rule have been granted. In actual practice, however, the trend toward independence for colonial areas here seems to be moving more slowly than in many parts of Asia and Africa. In 1954 representatives of the Latin American nations adopted a resolution condemning colonialism in the Latin American area.

The position of the United States with respect to Latin America represents an interesting case study in power relations, for, in addition to the establishment of direct sovereignty, the United States has at times maintained various degrees of protectorate-type control over individual Latin American states. Some aspects of the United States power position in Latin America are considered here.

Puerto Rico. Relations between the United States and Puerto Rico represent a somewhat unique variety of colonial control. The island of Puerto Rico has an area of 3,435 square miles, and a population of over $2\frac{1}{4}$ million persons. Because of the high birth and relatively low death rates, this population is increasing at the rate of 100 per cent every quarter century. Much of Puerto Rico's relief is of such rugged character as to handicap agriculture, and there are no known minerals to be profitably exploited on the island. Much of the agriculture is geared to commercial crops, such as sugar cane and tobacco, for which there is generally a higher cash return than is the case with production of food for local use. A land tenure system which permits considerable absentee land ownership also adds to the economic woes of Puerto Rico. On the other hand, the brightest spot in the island's economy has been the concerted effort toward industrialization, together with a government-sponsored land reform system which is breaking up many of the old estates. American industries in particular are attracted to Puerto Rico by the absence of income and other taxes, and by the availability of hydroelectric power and labor supplies. Despite this, however, the problem of a dense population and of competition with neighboring areas for export markets continues to work against Puerto Rico's economic advancement.

After the United States assumed control over Puerto Rico in 1898, the political status of the area was diminished, for the United States Congress failed to recognize the same degree of autonomy for Puerto Rico that it had experienced under Spanish rule. Not until 1917 were the people of Puerto Rico awarded United States citizenship. By the end of World War II political groups in Puerto Rico were divided in their views concerning the island's future political status—complete independence, statehood, or commonwealth status. The advocates of commonwealth status were victorious in the elections of 1948, and four years later Puerto Rico was officially established as a Commonwealth of the United States.

Under the terms of the commonwealth arrangement Puerto Rico became free to manage its own local affairs, although defense and foreign relations are still conducted by the United States. Puerto Rico has closer bonds with the United States than do the British dominions with the United Kingdom, for in the latter instance defense and foreign affairs are handled by the dominions themselves.

There is apparently little pressure for independence in Puerto Rico, largely for economic reasons. Under the commonwealth system Puerto Ricans are free to emigrate to the United States. Thousands each year take advantage of this emigration opportunity, the majority of them going to New York City. In Puerto Rico, as in Newfoundland, independence has been rejected by the voters because of the economic advantages to be gained by a political union with a larger country.

Cuba. The island of Cuba, lying to the south of Florida, has an area of 44,218 square miles and a population of close to 6,000,000. Unlike Puerto Rico, Cuba is not densely populated, and its agricultural potential is high. Much of the land is level or gently rolling and about one-third of Cuba is in cultivation. Sugar cane is Cuba's principal crop—a product which finds a large market in the United States.

A former Spanish colony, Cuba was under United States control from 1898 to 1901. Accompanying the proclamation of Cuba's independence in 1901 was the Platt Amendment, granting the United States the right to maintain coaling and naval bases on Cuban soil and to intervene in internal affairs "for the preservation of Cuban independence . . . for the protection of life, property, and individual liberty." This right was exercised in 1906, 1912, and from 1917 to 1922.

As a result of the Platt Amendment and of Cuba's economic position relative to the United States, the island existed in a protectorate-type status from 1901 until the development of the United States "Good Neighbor" policy in the mid-1930's. Even since the abrogation of the Platt Amendment Cuba has continued in a position of economic dependence upon the United States. The United States normally accounts for over half of Cuba's sugar exports, and a majority of the capital invested in the Cuban sugar industry is furnished by Americans.

Panama.   In 1903 United States intervention in a revolt by Panamanians against Colombia led to the establishment of Panama's independence and the subsequent granting to the United States by Panama of a lease in perpetuity on a ten-mile-wide strip of land across the Isthmus of Panama, through which an interoceanic canal was to be constructed. The Colombian government had previously refused permission for United States construction of the canal, and a group of Panamanians then struck for independence, partly on the grounds of this refusal. The fact that the United States actively prevented quashing of the revolt by the Colombian army was a clear case of direct United States intervention in the affairs of a Latin American nation. In 1921 the United States paid to Colombia $25,000,000 as compensation for the United States role in the Panama revolt.

Since 1903 United States influence in Panama's affairs has been undeniably strong. Virtually all of Panama's exports go to the United States, and about 70 per cent of its imports are from the United States. The Canal Zone itself plays an important role in Panama's economy, bringing a source of revenue into an otherwise poor nation. Disorders in Panama have at times been checked by American intervention, including the supervision of Panamanian elections. However, since 1934, the United States has followed a "hands off" policy with regard to Panama's affairs. Following World War II, when the government of Panama refused permission to the United States to maintain military bases outside the Canal Zone, the Americans acquiesced, although by so doing they were forced to abandon installations constructed at considerable cost within Panama. They thereby refuted communist claims that Panama was an American "satellite" state.

Other Areas of United States Control.   During the early part of the twentieth century the United States several times sent military forces to the Middle American republics for the purpose of maintaining law and order and "to protect foreign lives and property." In 1905 United States officials took charge of financial affairs in the Dominican Republic, and from 1916 to 1924 the country was occupied by American marines. During most of this period it was administered by a United States military government. United States troops occupied Haiti from 1915 to 1934 and Nicaragua from 1912 to 1925 and 1926 to 1933. No national government, operating under such conditions, can afford to be openly antagonistic to the occupying power.

A further extension of United States control in Latin America took place on the eve of American entry into World War II. At that time Great Britain granted ninety-nine-year leases for the establishment of United States military bases on certain British possessions, in exchange for the "loan" to Britain of fifty over-age destroyers. These bases are located in the Bahamas, Jamaica, Antigua, St. Lucia, Trinidad, and British Guiana. Although most of these installations are no longer operational, the United States has the right to reoccupy them in time of trouble until the year 2039.

Despite the various incidents of strong United States pressure in Latin America, relations between the United States and the Latin American republics improved considerably with the inauguration of President Roosevelt's Good Neighbor policy in 1934. A number of the republics were allied with the United States in World War II, and all are joined with one another and with the United States in a mutual defense alliance (Rio Pact). In 1953 the United States supplied half (by value) of Latin America's total imports, and received 45 per cent of its exports. In the same year United States investments in Latin America came to over 6 billion dollars. Such figures indicate the magnitude of the economic bonds which unite Latin America with the United States.

Particularly in the years since World War II the United States has followed a policy of large-scale economic and technical assistance to the twenty Latin American states. Much of this assistance has been carried out through the Organization of American States, a regional group set up in 1948 to co-ordinate economic, social, and other activities within and among the twenty-one member countries. In addition to contributing 70 per cent of the operating costs of this organization the United States has advanced large amounts of capital to individual Latin American republics. Further, United States officials have worked through diplomatic channels to destroy the specter of United States imperialism and to promote an atmosphere of mutual self-respect between the United States and the Latin American states.

Although considerable progress has been made in the improvement of inter-American relations, the situation is complicated, first, by long-term objectives of United States foreign policy and, second, by the various problems which face the Latin American governments. Concern in the United States over containment of communist pressure in Eurasia has meant that a relatively small proportion of foreign aid has gone to Western Hemisphere nations. Many Latin American officials have resented the fact that, because their countries are geographically removed from what is considered in Washington as the major zone of power conflict, they have received far less help from the United States than have such countries as Great Britain, Greece, Iran, and Japan. Together with this have been problems within the Latin American states, such as inflation, communism, dictatorships, and friction between individual countries. Because of these many factors it is no longer possible to lump the nations of Latin America together under the heading "United States Power Sphere."

TERRITORIAL PROBLEMS

The ability of a capital to control outlying areas can, of course, be demonstrated by the degree of political unity of the country concerned. With the exception of Panama's separation from Colombia in 1903, no state of Latin America since 1844 has had one of its sectors detach itself from the capital's control and become independent. Peripheral areas, however, have been detached from one country and joined to another, often with accompanying wars. In this section Latin America's major territorial conflicts of the past seventy-five years will be considered.

The Atacama

One of the most serious territorial disputes which has taken place in Latin America involved Chile, Peru, and Bolivia in a contest over the northern Atacama Desert area (Figure 26). This dispute was particularly significant, not only because of its violence and of the major territorial changes which followed it, but also because it proved to be one of the few territorial wars of modern times which ultimately was a financial success for the aggressor nation.

Prior to the late 1870's Peru controlled the northern Atacama, including the port of Arica, with its nearby oasis of Tacna. Bolivia had sovereignty over the central sector of the desert, while the southern portion was Chilean territory. The Atacama had been relatively unimportant economically, except for some silver and copper mining and a few coastal ports, but after 1860 the exploitation of the desert's sodium nitrate deposits led to a wild scramble for control of the territory. Both the Chileans and Peruvians were active in developing the nitrates, which had world-wide demand for use as fertilizers, while the Bolivian government was interested in collecting taxes on mines operated by Chilean and Peruvian organizations within Bolivian territory.

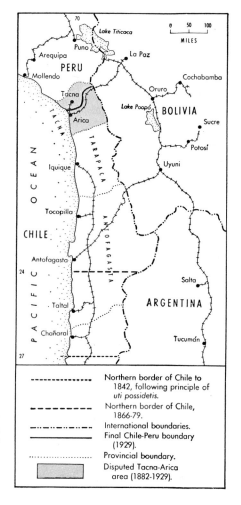

Figure 26. The Atacama. (After Borch-
ard, *Foreign Affairs*, I (Sept., 1922).
Copyright by Council on Foreign Relations.)

Ill-defined boundaries and the opportunity for quick profits inevitably
led to conflict. In the bitter War of the Pacific (1879–84) Chile attacked
Peru and Bolivia and eventually was victorious. As a result Bolivia lost
control of its coastal province, including the port of Antofagasta (Bolivia's
only outlet to the ocean), and Chile's northern border was extended 350
miles along the Pacific coast to the port of Arica. Thereafter the nitrate
deposits were entirely within Chilean territory, and for the next thirty years
—until the development of a method of recovering nitrogen from the air—
Chile realized enormous profits from the export of nitrates from the Atacama. Bolivia, cut off from the sea, was in a serious position, since the
country's economy is dependent upon the export of minerals. Eventually

the Chilean port of Arica was made a free port for Bolivia's foreign trade. By the terms of the treaty ending the War of the Pacific a plebiscite was eventually to be held in the Tacna-Arica area to determine its ultimate disposition between Chile and Peru. For over four decades, however, Chile refused to permit the plebiscite, and relations between Chile and Peru became severely strained. Finally, in 1929, as a result of strong diplomatic pressure from the United States, the Tacna-Arica area was divided, with Tacna reverting to Peru.

The Argentine-Chilean Boundary

This second dispute is noteworthy, not only because of the friction it engendered between neighboring states, but also because of the careful treatment given in the final arbitration award to the problem of ambiguous geographic terminology. The Andes Mountains form what would seem to be an ideal natural boundary separating Chile from Argentina; only in the extreme south are the Andes sufficiently low to form an ineffective barrier range. Article 1 of the 1881 treaty between Chile and Argentina states "The frontier line shall run . . . along the highest crests . . . which may divide the waters, and shall pass between the slopes which descend on either side."[10]

Unfortunately, the line joining the highest crests of the Andean cordillera does not always divide the watersheds. Particularly in the southern sector of the boundary, some westward-flowing rivers have eroded their valleys headward to a point where they drain areas well to the east of the line connecting the highest crests. The Chileans claimed that the term "highest crests" should be construed to mean only those highest crests which divided the waters; between such crests the boundary should naturally follow the watershed division. Argentina, on the other hand, maintained that "highest crests" meant just that—regardless of drainage divides. Both Chile and Argentina prepared for war, but eventually they agreed to submit the dispute to the Queen of England, and in 1902 a settlement was reached. In gratitude for the averting of war, the peoples of Chile and Argentina erected a colossal "Christ of the Andes" statue in Uspallata Pass, the main route through the mountains between Buenos Aires and central Chile.

The Upper Amazon

One territorial dispute which has not been completely settled concerns the upper drainage basin of the Amazon, where the borders of Colombia,

---

[10] Quoted by S. Whittemore Boggs, *International Boundaries* (New York: Columbia University Press, 1940), p. 86. For a full discussion of this controversy see this work, pp. 85–93; also Gordon Ireland, *Boundaries, Possessions and Conflicts in South America* (Cambridge: Harvard University Press, 1938), pp. 17–27; and Sir Thomas Holdich, *The Countries of the King's Award* (London: Hurst and Blackett, Ltd., 1904).

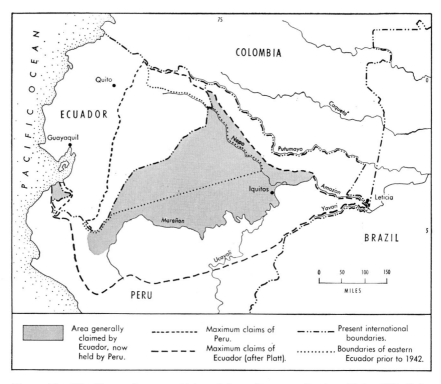

Figure 27. The Upper Amazon. (Adapted from Bowman, *Foreign Affairs*, XX (July, 1942), copyright by Council on Foreign Relations; and Platt in *Geographic Aspects of International Relations*, ed. Colby, The University of Chicago Press, copyright 1938 by University of Chicago.)

Ecuador, and Peru meet (Figure 27). Although the international boundaries in the northern sector of the Amazon basin generally follow drainage divides, this is not the case in the western part of the basin. During colonial times Spanish explorers crossed the Andes from the Pacific coast, moving downstream along the Amazon tributaries, and the boundaries of the Peruvian viceroyalty were extended several hundred miles east of the watershed dividing the Atlantic and Pacific drainage areas. The most direct route from Spain's western settlements to the upper Amazon lay across the mountains (at an elevation of over 10,000 feet) through Quito, to the main headwater of the Amazon. The difficulties of this route, however, were increased by the presence of hostile Indians, and gradually a Spanish route was developed from Lima, Peru, eastward across the mountains to the Ucayali River, which is navigable for a considerable distance upstream from its confluence with the Amazon.

As in other sectors of South America, international boundaries in this area were extremely obscure at the time of independence for the republics. Under Spain, title over the disputed upper Amazon basin area was established with the provincial government at Quito, and this jurisdiction was recognized as having passed to the Ecuadorian nation after the winning of independence. Although Ecuador continued its claim to the upper Amazon region on the basis of historical jurisdiction, its sovereignty was challenged by Peru and Colombia. During the nineteenth and early twentieth centuries, Peruvian settlers moved down the Ucayali to establish the river port of Iquitos and develop other parts of the upper Amazon basin, while Ecuador, despite its more direct access to the region, did little to colonize what it claimed was the eastern sector of the Ecuadorian nation. After 1900 Peru took active steps to extend jurisdiction over the upper Amazon basin. Eventually these actions led to complications with both Ecuador and Colombia.

Colombia in 1927 agreed to recognize Peru's claims to what had been eastern Ecuador. In return Peru ceded to Colombia a strip of territory in the disputed area, by means of which Colombia's border was moved southward to the Amazon River, giving it control over the port of Leticia. The solution was mutually satisfactory, for Peru's claims to the territory were strengthened and Colombia acquired navigation rights on the Amazon.

The principle of *de facto* control of what used to be eastern Ecuador was demonstrated by the Peruvians who effectively settled the area. In 1942 this control became *de jure,* for Ecuador officially relinquished claims on territory as far upstream on the Amazon tributaries as is navigable to launches. By such action Ecuador lost contact with the Amazon River. Peru now claims all of the territory east of the Andes still controlled by Ecuador, again on the basis of settlement, but the Ecuadorian government has remained adamant in its refusal to accede to these demands. Within this disputed area is a small but valuable oil field. Future economic development of the upper Amazon basin could possibly cause further territorial disputes between the interested nations and may lead to armed warfare in northwestern South America.

The Chaco

A territorial dispute which led to a bloody war between Bolivia and Paraguay involved the northern portion of the Gran Chaco, lying north of the Pilcomayo River and west of the Paraguay River (Figure 28). Bolivia's claims to this area were based on the principle of *uti possidetis,* for the original Spanish division of Bolivia had jurisdiction eastward to the Paraguay River. On the other hand, Paraguay claimed the area as hers by virtue of early exploration and settlement. Treaties attempting to divide the northern Chaco between the two countries had been signed in 1879,

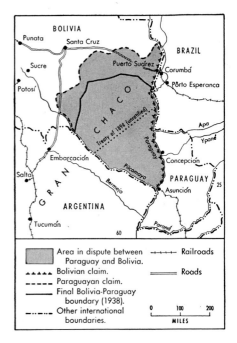

BOLIVIA

Punata   Santa Cruz

BRAZIL

Sucre   Puerto Suárez   Corumbá

Potosí   Pôrto Esperanca

C H A C O

Treaty of 1894 (unratified)

Apa

Ypané

Embarcación   Concepción

Salta

Bermejo   Paraguay   Picomayo

PARAGUAY   25

ARGENTINA   Asunción

Tucumán   Paraná   60

Area in dispute between Paraguay and Bolivia.   ┄┄┄ Railroads
▲▲▲▲ Bolivian claim.   ══ Roads
┄┄┄ Paraguayan claim.
──── Final Bolivia-Paraguay boundary (1938).
─··─··─ Other international boundaries.

0   100   200
MILES

Figure 28. The Chaco. Note the extensive use of rivers to mark boundaries. (After Schurz, *Foreign Affairs*, VII (July, 1929). Copyright by Council on Foreign Relations.)

1887, and 1894, but none of them had been ratified by both nations. In 1932 war between Bolivia and Paraguay broke out, and despite the best efforts of the League of Nations and other international bodies, continued for three years, until both nations were exhausted and a mediation was effected. Paraguay received about three-fourths of the northern Chaco area, although the contested portion of the Andes foothills, containing known oil reserves, remained with Bolivia. At Paraguay's insistence Bolivia was effectively blocked from utilizing the Paraguay River route to the Atlantic, when it was forced to relinquish control of the west bank of the river to Brazil.

Promises of extensive oil reserves in the Chaco have never materialized, and despite the three-year-long conflict (1932–35) for its control, the region remains of little economic value even today. Throughout the practically level area precipitation is seasonal and erratic; the western portion is both too arid and too remote for the development of an extensive grazing economy, while much of the eastern part is subject to widespread floodings. Unlike the War of the Pacific, the Chaco War was a bitter contest for a practically valueless prize.

British Honduras

The most serious territorial controversy in Middle America concerns

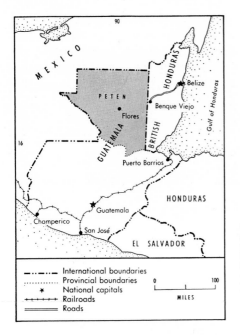

Figure 29. Guatemala and British Honduras. Note the isolation of Petén. (After Harrison-Church, *Modern Colonization,* Hutchinson's University Library and Longmans, Green & Co., 1951. Used by permission.)

Guatemala and British Honduras (Figure 29). Early British claims to what is now British Honduras were based upon exploration and occupation, although the first British inhabitants of the area were mostly pirates and logwood cutters. In the latter part of the eighteenth century Spain granted certain rights to British settlers along this part of the coast, but continued to maintain its rights to sovereignty over the area, and Britain continued to recognize this sovereignty even after Mexico and Guatemala had won their independence from Spain. During the nineteenth century Spain refused to discuss sovereignty claims with Britain. However, Guatemala as early as the 1820's laid claims to the British-occupied region, on the grounds that Guatemala was the rightful heir to all lands which had been under Spanish control between Mexico and the El Salvador and Honduras borders.

Despite the disputed sovereignty over British Honduras a treaty was signed by Great Britain and Guatemala in 1859, defining the international border as that which existed previous to January 1, 1850, and signifying the intentions of the signatory powers to co-operate in the construction of a road from Guatemala City to the Atlantic coast. The road, however, was never constructed, and a British offer to Guatemala of £50,000 in discharge of Britain's obligations for its sector of the road was not accepted within the agreed time limit by the Guatemalan government.

Since 1933 Guatemala has pressed her claims for "return" of British Honduras to Guatemalan control. These claims are based on more than legalistic maneuvers. British Honduras effectively shuts off the Guatemalan department of Petén, covering one-third of the country, from ready access to the Caribbean. Petén occupies the northeastern lowland of Guatemala and has few communication links with the highland sector of the country to the southwest. Its normal outlet would seem to lie eastward to the Caribbean, but this route is blocked by the British colony.

Problem Areas

The politico-geographic problems of Latin America may be grouped under three headings: present territorial disputes; changing status of colonial areas; and rival claims in Antarctica. Although Antarctica obviously lies beyond the limits of Latin America, it is included here because two of the Latin American republics are serious contenders for territory in this area.

Present Territorial Disputes

Present territorial conflicts in Latin America revolve about three principal areas: Guatemala's claims to British Honduras; the upper Amazon basin; and the Falkland Islands. In these cases it is doubtful that any major changes will take place in the near future, but all three represent potential areas of friction. The Guatemala-British Honduras situation has already been described (see page 101). In the decade of Guatemala's left-wing government (1944–54) there were indications that the dispute might eventually develop into some forcible expression of Guatemalan nationalism, but since then there has been little active controversy over this question. Britain has constructed the promised road from Belize westward to the Guatemalan border, but no connecting roads have been built in Petén. The political and economic situation might be aided by the improvement of port facilities at Belize, capital of British Honduras, and the designation of its harbor as a free port for Guatemalan products. Meanwhile, the latent expansionism of Guatemala faces determined British resistance regarding sovereignty over British Honduras.

With respect to the upper Amazon, Colombia seems satisfied with present arrangements, but future trouble may well develop between Ecuador and Peru. Again nationalist emotions in either nation could lead to a renunciation of the 1942 Rio Pact. Ecuador might reassert her sovereignty over all of her former eastern territory, or Peru might attempt to move Ecuador's borders farther west to the Andes. Border skirmishes between the two republics continue to take place at intervals, and the situation in this sector remains unsettled.

Controversy over the Falkland Islands in the southwestern Atlantic involves Argentina and Great Britain. Although the islands were claimed by Argentina at the time of its independence, Britain landed troops on the Falklands in 1833 and declared them to be British territory. The local population was forced to emigrate to Argentina, and in time Britain developed the area into a major naval, coaling, and wireless station. In the years since World War II Argentina has revived the issue of sovereignty over the Falklands, the Argentinians insisting that Britain occupied the islands illegally over a century ago, and should therefore evacuate them in favor of their rightful owners. This dispute has perhaps less potentialities for trouble than have the Guatemala-British Honduras and the upper Amazon controversies, though it would certainly add to Argentina's prestige if the nation were successful in dislodging Britain from the area.

Changing Status of Colonial Areas

Pressure for independence by the colonial peoples of Latin America has not been strong. The United States and the west European powers who control territory in this area have reached various stages of compromise in their efforts to ward off genuine hostility and possible revolt in any of their possessions. A movement is under way for a union of the British West Indies into a British Caribbean Federation, although the mainland colonies of British Honduras and British Guiana, as well as the British Virgin Islands, may not be included in such an organization. There would be a single governor general and a unified customs administration. The various groups— Barbados, Jamaica, the British Leeward Islands, Trinidad and Tobago, and the British Windward Islands—would be included in one economic union. Such a move would insure a greater measure of self-government and of economic strength than is generally possible within the separate island administrations, and would represent a step in the direction of independence or dominion status.

On the mainland of South America the British adopted a policy of local self-rule for British Guiana in 1953, but they soon revoked the new constitution as a result of the emergence of a dominant left-wing party there. This party, drawing its support primarily from the sugar workers of the country, appeared to have procommunist tendencies, and British officials felt that such an administration, capitalizing on local economic conditions, could pose a dangerous political threat to Latin America. Although with the suspension of the constitution the possibility of a communist-oriented government coming to power in British Guiana was removed, two problems still remain unsolved. The first concerns the political future of British Guiana itself, for pressures here are strong for the eventual attainment of self-rule. The second problem relates to other colonial areas in Latin America which are approaching self-rule. Will there also be a tendency in these countries where the average standards of living are low to support left-wing political parties and, thus, as in British Guiana, offer the possibility of procommunist regimes coming to power?

France regards the islands of Martinique and Guadeloupe as integral parts of the French Republic, thereby granting local inhabitants the right of representation in the French Assembly. The islands of the Dutch West Indies or Netherlands Antilles—Aruba, Bonaire, and Curaçao off the coast of Venezuela, together with St. Eustatius, Saba, and the southern half of St. Martin in the Leeward Islands—have formed a loose political union, which exists as a theoretical equal of the Netherlands itself. The Netherlands Antilles are subject to the Queen of the Netherlands, not to the Dutch government, although in practice, foreign and defense affairs are still managed by the Netherlands. Negroes have full voice in the West Indies government. However, the eventual political status of the Dutch West Indies (and of Surinam, or Netherlands Guiana, on the South American mainland) remains to be worked out with the Netherlands.

Rival Claims in Antarctica

The Antarctic continent, with an area of over five million square miles, has, until recently, been completely uninhabited. There are no known areas in which plant life of any kind can exist. Mineral and fuel deposits are still largely unknown, and the entire continent is of little economic consequence. Bases for fishing fleets are not located on the Antarctic mainland itself but on nearby island groups, such as the South Sandwich and South Orkney islands and Deception Island. The only present value the area would seem to possess is in connection with weather stations, since Antarctica is of importance to meteorologists in the making of long-range weather forecasts.

The prospects of the future economic and military value of Antarctica, however, have led to announcements of territorial claims by various nations since the beginning of the twentieth century. Each of the claimants has resorted to the use of the Polar Sectors, the various boundaries of which radiate out from the South Pole (Figure 30).

Within recent years, disputed territorial claims on this barren area have led to incidents which might easily have precipitated armed conflict. In 1925 Argentina laid claim to a sector south of the eastern Atlantic and of South America, despite the fact that this sector was part of an area which had previously been designated as the Falkland Island Dependencies by the British. In 1940 Chile also claimed a sector of Antarctica, although most of it occupies area of the Falkland Island Dependencies and the region claimed by Argentina.

The British, French, Norwegian, and Australian claims to sovereignty

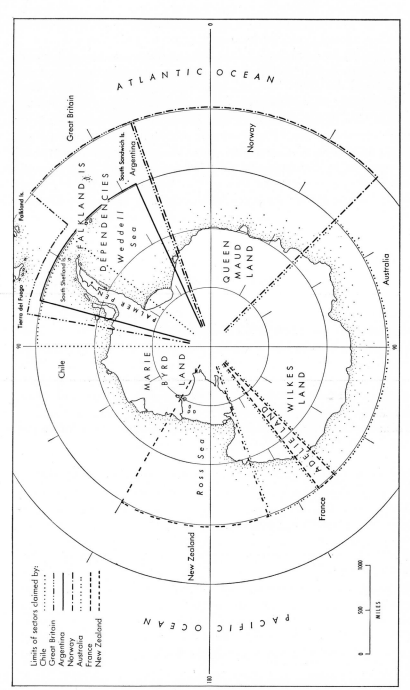

Figure 30. Territorial Claims in Antarctica.

are based for the most part on the principle of discovery, although in the case of the Falkland dependencies there is some historical controversy as to what nationality the captain was who first sighted the mainland here. On the other hand, Argentina and Chile base their demands for sovereignty on the grounds of effective occupation. The Argentinians have operated a weather station on an island close to the mainland since 1904, and the Chileans a whaling station on Deception Island since 1906, though neither establishment was actually on the Antarctic mainland. In more recent years, however, both Chile and Argentina have begun to operate year-round weather stations on the Antarctic mainland itself, thereby fortifying their respective claims to effective occupation. The British also have a year-round weather station on Palmer Peninsula within the sector claimed by all three contesting nations. As interest in Antarctica increases, so also will the friction over rival territorial claims.

BIBLIOGRAPHY

BURNS, SIR ALAN. "Towards a Caribbean Federation," *Foreign Affairs,* XXXIV, No. 1 (October, 1955), 128–41.

This is a comprehensive discussion of the proposed British Caribbean Federation.

CAMPBELL, JOHN C. "Nationalism and Regionalism in South America," *Foreign Affairs,* XXI, No. 1 (October, 1942), 132–49.

This article considers some basic features of the political areas in South America, including national cohesion and boundaries.

DAVIS, KINGSLEY. "Latin America's Multiplying Peoples," *Foreign Affairs,* XXV, No. 4 (July, 1947), 643–55.

A discussion of future population growth, and some of the ensuing political and economic problems.

HERON, DAVID WINSTON. "Antarctic Claims," *Foreign Affairs,* XXXII, No. 4 (July, 1954), 661–68.

A brief summary of the bases for territorial claims in the Antarctic, and a description of existing demands as of 1952.

IRELAND, GORDON. *Boundaries, Possessions and Conflicts in South America.* Cambridge: Harvard University Press, 1938.

———. *Boundaries, Possessions and Conflicts in Central and North America and the Caribbean.* Cambridge: Harvard University Press, 1941.

Two basic reference books for detailed descriptions of Latin American boundaries and territorial disputes.

JAMES, PRESTON E. *Latin America.* New York: The Odyssey Press, 1950.

The outstanding regional geography of Latin America.

JAMES, PRESTON E., and FAISSOL, SPERIDIAO. "The Problem of Brazil's Capital City," *The Geographical Review,* XLVI, No. 3 (July, 1956), 301–18.

The geographic factors of the site for Brazil's new capital city.

KAIN, ROBERT STUART. "Bolivia's Claustrophobia," *Foreign Affairs,* XX, No. 4 (July, 1942), 757–62.

A discussion of Bolivia's efforts to secure outlets to the sea.

PLATT, ROBERT S. "Conflicting Territorial Claims in the Upper Amazon," in *Geographic Aspects of International Relations,* ed. C. C. COLBY. Chicago: The University of Chicago Press, 1938.

A detailed account of this border dispute prior to World War II.

PLATTE, RAYE R. "The Guatemala-Honduras Boundary Disputes," *Foreign Affairs,* VII, No. 2 (January, 1929), 323–27.

———. "The Guatemala-Honduras Boundary Disputes," *The Geographical Review,* XXIII, No. 2 (April, 1933), 306–09.

Two detailed accounts of one of Central America's important boundary controversies.

5

THE COLONIAL POWERS OF EUROPE

● In the years since World War I the pattern of colonialism throughout the world has been radically changed. Many of the formerly dependent areas have achieved self-rule; other states, once independent, have passed under foreign domination. The empires of Japan, the United States, and of several of the western European nations have been substantially reduced in size and population, while the Soviet Union and China have emerged as centers of new colonial systems, in which the status of dependence is masked by such terms as "democracies" and "people's republics." These various changes in sovereignty have had far-reaching effects on the dependent or formerly dependent areas, on the mother countries, and on the general pattern of power areas existing throughout the world.

The history of empire development since the mid-fifteenth century has been associated largely with the maritime states of Europe. From these states explorers and traders went out to other continents and island areas, claiming these territories in the name of their homeland countries. The political partitioning of the non-European world was a long and complicated process, accompanied by a great number of territorial disputes, purchases and exchanges, and colonial wars. In the shifting patterns of control Spain and Portugal emerged as the early dominant powers, to be followed first by the Netherlands and then by France and Britain. Other European nations also entered the race for colonies. By the end of the nineteenth century practically all of the land area of the globe had been politically partitioned, with a large portion passing under the sovereignty of the European states. It is with the changing pattern of European colonial control that this chapter is concerned.

There are five major European colonial empires—those of Britain, France, Belgium, Portugal, and Spain. The Netherlands and Italy are former colonial powers which retain only vestiges of earlier overseas holdings. Germany, another former colonial nation, lost all its foreign territories after World War I. Denmark's area of overseas control is large in size but small in population and in economic importance. Norway controls only the Spitsbergen archipelago and several small islands in the Arctic and Antarctic areas (Table 1).

The relationships between the European colonial powers and their overseas possessions may be considered from several points of view: (1) the value of the possessions to the mother country, (2) the colonial policies followed in the administration of overseas areas, and (3) the effects of empire changes on world power alignments. A brief discussion of these topics is given below.

(1) The various assets which overseas territories represent to the mother country were listed on page 57 and comprise both the geographic aspects of the territories (location, natural resources, population totals and types) and the political ties which link them with the controlling powers. Some European possessions, such as Gibraltar, Cyprus, and Aden, have strategic military locations; others, such as Britain's Nigeria and the Belgian Congo, are rich in agricultural and mineral resources. Population factors are important because of the market potential economically-advanced colonial peoples can offer the mother country, and also because of the possible use of these peoples as a source for cheap labor or manpower for the armed forces.

Naturally the assets and liabilities of overseas territories to the European states may vary widely with changing political conditions. The Netherlands East Indies was once of great economic value to the Netherlands, while Indochina was of key importance to France. Yet in time both of these areas came to represent liabilities, because of the great costs involved in combating local struggles for independence. Territories which have attained independence may continue to be of economic and military value to the European states, because of investment and market opportunities and of the availability of sites for military bases. Iraq, Egypt, and the Union of South Africa represent areas in which Britain retained important economic and military influence after the achievement of self-rule; in all three countries, however, this influence has declined considerably since the end of World War II.

(2) The colonial policies of the major European powers are described in some detail in Chapter 12. Britain has taken the lead in promoting self-rule among its possessions, or in granting local representation on governing councils in areas where complete self-rule is still far in the future. Both France and the Netherlands have inaugurated somewhat nebulous "unions," in order to tie dependent areas more closely to the mother country. Portugal

Table 1

OVERSEAS POSSESSIONS OF THE EUROPEAN COLONIAL POWERS

	Area (sq. mi.)	Population (1955 estimates)
The British Commonwealth and Empire	12,056,342	644,129,000
. . Self-governing Commonwealth countries		
United Kingdom (Great Britain and Northern Ireland)	94,212	51,172,000
Australia	2,974,581	9,138,000
Canada	3,845,774	15,439,000
Ceylon	25,332	8,478,000
Federation of Malaya	50,598	5,980,000
Ghana (former Gold Coast and British Togoland) .	91,840	4,576,000
India (republic)	1,267,089	380,000,000
New Zealand	103,736	2,122,000
Pakistan (republic)	364,737	77,200,000
Union of South Africa	472,733	13,540,000
Great Britain and possessions (crown colonies, protectorates, trust territories, etc.)	2,357,493	125,368,000
Europe		
Channel Islands (Jersey, Guernsey)	75	101,000
Isle of Man	221	56,000
Gibraltar (colony)	2	25.000
Malta (colony)	122	317,000
Asia		
Cyprus (colony)	3,572	517,000
Aden (colony)	80	160,000
Aden Protectorate (incl. Socotra)	105,000	650,000
Singapore (state; incl. Christmas Isl.)	289	1,189,000
North Borneo (colony; incl. Labuan)	29,386	370,000
Brunei (protected sultanate)	2,226	56,000
Sarawak (colony)	47,069	609,000
Hong Kong (colony and leased territories) . . .	391	2,290,000
Africa		
Federation of Rhodesia and Nyasaland[a]	489,069	6,970,000
Southern Rhodesia (self-governing colony) . .	150,327	2,360,000
Northern Rhodesia (protectorate)	290,300	2,100,000
Nyasaland (protectorate)	48,442	2,510,000
Bechuanaland (protected territory)	275,000	293,000
Basutoland (protected territory)	11,716	590,000
Swaziland (protected territory)	6,705	212,000
Tanganyika (trust territory)	362,674	8,250,000
Kenya (colony and protectorate)	224,960	6,000,000
Zanzibar (protectorate; incl. Pemba)	1,020	276,000
Uganda (protectorate)	93,981	5,450,000
British Somaliland (protectorate)	68,000	640,000
Nigeria (federal colony)	339,156	30,500,000

[a] The federation is in a transition stage between the self-governing countries and the colonial possessions, since it has internal self-government, while the United Kingdom is responsible for external affairs.

Table 1 (continued)

OVERSEAS POSSESSIONS OF THE EUROPEAN COLONIAL POWERS

	Area (sq. mi.)	Population (1955 estimates)
British Cameroons (trusteeship territory) . . .	34,080	1,470,000
Sierra Leone (colony and protectorate)	27,924	2,050,000
Gambia (colony and protectorate)	4,003	264,000
Indian Ocean		
Mauritius (colony)	809	555,000
Seychelles (colony)	156	37,000
Maldive Islands (protected sultanate)	115	89,000
Pacific Ocean		
Fiji (colony)	7,040	333,000
Gilbert and Ellice Islands (colony; incl. Phoenix and Line isls. and Ocean Isl.)	369	37,000
Pitcairn Island	2	150
New Hebrides (condominium with France) . . .	5,700	50,000
Canton and Enderbury islands (condominium with United States; included in Gilbert and Ellice Islands colony)	27	300
Tonga (protected kingdom)	269	53,000
British Solomon Islands (protectorate)	11,500	104,000
Atlantic Ocean		
Bermuda (colony)	22	40,000
Falkland Islands (colony; incl. South Georgia) . .	6,068	2,500
St. Helena and dependencies (colony)	119	5,400
Middle America		
British Honduras (colony)	8,867	78,000
British Guiana (colony)	82,997	495,000
Bahamas (colony)	4,404	90,000
British West Indies:		
Barbados (colony)	166	227,000
Jamaica and dependencies (colony)	4,706	1,552,000
Trinidad and Tobago (colony)	1,979	710,000
Leeward Islands (colony)	423	125,000
Windward Islands (colony)	820	307,000
Australia and possessions (see Table 17)	3,158,144	10,857,950
New Zealand and possessions (see Table 17) . . .	105,072	2,238,500
Union of South Africa and possessions	790,458	13,992,000
Southwest Africa (mandate)	317,725	452,000
The French Union[b]	4,317,638	84,210,000
France (incl. Corsica)	213,009	43,216,000

[b] The former associated states of Vietnam (South), Cambodia, and Laos became independent countries in 1954. The former protectorates of Morocco and Tunisia were granted full sovereignty in 1956.

Table 1 (continued)

OVERSEAS POSSESSIONS OF THE EUROPEAN COLONIAL POWERS

	Area (sq. mi.)	Population (1955 estimates)
Algeria (northern departments and Southern Territories)	846,124	9,390,000
Overseas Departments		
Martinique	425	240,000
Guadeloupe and dependencies	687	230,000
French Guiana	35,000	28,000
Réunion	970	276,000
Overseas Territories		
French West Africa	1,831,100	18,100,000
Mauritania	416,100	560,000
Senegal	80,600	2,200,000
French Guinea	106,200	2,340,000
Ivory Coast	123,300	2,240,000
Upper Volta	106,000	3,260,000
French Sudan	460,500	3,600,000
Dahomey	43,800	1,620,000
Niger	494,600	2,280,000
French Equatorial Africa	969,000	4,560,000
Gabon	103,000	420,000
Middle Congo	132,000	700,000
Ubangi-Shari	238,000	1,100,000
Chad	496,000	2,340,000
French Somaliland	8,500	66,000
Madagascar and dependencies	227,950	4,550,000
Comoro Islands	834	170,000
French Oceania	1,544	65,000
New Caledonia and dependencies	7,202	64,000
St. Pierre and Miquelon	93	4,700
Condominium		
New Hebrides (with Great Britain)	5,700	50,000
Trusteeship Territories		
French Cameroons	169,500	3,200,000
French Togoland	21,200	1,064,000
The Belgian Empire	937,686	25,441,000
Belgium	11,779	8,841,000
Belgian Congo (colony)	904,991	12,300,000
Ruanda-Urundi (trusteeship territory)	20,916	4,300,000
The Portuguese Empire	839,248	21,058,000
Portugal (incl. Azores and Madeira)	35,414	8,725,000
Overseas Provinces		
Cape Verde Islands	1,557	168,000

Table 1 (continued)

OVERSEAS POSSESSIONS OF THE EUROPEAN COLONIAL POWERS

	Area (sq. mi.)	Population (1955 estimates)
Portuguese Guinea	13,948	540,000
São Tomé and Príncipe	372	53,000
Angola	481,350	4,260,000
Mozambique	297,731	6,000,000
Portuguese India (Goa, Damão, Diu)	1,538	643,000
Macao	6	200,000
Portuguese Timor	7,332	469,000
The Netherlands Union	227,910	11,807,000
The Netherlands	13,025	10,670,000
Surinam (autonomous territory)	55,144	250,000
Netherlands Antilles (autonomous territory: Curaçao, Aruba, Bonaire, St. Eustatius, Saba, and southern part of St. Martin)	366	187,000
Netherlands New Guinea	159,375	700,000
Denmark and Possessions	857,116	4,480,000
Denmark	16,576	4,422,000
Greenland (integral part of Danish kingdom) . . .	840,000	25,000
Faeroe Islands (autonomous territory)	540	33,000
The Spanish Empire	322,335	29,295,000
Spain (incl. Canary Islands)	194,945	28,850,000
Spanish Guinea (colony: Río Muni, and Fernando Po and nearby isls.)	10,830	206,000
Spanish West Africa (governorate: Ifni, Spanish Sahara (Río de Oro, Saguia el Hamra), and Southern Zone of Morocco)	116,478	96,000
Spanish Possessions in North Africa (incl. Ceuta and Melilla; and isls. of Alhucemas, Chafarinas, and Peñón de Veléz de la Gomera)	82	143,000
Norway and Possessions	149,298	3,411,400
Norway	125,064	3,408,000
Spitsbergen (Svalbard)	23,979	(winter) 3,400
Jan Mayen Island	141	10
Bouvet Island	22	—
Peter I Island	92	—
Italy and Possessions	314,586	49,050,000
Italy	116,311	47,780,000
Somalia (Italian Somaliland; trusteeship territory) .	198,275	1,270,000

has adopted an *assimilado* policy, under which a colonial subject may become "civilized" or assimilated, that is, acquire education and adopt a European way of life. Belgium has denied the vote to both white and non-white inhabitants of its territories, until such time as the nonwhites are prepared to take part in the administration of these areas. Spain continues, as it has in the past, to administer its colonies with little or no native representation.

The contrast between the colonial policies of Britain, on the one hand, and those of France (and to a less extent of Portugal, Belgium, Spain, and the Netherlands) on the other, points up a fundamental difference in political thinking. Whittlesey contrasts the two major colonial systems in Africa by describing "Indirect Rule," practiced by the British, as ". . . government which leaves the African political structure untouched, except for supervision by British political officers, organized not to supersede the indigenous government, but to parallel and supplement it," and "Direct Rule," practiced by the French, as ". . . exerted through a governor and his subordinates. . . . All responsible officials directly engaged in administering government are Europeans, except the men immediately in control of the smallest units . . . in order to integrate the colonies with the home country in the fullest possible degree."[1] In the system of direct rule local peoples are indoctrinated with the language and customs of the mother country and there is a tendency of disrupt tribal organizations. The process of detribalization may work considerable hardships on the colonial peoples, for at some stage of "Europeanization" they give up their former culture, and yet as Africans do not receive the full economic and political benefits of the European way of life. Direct and indirect rule are also applied in other parts of the world where dependent areas exist.

(3) The effects of empire changes on world power alignments may be summed up as follows: as a result of empire losses since the end of World War I the power position of the western European colonial nations has declined relative to other parts of the world, particularly Anglo-America, the Soviet Union, southern Asia, and North Africa. Since these colonial nations are members of various Western military alliances, this declining power position is important to the Cold War. Not only have several of the European states been forced to adjust their economies in recent years as a result of losses of colonial markets, investments, and sources for raw materials, but also, in the military and political sense, their leaders can no longer speak for the large areas and populations formerly under their control.

United action on the part of noncommunist countries in the face of communist expansion is one of the most significant aspects of the changing

---

[1] Derwent Whittlesey, *The Earth and the State*, p. 379. Used by permission of Henry Holt and Company, copyright 1944.

colonial pattern. The difficulties confronting the European states with respect to communist pressures differ widely from the difficulties which exist in southern Asia or Africa, where new states, having achieved independence from the Europeans, are struggling with local problems of national development. These different problems have been well recognized by communist political leaders, who often pursue one type of policy in dealing with the Europeans and another type with dependent or recently independent countries.

The degree of political and military unity existing between the European nations and their former possessions varies from place to place. Some states, such as Canada, Australia, and New Zealand, have continued to maintain close economic and military ties with their former mother country, but many others, as, for example, Indonesia, Cambodia, and Burma, have not. An additional factor of disunity in former imperial areas are the international tensions which have developed between newly independent states over such matters as control of territory and treatment of minority groups. The India-Pakistan and Israeli-Arab disputes are examples of this type of centrifugal force. The net effect has been to accentuate the differences in interests between states of the noncommunist world, and to complicate efforts to unite them in common action in the face of communist aggression.

In the sections which follow the various colonial systems of western Europe will be considered in terms of both the mother country and the relationship between the mother country and its overseas possessions. More complete descriptions of the dependent states appear in the chapters on the regions in which they are located.

GREAT BRITAIN AND THE COMMONWEALTH

In the early 1920's Great Britain was the seat of an empire in which the overseas possessions measured 13,600,000 square miles in area (26 per cent of the land area of the globe, excluding Antarctica), with a population of 460,000,000. By 1957 this empire had been reduced to approximately 2,357,000 square miles, containing about 125,000,000 inhabitants, so that it ranked second in size and second in population among the colonial systems of the world (Figure 31). Sixteen independent nations, dominions, and commonwealth republics have been created from the British Empire of the 1920's, but most of these have continued within the framework of the British Commonwealth. Several other overseas possessions are destined for independence within the Commonwealth in the near future.

The United Kingdom

The United Kingdom, located off the coast of northwestern Europe, is composed of Great Britain (England, Wales, and Scotland), Northern

Figure 31. The British Commonwealth: Changes Since 1921.
For the present status of world empires, see map on inside cover.

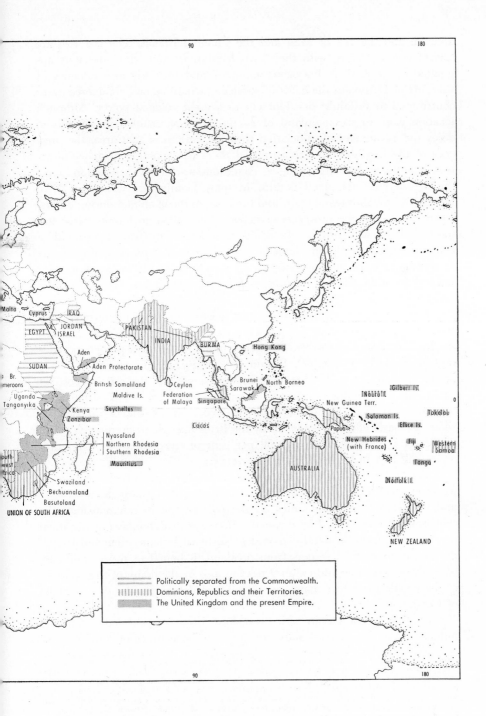

90   180

Malta
Cyprus   IRAQ
JORDAN
EGYPT   ISRAEL   PAKISTAN
Aden   INDIA   BURMA   Hong Kong
SUDAN
Aden Protectorate
Br.
meroons   British Somaliland   Brunei   North Borneo
Uganda   Maldive Is.   Sarawak   Gilbert Is.
Tanganyika   Ceylon   New Guinea Terr.
Kenya   Federation   Singapore   0
Zanzibar   of Malaya   Solomon Is.   Tokelau
Seychelles   Ellice Is.
Cocos   Papua   New Hebrides   Fiji   Western
Nyasaland   (with France)   Samoa
Northern Rhodesia   Tonga
outh   Southern Rhodesia   Mauritius   AUSTRALIA
west   Swaziland   Norfolk I.
rica   Bechuanaland
Basutoland
UNION OF SOUTH AFRICA   NEW ZEALAND

Politically separated from the Commonwealth.
Dominions, Republics and their Territories.
The United Kingdom and the present Empire.

90   180

Ireland, and the Isle of Man and the Channel Islands. The last two are special political units, with their own legislatures and with governors appointed by the Crown. Location, resources, and the early pre-eminence of this part of Europe in the fields of science, navigation, and commerce, have contributed to Britain's[2] development as a great colonial power. Although location close to the mainland of western Europe enabled the British to enjoy the advantages of association with the nations of that area, the presence of the English Channel permitted them the opportunity to withdraw from Continental affairs whenever conditions warranted such action. Thus the British have remained neutral in some Continental wars, and have succeeded in withdrawing their land forces from the mainland during others, when faced with the prospects of defeat. Since 1066 no foreign army has successfully invaded Britain.[3] In addition to defense the waters surrounding Britain have provided opportunities for overseas trade and commerce. Some of the major trade routes of the world pass close to the British Isles, and since the middle of the seventeenth century Britain has been a leading maritime power.

The advantages of Britain's insular location are partially offset by the country's small area and limited resources. Including Northern Ireland, the total area amounts to 94,000 square miles, and with a present population in excess of 51,000,000, Britain has an average density of over 540 persons per square mile. Climate, soils, and slope, and the relative costs of agriculture have limited crop land to about 30 per cent of the total area, thereby affecting the nation's capacity to feed itself. During World War II, when strenuous efforts were made by the British people to produce as much foodstuffs as possible, well over 50 per cent of the nation's food requirements still had to be imported from overseas.

The United Kingdom represents a situation in which centripetal forces are well developed. The limited area, the strong circulatory system, and the sense of national unity on the part of the British outweigh the centrifugal forces created by regional differences or differences in historical development, as in Scotland and Wales. Northern Ireland, inhabited largely by the descendants of settlers from Scotland, is bound to the British Isles not only by economic and cultural ties but also by the desire of the majority of the people there to remain free of political domination by the Republic of Ireland.

Britain's limitations in agriculture have been compensated in part by industrial and commercial activities, and by the earning of "invisible in-

---

[2] The term "Britain" is used here synonomously with the United Kingdom.
[3] The waters which protect Britain from invasion by enemy armies have, of course, had little effect on air operations. During World War II the German *Luftwaffe* proved that the barrier function of the English Channel was fast disappearing, and the development of rocket artillery toward the close of the war further established this fact. Postwar experiments with atomic and hydrogen bombs have virtually ended the possibility of British isolation in the event of future warfare on the Continent.

come" through such services as tourism, insurance and banking activities, and foreign investments. The Industrial Revolution came early to Britain, and its development was aided by the presence of extensive coal measures as well as by a moderate amount of iron-ore resources. In the nineteenth century Britain became a coal-exporting nation. By the mid-twentieth century, however, many of the more accessible measures have been exhausted, labor costs are high, and the process of mechanization has been slow; as a result the British must normally import a portion of their coal. Other mineral and fuel resources are almost completely absent in Britain, adding to the list of commodities the British must import in order to maintain their industrial economy. Before World War II Britain was able to maintain a favorable balance of payments, but in the years since 1939 this has generally not been true. Loss of foreign investments and overseas markets, together with wartime destruction and the expense of maintaining armaments for the Cold War, have hindered postwar economic recovery, with the result that considerable financial assistance from the United States since the end of World War II has been necessary to permit Britain to fulfill its domestic and overseas commitments.

In the development of its empire the British nation has been fortunate in both the number and the quality of its population. From the early seventeenth to the early nineteenth century, while Britain still possessed a primarily agricultural economy, there was a considerable excess of population in terms of available employment. Thus there was a strong incentive for emigration overseas. The advent of the Industrial Revolution in the nineteenth century meant increased opportunities for employment in Britain itself, but at the same time the population also increased rapidly. During the half century from 1851 to 1901 the combined population of England and Wales increased by over 80 per cent.

The concern of British settlers in overseas territories for the advancement of orderly government and for the development of the land they inhabited led them to establish stable political and economic systems in these areas. Despite certain weaknesses in some areas, such as economic exploitation and retention of the color bar, the British have ranked among the best colonizers in the world, in terms of effective utilization of the land, treatment of colonial peoples, and political administration.

Ireland

The turbulent history of the island of Ireland is reflected in its political division into a northern and a southern sector, and in the continued agitation in the south for unification of the entire area into one state. The island has an area of 31,840 square miles and a population of just under 4,500,000. About one quarter of the land is in cultivation. In the past Ireland has had difficulty in feeding its people: in 1830 there were more than 8,000,000 inhabitants on the island, but repeated potato famines during the next two decades resulted in the emigration of over half the population—a majority of them to the United States. Other than agricultural land Ireland has few resources, except peat and some water-power potential. The Irish have thus experienced considerable difficulties in developing industries, and, particularly in the central and southern parts of the island, they have preserved a predominantly agricultural economy. Northern Ireland has undergone some industrialization, and is important for its shipbuilding and linen industries. The economic advances made here are significant in terms of possible unification of the island.

The Republic of Ireland, occupying the central and southern portion of the island, contains 84 per cent of the total area and 68 per cent (1951 figures) of the population, and is overwhelmingly Catholic; while Northern Ireland, an integral part of the United Kingdom, has a population which is about 70 per cent Protestant (Figure 32). The island was divided in 1920 in response to demands by the people of the central and southern sectors that they receive self-government. Plebiscites were held in each of the island's thirty-two counties, and in six northern counties a majority elected to remain with Britain. The boundary was finally delimited on the basis of old county boundaries, so that many people who had wished to be in southern Ireland found themselves included in the north. Although from the standpoint of origin the Ireland-Northern Ireland border was historical in nature, it represented a superimposed boundary with respect to the cultural aspects of the area, for it failed to separate effectively the Catholics from the Protestants. As a result the border has contributed to the tension existing between the northern and southern counties.

The central and southern portion of the island has been known by several names—the Irish Free State (1922–37), Eire (1937–49), and the Republic of Ireland since 1949. It was set up as a dominion in 1922, but later it chose to sever all connections with the Commonwealth, except those of an economic nature. Since 1922 the people of the Republic of Ireland have agitated continuously for elimination of the island's division and inclusion of Northern Ireland within the Republic. This proposal has been resisted both by the British, who wish to maintain military and economic ties with Northern Ireland, and by a majority of the people of Northern Ireland itself. The latter are not attracted by the possibilities of being a definite religious minority in a united Ireland; more important, perhaps, is the fact that the standard of living in the north is considerably higher than in the south. Political unification with the other units of Great Britain has been important to Northern Ireland's economy; if union with the Irish Republic ever were carried out the average income per capita might undergo a considerable decline.

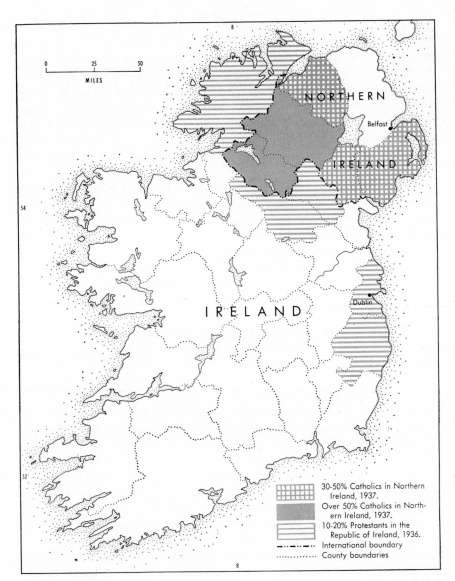

0   25   50
MILES

8

NORTHERN

Belfast

IRELAND

54

IRELAND

Dublin

52

	30-50% Catholics in Northern Ireland, 1937.
	Over 50% Catholics in Northern Ireland, 1937.
	10-20% Protestants in the Republic of Ireland, 1936.
—·—·—·	International boundary
·············	County boundaries

8

Figure 32. The Partition of Ireland. (After Stoneman, "The Partition of Ireland," Doctoral dissertation, Clark University, 1950. Used by permission.)

The British Commonwealth of Nations

A unique empire relationship has been evolved by Great Britain with respect to its overseas possessions. As a result of wide differences in economic and political conditions throughout the areas under British control, a Commonwealth arrangement was established in 1931, consisting of the United Kingdom, the dominions and republics, the colonies, protectorates, and protected territories, and the territories under trusteeship. Of the overseas units, the dominions and republics are self-governing, while the colonies, protectorates, protected territories, and trusteeships constitute what is left of the British Empire. By September, 1957, there were seven dominions—Australia, Canada, Ceylon, Ghana (formerly Gold Coast), the Federation of Malaya, New Zealand, and the Union of South Africa—together with India and Pakistan, which since independence have declared themselves to be republics.

The dominions of the British Commonwealth are defined as "autonomous communities within the British Empire, equal in status, in no way subordinate to one another in any aspect of their domestic or external affairs, though united by a common allegiance to the Crown." India and Pakistan as sovereign independent republics recognize the Queen as symbolic head of the Commonwealth, but differ from the dominions in that the Queen is not titular head of their countries and administration is not carried out in her name. In actual practice membership of the independent units in the British Commonwealth of Nations carries with it no mandatory restrictions, and members may at any time withdraw from the Commonwealth. Defense and foreign affairs are handled by the individual units, although military activities may be co-ordinated in times of war. Economic and cultural ties also continue between Britain and the dominions and republics, resulting in mutual benefits for the Commonwealth members.

The British colonial possessions are located, for the most part, in three areas: central and southern Africa, the Caribbean basin (including the Guiana coast), and southeast Asia and the southern Pacific Ocean. Some of these are of particular importance as military bases. Because of the low average income of most of the inhabitants of the colonies and protectorates, the market potential of many of these areas is still small. It is perhaps paradoxical that as the local peoples advance their economic status (thereby increasing the market potential) they also hasten their political independence from Britain.

A study of the political structure of the British Empire reveals both the great flexibility in type and degree of control and the constantly changing nature of control as overseas areas move toward self-rule. The exact number of units in any one category of dependency changes from year to year, as the British adjust to the demands and abilities of the dependent peoples. Some areas are in the process of becoming completely free from associations with the Commonwealth, others are on the road to dominion or republic status, and still others will become incorporated within the borders of neighboring territories. By adjusting the conditions of territorial control, Britain has succeeded in preventing widespread unrest in its possessions and in retaining the friendship and co-operation of most of the states which were once dependent territories.

Britain's trusteeship territories (formerly League of Nations mandates) are in central Africa, and include Tanganyika, the British Cameroons, and British Togoland, with a total population of over 10,000,000. Togoland is now a part of Ghana. Economically and politically the territories are treated as parts of the Commonwealth, although annual reports on certain of the territories' activities must be made to the United Nations.

Since 1921 a number of areas have become completely separated from Britain's imperial system. The Class A mandates, which included Iraq, Transjordan, and Palestine, eventually became independent but not Commonwealth members, although the first two continued to maintain certain military ties with the British. The Irish Republic became a sovereign independent area in 1949, completely free of Commonwealth connections except for continued membership in the sterling bloc. Egypt, Burma, and Sudan have likewise ended their Commonwealth associations, thereby reflecting the strong desires for complete freedom of action by the governments of these areas.

The Significance of the Commonwealth to Britain. The economic value of the Commonwealth to Great Britain is not as great as it once was. During the nineteenth and early twentieth centuries the colonies served (1) as suppliers of raw materials, such as grains, tin, rubber, diamonds, gold, sugar, cotton, and wool; (2) as markets for the mother country's industrial products; and (3) as areas for investment by British capital. In recent decades, however, the situation has changed. Such areas as Canada, Australia, New Zealand, and the Union of South Africa have advanced to the point where they can supply most of their required industrial items, and Canada is actually beginning to emerge as an exporter of finished industrial goods in competition with Britain. Markets for Britain's manufactured goods in India and Pakistan are also growing scarcer, due in part to the growing ability of these countries to supply their own needs. In 1920 Britain's trade with Commonwealth members amounted to 60 per cent by value of its total foreign trade; by 1953 this figure had declined to 48 per cent, of which nearly two-thirds was with the now-independent dominions and republics.

The independent Commonwealth members are still joined with Great Britain and its empire in the sterling bloc, an economic arrangement whereby the member nations extend preferential tariff agreements to one another and adopt a common monetary policy, maintaining their currencies in fixed relation to the pound sterling. The economic advantages of membership in the sterling bloc have been a factor in Britain's reluctance to be associated too closely with economic organizations among the nations of the west European mainland.

The Commonwealth is also important to Britain in terms of military and political activities, as well as prestige purposes. During the past two world wars the Commonwealth has supplied large quantities of men and equipment for use against Britain's enemies, and in peacetime the British, through the use of certain Commonwealth areas, have been able to maintain a world-wide system of military bases. The British Crown still represents a symbol of allegiance for hundreds of millions of people, and London, as the seat of the Commonwealth, continues to be one of the great capital cities of the world.

Mention has already been made of the inevitability of centrifugal forces developing within such global political systems as the overseas possessions and associated countries of the European powers. Within the British Commonwealth such forces are represented by a number of different situations —the rise of "neutralism" in India and Ceylon, the isolationist tendencies of the Union of South Africa, the struggles for political control of Cyprus, the challenge of Arab nationalism to British power in the Middle East and of Latin American nationalism to British control in portions of the Western Hemisphere. Despite these forces, however, the British Commonwealth remains a political entity of great size and population, a symbol of wise colonial policy which has effected the transformation of what was once the world's largest empire into what is now the world's largest political association of independent and dependent states.

Lifelines of the Commonwealth. The pattern of Commonwealth territories—both past and present—is closely linked with the maintenance of lifelines, by means of which trade and the movement of military supplies and personnel are carried out. These lifelines are primarily ocean routes, although they are augmented by airways and, in certain areas, by rail and highway routes as well. The strategic importance of the lifelines has declined somewhat in recent years, because of the lessening of the overseas territories' dependence on Britain and because of the ability of hostile air power in time of war to render certain of these lines ineffective to the Commonwealth countries.

One of the most important lifelines is that which crosses the North Atlantic, linking Great Britain with Canada. As a supply line this route— which also connects with the United States—has been of immense value to Britain during time of war. A second lifeline passes through the Mediterranean, the Suez Canal, and the Red Sea to the Indian Ocean and beyond to the Far East. The route is guarded by a series of strategic bases, such as Gibraltar, Malta, and Aden, but because of the rise of nationalism in areas flanking this route and of the proximity of potentially hostile air bases, Britain's ability to guard the line has been seriously weakened. In a future conflict the Mediterranean route might well prove completely useless to the Commonwealth. Not only in the Mediterranean and the Middle East have British bases been threatened. India and Ceylon have also interfered with Britain's use of its bases in their respective territories, and as a result Britain has begun the development of a major air base in the Maldive Islands, southwest of India, in the Indian Ocean.

A third British lifeline connects Britain with southern Africa and Australasia. Like the Mediterranean-Red Sea route, it has numerous bases and commercial ports along its course, and at times when the Mediterranean route cannot be utilized this lifeline has served as an alternate to the Indian Ocean. Another lifeline passes across the Atlantic, through the Panama Canal, and across the Pacific to Australia and New Zealand, while a fifth lies across the South Atlantic to the Falkland Islands and Antarctica. Bases and commercial ports are farther apart on these last two routes, and these lifelines have never been of as much importance to Britain as have the others. A final route, which is being developed as an alternative military supply line between Britain and the Indian Ocean, lies across central Africa from the Gulf of Guinea to the east coast ports of Kenya and Tanganyika. This route, which would be used as an emergency lifeline, would require the transshipment of cargo from ships to overland carriers in west Africa and from these carriers back to ships on the east coast (see also page 337).

FRANCE AND THE FRENCH UNION

The French Empire, like the British, has been undergoing major changes since the end of World War II. The strong nationalism in the overseas possessions and the weakened power position of France itself after defeat and occupation by the Germans resulted in the gradual decline of French power in southern Asia and in North Africa. Unlike the British, the French were unwilling to accede to demands by colonial peoples for complete independence; instead a French Union was established, within the framework of which certain territories would become autonomous units. These concessions to nationalist movements, however, were not great enough to stem the rising tide of insurrection, and France was eventually forced to relinquish much of its control both in Indochina and in North Africa.

The French Nation

France's location makes it both a maritime and a continental power. The nation faces on three bodies of water—the Atlantic, the Mediterranean, and the English Channel—while on its land borders it touches nine nations. For over a thousand years portions of France's land borders, particularly in the east, have been the scenes of frequent warfare and territorial change (see Chapter 6 for a discussion of this eastern border). Three disastrous wars with Germany in less than seventy-five years have affected both the material and the psychological position of the French, and many of France's internal and external problems since 1945 can be traced to the devastating aftereffects of German aggression.

As a result of the historical rivalry between France and Germany, the economic position of the French nation has been of particular importance to its political development. Economic production, particularly in the industrial fields, represents one of the major elements of a state's war potential, and France's ability to defend itself against German aggression (either by maintaining high levels of French output or by reducing those of the Germans) has been a significant aspect of the nation's security.

The French nation possesses considerable natural resources, including iron ore, potash, coal, bauxite, and forests, as well as large areas where both soil and climate render conditions suitable for agriculture. The nation's energy output has been augmented in recent years by increased development of its water-power potential. French industrial production, however, is normally less than that of Germany. After World Wars I and II France sought to gain control of industrial facilities in the Saar, primarily to effect a greater equalization of output with Germany. In 1945 France also sought to impose limits on the degree to which German industry could expand in its postwar recovery, but these efforts were largely unsuccessful, and by 1950 steel production in West Germany had surpassed that of the French.

Population potential is another aspect of France's power position. The population has grown relatively slowly during the past century. In 1861 it numbered 37,400,000; in 1955 it was 43,216,000, representing an increase of less than sixteen per cent in ninety-four years. This slow population growth has had an adverse effect on France's power status, in that it has been a check on the availability of manpower to maintain the nation's economy and to serve in its armed forces. France has an area of 213,000 square miles with an average population density of just over 200 persons per square mile —a figure which is low for the nations of northwest Europe. The lack of population pressure has been partly responsible for the relatively small-scale emigration of colonists to France's overseas possessions, with the exception of those in North Africa.

France has been a unified nation for over six centuries, and there are strong centripetal forces here based on national sentiment, centralization of power, and ethnic unity. The Paris Basin, which is the principal core area of the country, also serves as the economic and political center of France. The centralization of control here is augmented by the political subdivision of the country into ninety departments, no one of which is in a position to seriously challenge the authority of the national government. Despite physical and economic differences throughout the nation, there is a well-developed circulatory system, based primarily on the transportation facilities and on the extensive use made of radio, newspaper, and other communication media.

Figure 33. France: Language Minorities. (After Van Valkenburg, *Elements of Political Geography,* copyright 1939 by Prentice-Hall, Inc. Used by permission.)

Religion also constitutes a unifying element, since practically all of the French are Roman Catholic. Language, on the other hand, does not produce the same degree of cultural cohesion. Although over 90 per cent of the inhabitants speak a dialect of French, there are important minorities along the borders which speak foreign tongues. In Alsace and eastern Lorraine much of the population speaks either German or Alsatian, a dialect akin to German, and in the eastern part of the French Riviera are many Italian-speaking groups. There are thousands of Spanish-speaking people in southern France at the eastern end of the Pyrenees, while in the western end are the Basques, a distinct ethnic group also inhabiting northern Spain. Finally, in the northwest are people who speak Celtic, or Breton (Figure 33).

In France, as in other countries, these ethnic differences represent centrifugal forces, which, particularly in times of crisis, tend to weaken the unity of the nation.

The French Union

Prior to World War II the political framework of the French Empire was far less complex than that of the British Commonwealth, for there existed a relatively simple mother country-colony relationship between France and its possessions. Although Syria and Lebanon, former League of Nations mandates, became independent at the end of World War II, the remaining empire was the largest in area in the world, measuring over 4,000,000 square miles, with a population of some 80,000,000 people. In 1946, in response to pressures for increased self-rule in some of the colonial areas, the Paris government established the French Union, consisting of Metropolitan France, Algeria, the overseas departments, the overseas territories, the trusteeship territories, the Anglo-French condominium of New Hebrides, and the associated states and protectorates.

Nowhere in the organizational framework of the French Union was there a provision for attainment of dominion status or of eventual independence. The Union's purpose was ". . . to enable each territory to develop freely along democratic lines, while remaining linked to France by common interests."[4] The concept of "linked by common interests" can obviously mean many things to many persons; even to French officials its definition apparently varied widely. It was partly because of the ambiguity of the political relationships that were envisioned between France and its overseas possessions at the time of the Union's establishment that so much local resentment developed against the French in Indochina and in North Africa.

Northern Algeria is divided into twelve departments. These and the four overseas departments—Martinique, Guadeloupe, French Guiana, and Réunion—are considered as integral parts of France and send representatives to the French National Assembly. French policy with respect to these areas, as well as to the overseas territories, has been one of assimilation, attempting to bring all inhabitants within the social, cultural, and political family of France. In view of the low cultural levels of many of the colonial peoples the actual implementation of this policy has taken place only on a small scale.

In the trusteeship territories there has been less attempt at assimilation, and up until recently France's control has been more of the protectorate type, leaving native institutions relatively unchanged. The establishment of French Togoland as a republic within the French Union in 1956, however, may herald a change in this policy.

[4] *The French Union*, French Information Service, 1949, p. 1.

In the former associated states of Cambodia, Laos, and Vietnam and in the protectorates of Tunisia and Morocco there was little interference with local institutions. The inability of the French to come to an agreement with local political leaders on the terms of the political status of the associated states and protectorates led to the gradual weakening of political ties between these areas and the mother country. By 1956 France had officially ended its rule in Morocco and Tunisia and in the states of Indochina. In a last effort to retain something of its influence in the two North African territories, the French government maintained it was still linked to Morocco and Tunisia by ties of "interdependence," although, as in former times, the actual nature of these ties was not clearly determined.

Assets and Liabilities of the Union. The importance of the French Union to France might be summed up in the three terms—prestige, manpower, and commerce. Although the majority of the French people has never been particularly "colony conscious," the overseas possessions have always been a source of national pride. Countering this, however, have been certain Union liabilities, such as the long slow retreat in Indochina (see page 404) and the rebellions in North Africa (see page 302), which have harmed, rather than enhanced France's prestige.

The French have long looked to overseas possessions as sources for military manpower. Non-European troops have been important to the maintenance of French power throughout its world-wide empire. Since World War II, however, the Union has been more of a liability than an asset to France in this respect. The Indochina war cost the French army (including the Foreign Legion) 32,500 dead, and necessitated the deployment of several French divisions to that area, some of which had to be withdrawn from western Europe, where they were intended for use with the North Atlantic Treaty Organization. A number of French divisions have also been sent to North Africa in recent years to cope with Arab uprisings there.

The Union is France's greatest trade partner, accounting for about one quarter of the nation's imports and nearly forty per cent of its exports. From the Union comes iron ore, phosphate, grain, wine, sugar, and graphite. Continued improvement in the standard of living of the colonial peoples in the Union will mean greater markets for French exports, and thus increase the potential economic value of the overseas possessions to France. On the other hand, the political disturbances within the overseas possessions have been reflected in trade statistics. French trade with South Vietnam in 1955, for example, was half that in 1952.

THE BELGIAN EMPIRE

Belgium's history of colonial control dates back only to the late nineteenth century. The nation's independence was not achieved until the 1830's, and in the decades which followed Belgium's leaders devoted their energies to building up their country's economic level, giving little attention to the acquisition of colonial areas. In 1878, however, Belgium's King Leopold sent the noted explorer Henry Morton Stanley into the Congo River basin to supervise the establishment of Belgian outposts and to explore the area more fully. At the Berlin Conference of 1884–85 Leopold was declared sovereign of the Congo Free State, and for over twenty years he controlled the region as his own private estate. Not until 1908 did the Belgian government assume responsibility for the large tropical area.

At the end of World War I Belgium was awarded a League of Nations mandate over Ruanda-Urundi, a former German possession adjoining the Belgian Congo in central Africa. Inclusion of this region within the Belgian empire brought the total of Belgium's overseas possessions to 926,000 square miles, so that it now ranks third in size among the empires of the European states.

Belgium is an industrial nation in northwestern Europe, with only a small stretch of coast on the North Sea. It has an area of nearly 12,000 square miles and a population of some 9,000,000 persons. Despite the high average population density, Belgium's industrial structure—based on the presence of extensive coal deposits—normally provides sufficient employment opportunities for the bulk of Belgian workers. Thus the nation has had little need for an empire as a settlement area for surplus population.

Belgium's colonial policy in the Congo is described in detail on page 337. Because of the low stage of cultural development of the Congolese, the Belgians have not faced the demands for self-rule which have been made of other European colonial powers. Economically, the region is only beginning to be developed; in 1953, for example, it accounted for less than eight per cent by value of Belgium's total foreign trade. Because of the great potential wealth of the Congo, however, the Belgians, particularly since World War I, have become increasingly concerned with the development of this overseas possession, and Belgium is gradually assuming the aspects of a major colonial power. Here, as in the case of the African territories of the French Union, greater purchasing power of the inhabitants and emigration of more Europeans to the colonies will in time greatly augment the trade value of the Congo to Belgium. Because of its mineral, agricultural, and power resources this area is one of the most valuable colonial possessions still left to the nations of western Europe.

THE PORTUGUESE EMPIRE

Portugal's empire, like that of the Belgians, is remarkable in that few forces exist for the removal of the colonial areas from Portuguese control. Portugal's constitution officially bars the cession of any of the overseas territories to foreign powers, and no programs have been set up for the establishment of independence. To counter the demands of its African peoples for increased economic and political opportunities, Portugal has inaugurated an *assimilado* policy. When vocal political groups begin to develop in the African territories, the long-term effectiveness of Portugal's plans for retaining control of its empire will then be put to the test.

Portugal itself has an area of 35,000 square miles and a population of over 8,700,000. The people are united by language and religion, and Lisbon, the capital, is also located in the nation's major core area. Thus Portugal, unlike Spain, has few centrifugal forces within its borders to threaten national cohesion. Much of the country is mountainous, and little of its estimated mineral wealth has yet been exploited. Except for textiles, industrialization is not well developed, and the per capita income is low compared with that of the nations of northwestern Europe. Although the country has a long indented seacoast on the Atlantic and is important for its fisheries, Portugal has not been a major maritime power for nearly four centuries. Its governments have lacked the resources needed to administer a large and far-flung empire, and much of the impetus for colonial development has been furnished by the Church or by chartered commercial companies, such as the Mozambique Company, which up to 1942 exercised political control over a large portion of Mozambique.

Portugal's historical alliance with Great Britain provided the protection of the British fleet and saved at least a part of the African possessions from annexation by other European powers. In recent years Portugal has also maintained close military relations with the United States. Portugal is a member of the North Atlantic Treaty Organization, its principal contribution being the granting of permission to the United States to build and maintain an air base in the Azores Islands. Lobito, on the coast of Portuguese Angola, may also be developed as a western terminus for one of the wartime supply routes across the African continent which are now in the process of construction. (See also the discussion of Portugal itself in Chapter 7.)

Portugal was the first nation in Europe to develop an overseas empire. Early in the fifteenth century Portuguese expeditions began exploring the west coast of Africa in an effort to discover a sea route to India, and in subsequent years Portuguese colonies were established in Africa, Asia, and the East Indies. Brazil was Portugal's one possession in the Western Hemisphere. Many of these territories were eventually lost, but Portugal still retains a considerable colonial area for development. The decline of Portugal's empire after the middle of the sixteenth century was occasioned by a number of factors, including the gradual depletion of manpower in the nation as a result of prolonged military campaigns and the persecutions and expulsion of Jews, whose wealth and skills had formed an important base for Portugal's expansion. Other countries, with greater resources and manpower, supplanted Portugal as the seats of world empires.

Of the 804,000 square miles of Portugal's overseas territory, 99 per cent lies in Africa and off the African coast. Angola (with its northern exclave of Cabinda) and Mozambique are the two largest Portuguese territories. Others are Portuguese Guinea, located on Africa's west coast, the Cape Verde Islands, lying west of Dakar in the Atlantic Ocean, and the islands of São Tomé and Príncipe in the Gulf of Guinea.

Portugal's well-known overseas possession, the Azores Islands, lies 1,000 miles west of Portugal itself, and is an important air stop for transatlantic flights. The islands are administered as districts of Portugal itself. Likewise, the Madeira Islands, southwest of the Azores, are considered as part of Portugal. In the Far East are the Portuguese enclaves along the Indian coast (Goa, Damão, Diu), the peninsula of Macao on the coast of south China, and Portuguese Timor, the eastern portion of an island in the Malay Archipelago. The total population of Portugal's overseas possessions (including the Azores and Madeira) is about 12½ million. Although the colonial peoples in Portugal's overseas possessions are generally at a low stage of cultural development, the empire ranks as Portugal's leading trade partner, accounting in 1953 for about eighteen per cent by value of its foreign trade. Employment opportunities in Portugal are insufficient to satisfy the needs of the present population, and there has been pressure for emigration to the African colonies. If agricultural, mineral, and power resources in Portuguese Africa are further developed, the empire may in time prove to be an important asset to the people of Portugal.

THE SPANISH EMPIRE

Spain, whose empire ranks well down in size among those of the western European states, was once the greatest maritime power of the Continent. In 1494 in the Treaty of Tordesillas Spain was awarded all newly-discovered lands west of 50° west longitude; as a result Spain's colonial possessions were confined largely to the Western Hemisphere. The Philippines were the only major Spanish possession in the Far East. Spanish ships also sailed along the west coast of Africa, and this exploration led to the establishment of colonies to the south of Morocco and in the area of the Gulf of Guinea.

The defeat of the Spanish Armada by the British in 1588 spelled the end of Spain's dominance of the seas, but the nation continued to control much of its overseas possessions until the nineteenth century, when a majority of the Latin American states achieved independence. Later, as a result of the Spanish-American War, Spain was forced to withdraw completely from Latin America and from the Pacific. Thus, since the beginning of the twentieth century Spain has had only its African possessions left to develop.

The Spanish nation has an area of 195,000 square miles and contains about 29,000,000 people. These figures include the Balearic Islands in the western Mediterranean, as well as the Canary Islands in the Atlantic. The tremendous energies expended by the nation in colonial activities three and four centuries ago are no longer evident either in its domestic or its overseas activities. Despite the country's size, population, and resource base —which includes such raw materials as coal, iron ore, copper, lead, zinc, and mercury—Spain's economy is at a low stage of development. The per capita income is among the lowest in Europe (see also Chapter 7). The difficulties Spain has faced in adjusting to economic, social, and political problems of the mid-twentieth century have been reflected in its relations with its empire. "Assimilation" and "monopoly" are terms which may best describe Spanish colonial policy. Both the Balearic and Canary islands are administered as an integral part of Spain. In other areas attempts have been made by both Church and State to Christianize the inhabitants and instill in them something of Spanish culture. Non-Spanish commercial enterprises are discouraged from operating in the overseas territories, and there has been no attempt to prepare the local peoples for self-government.

In 1956 the Spanish government announced the ending of its protectorate over Spanish Morocco. The remaining territories—Spanish West Africa, Spanish Guinea, together with three coastal enclaves in Morocco and three offshore islands—have a combined area of 127,000 square miles and a population of about 450,000. However, Spain's possessions are of relatively little economic value, and the Spanish people themselves are not particularly concerned with the nation's colonial activities. Río de Oro in Spanish West Africa is important as a base for fishing fleets, and Spanish Guinea exports agricultural products such as cocoa and coffee.

THE DANISH EMPIRE

Located on the sandy Jutland Peninsula between the North and Baltic seas, Denmark has a physical environment characterized by relatively infertile soil (which Danish farmers at great expense have made extremely productive), a long coast line with many offshore islands, and a virtual absence of minerals and power fuels. With a population of about 4,400,-000, Denmark has a national economy based on intensive agriculture and the export of dairy products, bacon, eggs, and vegetables, on high-grade manufactured goods (ships, diesel engines, china), on fishing, and on the maintenance of a moderate-sized merchant marine which is important in international shipping activities.

Denmark's border problems with Germany are described in Chapter 8.

The Danish people are united in language and religion. Perhaps equally important as a centripetal force, however, has been the need for national cohesion in the face of German expansionist pressure to the south. Unlike most peninsular areas, Jutland is politically partitioned and the Danes have no natural defenses against the Germans. Denmark's national sovereignty has in the past depended largely upon the cultural and political strength of the Danish people and upon the support Denmark has received from other countries at times when its existence has been threatened. The nation's capital, Copenhagen, is located on an island in the eastern part of the nation. It is, however, the historical political and cultural center, about which is concentrated over one quarter of Denmark's population.

Danish control of overseas territories dates back to the late fourteenth century, when Iceland became a colony. Later colonization efforts led to the establishment of Danish territories in Greenland, the Faeroes, the West Indies, and Africa. The African possessions, acquired in the seventeenth century, were only held for a short time, but the other territories remained under Danish control down to the twentieth century. In 1917 the United States acquired possession of the Danish West Indies (now known as the Virgin Islands), and the following year Iceland became a sovereign state, joined in a political union with Denmark.[5]

Greenland and the Faeroe Islands, Denmark's remaining overseas territories, measure 840,500 square miles in area. Both are important as sites for bases in the defense of the North Atlantic, but neither one is of great economic importance to Denmark, except for the fishing activities carried on by the local peoples. In 1953 Greenland was officially made an integral part of the Danish nation, and the area's approximately 25,000 inhabitants were thus politically (if not culturally) assimilated within Denmark itself. The Faeroe Islands received local autonomy in 1948. The Faeroes are economically dependent upon Danish subsidies and there is little pressure here, or in Greenland, for national independence.

THE NETHERLANDS EMPIRE

The Netherlands, like Spain, is an important colonial power of the past. In the early seventeenth century Holland had built up a great overseas empire in the Western Hemisphere, Africa, and the Far East. Although the African and most of the Western Hemisphere possessions were eventually lost to other powers, Dutch holdings in the East Indies were retained through World War II, while the western portion of New Guinea and a few possessions in Latin America still remain under Dutch control.

---

[5] The establishment of Iceland in a commonwealth-type relationship with Denmark preceded similar British, French, American, and Dutch organizations by a number of years. In 1944 Iceland became completely independent of Danish political ties.

The Netherlands itself is a relatively small European state, with a high population density of nearly 800 persons per square mile. The Dutch economy—based on intensive utilization of domestic resources—consists primarily of commercial activities (both intra-European and overseas), agricultural exports—such as dairy products, fruits and vegetables, and flowers—and high-grade manufactured goods, particularly ships, machinery, and electrical equipment. The Netherlands has few resources for heavy industry; coal production is insufficient for domestic needs, and there is practically no iron ore, ferro-alloys, or petroleum (see Chapter 6 for a discussion of Dutch territorial problems).

Prior to World War II the Dutch empire measured over 800,000 square miles and contained nearly 80,000,000 persons. The wealth of the Netherlands East Indies was an important element of the nation's economy, for the colony served as an area for emigration, a market for exports, and a source for raw materials and investment opportunities. On the eve of World War II there were over 230,000 Dutch nationals living in the East Indies, and from that area came such valuable products as tin, petroleum, rubber, sugar, and quinine. The Dutch were leaders among the European powers in the art of colonial administration, partly as a result of their concern for health, education, and economic progress of the local peoples. However, the political policies of The Hague government were conservative, and there was little thought given to native self-rule, other than that connected with local affairs. Thus the Netherlands' colonial policy, lying somewhere between the "autonomy" of the British and the "assimilation" of the French and Portuguese, contained some of the negative features of both systems. The Dutch made relatively few attempts to indoctrinate their colonial peoples with Dutch culture; rather, they respected local institutions and did what they could to protect them. On the other hand, the Dutch were unwilling to face the logical outcome of local economic and political progress, namely, that the people would in time reach a point where they would actively demand self-rule.

During World War II the Netherlands East Indies were occupied by the Japanese. Following the war Holland was unable to re-establish effective control over its possession. In 1949 the entire area, with the exception of western New Guinea, became independent (see also Chapter 15). The remaining Netherlands' overseas territories have an area of 215,000 square miles and a population of about 1¼ million persons. In addition to western New Guinea (159,000 square miles), the Dutch territories are confined to Surinam in northern South America and to the Netherlands Antilles, consisting of the Caribbean islands of Aruba, Bonaire, Curaçao, Saba, St. Eustatius, and the southern half of St. Martin. Both Surinam and the Netherlands Antilles have local autonomy, with the Dutch retaining control of defense and foreign affairs.

OTHER EMPIRES

Italy and Norway are the other two west European powers controlling overseas territories. In the years immediately prior to World War II Italy controlled 1,287,000 square miles of colonial territory, with a population of over 12 million. The Italians came late into the race for African colonies. Their first acquisition (Eritrea) was not made until 1882. Later Italy also annexed Italian Somaliland, Libya, the Dodecanese Islands, and Ethiopia. The Italian Empire, although of relatively little economic value, served to strengthen Italy's sense of national pride. With the nation's defeat in World War II, all colonial possessions were taken away. In 1950 Italy was granted a ten-year United Nations trusteeship over former Italian Somaliland (Somalia), with an area of 198,000 square miles and a population of 1¼ million. Thus the nation is no longer an important colonial power: if Somalia receives its independence in 1960, Italy will have lost its last overseas territory.

Norway is a long, narrow, mountainous country in northern Europe. Despite the centrifugal forces resulting from shape, from the location of the capital, Oslo, in the southeastern part of the nation, and from poor land communications to the northwestern and northern areas, Norway is a relatively cohesive state. Most of the people are united by ties of language, religion, and national sentiment. The majority lives in the central and southern parts of the country, and there are no large population centers across Norway's land borders in Sweden or the Soviet Union to attract the Norwegians away from Oslo. With an area of 125,000 square miles and a population of about 3,400,000, Norway's few resources consist of water power and moderate quantities of iron ore, pyrites, copper, lead, and zinc. Arable land is limited to less than five per cent of the total area, but fishing and shipping activities are important. One of the Norwegian government's problems has been to protect the nation's offshore sovereignty (claimed out to the four-mile limit) from encroachment by foreign fishermen.

Norway was granted sovereignty in 1925 over the group of islands in the Arctic Ocean collectively called Spitsbergen (or Svalbard), with the provision that they be permanently demilitarized and that certain other powers be granted economic rights there. The chief resource of Spitsbergen is coal, some of which is exported to Norway (the nation has practically no domestic coal supplies) and some to the Soviet Union. The Norwegians also control Jan Mayen Island (uninhabited except for Norwegian meteorological personnel), located between northern Norway and the coast of Greenland, tiny Bouvet Island in the South Atlantic, and Peter I Island in the Antarctic Ocean. Norway's maritime interests are reflected in the fact that all of her overseas possessions are insular. The territories have a total area of 24,000 square miles and a population of less than 3,500 persons.

BIBLIOGRAPHY

Bowman, Isaiah. "Population Outlets in Overseas Territories," in *Geographic Aspects of International Relations,* ed. C. C. Colby. Chicago: The University of Chicago Press, 1938.

This article discusses the general value of colonies as outlets for surplus population and as trading areas.

Fawcett, C. B. "Life Lines of the British Empire," in *New Compass of the World,* ed. Weigert, Stefansson, and Harrison. New York: The Macmillan Company, 1949, pp. 238–49.

A description of the major lifelines connecting Great Britain with the various units of the Commonwealth.

Hodson, H. V. "Eire and the British Commonwealth," *Foreign Affairs,* XVI, No. 2 (April, 1938), 525–37.

The basic causes of friction between Eire (now the Republic of Ireland) and Great Britain, and the factors of mutual interdependence between the two areas.

Hoffman, George W. (ed.). *Geography of Europe.* New York: The Ronald Press Company, 1953.

Van Valkenburg, Samuel, and Held, C. C. *Europe.* New York: John Wiley & Sons, Inc., 1952.

Two regional geographies which provide background material on the mother countries of the colonial empires.

Whittlesey, Derwent. *The Earth and the State.* New York: Henry Holt and Company, 1944, Chapter 5, "The Coastland and World Power."

Problems of European colonization, with special emphasis on Great Britain.

Wright, Quincy. *Mandates and the League of Nations.* Chicago: The University of Chicago Press, 1930.

A standard work on the mandate system.

6

WESTERN EUROPE'S "MIDDLE KINGDOM"

● Between the Mediterranean and the North Sea lies one of the most complex politico-geographic areas of the world. Here in western Europe's "Middle Kingdom"[1] boundaries of language, religion, and nationality overlap one another in complicated patterns. Political units have been characterized by complex shapes and by frequent border changes, and problems of territorial control are often magnified to the point where bitter international disputes arise over the possession of small pieces of territory. The scars of past conflicts are still much in evidence in the desires and fears of the local inhabitants, in the pattern of political control, and in the attitudes of the western European governments toward matters of present and future sovereignty in this area. A number of basic politico-geographic principles may be illustrated by a discussion of territorial control here. For this reason, and because of the repercussions which sovereignty disputes have had in other areas, the region is treated as a separate entity.

The area of Lothar's Middle Kingdom included what is now eastern France, western Germany, the Benelux countries (Belgium, the Netherlands, and Luxembourg), the Saar, Switzerland, northwestern Italy, and Monaco. The region has been the scene of some of Europe's most perplexing territorial problems, among them Alsace-Lorraine, the Saar, and the Benelux-German and French-Italian border areas. Because of territorial conflicts which arose out of World War II, this region has been of particular significance on the international scene within recent years. Disputes involving Germany, France, and the Benelux countries have had considerable effect on

---

[1] So called because it corresponds generally to the Middle Kingdom awarded to Lothar at the breakup of Charlemagne's empire.

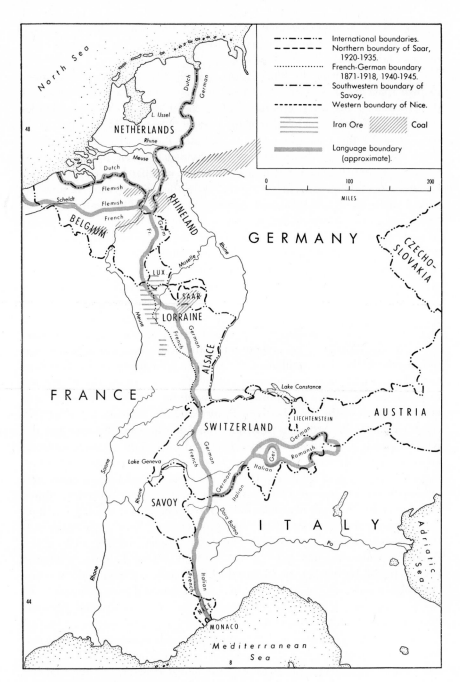

Figure 34. The "Middle Kingdom."

the process of welding together a strong west European military and eco-nomic alliance, for these boundary problems only serve to perpetuate ani-mosities between the Western powers.

Only once during its long history was the entire area unified under its own ruler. That was from 843 to 855, when Charlemagne's empire was divided among his three grandsons after the Treaty of Verdun. Charles received the western portion, Louis the eastern, while the Middle Kingdom, lying between the two, was given to Lothar (Figure 34). After Lothar's death in 855 the Middle Kingdom was divided between the eastern and western empires. France eventually evolved out of what had been the west-ern portion of Charlemagne's empire, while the eastern zone is now in-cluded in Germany, Austria, and northwestern Italy. The central belt be-tween these two sectors, however, has never been effectively absorbed by its more powerful neighbors, nor has it been reunified. Instead it remains a buffer zone, a scene of frequent warfare and of boundary change. Its stra-tegic location, its natural resources and economic development, and its vari-ety of peoples make it too important an area to be left for long in peace.

Surface Configuration

The distribution of upland and lowland areas has had a major his-torical role in the development of the region's political patterns. The Alps cross Switzerland in an east-west direction, then turn south in a long arc to mark the French-Italian border. North of the Alps is a series of low mountain blocks—the Jura between France and Switzerland, the Vosges in eastern France, the Ardennes in Belgium and northeastern France, and the Rhine uplands in western Germany. The need for communications between areas separated by these uplands has focused attention on the connecting gaps and passes, and countless battles have been fought by soldiers and diplomats for control of these important routes. Alsace-Lorraine stands guard over two historic invasion routes into France, the so-called Lorraine Gate between the Vosges and the Ardennes and the Saverne Gap through the Vosges itself. To the south, between the Vosges and the Jura, is the Burgundy Gate, watched over by the fortified city of Belfort. Along the French-Italian border lies the former duchy of Savoy controlling the western approach to the Alpine passes of Mt. Cenis and Little St. Bernard. At the southern end of the Alps Monaco adjoins the coastal road between Nice, France, and Savona, Italy.

Between the Ardennes and the North Sea is a lowland about 100 miles wide at its narrowest point. Here are the fields of Flanders and of Water-loo, situated on the historic invasion route across Belgium. To the east the lowland broadens out into Holland, and beyond this lies the North Ger-man Plain. Holland's defenses used to depend not on mountains but on water. Over one-third of the nation lies below sea level, and throughout the other sectors numerous rivers and canals form potential lines of resistance. In times of invasion the Dutch have opened the dikes to flood the lowland areas and then retreated to high ground behind the water barriers. The tools and tactics of modern warfare, however, cannot easily be inhibited by such methods, and today the Dutch must rely on diplomacy and powerful allies for their security.

Natural Resources

The struggle for control of mineral and power resources has been an important element in the political pattern of this area, particularly during the twentieth century. The French province of Lorraine contains valuable iron ore reserves; a part of this deposit also extends into southern Luxembourg. Good coking coal exists in the Saar Basin, central Belgium, northwestern Germany, and southern Holland. The proximity of these resources to one another has enabled a large number of iron and steel centers to be developed in many places throughout the northern part of the Middle Kingdom. Other resources include timber, water power, potash, and small amounts of petroleum. Timber and water power figured prominently in Belgian and Luxembourg territorial claims after World War II. Potash and some petroleum are found in Alsace. The presence of zinc along the Belgian-German frontier led to the formation of the neutral territory of Moresnet (see page 143), since neither Belgium nor Prussia would agree to have the resource remain within the borders of the other state.

Ethnic Features

Language, religion, and nationality are significant factors in the political complexities which have existed in the Middle Kingdom. The political effects of ethnic differentiation have varied considerably. Thus, for example, religious differences were once of major significance in dividing peoples in this area, but in recent times this has declined considerably in political importance. Likewise, nationality, the sense of "belonging to" a particular nation, may become less intense—or perhaps disappear almost completely— with the passage of time, as occurred in those sections of Luxembourg which were included within Belgium in 1839 and have since remained there.

The political effects of linguistic patterns in this part of Europe do not follow any prescribed form. The three major tongues are French, German, and Italian. The French-speaking area extends outside of France into southern Belgium, western Switzerland and northwestern Italy. German dialects are dominant in parts of southeastern Netherlands, eastern Belgium, Luxembourg, the Saar, northern and central Switzerland, and part of the

French provinces of Alsace and Lorraine. Italian is spoken across Italy's borders in southeastern France and southern Switzerland. In addition there is Dutch, spoken throughout most of the Netherlands; Flemish, a language akin to Dutch, which is spoken in northern Belgium and northeasternmost France; and Romansh (Rhaeto-Romansh), an ancient tongue prevailing among the mountain people of eastern Switzerland. Many of the peoples of this part of Europe are bi- or even tri-lingual, illustrating the strong cultural cross currents that exist here.

Language, as a reflection of cultural ties which bind people together, may be important in strengthening bonds of national sentiment, even across international borders. Such has been the case with the German-speaking people of eastern Belgium, who have often felt stronger ties with Germany than with Belgium, or with the Flemish people of northeastern France, who look eastward to Belgium as the source of their national sentiments. In many instances, however, language-nationality relationships in this area exist only slightly or not at all. The German-, French-, and Italian-speaking peoples of Switzerland retain their allegiance to the Swiss nation, rather than with bordering areas of similar linguistic characteristics. Likewise, the German-speaking peoples of Luxembourg have strong ties with their own nation rather than with Germany, and the French-speaking Walloons of Belgium are pro-Belgian rather than pro-French.

In terms of religion, most of the population of the Middle Kingdom is Roman Catholic. Protestants predominate only in northwestern Germany, the Netherlands, and northern and central Switzerland. In the Netherlands the ratio is about three Protestants to two Catholics, while in Switzerland approximately the same ratio exists, again in favor of a Protestant majority. Jewish minorities are present throughout the entire area. Although a few of the nations have Catholic political parties, religious differences within and between the various countries generally have few important political repercussions, except in such matters as education.

Nationality is often difficult to assess with respect to the populations of particular areas. Although linguistic ties are on many occasions helpful in determining national sentiments, economic and historical factors may also be important. In the years immediately following World War II, for example, the French nation tried with some success to develop sympathies among the Saarlanders for separation from Germany and union with France. At that time Germany was a defeated nation with few economic and political prospects, and many Saarlanders were at least temporarily affected by the favors shown them by the Paris government and by the obvious contrast between a defeated Germany and a more economically stable France. The gradual revival of the West German economy, however, tended to weaken most of the pro-French sympathies in the Saar. A somewhat analogous situation exists along the eastern French Riviera, where many of the Italian-speaking people had strong pro-Italian sympathies when Mussolini was at the height of his power, but since World War II have much preferred to remain in France rather than become involved with Italy's political and economic problems.

In few other parts of the world has so much attention been paid to the national desires of the inhabitants of disputed areas in order to develop stable political borders. In 1860 plebiscites were held in Savoy and Nice on the question of union with France; in 1919 the people of Eupen-Malmédy voted for union with Belgium; and in 1935 and 1955 plebiscites were held in the Saar to determine the political future of the area.

Plebiscites, of course, do not always indicate the choice of peoples living in disputed areas, first, because they may not be carried out under conditions permitting free choice and, second, because the alternatives offered the inhabitants may not include what they desire most, such as independence or at least autonomy which will permit them to develop their own cultural and political organizations.

Political Features

Because of the great number and complexity of the boundaries in this region and the frequent changes in boundary locations, it is difficult to generalize as to their origin or cultural relationships. Many follow rivers or mountain crests; others are historical in origin. Due to the long history of settlement in the Middle Kingdom, antecedent boundaries do not exist. Practically all have been superimposed across existing ethnic patterns, although in a few instances—as, for example, along parts of the Alpine border between France and Italy—the boundaries which were drawn to follow physical features also separated linguistic groups from one another. Along some superimposed boundaries ethnic groups have gradually adjusted themselves to the political division. Thus portions of the German-Dutch border, undisturbed for a long period of time, gradually changed from a superimposed to a consequent type of boundary, since Germans came to predominate in areas to the east, and Dutch among groups living to the west.

In the absence of strong unifying forces the tendency has been to perpetuate medieval political alignments of many small, complicated political units, with resulting "microterritorial" problem areas, involving small bits of territory and population. These problem areas have been particularly significant to the functioning of economic systems here. The Dutch bridgehead at Maastricht, for example, has in the past interfered with Belgium's use of the Meuse River for shipping operations (Figure 6), while to the north the Belgian enclave in the Netherlands complicates the problems of Dutch customs control (Figure 5). Another example of the microterritorial political pattern was the creation of the neutral territory of Moresnet in 1815, a one and one-half square-mile area between Belgium and Prussia. It was administered as a condominium by Belgium and Prussia (later Germany) until after World War I, when, as a result of a boundary shift, it was incorporated within Belgian territory. Despite the difficulties produced by these and other territorial peculiarities, there have been few efforts made to simplify the political pattern, with the result that various sources of friction remain between the interested nations.

Economic Development

International boundaries may inhibit resource development by separating mineral deposits or power sites from potential capital, markets, or processing plants. Such obstacles to the free movement of goods and capital in western Europe have in the past been partially avoided by the formation of international cartels. Under these control of production and marketing facilities are centralized in one organization and agreements worked out with various governments to permit free movement of goods and capital across national borders. The political areas, particularly from Switzerland to the North Sea, are closely bound together by railroads, highways, and canals, and many aspects of their economies complement one another.

Since the end of World War II a new trend has appeared in western Europe—a movement by national governments toward economic and military unity. Despite the various antagonisms and territorial claims in this area, officials have been motivated by common interests and fears to undertake international action. The Benelux Economic Union, the Schuman Plan,[2] the Western European Union,[3] and the proposal for the gradual establishment of a common market among the Schuman Plan nations are all steps towards unification which may bring an end to western Europe's long history of territorial problems.

POLITICAL REGIONS

For the sake of clarity the Middle Kingdom is divided here into five political regions: Benelux, the Saar, Alsace-Lorraine, Switzerland, and the French-Italian border area. Each region will be considered briefly in terms of centrifugal and centripetal forces operating within it and of basic politico-geographic elements illustrated by its past and present development.

Benelux

The three Benelux nations (Belgium, the Netherlands, Luxembourg) illustrate well the principles of unity and division within a border area.

---

[2] A customs union formed in 1953 by France, the Benelux countries, West Germany, and Italy with respect to coal, iron and steel, and scrap iron.
[3] An international military organization organized in 1955, embracing the armed forces of the six Schuman Plan nations and Great Britain.

Location has proved both a blessing and a curse, for in peacetime proximity to Germany, France, and Britain has enabled the Benelux countries to achieve high levels of economic development. In wartime, on the other hand, parts of the region have repeatedly suffered from invading forces. In the face of recurrent danger from bordering powers, the Benelux nations have long been under pressure to unite their efforts economically, militarily, and politically. Differences in their cultural, economic, and historical backgrounds, however, have served in the past to keep them apart.

Protestant Holland won its independence from Spain in 1648, and subsequently developed one of the great colonial empires of the world. The Catholic states of Belgium and Luxembourg remained under foreign domination until the Congress of Vienna (1815), following the defeat of Napoleon, when the victorious powers, desiring a strong buffer state along France's northeastern border, united the two areas with Holland into what was then termed the United Netherlands. This attempt at political unity soon failed, and in 1830 the peoples of Belgium and Luxembourg revolted. Nine years later the independence of Belgium was officially recognized. Luxembourg maintained a personal union with the Netherlands until 1868, when a constitution was drawn up declaring the former an independent state. Memories of the ill-fated United Netherlands served to dampen enthusiasm among the peoples of all three countries for subsequent attempts at unification during the remainder of the nineteenth and in the early twentieth centuries.

The Benelux-German Border. The pattern of territorial control along the border separating Germany from the three Benelux states illustrates the complexities of political sovereignty in this part of the world. At the end of World War I the Belgian-German boundary, which had been delimited in 1815, was rectified in favor of Belgium, the recent victim of German aggression. In addition to annexing Moresnet, Belgium received control of the small areas of Eupen, Malmédy, and St-Vith (Figure 35). These areas totaled about 400 square miles, but they brought timber and water-power resources within the Belgian borders. Between the towns of Eupen and Malmédy was a railroad which, although Belgian-controlled, passed several times across the German border, thus creating enclaves of German territory between the right-of-way and the Belgian border.

Several thousand German-speaking people living in the Eupen area were included within Belgium following the territorial transfer. After the rise of Hitler in the early 1930's German political propaganda was directed toward the return of these areas to the Fatherland. In 1940, following Germany's second invasion of Belgium in twenty-six years, the Eupen-Malmédy sector (including St-Vith) was reannexed by the Germans. Five years later it was returned to Belgium. Territorial shifts such as these are typical of this Middle Kingdom area.

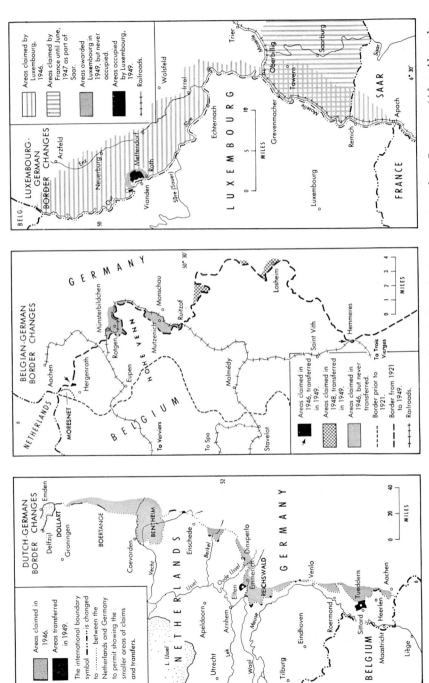

Figure 35. *The Benelux-German Border.* In 1956 most of the Belgian-held territories were returned to Germany. (After Alexander, *The Geographical Review,* XLIII (Jan., 1953). Courtesy of American Geographical Society.)

During World War II the Netherlands, Belgium, and Luxembourg were invaded and occupied by the Germans. At the end of the war the Netherlands demanded 648 square miles of territory from Germany as compensation for the more than 14 billion dollars worth of damage done to that country by the Germans between 1940 and 1945. Luxembourg asked for 140 square miles of land, while the Belgians desired eleven square miles. The total German-speaking population involved in these claims amounted to about 150,000 persons. Economic motives formed the basis for most of the Netherlands' claims. The Dutch wanted coal deposits, timber reserves, and control of German waterways, which would permit the drainage of several areas in northeast Holland and the construction of a channel to the Dutch port of Delfzijl. The Netherlands also desired to straighten out the Dutch-German frontier and reduce its length. The Belgians wanted timber supplies and a chance to eliminate German enclaves in the Eupen-Malmédy sector along its eastern border. Luxembourg also wanted timber, as well as water power for a proposed hydroelectric plant on the Our River, which flows between Germany and Luxembourg.

Many officials in the Benelux countries, as well as elsewhere, were frankly doubtful of the feasibility of these demands. They were worried about the inclusion of so large (and presumably unfriendly) a German minority within the Lowland countries. They were also apprehensive lest the Germans move to reconquer these lost areas as soon as Germany was in a position to do so. In March, 1949, a commission of the Western powers sanctioned a series of thirty-one minor changes in the Benelux-German border, involving a total of fifty-two square miles and some 13,500 German-speaking inhabitants (Figure 35). The largest share of this territory (twenty-six square miles) went to the Netherlands. The Belgians were granted all their demands, but by this time public opinion there had reached a point where it was deemed unwise to accept nearly 4,000 unwilling Germans into the country. Consequently the few areas Belgium finally incorporated into its territory were largely unoccupied. Luxembourg also declined to occupy inhabited areas awarded to it, and confined its annexations to a small forest strip.

The Western powers stipulated in 1949 that these border adjustments would be confirmed or modified by terms of the final settlement with Germany. There seems little chance that the original claims for nearly 800 square miles of German territory will ever be revived. In 1956 Belgium returned to West Germany most of the areas it had annexed; but the other border changes may very likely be permanent. Approximately 10,000 Germans have been separated from their homeland by the shift of frontiers and are now in the Netherlands. It is not unlikely that in years to come these former German citizens may agitate strongly for the return of their lands to Germany.

The Benelux Union. The interaction of centrifugal and centripetal forces in northwestern Europe has been clearly evidenced in the development of the Benelux Union. Prior to the end of World War I Luxembourg had been joined economically with Germany, but in 1920 it severed these ties and united with Belgium in an economic union[4] as the first major step toward unification of the Benelux area since 1830.

During the interwar years there was much discussion about economic unification of the Belgian-Luxembourg area with the Netherlands. However, many of the same antagonisms between Belgium and the Netherlands, which had split the United Netherlands in 1830, were still present: cultural differences, economic competition, and dissatisfaction over the functioning of certain border areas. World War II provided the necessary centripetal action. The sense of international unity born out of the common suffering the peoples of the three nations had undergone during the Nazi occupation, and the realization of the economic benefits which would accrue through the pooling of resources successfully overcame the obstacles to united action, and on January 1, 1948, the Benelux Union was inaugurated.

Serious problems were faced by the Benelux leaders in their efforts to arrange for the elimination of all trade barriers between Belgium-Luxembourg and the Netherlands. The latter had been badly damaged in World War II, its East Indies empire was in revolt, and the national economy was in a weak position. Belgium and Luxembourg, on the other hand, had emerged from the war with relatively little destruction, and their factories were in full production. Belgium still controlled its rich Congo possessions, and in 1948 the Belgian-Luxembourg area had one of the strongest economies in Europe.

In addition to these immediate conditions, there were long-standing problems of economic competition. Rotterdam in the Netherlands and Antwerp in Belgium have been traditional seaport rivals, particularly in handling the rich Rhine River trade to and from west Germany. Before World War II Belgium and Luxembourg were primarily industrial nations, while the Netherlands placed more emphasis on agriculture. After 1945 the Dutch, faced with a population increase which added 40,000 new workers per year to the labor force, felt that the only course for them to take was industrialization. Yet if the Netherlands built new industries these would compete with already-existing plants in Belgium and Luxembourg. Finally, the Netherlands had developed a high-grade dairy and fruit and vegetable export business, while Belgium and Luxembourg had not. To remove all tariffs would have meant that the latter would soon have been flooded by low-priced Dutch products. Despite these basic economic problems restrictions were gradually lifted on the interchange of practically all commodities. Vol-

[4] An economic union is similar to a customs union in that duties are removed on all goods passing between member nations. In addition, an economic union involves a reciprocal adjustment of price and wage levels in member states and common monetary and financial policies.

untary unification of areas of similar size and population has always been extremely difficult to achieve. The success of the Benelux planners indicates the new direction in which political units in western Europe are beginning to move.

The Saar

The Saar, located to the southeast of Luxembourg, has been one of the historic disputed areas between France and Germany. Since late in the ninth century the region has been associated with the Germans, although for brief periods during the reigns of Louis XIV and Napoleon it was included within France. The great majority of the people are German in speech and culture.

The Saar is of military importance to its neighbors since it controls eastern approaches to the Lorraine Gate, a lowland passageway between Germany and France which has figured prominently in wars between the two areas. It is of economic importance because of its great coal reserves and its steel mills (Figure 36). It is also something of an economic link between France and Germany: international rail and waterways pass through the Saar, much of the area's coal (mixed with coking coal from the German Ruhr) is used to smelt the iron ore of the French province of Lorraine, and the Saar's deficiencies in food are normally met by imports from Lorraine.

The French government at the time of the Versailles Conference in 1919 put forth claims to the Saar, partly on the grounds of war reparations and partly in order to reduce Germany's national power potential. French coal fields in the northeastern part of the nation had been badly damaged by the Germans, and the French government feared that without ready access to coal reserves France would be seriously handicapped in any future efforts to maintain industrial equality with Germany. In the final peace settlement in 1920 a 730-square-mile area within the Saar Basin was taken from Germany and placed under the administration of the League of Nations for a period of fifteen years. The French were awarded ownership of the coal mines during the fifteen-year period in order to satisfy their economic demands. Thus the Saar, whose cultural, economic, and political ties had for centuries been with Germany, became an internationalized area with its economy oriented toward France.

Several important questions may be raised with respect to the treatment of the Saar problem after World War I. First, should a defeated nation be divested of an integral part of its national territory in order to weaken its power potential? Second, can a nation achieve security by acquiring territory or resources from a rival power? Third, in a buffer zone such as the Middle Kingdom, is international control of disputed areas a workable solution to territorial conflicts?

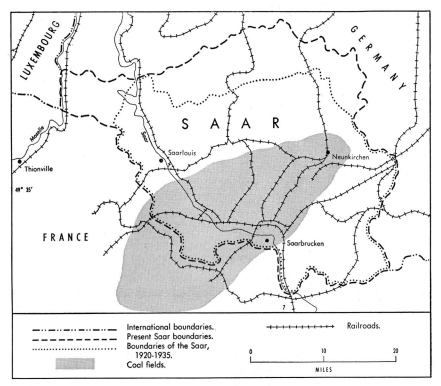

Figure 36. The Saar. (After Held, *The Geographical Review*, XLI (Oct., 1951). Courtesy of American Geographical Society.)

The answers are difficult to find, for national power is a complex and changing phenomenon, and each territorial dispute has its own individual elements of motives, desires, and justice. The delegates at Versailles apparently had some concern for the feelings of the Saarlanders, first, when they placed the area under League supervision rather than awarding it directly to France and, second, when they provided for a plebiscite to be held in 1935 to determine the Saar's future status. Some of the weaknesses of international control of territory were illustrated in the case of the Saar. Although international organizations generally provide well-run administrations, the national aspirations of the peoples of the internationalized area often remain unsatisfied. Furthermore, the conflicting powers themselves are frequently dissatisfied with a solution involving international control of a disputed area, for it fails to satisfy either one's territorial demands. One power, however, may in time accept international administration, if the alternative to this is that the other power will obtain complete control over the area.

In the 1935 plebiscite over 90 per cent of the voters favored return of the Saar to Germany. The exchange was effected in the same year, and control of the coal mines was returned to the Germans. The resource and industrial output of the Saar contributed to Germany's economic and military build-up prior to and during World War II.

The territorial problems of the Saar following World War II differed in certain respects from those of the post-World War I era. French troops took over control of the area from the Americans in July, 1945. After some border rectifications, the Saar territory measured 991 square miles in area, somewhat larger than the region detached from Germany in 1920. The population numbered 943,000, most of them German-speaking. In the fall of 1947 a local parliament was elected, with a large majority of the votes going to parties committed to economic union with France. Candidates of pro-German political parties, however, were denied the right to seek office in the Saar. In December of that year French occupation troops were withdrawn, and in January, 1951, an autonomous Saar was officially established. The area was free to manage local affairs, but it was tied to France in an economic union. The French government was to manage the Saar's defense and foreign policies.

In the years following World War II the French made several moves to strengthen the bonds between France and the Saar. They invested heavily in the area, they denied themselves the privilege of dismantling Saar factories, and they made efforts to improve the living conditions of the Saarlanders and to hasten the revival of industries in the area. On the other hand, they continued to deny the right of pro-German political parties to take part in the Saar government, and within a few years the Saarlanders —many of whom had been glad to accept French help in 1945–46—grew increasingly restless under France's control.

During the early 1950's, as France and West Germany became member states in international economic and military organizations, the Saar situation grew increasingly tense. The area's industrial importance to France may be illustrated by the fact that in 1955 the Saar produced 32 per cent as much coal and 25 per cent as much steel as the French nation itself. Including the Saar output France's steel production that year equaled 73 per cent of West Germany's; if the Saar were included with West Germany the French percentage would have dropped to 51. To West German officials, however, one of the difficult aspects of French control of the Saar was that it weakened Germany's position with regard to the Polish and Soviet seizures of German territory east of the Oder and Neisse rivers. Protestations by West German leaders against the unilateral action in the east were met by communist propaganda against French behavior in the west.

After many consultations between French and West German officials over the area's future, the Saarlanders in the fall of 1955 were offered a plebiscite, in which they were to accept or reject an international status for the area under the administration of the Western European Union, until such time as a final German Peace Treaty was worked out. There is a striking similarity between this proposal and the administrative framework under which the Saar existed from 1920 to 1935. Prior to the holding of the plebiscite pro-German political parties were again permitted in the Saar.

In October, 1955, the Saarlanders rejected the proposed statute by a vote of just over two to one. There were many reasons for this, among them a lack of faith in the newly-organized Western European Union, the cultural affinities of the Saarlanders with the Germans, and the continually expanding economic strength of West Germany. Pro-German political parties soon won control of the Saar parliament, and in June, 1956, a Franco-German agreement was finally drawn up providing for the return of the Saar to Germany on January 1, 1957, and its establishment as the tenth state in the West German Republic. The economic union with France was to be gradually abolished over a three-year period. The French, however, were assured of access to coal from mines in the Saar for at least twenty years, and trade between France and the Saar remains duty-free. The only stipulation was that, if the value of exports or imports between the two areas exceeds the respective values of 1955, duties will be levied against the excess amount. Also included in the agreement was the provision for German assistance in canalizing the Moselle River, thereby affording the Lorraine industrial district ready access to the Ruhr coal supplies and markets of West Germany. The settlement of this last major legacy of World War II's territorial problems in western Europe is another example of the trend toward international co-operation which has developed in this area.

Alsace-Lorraine

The name Alsace-Lorraine refers to a 5,600-square-mile area to the south and southeast of Luxembourg and the Saar, which, like the Saar, has several times been a source of bitter dispute between France and Germany. The province of Alsace stretches to the west of the Rhine River, and includes not only the Rhine lowlands paralleling the river but also the eastern slopes of the Vosges Mountains. The region is important for agriculture (grain, tobacco, fruit), for potash, most of which is manufactured into fertilizer, and for its small petroleum reserves. It is also of military importance because of its control of the Saverne Gap through the Vosges Mountains into east central France. Lorraine is a gently rolling plateau area, whose major economic significance lies in its great iron ore deposits. Like the Saar, it is strategically located with regard to the Lorraine Gate between France and Germany. In the territorial disputes over Alsace-Lorraine only the Moselle department in eastern Lorraine has been involved; the rest of the province has remained French during all boundary shifts (Figure 37).

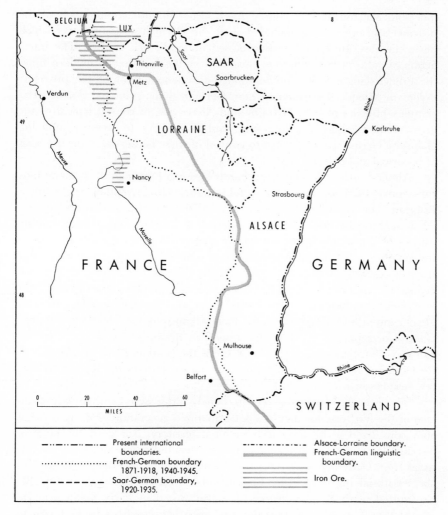

Figure 37. Alsace-Lorraine. (After Hartshorne, *World Politics*, II (Jan., 1950). Courtesy of Princeton University Press.)

Alsace-Lorraine has been an historic transition area between French and German cultural and political developments. After the breakup of Lothar's kingdom Alsace was included in the Germanic realm for the greater part of eight centuries, although for some years during the thirteenth century the ten major cities of Alsace were practically independent units within the Holy Roman Empire. In 1648 Alsace was officially joined to France; two centuries later, however, a majority of the inhabitants still continued to speak a German dialect. Sectors of Lorraine also won varying degrees of independence during the Middle Ages, although throughout much of the province's history it was included with the German-speaking areas which lie to the east. In 1766 Lorraine passed under French control. The inter-action of cultural forces here is illustrated by the fact that in modern times the French language has predominated throughout most of the province, except in Moselle department where German is the principal tongue. The complex histories of both Lorraine and Alsace are, of course, typical of the areas of the Middle Kingdom, and tend to give rise to greatly conflicting claims by Germany and France to control of these border areas on the basis of historical and cultural ties.

Alsace-Lorraine has changed hands between France and Germany four times since 1870. By the Treaty of Frankfurt (1871), ending the Franco-Prussian War, victorious Germany annexed the Alsace-Lorraine area, there-by weakening France's defensive position and at the same time gaining control of Lorraine's valuable iron ore reserves. The inhabitants of Alsace-Lorraine were, for the most part, strongly opposed to the German move, but their opinions were never solicited. At the time of the delimitation of the Franco-German border in 1871 considerations of military strategy and, to a less extent, the location of the French-German language boundary were of greater importance to the German officials than were the iron ore resources.[5] Control of a part of the Lorraine resources, however, was of great signifi-cance to Germany's industrial build-up in the years prior to World War I, for Germany possessed good coking coal, particularly in the Ruhr area, but few supplies of iron ore.

The French, of course, were extremely bitter over Germany's annexa-tion of the territory, for they saw a Germanized generation grow up in what they considered to be their own national territory. Not until the close of World War I was France in a position to demand reannexation of the lost areas from Germany. The return of Alsace-Lorraine to France did not end the territorial problems. The French government has always been highly centralized, with a great degree of power vested in Paris, while prior to World War I Alsace and Lorraine had been permitted by the Germans to set up their own local parliaments. In Alsace particularly a movement developed in the 1920's in favor of autonomy for the area. Many Alsatians felt that their land would continually oscillate between France and Ger-many unless the local inhabitants were free to manage their own affairs. The French moved decisively against this threat. Through arrests and the suppression of newspapers they were able to stamp out the movement, at

---

[5] See Richard Hartshorne, "The Franco-German Boundary of 1871," *World Politics*, II, No. 2 (January, 1950), 209–51. The inclusion of much of the iron ore within Germany appears to have been almost accidental, a coincidence resulting from locating the border according to strategic considerations. In 1871 the Lorraine ores were being used by the French for iron production, but until the discovery of the Thomas-Gilchrist process in 1878 it was not possible to utilize the resources with their high phosphorous content for the production of steel.

least on the surface, although many elements went into hiding and continued their agitation in secret.

The third war between France and Germany in less than seventy years broke out in 1939, and after the Nazi conquest of France in June, 1940, Alsace-Lorraine was reannexed by the Germans. Five years later, Germany was again a defeated nation and the territory was returned to France.

In unhappy areas such as this the principal sufferers are the inhabitants themselves. Not only is the political structure of the region damaged, but also the economic and social foundations. New tariffs and government policies suddenly present themselves to the businessman. Old markets are gone and new ones must be found; health and education facilities suffer. Persons in responsible positions may be removed from their jobs, imprisoned, and sometimes executed. If this happens once in a generation the results may be serious. If it happens four or five times the entire social framework of the area is severely tested.

In the case of Alsace-Lorraine it is difficult to determine the real desires of the population—if indeed a common desire exists. Certainly the French government has never exerted itself to win the friendship of the peoples of Alsace-Lorraine as much as it has in the case of the Saarlanders. Probably Paris has felt more secure in the loyalties of the inhabitants of Alsace-Lorraine. Yet here, as in other parts of the Middle Kingdom, interest in independence, or at least political autonomy, remains strong. Long before their history of political vacillation between France and Germany Alsace and Lorraine possessed their own cultural and political characteristics, and many of the peoples there will continue to press for recognition of their area's uniqueness so long as the present political framework of western Europe exists.

Switzerland

The Swiss nation represents a unique politico-geographic situation, for despite its intricate political pattern and the presence of diverse linguistic and religious groups within its borders the nation has overcome the internal centrifugal forces so common to this sector of Europe, and has maintained its boundaries intact through several major European conflicts (Figure 38). Independent since the late thirteenth century, Switzerland has had no serious territorial problems since 1815, and has been involved in none of the wars which have been waged since that time among the nations of Europe.

Although often thought of as a predominantly Alpine country, Switzerland actually has three principal geographic regions—the Alps in the south, the Jura Mountains in the west, considerably lower in relief, and the Swiss Plateau, comprising about one-third of the country, which extends

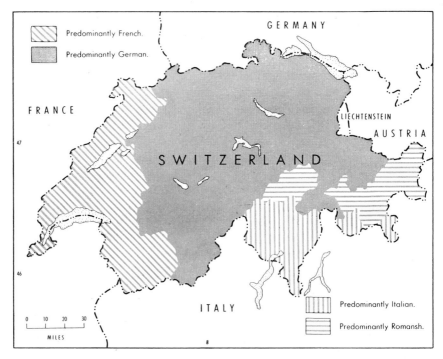

Figure 38. Switzerland: Language Patterns. (After map in *Focus*, VI (Sept., 1955). Courtesy of American Geographical Society.)

northeast-southwest between the Jura and the Alps. Within this plateau area, most of which is less than 2,000 feet in elevation, live over three quarters of the nation's population. There are practically no mineral resources in Switzerland, and hydroelectric power is the only important source of energy. With a population of over 4,750,000 Switzerland must depend on high-grade manufactures, such as machinery and watches, on specialized agriculture, on international transit freight, and on tourism as major sources of revenue.

Location in and adjacent to the Alps once helped to isolate the Swiss from their more powerful neighbors, but with modern transportation the nation has become an important link in Europe's east-west and north-south road, rail, and air routes. By its long-term policy of neutrality Switzerland has developed a role as the site for international organizations and conferences. During its lifetime the League of Nations was located at Geneva, as are also the headquarters of the International Red Cross and certain agencies of the United Nations. Major international conferences have been held at Geneva, Lausanne, Montreux, and other Swiss cities.

Switzerland's borders are typically complex and irregular, like many others in the Middle Kingdom. In the north a Swiss bridgehead at Schaffhausen extends across the Rhine toward Germany, and within this are two tiny enclaves of German territory. To the northwest a glacis stretches across the main crest of the Jura Mountains toward France, while to the south a much larger glacis projects into the North Italian Plain. Thus, like the Benelux countries, Switzerland retains certain vestiges of medieval political units, some of which appear anachronistic in the current world political pattern, with its emphasis on efficiency of economic and political operations. A further example of the complexity of this area is the existence of Liechtenstein, a sixty-one square-mile country lying between Switzerland and Austria. Independent since the early eighteenth century, Liechtenstein is joined with Switzerland in a customs union.

The attitude of the Swiss people is one of the most remarkable features of this nation. Despite the diversities of language and religion, the sense of unity contrasts sharply with the shifting political loyalties of many other peoples of the Middle Kingdom. One reason for this may be the national pride of the Swiss peoples in the fact that their forefathers achieved independence without help from outsiders and that this independence has been maintained for over six and a half centuries. Another reason for the lack of stronger centrifugal forces in Switzerland is the factor of neutrality—the benefits of freedom from entanglement in Europe's conflicts would provide a strong motive for continued national unity. Associated with this are the advantages of Switzerland's economic position, particularly in international banking, investments, and trade. Thus in Switzerland, as in Belgium, Canada, and other areas, the economic and political benefits of national cohesion outweigh the divisive forces of cultural differences.

The French-Italian Border Area

Along the French-Italian border disputes over territorial control have involved two sectors, the 6,500-square-mile Savoy area in the north and the small province of Nice along the Mediterranean coast. Between Switzerland and the Mediterranean the Maritime Alps trend north-south in an unbroken chain with few practical passes across them. Mountainous areas at lower elevations extend for a considerable distance east and west of the main chain, and within these upland regions relatively isolated political units have developed. Savoy, located south of the Swiss border and to the west of the main chain of the Alps, is perhaps the most famous of these political units. Communications between Savoy and France are considerably easier to maintain than between Savoy and Italy. The principal markets for Savoy's exports are in France, and the majority of the population is French-speaking. Nevertheless, throughout much of its history the area has been associated with the Italian states to the east. To the south, Nice is also separated from Italy by mountains. As in the case of Savoy, lines of communication with France are more easily maintained than are connections via the coastal road with Italy.

In 1859 the French king agreed to support the Italian states in their struggle for independence from Austria in exchange for the territories of Nice and Savoy. However, the French forces were withdrawn from the struggle before victory for the Italians had been achieved. Despite Italian protests, the French held plebiscites in the two areas to determine popular sentiment concerning union with France. The results of both plebiscites were pro-France, and Savoy and Nice were incorporated subsequently within the French nation. The areas were later the source of considerable friction between Italy and France. Mussolini used them to build up anti-French propaganda in the 1930's, reminding the Italians that both areas were historically a part of Italy and that France annexed them after a broken promise.

The French-Italian border problems have never been as serious as those between Germany and her western neighbors, partly because of the mountain chain between France and Italy and the relative lack of resources in the border areas. The linguistic boundary corresponds fairly closely to the political one, and the Alps form a rather effective barrier between France and Italy. At the end of World War II France annexed from Italy five small areas along the crest of the Alps as compensation for war damages. These areas contained a total of 370 square miles and a population of 3,620 persons (Figure 39), most of them Italian-speaking. From north to south these areas were: (1) Little St. Bernard Pass, (2) Mt. Cenis Plateau, (3) Mt. Thabor, (4) Mt. Chaberton, including the Montgenèvre Pass, and (5) the upper valleys of the Tinée, Vésubie, and Roya rivers, including the Tende Pass.

Through these border changes France gained control of several important passes as well as water-power sites. Special clauses were included in the treaty to insure that Italy would continue to receive electricity from her former hydroelectric installations. The moderate nature of the French demands and the fact that provisions were made to prevent undue hardship to the Italian economy because of the territorial transfers have resulted in an apparent absence of bitterness on Italy's part with regard to its losses. The intelligent handling of the whole territorial question here could serve as an excellent example to contesting nations in other parts of the world whose ambitions are less restrained.

Monaco. Along the Mediterranean coast is Monaco, another relic of the medieval political pattern. This nation, with an area of 370 acres and a population of 19,000, is joined in an economic union with France. It is famous for its gambling casino. Perhaps Monaco's reputation as a distinct political entity has helped to prevent French attempts to incorporate it within the territorial jurisdiction of the French nation, which surrounds it on all but its seaward side.

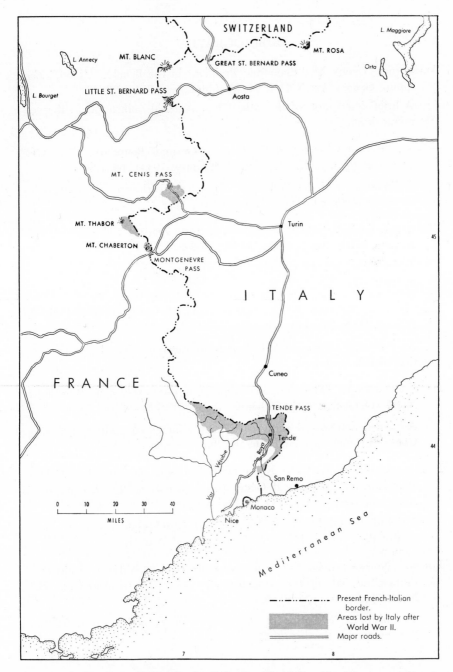

Figure 39. The Franco-Italian Border Following World War II. (Courtesy of French Press and Information Service.)

BIBLIOGRAPHY

ALEXANDER, LEWIS M. "Economic Problems in the Benelux Union," *Economic Geography*, XXVI, No. 1 (January, 1950), 29–36.

A brief description of this attempt at regional unification at the economic level.

———. "Recent Changes in the Benelux-German Boundary," *The Geographical Review*, XLIII, No. 1 (January, 1953), 69–77.

A discussion, with detailed maps, of the territorial claims by the Benelux countries against Germany after World War II.

BIERMANN, CHARLES. "The Franco-Swiss Free Zones," *The Geographical Review*, XIII, No. 3 (July, 1923), 268–377.

A description of the complex economic arrangements in southwestern Switzerland.

HARTSHORNE, RICHARD. "The Franco-German Boundary of 1871," *World Politics*, II, No. 2 (January, 1950), 209–51.

An extremely thorough, well-documented examination of the delimitation of this boundary.

HELD, COLBERT C. "The New Saarland," *The Geographical Review*, XLI, No. 4 (October, 1951), 590–606.

An excellent regional study of the area, including political pressures. Contains a map of changes in the Saar boundaries, 1945–49.

HOFFMAN, GEORGE W. "The Netherlands Demands on Germany: A Post-War Problem in Political Geography," *Annals of the Association of American Geographers*, XLII, No. 2 (June, 1952), 129–53.

A detailed, well-documented account of Dutch demands for rectification of their eastern border following World War II.

POUNDS, NORMAN J. G. "The Origin of the Idea of Natural Frontiers in France," *Annals of the Association of American Geographers*, XLI, No. 2 (June, 1951), 146–58.

The historical evolution of the concept of France's eastern frontier. Extremely well documented.

7

THE MEDITERRANEAN BASIN

● The Mediterranean Sea washes the shores of three continents—Europe, Asia, and Africa. Across it pass the lifelines of several European empires, and on its coast lands and islands there exists a wide variety of physical elements, ethnic groups, and economic interests. Because of the great diversity of geographic features and the long history of political development here, patterns of territorial control are extremely complex in terms of both form and stability. Ethnic and political boundaries often have little relationship to one another, giving rise to friction between countries and between groups within a single country. Political units, within the Basin itself and in other areas, have frequently engaged in territorial expansion here, and as a result disputed sovereignty is a characteristic feature of this part of the world. Finally, the ideological struggles of the Cold War are manifest in this area, as Western and Soviet spheres of influence come into close proximity with one another and as international communism capitalizes on the poverty and political instability in many of the countries of the Mediterranean region.

The limits of the Mediterranean Basin area, of course, inexact, and must be arbitrarily fixed to suit the purposes of the description. In this chapter the Basin comprises the Mediterranean itself, the Adriatic, and the coast lands from the Iberian Peninsula through southern Europe to and including Turkey. The Black Sea area, with the exception of northern Turkey, will not be included, for many of its political attributes differ from those of the Mediterranean region. Likewise, Israel and the Arab areas of southwest Asia and North Africa are considered in Chapter 11 and will be treated only with few details here.

Physical Elements

Location. The Mediterranean Sea at various times in history has been of great significance as an area of transit between the three continents which border it. This transit role, of course, is augmented by the waterway's proximity both to the Indian Ocean and to the Black Sea. The Mediterranean is also accessible by historic overland routes to such areas as northern France, Switzerland, Austria and the Danube Basin, Iraq and the Persian Gulf oil region, and the Nile Valley-Red Sea area. As a result, developments in the Mediterranean Basin are often of considerable importance to political control in these other sectors as well. Because of the many strategic areas which converge upon it, the Mediterranean has been the scene of some of the great military struggles of world history, and even today it is a region of potential great-power conflict.

Landforms. The diversity of landforms within the Mediterranean Basin is reflected both in the land and sea bodies—peninsulas, islands, isthmuses, and straits—and in the various plain, plateau, hill, and mountain areas. The political significance of these landforms was greater in the past than during the present era of air transportation and of large national political units. Thus, for example, the British-controlled island of Malta in the central Mediterranean was for a long time an important center of naval power in this area, but with the advent of air warfare land-based enemy planes are all but able to neutralize the military advantages of the island in time of war. On the other hand, landforms still retain political significance in certain parts of the Mediterranean area, as, for example, in their barrier function between Spain and France, in the isolation of Albania from Greece and Yugoslavia, and in the centrifugal effects of surface configuration within several states.

Peninsulas and islands may serve as bridgeheads for the overseas expansion of a state's influence and political control; on the other hand, because of exposed position, they may invite attack and occupation by hostile powers. Thus Cape Bon in northeastern Tunisia served as a base for the Allied invasion of Italy in World War II, while the Gallipoli Peninsula at the Dardanelles was the initial point of attack by the British against the Turks in 1915. Likewise, Italian control of Saseno Island in the Adriatic between the two world wars was an important factor in the maintenance of Italian power in Albania during that time.

Straits connecting major bodies of water have historically been areas of contested sovereignty. In the Mediterranean the two most famous are the Strait of Gibraltar and the Turkish-controlled Straits, consisting of the Dardanelles, the Sea of Marmara, and the Bosporus. The international contests for control of these straits are discussed later in the chapter. Another important strait is that of Otranto, 47 miles in width, at the entrance to the Adriatic. Since 1870 the Italians have consistently sought to maintain control over the Strait of Otranto in order to strengthen their power in the Adriatic area.

The factor of physical diversity may also be found in the coast lands of the Mediterranean and in the surface configuration behind the coasts. Indented coasts, along which some level areas exist, were utilized early in the development of city states. From these sites the city states embarked to found colonies in other coastal areas. In contrast are the precipitous coasts, such as Dalmatia on the eastern shore of the Adriatic, along which the mountains parallel the coast line, affording few level areas and offering poor connections with the interior. Where small harbors exist along such steep coasts they commonly are pirate strongholds. Straight, harborless coasts have generally discouraged development of maritime powers, except insofar as powerful land nations have developed along the coasts and have found their need for maritime activities great enough to overcome the physical disadvantages. Such was the case of Rome, where, despite the lack of good natural harbors, strong maritime development took place.

Numerous highland areas surround the Mediterranean Basin. Around and through these areas important lowland gateways such as the Rhône-Saône Valley, the Alpine passes, and the Vardar-Morava corridor, connect the Mediterranean with other regions. The most important of these mountains and lowlands are shown in Figure 40. Many of the lowland routes have been of historical importance both as avenues for expansion of power outward from the Mediterranean Basin and for invasion into the Basin from other areas.

Climate and Soils. The climate of the Mediterranean is generally characterized by winter rainfall and summer drought, although over such a large area there are wide variations of temperature and precipitation. In many lowland areas precipitation is frequently insufficient for agriculture, and in many level sectors inadequate drainage has resulted in high water tables, thereby necessitating expensive drainage operations if such areas are to become productive. Steep slopes severely limit arable land throughout much of the Mediterranean Basin and both soil erosion and soil exhaustion are prevalent here, thus contributing to the poverty of the people.

Ethnic Groups

Some of the world's oldest civilizations began in and about the eastern Mediterranean. As soon as man had mastered the art of water transportation, ships began to travel around the periphery of the Mediterranean, and later directly across it. Soon settlements sprang up in coastal areas progressively farther westward toward the Strait of Gibraltar. Expansion by sea was

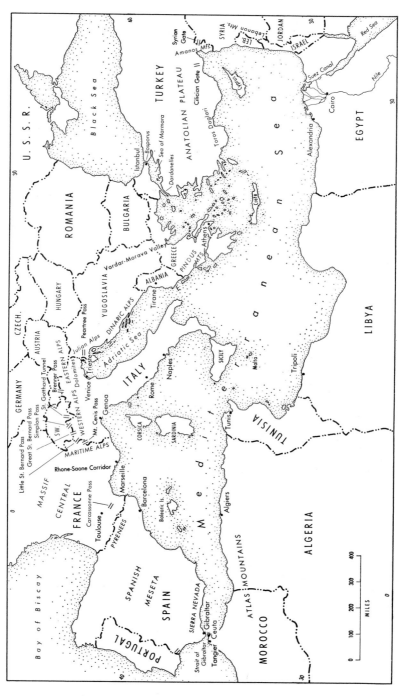

Figure 40. The Mediterranean Basin, Showing Surrounding Highlands and Lowlands.

later matched by expansion by land on the part of such groups as the Macedonians and the Arabs, as well as by groups from outside the Basin—the Goths, the Huns, and the Slavs. The population of the Mediterranean Basin has grown to the point where it numbers roughly 125 million persons, representing over a dozen nationalities and languages and four major religions—Roman Catholic, Greek Orthodox, Moslem, and Jewish.

The lack of conformity between political and ethnic patterns is evident in many parts of the Basin. In Spain three languages (Castilian, Catalan, and Galician) are spoken, and there is a large Catalan-speaking minority across the border in France as well. Italian-speaking groups inhabit southern France as well as the French island of Corsica and the former French protectorate of Tunisia on the North African coast. Until the end of World War II there were also Italian minorities along the Adriatic coast of Yugoslavia. Greeks and Albanians intermingle along the border between the two countries, and there are large numbers of Albanians in Yugoslavia.

Throughout most of the Basin settlement patterns have remained fairly stable for a long time, regardless of changes in political control. Greeks, for example, have lived on Cyprus for centuries, despite the fact that the island has been under Turkish and, recently, British sovereignty. Greeks also inhabit the Dodecanese Islands in the Aegean Sea, even though here too foreign control (first Turkish, then Italian) continued down to the end of World War II. Naturally, such ethnic patterns have at times caused intranational or international friction, as in the movements in Spain for Catalan autonomy, in Greece for border alterations, and on Cyprus for changes in the island's sovereignty.

Economic Interests

The Mediterranean Basin is relatively poor in natural resources for industry and agriculture. The limits of arable land have already been noted. Much of the potentially valuable soil has been harmed by poor agricultural techniques. Outmoded land tenure systems have hindered the rise of a land-owning peasant class, which might represent a force for political stability in many of these countries. Together with limited resources are the factors of large populations and rapid population increases in many Mediterranean areas. In Italy, for example, the population—which approaches 50,000,000—is increasing at a rate of over 350,000 per year, placing heavy strain on the nation's resources and development.

Important reserves of coal and minerals are available only in Spain, France, Turkey, and Morocco; in all of these countries except France lack of available capital has prevented large-scale utilization of these resources. There is practically no petroleum whatever within the Basin, and water power remains largely undeveloped except in France and Italy. These two nations are also the only ones in which major industrial development has occurred, although in Spain, Israel, Egypt, and to a lesser extent Greece and Turkey, industries are beginning to be built up. In many parts of the Mediterranean Basin there are large numbers of poor people,[1] with the result that communism has had considerable success in exploiting popular discontent, particularly in Italy and Greece.

DEVELOPMENT OF THE MODERN POLITICAL PATTERN

The history of the Mediterranean Basin dates back over five thousand years to the time when the Basin was the scene of the beginnings of Western Civilization. During the early years of the Christian era the Romans succeeded in unifying most of the Basin under their control, and in the centuries which followed other empires, notably those of the Arabs, the Turks, and the Venetians, were spread over various parts of the Mediterranean coast lands and islands. However, few vestiges of these former empires remain in the political pattern of the area. Capital cities, such as Rome, Athens, and Ankara, as well as some of the provincial boundaries, still exist as relics of the past, but most political features are of more modern origin.

At the start of the nineteenth century the Mediterranean was of relatively little significance in terms of world power relations. The opening of a sea route around Africa to the Far East, the development of the Americas, and the predominance of political and commercial activities in the Baltic-North Sea area had resulted in a gradual decline in importance of the Mediterranean Basin from the early sixteenth century. The great struggles between nations for control of valuable territories had shifted to other parts of the world. Not until the opening of the Turkish Straits to neutral shipping in 1859 and the completion of the Suez Canal ten years later was there a revival of the Mediterranean's historic role as a route of transit between western Europe and the land masses to the east.

Three basic trends have developed with respect to the modern pattern of political control in the Mediterranean area. These are (1) the expansion of colonial powers, including those located within the Basin and those in other parts of Europe, (2) the rise of unified independent states, and (3) the extension of Cold War pressures into the Basin.

The expansion of colonial powers in the Mediterranean area began with the British acquisition of Gibraltar from Spain in 1704 and of the island of Malta from France in 1814. In addition to Britain, France, Italy, Spain, and Greece have also won control of areas in the Basin, and since World War II the Soviet Union has established holdings here as well. Most of the empire activities have taken place on the eastern and southern shores of the

---

[1] Representative per capita incomes in 1953 were: Spain, $471; Italy, $298; Greece, $174; compared with $1,911 for the United States.

Mediterranean, and therefore are covered in Chapter 11. The impacts of this colonialism have, however, been felt throughout the Mediterranean lands. Thus, Italy's failure to win important territorial concessions in the Middle East after World War I strongly influenced that nation's determination at the Versailles Conference to press for territorial gains in Europe. More recently the decline of British military power in Palestine and the Suez area has bolstered Britain's decision to retain control of Cyprus, even in the face of strong opposing pressures.

The development of unified, independent states in the Mediterranean Basin is a process which has been going on for a long time. At the beginning of the nineteenth century Portugal, Spain, and Turkey had already been unified, self-governing states for many years; the other sovereign nations of the area have achieved their present political status since 1800. Many of the now independent states have been faced with problems of unstable boundaries or of "unredeemed" areas, in which peoples having cultural ties to one country remain under the control of another state. The recurrent problems of territorial control in such areas have contributed greatly to the politico-geographic complexities of the Mediterranean region.

The extension of Cold War pressures into the Basin is associated with the changing power complex of this area. Throughout its history the Mediterranean has been the scene of conflict between land and sea powers, as political areas located within the Basin have sought to expand their territorial holdings and as non-Mediterranean peoples have invaded and occupied its coastal and island territories. Although air power has now added a third dimension to warfare, the essential land-sea basis for conflict still remains in this area. In recent years land power has been represented primarily by the Soviet Union and its satellites, moving out from bases to the north and east of the Basin, while sea power is present in the opposing forces of the United States and Britain, augmented by those of other NATO powers. Thus, superimposed on demands for independence, for border changes, and for annexations of territory within the Mediterranean area, there is a basic power shift in the Basin, represented by a decline in the British, as well as the French and Italian, empire, by the strengthening of United States influence, and by the ever-present threat of Soviet expansion into the area.

POLITICAL UNITS OF THE NORTHERN MEDITERRANEAN BASIN

In the sections which follow most of the states in the northern part of the Mediterranean Basin will be considered in terms of the internal and external aspects of political control. These states are: Spain, Portugal, Italy, Albania, Greece, and Turkey. France and Yugoslavia are omitted here, as they are treated in other chapters. Particular attention will be given to problems concerning disputed territory.

The Iberian Peninsula

The Iberian Peninsula, cut off from the rest of Europe by the Pyrenees barrier, forms a relatively isolated geographic unit, yet one in which centrifugal forces have been effective in preventing political and cultural cohesion. Among these forces are diversity of landforms and differences in climate, economic activities, and historical development. Five principal languages are spoken: (1) Catalan, in northeast Spain, (2) Castilian, in central and southern Spain, (3) Galician (a dialect of Portuguese), in northwest Spain, (4) Portuguese, in Portugal, and (5) Basque, the language of approximately 2,000,000 people who inhabit the western Pyrenees in both Spain and France. Although they have no history of political independence, the Basques have for many centuries resisted efforts to assimilate them within the cultures of the French and Spanish states.

Madrid, the Spanish capital, was purposely located during the late Middle Ages in the geographic center of the Iberian Peninsula, in order to strengthen centripetal pressures in that area. As early as the thirteenth century, however, Portugal, facing the Atlantic, had become an independent state, and except for an eighty-year period of union with Spain, it has remained a separate nation since that time. A third political unit on the peninsula, the British possession of Gibraltar,[2] was established early in the eighteenth century. In addition to the physical and cultural forces of diversity is the fact that there is no one primary core area in Iberia and that even in modern times the circulatory system is poorly-developed here. Thus regional differences continue to influence strongly the attitudes and desires of a majority of the people.

Although they were once important world powers, Spain and Portugal have made relatively little economic or political progress within recent times. The harbors of the two countries no longer serve the great trade routes of the world. Both states have for many years been controlled by dictators, and the long acceptance by the Spanish and Portuguese of existing conditions contrasts sharply with many other areas of the world, where, since the mid-1930's, continued poverty and political oppression have led to widespread popular unrest and violence. The factors of location and of protection behind the Pyrenees have meant that Spain and Portugal are less exposed to the dangers of possible invasion from the Soviet Union and its satellites than are other states of western Europe. Nevertheless, Portugal is a member of NATO, and both Portugal and Spain have permitted the United States to maintain military bases within their borders. (See also Chapter 5 for a discussion of the roles of Spain and Portugal as colonial powers.)

---

[2] The mountain state of Andorra in the east-central Pyrenees might also be considered as part of the peninsula. Protected by surrounding mountains this Catalan-speaking nation, with an area of less than 200 square miles and a population of about 5,000, has a history of independence which dates back to 1278.

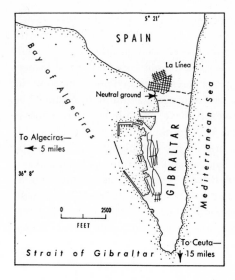

SPAIN

5° 21′

Bay of Algeciras

La Línea

Neutral ground →

To Algeciras—
◄— 5 miles

36° 8′

Mediterranean Sea

GIBRALTAR

0   2500
FEET

Strait of Gibraltar

To Ceuta—
▼ 15 miles

Figure 41. Gibraltar.

The Strait of Gibraltar. One of the most strategically important areas
of the western Mediterranean Basin is the Strait of Gibraltar, a waterway
eight miles wide at its narrowest point, which connects the Atlantic with the
Mediterranean. Spain occupies the northern coast, except at the extreme
east, where the British-controlled peninsula of Gibraltar is located. The
southern coast is occupied by the former Spanish Morocco, which since 1956
has been a part of the independent state of Morocco. The Spanish continue
to maintain sovereignty over a coastal enclave about the city of Ceuta. At
the western end of the African coast is located the city of Tangier (see
page 288).

For centuries the strait has been an historic passageway for political and
military movements both in a north-south direction between Europe and
North Africa, and east-west between the Atlantic and the Mediterranean.
The Vandals moved southward across the strait early in the fifth century in
an encircling movement toward Rome. Three centuries later the Moors advanced northward from Africa to Europe. The waterway represents a transition point between European and North African cultures, and something
from each continent has managed to filter across to the other.

The British Rock. Great Britain occupied the 2¾-mile long Gibraltar
Peninsula (including the famous Rock) in 1704, and has retained it ever
since, despite periodic pressures from Spain for its return (Figure 41). Composed of limestone, the Rock rises to over 1,400 feet and is honeycombed with
corridors, rooms, ammunition and storage dumps. The normal peacetime
population is about 25,000. Although a majority of the population speaks
Spanish, the people are not Spaniards by origin or in sympathy. When Britain first established Gibraltar as a fortress the Spanish population living there

voluntarily withdrew, and the area was repopulated by immigrants—mostly from the Italian city of Genoa. Gibraltar is connected by a land bridge with the Spanish mainland, and many Spanish workers who earn their living on Gibraltar live in the Spanish city of La Línea at the northern end of this bridge.

Spanish nationalism in recent years has manifested itself in sporadic demonstrations and in demands for the return of Gibraltar to Spain. The indigenous people of Gibraltar apparently have no wish for such a move. Nor would the 12,000 Spanish workers who commute daily to the Rock welcome the transfer, for wages on Gibraltar are far higher than could be earned in Spain. For the British the Rock is still important as a supply and maintenance base and as a symbol of British power, but its military significance has declined in relation to other less vulnerable bases of the British Commonwealth. In any future world conflict Gibraltar might be completely neutralized by hostile control of the Spanish mainland or by atomic attack on the base itself.

Italy and the Adriatic

The Italian Nation.   The peninsular nation of Italy has often experienced territorial instability and change. Its relations with the areas which surround it on its land and sea borders have been greatly influenced by two historical trends—first, the fear that these areas might be used as bases for launching attacks against Italy itself and, second, Italian desires to expand the nation's political control to nearby areas, some of which have in part been occupied by Italians, and which were once part of the Roman Empire. On its land borders the nation is separated by the Alps from four neighbors—France, Switzerland, Austria, and Yugoslavia. Across the narrow Adriatic Sea lie Yugoslavia and Albania. The French island of Corsica is situated fifty miles west of the Italian mainland, and the former French-controlled North African coast is less than 100 miles across the Mediterranean from Sicily. Finally, sixty miles to the south of Sicily is the British island of Malta.

Italy's location makes it something of a transitional area between central Europe and the Mediterranean. The climate of northern Italy is continental rather than Mediterranean, and much of the economy of this area is closely tied with that of France, Switzerland, and Austria. Although the Alps surround Italy on its land boundaries, communications through and around the mountains are not difficult to maintain; the numerous valleys of the Italian border regions are populated by French-, German-, and Slavic-speaking peoples as well as Italians. Italy's continental neighbors, particularly France and Austria, for many centuries controlled important sections of what is now the Italian state, and the political and military activities of these nations in Italy constituted one of the principal causes for the late unification of the peninsula into an independent national state.

The location of Italy is of great importance in terms of power alignments in the Mediterranean, for the nation practically bisects the water body
in its narrow central sector. The military aspects of this location were of significance to British and Allied dominance in the Mediterranean in World
War I, when Italy was allied with Britain, and in World War II, when Italy
and Britain were enemies. Since 1949 Italy has been a member of the North
Atlantic Treaty Organization and has provided bases for naval operations
by NATO members in the central Mediterranean.

The nation possesses few of the important requirements for national
power. There is virtually no petroleum in Italy, only small amounts of low-
grade coal, and insufficient iron ore to meet domestic needs. Water power is
the only readily available power source, although utilization of natural gas is
becoming increasingly important. Much of Italy's soil is exhausted or subject
to severe erosion, the system of land tenure is only gradually being modern-
ized, and, although forty-five per cent of the nation is in crop land, food
production is insufficient to satisfy domestic needs.

Italy's population of some 48,000,000 places considerable strain on the
nation's resources. Large numbers of Italians have emigrated to foreign
countries; Italian workers also migrate as "temporary residents" to other
European nations in order to secure employment. It was an Italian hope
that the acquisition of overseas territories would provide an outlet for surplus population. Prior to the outbreak of World War II, however, less than
200,000 Italians (0.4 per cent of the population) resided in Italy's colonial
areas. One of the important political aspects of Italy's population pressure
is, of course, the effect of this pressure on the nation's economic structure.
There is in Italy a large Moscow-oriented Communist Party, which skillfully capitalizes on the fears and discontents of the Italian people. Thus
here, as in other countries of the noncommunist world, the failure of the
Italian government to provide adequately for the needs of the great mass
of the population could lead to a strengthening of internal communism and
eventually a possible weakening of the military and economic ties between
Italy and the Western nations.

Political Features. Italy's political features reflect the complicated
pressures which exist here. The internal forces of unity and diversity, the location and functioning of international boundaries, and the changing pattern of overseas territories show clearly the effects of diverse geographic elements and the varying power positions of Italy throughout its history. Major
centripetal forces include a strong concept of nation, a single language and
religion, and a relatively well-developed circulatory system. The capital is
centrally located geographically, although it is too far south in relation to the
political or economic balance. The principal core area of Italy is the Po
basin, containing approximately forty per cent of the nation's population.
Other core areas are Tuscany (including Florence and Pisa), the Tiber low-

lands around Rome, and Campania in the southwest, centered on Naples.

Italy's physical features have contributed somewhat to regional isolation, but more important centrifugal forces are the climatic and economic differences between the Po basin of the north and the hills and coastal plains of the central and southern areas. The northern Italians, with their greater economic development, often feel themselves to be culturally superior to the people of central and southern Italy; one political effect of this has been the resentment among north Italians toward government-sponsored programs for the economic and social betterment of the south.

Italy's land boundaries are largely physical in character, following mountain divides. The complex ethnic patterns in the Italian border areas and the desires for control of resources and of passes have led to a great number of territorial disputes between Italy and France, Austria, and Yugoslavia. The controversies with France are treated in Chapter 6, those with Austria in Chapter 8; the Italo-Yugoslav border is considered on page 173. Ethnic and strategic considerations have also figured prominently in Italy's control of nearby coasts and islands. Italian territorial ambitions in the Adriatic have centered on the Adriatic islands and on the coast lands of Yugoslavia and Albania. Corfu, a Greek island in the Ionian Sea, has also been coveted by the Italians because of its strategic location with regard to the Strait of Otranto. To the west an historic objective has been the annexation of Corsica with its Italian-speaking population, which was lost to the French in the eighteenth century. In the south possession of Malta has often been cited by Italians as a principal requirement of Italian dominance in the central Mediterranean.

The Italian Empire. After the unification of Italy in 1870 the Italians, like the Germans, desired an overseas empire as a mark of national prestige, as an area for investments, and as a market for exports. Germany's territorial successes prior to World War I—and again under Hitler—served further to whet Italy's appetite for imperial development, as did the growth of the British, French, Belgian, and Portuguese empires. Many Italians, comparing the poverty of modern Italy with the grandeur of the Roman Empire, convinced themselves that a revival of the power and prestige of Roman times was possible in twentieth-century Italy, and they preached, wrote, and worked toward this goal.

In Africa, Italy acquired Eritrea along the Red Sea coast by conquest and Italian Somaliland by occupation and treaties, while Libya was won from the Turks just prior to World War I. In 1935 Ethiopia, one of Africa's few independent states, was invaded and conquered by Italian forces based in Eritrea and Italian Somaliland. The success of Italian moves here was occasioned in part by the fact that these African areas had not been effectively claimed by other European powers, since they had little demonstrable economic or strategic value. They also proved to be of little economic importance to the Italians in terms of resources, settlement areas, or markets. Following World War II the territories were taken from Italy, although the Italians were later awarded a ten-year trusteeship over Somalia—the former Italian Somaliland (see Chapter 12).

In the eastern Mediterranean Italy won from Turkey the Dodecanese Islands (including the island of Rhodes) at the same time as it acquired Libya. The islands, inhabited by Greeks, are of little economic value, but the Italians hoped to use them as a springboard for the expansion of their power into Turkey—an operation which was never successful. For over three decades the Dodecanese remained an Italian outpost in the eastern Mediterranean, but in 1944 Italy, by this time a defeated Axis nation, ceded them to the Greeks.

Expansion in the Adriatic Area.   In the Adriatic area Italian political ambitions and activities became extremely complicated. Italy's desire for domination here involved three sections—Trieste and the Istrian Peninsula, the Adriatic islands and coast land, and Albania on the Strait of Otranto at the entrance to the Adriatic.

Trieste and the Istrian Peninsula.   The Trieste controversy is one of the outstanding examples of Italian irredentism. The area about the head of the Adriatic, sometimes referred to as the Julian region, has been a maritime outlet for areas to the north and to the east, and from Trieste rail lines extend eastward to the Danube lowland, north to the Drava valley and Vienna basin, and westward to the Po lowlands. The close ties between this area and central Europe are illustrated by the fact that even in 1956 over two-thirds of the trade handled by Trieste was Austrian. Thus the Austrian people, as well as the Italians and Slavs, continue to be vitally concerned with the question of political control over the Trieste area.

The ethnic pattern in the Julian region reflects its historical development as a marchland area. Roman colonists came to the Adriatic littoral in the first centuries of the Christian era, while Slovenes moved here from the east during the seventh and eighth centuries. From such ancient roots the modern ethnic division developed, with surprisingly little variation or intermixture. In general, the Italians inhabited the coastal lowlands from the Isonzo River eastward to Pola at the tip of the Istrian Peninsula, while the Slovenes, a Slavic people, lived in the uplands behind the coastal plains.

For nearly three centuries prior to 1919 Trieste and most of the Istrian area were under Austrian control. At the end of World War I Austria and Hungary were drastically reduced in size, and both Italy and the newly-created state of Yugoslavia put forth claims to this area. The Yugoslavs maintained that their nation was heir to this part of the former Austro-Hungarian Empire, and further that Trieste and Fiume were the only seaports available to them while Italy had other harbors to develop. Italy, however, insisted on its ethnic and strategic rights here, and the Italo-Yugoslav

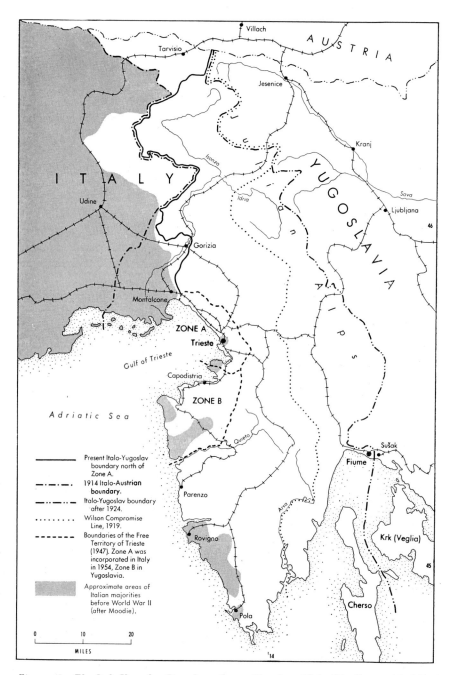

Figure 42. The Italo-Yugoslav Boundary Area. (Based on Kish, *The Geographical Review*, XXXVII (Jan., 1947), courtesy of American Geographical Society; and Moodie, *The Italo-Yugoslav Boundary*, George Philip & Son, 1945. Used by permission.)

boundary was eventually delimited so as to give Italy control of almost the entire Julian region. Over half a million Slovenes thus came under Italian jurisdiction. The nearby port of Fiume was set up as a "free state," but within a few years the Italians annexed this as well (Figure 42).

With the ending of World War II the question of sovereignty over Trieste and the surrounding areas was once again raised. Much the same arguments were used as in the years following World War I. Eventually, by the terms of the Italian Peace Treaty Yugoslavia received most of the area which prior to 1919 had belonged to Austria-Hungary, although Trieste and the coastal regions near it—containing a predominantly Italian population— were constituted as the Free Territory of Trieste and placed under United Nations control.[3] Until such time as a governor could be appointed for the Free Territory, the area was divided into two zones—Zone A, including Trieste itself, which was occupied by American and British forces, and Zone B, to the southeast, occupied by the Yugoslavs. Most of the Italians living in the coastal areas east of Trieste subsequently moved to Italy itself, thus breaking the historical ethnic pattern here.

As in Korea and Germany, the provisions for a unified territory of Trieste were never carried out, due to the inability of the Western and communist powers to agree on the details of implementation. In October, 1954, after numerous proposals for the area's future had been considered, the territory was permanently divided, with Zone A being incorporated within Italy and Zone B into Yugoslavia. A minor correction in the border between the two zones, involving six square miles and about 4,000 Slovenes, was made in favor of Yugoslavia.

As has often happened in the past the principal victims of the settlement may be the Triestans themselves. Trieste will be maintained as a free port, but Yugoslavia is improving the facilities of its own port at Fiume (Rijeka) and will use this as the nation's outlet to the Adriatic. The occupation forces have been withdrawn from Trieste, and the economy of the city (population about 250,000) has subsequently declined. With the advent of economic depression may come widespread discontent on the part of the Triestans against the terms of the territorial settlement.

THE ADRIATIC SEA. Italy's attempts to dominate the Adriatic area have not been confined to the Julian region. At the close of World War I Italy demanded control of certain Adriatic islands as well as territorial concessions along the Dalmatian coast of Yugoslavia. Eventually the Italians were granted (1) an enclave about the Yugoslav city of Zara (now Zadar); (2) three northern Dalmatian islands (Cherso, Lussino, and Unie) control-

---

[3] The compromise on Trieste was closely tied to the question of the Italian Tyrol at the end of World War II. Austria had demanded return of the Tyrol from Italy, and the successful resistance by the Western powers to these demands partially compensated the Italians for their losses in the east to Yugoslavia.

ling the entrance to Fiume; (3) Lagosta and another southern Dalmatian island; and (4) the Pelagosa Islands in the mid-Adriatic, forty miles south-west of Lagosta. These unconnected points assured Italy of naval dominance in the Adriatic.

During World War II Italy extended its power farther east by annexing the western areas of defeated Yugoslavia and establishing a protectorate over the central portion of the nation (Figure 57). The end of the war, how-ever, saw the evacuation of Yugoslavia and the return of Zara and the Italian-controlled Adriatic islands to the Yugoslavs, coupled with a rising interest by Yugoslavia in the development of its maritime activities. Thus once again Italy is confronted by a strong power across the narrow Adriatic.

ALBANIA. A third objective of Italian expansion in the Adriatic area has been Albania, a mountainous country which was set up as an independ-ent state in 1913, largely to keep the landlocked kingdom of Serbia from reaching the Adriatic. The state is poor and undeveloped, tribal loyalties are often stronger than national ones, and large parts of the area have never been effectively organized either politically or economically. The principal *raison d'être* for Albania's independence was the international rivalry exist-ing over the control of this strategic portion of the Balkans.

During World War I Italy's ambitions to establish permanent control over Albania were eventually blocked by pressure from Britain, France, and the United States, and in 1919 the Italians were forced to content them-selves with possession of the Albanian port of Valona (Vlonë), across the Strait of Otranto from Italy, and of the island of Saseno (Sazan), at the mouth of the Bay of Valona. In this way Italy secured control of both sides of the Strait of Otranto.

Between the two world wars Italy expanded its influence in Albania, first by economic means, and later by assisting in the training of the Albanian army. To both Yugoslavia and Greece this Italian encroachment on the Balkan Peninsula was viewed with alarm. On Good Friday, 1939, Italian forces invaded Albania and soon subdued the nation. From here they later launched an unsuccessful attack against the Greeks, and in 1941 Albania pro-vided a base for Italian forces for their part in the Axis invasion of Yugoslavia.

Italian influence in Albania has not returned since World War II. Communist partisans in Albania helped to liberate the country from the Axis forces, and later Albania was occupied by the Red Army. A pro-Moscow government was installed, and by 1946 Albania had become a Soviet satel-lite state. Saseno and Valona were returned to Albania by Italy. Saseno is reportedly being developed as a submarine base from which communist craft could threaten the Mediterranean. Italian military supremacy in the Strait of Otranto has ended; through the waterway an "iron curtain" now extends, separating a Soviet-dominated state from non-Soviet areas.

Greece and the Eastern Mediterranean

Geographic and Historical Background of Greece. Greece, like Italy, contains elements of both continental and maritime environments. On its northern borders the nation adjoins Albania, Yugoslavia, and Bulgaria. The mountainous character of the border areas and the complex ethnic patterns here have resulted in historic conflicts of boundary location between the Greeks and their three northern Balkan neighbors. On the northeast Greece also adjoins Turkey: here again many territorial and ethnic problems have arisen. The mainland possesses a long coast line, and is surrounded by many Greek-inhabited islands.

With an area of 51,182 square miles, Greece has relatively few resources to support its population of about 8,000,000. Much of the land is mountainous and less than thirty-two per cent is classed as arable land. Level areas are often swampy and require extensive drainage operations before they can be made productive. Here, as in Italy, agricultural production suffers not only from the lack of available land, but also from poor agricultural techniques and lack of capital for such things as good seed and fertilizers. Greece has no coal or petroleum, and the water-power potential is not yet well-developed. The nation has a wide variety of minerals, such as iron ore, lead, zinc, and chromium, but none of these occurs in large quantities. The population increase is about 90,000 per year, and many Greeks have emigrated overseas in search of better economic opportunities. Others have turned to the sea for their livelihood, but the Mediterranean is not one of the rich fishing areas and Greece is not one of the great mercantile nations of the world.

Most of the people living within Greece are united by language, religion, and national loyalty. The frequent need for resistance to foreign aggression has also contributed a significant unifying element to the country. The principal areas of ethnic differences occur in the northern border regions. Centrifugal forces are strong here, due to the complex terrain, the differences in economic interests, particularly between northern and southern Greece, and the lack of transportation and other communication facilities throughout the nation. Athens, both the ancient and modern capital, is located in the principal core area, but because of the diverse topography population concentrations are scattered throughout the country. Macedonia, centering on Salonika in the northeast, represents a secondary core area, while among the less important ones are Epirus in the northwest, the various lowlands of Peloponnesus in the south, and the plain of Thessaly northwest of Athens.

After nearly four centuries of Turkish control the Greeks finally won their independence in 1829. During the following ninety years they were able to extend gradually the territory of their nation, winning control of various Aegean islands, Crete, Corfu, and the Ionian Islands, as well as both western and eastern Thrace, all of which areas were inhabited largely by Greeks. At the end of World War I the Greek-inhabited eastern Aegean Islands, including Lemnos, Samos, and Samothrace, were ceded to Greece. Return of the Dodecanese Islands at the end of World War II brought another segment of Greek population under the nation's control.

Before World War I many Greeks also lived in the vicinity of Smyrna on the western coast of Turkey. Following the war Greek troops occupied the Smyrna area in anticipation of the creation of a Greek "influence zone" here, but they were soon forced to withdraw in the face of renewed Turkish military strength. In 1923 there was an exchange of over 1¾ million Greeks living in Turkey with some 350,000 Turks living in Greece. Thus the Greek ethnic "bridgehead" in Anatolia was removed.

Not only on Crete and most of the Aegean Islands, but also on Cyprus is the population predominantly Greek. In addition to some 400,000 Greeks on Cyprus, there are also approximately 100,000 Turks. The island was under Turkish control from 1571 until 1878, when it passed into British hands.[4] The British have developed Cyprus into a major Middle East military bastion, but since 1955 they have been under strong pressure from Greek Cypriotes to permit a union of the island with Greece (see also page 184).

Land Boundaries of Greece. Greece's land boundaries have often caused difficulties to the nation. Because of the complex ethnic patterns existing in the border area, conflicts have arisen with Bulgaria over Thrace, with Yugoslavia over Macedonia, and with Albania over northern Epirus.

THRACE. In 1913, following the First Balkan War, Greece gained control over the former Turkish territory in western Thrace, and after World War I defeated Bulgaria was forced to cede eastern Thrace to the Greeks. This narrow strip of Greek territory, reaching eastward to Turkey, separates the territory of Bulgaria, a Soviet satellite state, from the Aegean. The territory is inhabited for the most part by Greeks, although in the mountain areas along the Greek-Bulgarian frontier, there are nomadic Bulgarian and Romanian peoples.

Northwestern Thrace includes a portion of the region known as Macedonia, a complex ethnic and political area. Greek Macedonia was the scene of a major population change in 1923, when over half a million Greek refugees from Turkey were settled in the northern part of this area. Immediately following World War II the mountainous area of Macedonia, bordering on northern Greece, Albania, Yugoslavia, and Bulgaria, was the site of guerrilla warfare, as communist forces from countries to the north of Greece

---

[4] Actually Turkey leased the island to Britain between 1878 and 1914, at the end of which time Britain formally annexed it. The following year Britain offered Cyprus to Greece as an inducement for Greek entry into World War I on the side of the Allies, but the offer was refused.

sought to overrun the nation. The presence of Macedonians, Albanians, and other non-Greek groups along the borders complicates the political situation, especially when Greece's neighbors use them to stir up trouble for the Athens administration (see page 251 for a discussion of the Macedonian problem).

NORTHERN EPIRUS. Relations between Greece and Albania have been strained for many years as a result of disputed sovereignty over northern Epirus, a mountainous area of about 3,000 square miles in southern Albania containing some 320,000 people. When the Albanian nation was set up just prior to World War I its southern boundary was delimited in such a way that a number of people having cultural affinities with Greece were included within the new state. Since 1913 Greece has frequently pressed for border rectifications so as to include these people within the Greek nation.

The ethnic characteristics of the people of northern Epirus have never been carefully determined. Surveys based on religion at the time of World War I showed that about forty per cent of the population were Greek Orthodox. Whether all of these, if given the choice, would prefer Greek to Albanian rule is, of course, impossible to predict. Another survey, made after World War I, estimated that about one-sixth of the population of southern Albania spoke Greek in their homes. In this case Greece might have fairly strong claims to the loyalty of most of the people. On the other hand, there is also a large number of Albanian-speaking people (sometimes estimated as high as 100,000) in northern Greece, thereby further contributing to the problems of delimiting an ethnic boundary between the two states.

The problem of the Albanian-Greek border must be viewed today in the light of its role as a sector of the "Iron Curtain" and therefore an area of tension in the Cold War. Greece has for the time abandoned its claims to parts of northern Epirus, but the ethnic problem may eventually be revived, as each nation still has sizable minorities in the other's territory.

Turkey and the Straits

Turkey's location in the northeastern sector of the Mediterranean Basin is strategically important because of the Straits, the nation's proximity to the Soviet Union, and its relationship to the countries of the Middle East. As a result of its military alignment with the United States and other NATO powers, Turkey has become an extremely significant area of Western influence in this part of the world—a check to Soviet expansion to the Aegean Sea and the Middle East, and a base for United States military strength in the troubled eastern Mediterranean.

With its population of over 23,000,000 and its reserves of chrome, molybdenum, and manganese, as well as its coal and water-power potential, Turkey possesses the basis for a relatively strong economic system. However, because of its history, and of the mountainous terrain throughout most of the country, modernization of Turkey's economic, social, and political structure has been slow, with the result that the average annual income remains very low. Much progress must still be made in such fields as education, health, and agricultural techniques before Turkey will have reached the level of development and per-capita income of the nations of western and central Europe (see page 309 for a discussion of the Kurds).

Centrifugal forces of distance, mountain barriers, and poor communication systems have hampered the development of strong political cohesion in Turkey. During the 1920's the national capital was moved from Constantinople to the ancient capital city of Ankara in the center of the nation, in order to promote a sense of independence from foreign control and to help in the unification of the various sectors of Turkey. With the expulsion of the Greeks in 1923 greater cultural unity was obtained among the Turkish population. The principal ethnic minorities remaining in Turkey are the Armenians and Kurds in the rugged eastern part of the nation.

Changing Power Status of Turkey. The Ottoman Empire, of which Constantinople (now Istanbul) was the capital, began its growth during the mid-fifteenth century, and about 200 years later had reached its maximum extent. At one time the Turks controlled an area from the Atlantic to the Persian Gulf and from the Hungarian Plain and the southern Ukraine to the southwestern corner of Arabia. By the end of the seventeenth century the Empire had begun to decrease in size, but not until after World War I did it completely disappear. Thus for nearly 500 years Turkey was a major power in the Mediterranean Basin.

From 1914 to 1918 Turkey fought on the side of Germany and its allies, after which Turkey was a thoroughly beaten nation, in no position to bargain at the peace conference. Control of the Straits was taken from the Turks in 1920 and placed in the hands of an international commission, and foreign zones of occupation (French, Italian, and Greek) were established along the nation's western and southern coasts.

The rebirth of Turkish power began in 1920, when a spirit of nationalism (occasioned in part by the severity of the terms of the Turkish Peace Treaty) began to sweep the country. Foreign occupation forces were eventually defeated by Turkish troops, and by 1923 Turkey was in a position to reassert its sovereignty. Under the strong leadership of Kemal Ataturk, Turkey adopted many customs of the Western nations, developed a strong military force, and by 1939 had again become an important power in the Middle East.

During World War II the nation remained neutral until the closing months of the conflict, when it declared war on Germany. Immediately following the war Turkey was subjected to heavy pressure by the U.S.S.R., particularly in connection with the Straits, for the Soviets wanted a share in the control and defense of this waterway. With the backing of the United

Figure 43. The Straits.

States, Turkey resisted Soviet pressure. American military and economic aid was granted to the Turks, and eventually Turkey became a member of NATO. One of the most powerful nations of the Middle East area, Turkey has regained much of its former significance as a key state in international power alignments.

The Straits. One of Turkey's most critical problems of territorial control has concerned the waterway connecting the Black and Aegean seas. This waterway lies entirely within Turkish territory, although the right of passage through it vitally affects all the nations which border the Black Sea. The Straits consist of three sections: the Dardanelles in the west, a 47-mile-long passage, at one point less than a mile wide; the Sea of Marmara, 125 miles long; and the 18-mile-long Bosporus in the east, less than 2,500 feet wide at its narrowest point (Figure 43). Istanbul stands on both the European and Asiatic sides of the Bosporus at its entrance into the Sea of Marmara. Since the middle of the fifteenth century Turkey has retained control of the Straits, and holds the threat of being able to "bottle up" Black Sea navigation when and if Turkish leaders deem such action necessary.

The history of Turkish policy toward the passage of foreign ships through the Straits is a long and intricate one. The defeat of Turkish forces late in the eighteenth century led to a relaxation of restrictions on foreign shipping in 1774, and the granting of permission for Russian merchant vessels to utilize the waterway. In 1859 permission was extended to all neutral shipping to pass through the Straits, thereby opening the Black Sea for the first time to world commerce. During World War I Turkey, a belligerent, closed the Straits to all Allied shipping, and Russia was cut off from Allied supplies. British naval and land units tried to force the Straits in 1915, but despite the high losses their efforts were unsuccessful. By the Treaty of Sèvres (1920) the Straits were demilitarized and Turkey lost complete control of their administration.

Two subsequent international conferences served to return control of the Straits to Turkey. The resurgence of Turkish nationalism led to the Treaty of Lausanne (1923), returning the waterway to Turkish administration. Thirteen years later Turkey found itself in a strong bargaining position, and the Lausanne Treaty was superseded by that of Montreux, permitting Turkey to fortify the Straits and to close them to warships of all countries when Turkey was at war or threatened by aggression. Soviet warships were to use the Straits in peacetime without restriction, but non-Black Sea powers could send only a limited naval tonnage at one time into the Black Sea.

During World War II Turkey exercised its right of closure, although Allied officials maintained that German vessels at times dismantled their armament, sailed through the Straits, and then reassembled it. The passage of Soviet warships through the Straits was denied, and in 1945 the Russians put forth demands for increased control of the Straits. They asked for a confederation, composed of powers bordering the Black Sea, to administer the waterway, although these powers consist only of the U.S.S.R., the satellite states of Bulgaria and Romania, and Turkey. The Russians demanded that a joint Soviet-Turkish defense be set up for the Straits and that they be open in peacetime only to warships of the Black Sea powers. The Turks, however, have resisted Soviet demands, and the Straits are still administered according to the Montreux Convention of 1936.

The Turkish-Russian Border Area. The mountainous region of northeastern Turkey is one of the most isolated parts of the nation, and an area in which strong centrifugal forces have at times developed with respect to Turkish control. The Armenians, an ethnic group which numbers about 2,500,000, inhabit the valleys and basins of northeastern Turkey and of the southwestern sector of Soviet Transcaucasia. Their isolation has helped them to retain their distinctive language and culture in the face of the numerous military activities and political changes which have taken place here through past centuries.

The Turkish-Soviet border stretches for 322 miles through this upland region (Figure 44). Controversy between Turkey and Russia over the location of this border dates back to 1878, when the Russians completed a century-long advance southward by annexing a Turkish-controlled sector, including the port of Batumi on the Black Sea coast. During World War I Russia and Turkey faced one another across the border. Russian forces ad-

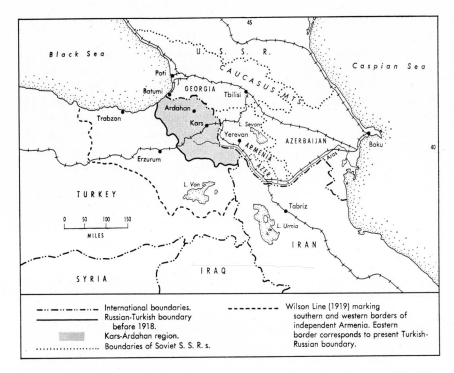

Figure 44. The Turkish-Russian Border Area. (Boundaries after Bowman, *The New World*, World Book Co., 1928. Used by permission.)

vanced into eastern Turkey and were aided by Turkish Armenians, still recovering from the terrible massacre inflicted on them by the Turks in 1894. The collapse of Russia in 1917 brought the return of Turkish troops and renewed pillage. In the Treaty of Brest-Litovsk, which defeated Russia signed with Germany and its allies, the Kars-Ardahan region, part of the sector won by Russia from Turkey in 1878, was returned to the Turks. The new boundary practically split the Armenians in two. After the surrender of Germany and the other Central Powers in November, 1918, the Brest-Litovsk Treaty was abrogated, but because of Russian internal difficulties the Turks continued to hold the Kars-Ardahan area.

Following World War II the Soviets asked for the return of Kars and Ardahan from the Turks. Despite its rugged terrain the area could be utilized by powers hostile to Russia for the construction of air bases only a few minutes flying time from the industrial oil fields and transportation lines of Soviet Transcaucasia. The Turks have held firm in their resistance to Soviet territorial demands. Although in 1953 the Soviet government officially abandoned its claims to changes in its border with Turkey, the region still remains a source of potential dispute, particularly if relations between Russia and Turkey should deteriorate at some future time.

The Armenians, of course, continue to be divided. Their hopes for political independence, like those of the Kurds, the Macedonians, and the Basques, seem to have little prospect of materializing. From Soviet Armenia Pan-Armenian propaganda is beamed westward, designed to attract the people of Turkish Armenia to the U.S.S.R., and, ultimately, to weaken Turkey's control over its Armenian area. One possible objective of Soviet propaganda would seem to be the incorporation of Turkish and Soviet Armenia into some sort of Soviet-dominated "Greater Armenian People's Republic."

Problem Areas

1. The Struggle for "Enosis" in Cyprus

The dispute over control of the island of Cyprus poses one of the most difficult problems of sovereignty since the end of World War II. The Greeks on Cyprus have been demanding that the island's status as a British crown colony be ended, and that *enosis,* that is, union of Cyprus with Greece, be carried out. The British, faced with the loss of other areas in the Middle East, turned to Cyprus as the site for their major military base in this part of the world. The harbor facilities on Cyprus are not extensive, but the island can be used as a deployment area for troops and for air bases. Although the Greek government has assured Britain that permission to maintain bases on Cyprus would continue to be granted should Cyprus be joined to Greece, the British contend that Greek governments change and that a future administration in Athens might deny Britain the use of the island. The Turks are also opposed to *enosis,* first, on the grounds that the status of the Turkish minority on Cyprus would be safer under British than under Greek control and, second, that the island lies but forty-two miles from the Turkish mainland. If Greece should someday come under a left-wing government a Greek-controlled Cyprus would be a threat to Turkey's security.

The Cyprus dispute has strained relations between Greece and Britain—traditionally friendly states and military allies in NATO—as well as between Greece and Turkey—also NATO allies. The British have offered the Cypriotes a liberal home-rule constitution. They have also suggested that they are willing to spend large sums of money in development of the island's resources, sums which Greece cannot possibly afford. The fact remains, however, that a plebiscite on Cyprus would probably show an overwhelming majority of the population favoring *enosis.*

The Cyprus dispute is, of course, related to other problems of control as well. The British have adopted a "tough" policy on the island, hoping to subdue the violence by force. If they are unsuccessful here they may face mounting insurrection in other parts of their empire as well, such as in British Guiana and Singapore.

One possible course of action is the partitioning of the island into Greek- and Turkish-occupied sectors, with the former uniting with Greece and the latter remaining under British control. Such a solution, however, although advocated by some officials, is opposed by the Greek majority on Cyprus, and could well lead to a far more explosive situation than that existing in Ireland. There are few islands in the world with moderate to high population densities which are politically divided, since the facts of geography constitute a strong centripetal force.

2. The Changing Political Status of Malta

Britain's island base of Malta in the central Mediterranean also may experience a change in political status, although here the change will take place within the framework of the British Commonwealth. With an area of 122 square miles (including the nearby islands of Gozo and Comino) and a population of nearly 320,000, Malta faces serious problems of economic survival. Most of the island's food must be imported, and the major source of income is from the British naval dockyard located here.

The Maltese, descended from the ancient Phoenicians, are divided in their political aspirations. One group favors dominion status for the island, while another is striving for incorporation within the United Kingdom—a status resembling that of Northern Ireland. In the latter case Malta would stand to gain from British social welfare benefits, although, on the other hand, the people would also have to pay high income taxes. The Maltese are Roman Catholics, and some opposition to the integration plan has come from the Catholic Church, which fears that its dominant position in matters of religion, education, and family life in Malta might be endangered if the island were a part of Protestant Britain. In February, 1956, a referendum was held in Malta, which resulted in a 3 to 1 vote in favor of union with Great Britain, but the desires of the Maltese people have not yet been fulfilled by the London government.

BIBLIOGRAPHY

"Cyprus: The Closed Issue?" The World Today, X, No. 9 (September, 1954), 372–81.

A discussion of the principal issues involved in the controversy for control of Cyprus.

EAST, W. GORDON. "The Mediterranean: Pivot of Peace and War," *Foreign Affairs,* XXXI, No. 4 (July, 1953), 619–34.

An interesting discussion of the changing strategic position of the Mediterranean.

ESMER, AHMED SUKRU. "The Straits: Crux of World Politics," *Foreign Affairs,* XXV, No. 2 (January, 1947), 290–303.

Summarizes the various controls on shipping in the Straits since the end of the 18th century, and considers Soviet post-World War II demands.

"Italy in Africa," *The World Today,* IV, No. 2 (February, 1948), 62–74.

The development of the Italian empire, and the value of the colonies to the mother country before World War II.

MOODIE, A. E. *The Italo-Yugoslav Boundary.* London: George Philip and Son, Ltd., 1945.

A detailed account of this border by one of the experts on the problem.

UNGER, LEONARD. "The Economy of the Free Territory of Trieste," *The Geographical Review,* XXXVII, No. 4 (October, 1947), 583–609.

A comprehensive survey of the economy of this disputed territory through World War II.

8

GERMANY AND AUSTRIA

● Germany and Austria occupy one of the key areas in the power complex of the European continent. The turbulent histories of both states have been characterized by numerous problems of territorial sovereignty, involving diverse ethnic patterns, national ambitions for economic and political status, and pressures by other states to contain—or, when possible, to reduce—the areas of German and Austrian control. Prior to 1848 Austria was one of the continent's leading nations; since the middle of the nineteenth century, however, Germany has emerged as the dominant state of central Europe, and most of the territorial problems in this area since 1864 have been associated with the expansions and contractions of the German borders. Since World War I Austria has lost its status as a major European nation, but Germany, despite its defeat in two world wars and its present divided condition, still retains much of its tremendous power potential. The future political pattern of Europe depends to a considerable extent on the avenues into which this German power potential is ultimately directed.

The development of the Austrian and German nations is interwoven with the history of the German-speaking peoples in Europe. In the tenth century the original core area of the Germans extended from the Elbe River westward to the present German-French language border, and from the North Sea south through northern Switzerland, present-day Austria, and even into parts of northern Italy. From this area the German-speaking groups gradually expanded to the northeast, east, and southeast. In many parts of the continent they managed to retain their cultural identity for centuries, even after the growth of nationalism in eastern and southern Europe and the incorporation of many people of German stock into non-German states. The German government, particularly after the country's unification in 1871, has often used the fact of German-speaking groups living in other countries (*Auslanddeutsche*) as justification for Germany's territorial ambitions in Europe (Table 2). The propaganda put forth by Pan-Germanists has argued that these *Auslanddeutsche,* because of their cultural affinities with Germany, should be permitted to become politically united with the *Vaterland.*

Table 2

GERMAN-SPEAKING PEOPLES LIVING BEYOND
GERMANY'S BORDERS IN THE EARLY 1930'S

Country	Population
Czechoslovakia	3,200,000 (1930)
Poland	1,300,000[a] (1935)
Russia	1–1,200,000 (1935)
Romania	745,000 (1930)
Yugoslavia	499,000 (1930)
Hungary	479,000 (1930)
Latvia	62,000 (1935)
Lithuania (excluding Memel)	33,000 (1931)
Memelland	25,000 (1930)
Estonia	16,000 (1934)

(Practically all German-speaking peoples in the areas listed above have been removed or killed since the beginning of World War II.)

Austria	6,330,000 (1931)
Switzerland	2,900,000 (1930)
France	1,250,000[b] (1930)
Saarland	770,000 (1927)
Luxembourg	297,000 (1935)
Italy	250,000[c] (1939)
Belgium	69,000 (1930)
Denmark	20,000[b] (1930)
Netherlands	12,000[b] (1930)

Census figures vary widely according to the particular definition of "German-speaking" peoples.
[a] Approximate figure. Includes Danzig.
[b] Approximate figure.
[c] Including Ladins.
Sources: Joseph B. Schechtman, *European Population Transfers, 1939–1945* (New York: Oxford University Press, 1946); *The Statesman's Yearbook, 1941;* information services of the Netherlands, Belgium, and Denmark.

Relations between Germany and Austria, the two major German-speaking states, have varied considerably through the centuries. On the one hand are cultural, historical, and economic bonds uniting them; on the other are conflicts of national interests, together with foreign pressures which have at times worked to prevent an *Anschluss* of the two nations. Each state has its own national individuality, yet there have always been strong centripetal forces drawing the two together. The Austrian Peace Treaty of 1955 takes cognizance of these forces by specifically forbidding any future political merger of Austria with Germany.

In the sections which follow Germany will be considered first, in terms of its national power potential and the evolution of the present pattern of political control here. Austria will then be treated with respect to its physical and cultural features and the changes of territorial control which have taken place in this area in recent decades.

Germany

The territorial area of Germany has changed many times during the twentieth century, and it is not unreasonable to assume that the Germany of the next decade may be of still different size and shape than it is today. Most Germans think of the German state as comprising the area which was contained within the 1935–38 boundaries. Following World War II this territory was divided into four parts: West Germany (the German Federal Republic), a sovereign democratic nation; East Germany (the German Democratic Republic), a satellite state of the Soviet Union; the area east of the Oder-Neisse line, now a part of Poland;[1] and the Saar, which became an autonomous area joined politically and economically with France. On January 1, 1957, the Saar was united politically with West Germany and became one of its constituent states. In Table 5 the areas and populations of these four divisions of Germany are listed.

Elements of German National Power

Location, Size, Shape. Germany occupies a central position in Europe, touching nine states and bordering on both the North and Baltic seas. Its location with regard to neighboring states has been both an asset and a liability (Figure 45). With its central location and with lowland routes and waterways connecting it with other areas, Germany has been able to profit from cultural associations with its neighbors, notably in political ideas, scientific developments, and philosophic and artistic trends. It has also, of course, benefited from economic ties with adjoining states. On the other hand, this location, together with the diversity of relief (particularly in central and southern Germany), contributed to the late political unification of Germany, for the region has long been a transit area for foreign armies and peoples, and it lacks well-defined boundaries within which cohesive forces could operate for political unity.

---

[1] The lower part of the Oder River and its tributary, the Neisse, form the border between Poland and East Germany. The territory of East Prussia, in what used to be northeastern Germany, was divided between Poland and the U.S.S.R. in 1945, with Russia receiving about forty-three per cent of the area, including the port of Kaliningrad, formerly Königsberg.

Figure 45. Germany and Austria: Physical Features.

Since 1871 no nation bordering Germany has been as strong economically as the Reich itself. As a result Germany has been in an advantageous economic position with regard to trade with its neighbors, particularly Luxembourg, the Netherlands, Switzerland, and Austria. German industrial exports have found ready markets in these and other adjacent states, and from them Germany has been able to obtain needed commodities, such as dairy products, fruits and vegetables, iron ore, and grains.

In terms of a nation's military and political expansion the existence of relatively weak neighbors is a definite asset. Since 1864 Germany on several occasions has been able to encroach on the territory of its neighbors, or to convince them by reason of its potential power that annexation of German territory, even when possible, would be a foolhardy act. Fear of reprisals from a revitalized German nation, for example, prompted the Belgian and Luxembourg governments in 1949 to refuse most of the small sectors of German territory awarded them by the Western powers as war reparations. One disadvantage of a central location is the possibility of a two- or three-front war, as occured in 1944–45 when Germany had to defend its eastern and western borders as well as its southern flanks.

Considered as a unit comprising both East and West Germany, the nation has an area of 138,000 square miles, or about seventy-four per cent of what it was in 1935–38. The shape resembles that of an hourglass, with an inward bulge in the east, where Czechoslovakia extends about 150 miles into the main body of the country, and a smaller one in the west where France projects eastward in the Karlsruhe area. Since Czechoslovakia is a Soviet satellite state the Czech indentation must be considered in West Germany's defense against possible communist attack.

Economic Features. In many respects Germany's economic strength was developed only after physical limitations had been overcome. Most of the soils are of moderate to poor fertility, but with wise agricultural practices these have been made productive to the point where the nation during the two world wars was able to achieve a high degree of self-sufficiency. Mineral and power resources are not abundant. Production of iron ore, copper, lead, and zinc are insufficient to meet domestic needs, and there is practically no petroleum. The highlands of central and southern Germany provide water power, much of which has been developed, but the nation's major fuel resource is coal—tremendous reserves of coking coal in the Ruhr, smaller supplies in the Saar and Silesia (now separated from Germany), and lignite, particularly in Saxony (part of East Germany). Other resources include potash, particularly from the Stassfurt area of East Germany, and timber from upland areas throughout the nation.

An important element in Germany's economic strength has been the development of science and technology, particularly in the electro-chemical fields, enabling the nation to utilize its great coal resources for the production of needed commodities, and to derive substitutes for such products as sodium nitrate and petroleum, which in time of war have been unobtainable. Wartime needs have greatly stimulated German economic development, particularly since the end of the nineteenth century, focusing attention on the build-up of heavy industries, on the role of government aid and supervision in strengthening the economic base, and on the search for new processes and commodities to aid Germany in time of conflict. The results of this continuous drive for a strong national economy have been that Germany was the dominant economic power in Europe before World War I, again before World War II, and within a few years after World War II West German steel production was once more the greatest in Europe (outside the U.S.S.R.).

Transportation facilities have been important in integrating Germany's internal economy and in tying it with other nations. Most of the major rivers flow north-south, and where necessary, have been canalized. East-west canals have been constructed to link the river systems with one another, and with Benelux, France, and Poland. The German rail and road networks are among the best in Europe, and together with the waterways these systems link the nation closely with its neighbors, particularly to the west. Before World War II overseas trade was maintained by an efficient merchant marine and by what was then one of the world's greatest overseas airlines. Within ten years of the war's end both were being rebuilt rapidly.

The economic development of Germany prior to 1914 and again from 1933 to 1939 was a major factor in Germany's ability to wage sustained war. In addition, the flexibility of its economy permitted the nation to shift rapidly from peacetime to wartime production. The French tried at the end of both world wars to place permanent limits on German industrial production as a means of restraining Germany's national power, but both times the attempts were unsuccessful. One of the Germans' key assets has been the Ruhr industrial complex, with its coal, its rail and water transportation net, and its iron and steel, chemical, and allied industries. Plans for international control of the Ruhr, made after Germany's world war defeats, have never prevented the restoration of German control and the eventual recovery of Ruhr production.

German economic power has been felt in other nations, often with political or military overtones. During the 1930's, for example, Germany achieved a position of economic dominance over many of the countries of southeastern Europe, and German overseas trade with Latin America, the Middle East, and the Orient was also greatly developed at that time. Economic contacts were frequently utilized as bases for espionage or dissemination of Nazi progaganda. In some countries, for example, Hungary, the powerful role Germany played in the national economy aided the local Nazi party in eventually assuming control of the country's government.

Economic objectives have played an important role in Germany's territorial ambitions, but it is easy to overemphasize the economic motives for territorial expansion in relation to such factors as military strategy or national prestige. The Germans went to great lengths, for example, to develop a colonial empire before World War I, yet these overseas possessions were never a major economic asset to the nation. Likewise, German annexation of eastern Lorraine in 1871 was based more on considerations of strategy than of the location of the iron ore reserves (see page 154).

After World War II Germany's economic power was handicapped

by the division of the nation and the separation of the Saar and the eastern areas. East Germany has been forced to gear its economic activities with those of the other members of the Soviet bloc, while West Germany has been free to build up an economy within the framework of the noncommunist world. In prewar days the area now constituting West Germany found the greatest market for its goods in what is now East Germany. In recent years, however, with trade across the Iron Curtain discouraged by the Western powers, West Germany has turned not only to the other nations of western Europe and to Anglo-America, but also to Latin America, Africa, and the Middle East.

Population. The population of East and West Germany combined amounts to about 70,000,000 persons. Only a negligible number of Germans is left in the Polish-controlled area east of the Oder-Neisse line. A large population has always been one of the elements of German power in terms of labor and military forces. The German people have an intense national consciousness, bolstered by a common language. This sense of unity has developed despite religious differences[2] and postwar territorial divisions. The 1945 division of the nation, dictated by outside powers, runs counter to the strong feelings of unity, and to a majority of the German people reunification is a primary goal, to be achieved as rapidly as possible.

Two aspects of the German population factor have been utilized by propagandists in justifying the nation's territorial demands. One is the need for living space or *Lebensraum* for the nation's large and energetic population. The concept of life as a fight for space was developed in the writings of Ratzel and his followers, and has been utilized by more recent German scholars and officials in explaining the nation's needs for additional territory. Associated with this *Lebensraum* has been the desire by German leaders to unite German-speaking groups living beyond the nation's borders within the framework of Germany itself, even at the cost of destroying other national units and incorporating large non-German groups as well.

One of the important developments with respect to population in postwar Germany has been the redistribution of peoples. Professor Chauncy Harris[3] describes four types of refugees in Germany: (1) *Displaced Persons,* who were non-German laborers brought to Germany during the war; (2) *Expellees,* German-speaking peoples who have been driven from their homes east of the Oder-Neisse line in the district which is now Polish territory or from other nations of eastern Europe; (3) *Refugees,* from East to West Germany; and (4) *Recent Refugees,* to West Germany from other areas behind the Iron Curtain. The displaced persons have mostly been

---

[2] The population of pre-Hitler Germany was divided roughly three to two in favor of Protestants over Catholics. In addition there were 500,000 Jews, of whom less than 25,000 now remain in the two German republics.
[3] Chauncy D. Harris and Gabriele Wülker, "The Refugee Problem of Germany," *Economic Geography,* XXIX, No. 1 (January, 1953), 10–26.

resettled in the west. Harris estimates that there are about 12,500,000 expellees, which figure includes about 7,500,000 persons from the area east of the Oder-Neisse line and 5,000,000 from other parts of eastern Europe. Of the total number of expellees, about two-thirds are in the West German republic. Refugees, who formerly lived in East Germany and who have crossed the border to West Germany—together with recent refugees from other areas of Soviet-dominated eastern Europe—are estimated to number over 2,000,000.

Political Features. Because of the frequent changes which have taken place in Germany's boundaries, and because of the great population transfers since World War II, it is difficult to analyze the functional aspects of the borders. The lack of prominent natural features to serve as boundary markers is evident everywhere except in the southeast, where mountains separate Germany from the Bohemian basin of Czechoslovakia. Rivers have often been used to mark German borders, but here, as with mountains, the physical features have not corresponded with the ethnic boundaries. The only border along which no serious problems of territorial control have developed since the unification of Germany is that with the historically neutral state of Switzerland—a border which for most of its length follows the Rhine River and Lake Constance.

The ties of language, culture, and national loyalty are the most powerful centripetal force within Germany. Regional differences are reflected in the various dialects and in the diverse economic and cultural outlooks, but they do not constitute strong elements of national disunity. Linguistic minorities within Germany's borders are extremely small. The only important minority group were the German Jews, who were violently persecuted under the Nazi regime.

Germany has several core areas, principally the Rhine valley, the Central Uplands (Hannover, Magdeburg), Saxony (Leipzig, Dresden), and the Berlin area. Other urban centers, such as Hamburg, Munich, and Nürnberg represent secondary core areas. Berlin, the capital of unified Germany (and still the capital of East Germany), lies well to the east of the major population concentrations, but is the historic capital of the Prussian state. Bonn, in the Rhine valley, is the capital of West Germany. The city is well located with respect to West Germany's population distribution, but it lacks the historical attraction of Berlin.

THE EVOLUTION OF THE GERMAN NATION

The Development of Germany to World War I

The various German states of central Europe were late in merging into one political entity. In 1815, at the Congress of Vienna, a Germanic Confederation, including both the German states and Austria, was organized under Austrian domination. By this time, however, the German state of Prussia, occupying much of north central and northeast Germany, had so increased in power that already it represented a challenge to Austria's position in central Europe. In the decades following the Vienna Congress Prussia moved gradually to eliminate Austria from the Confederation and to unite the German states in a Prussian-dominated nation.

Organization Under Prussia. With its powerful landholding aristocracy and its strong military system, Prussia represented something of a holdover from feudalism. The strength derived from wise leadership, a well-organized population willing to give blind obedience to the leaders, and a powerful military tradition were utilized by Prussia in its early territorial gains and in its rise to power in the nineteenth century. The development of the German nation and the subsequent expansion of this nation are in a sense the history of Prussian expansion. Prussian leadership was responsible for the creation of a unified Germany, and Prussian political and military officials—as well as Prussian civil servants—continued to play dominant roles in Germany after unification.

As a first step toward German unification the Prussians instituted a customs union (*Zollverein*) in 1833, which eventually united the German states into an economic unit, from which Austria was excluded. Next, in 1864 Prussia attacked Denmark, and the co-operation of the other German states in the war effort furthered the bonds of German unity. Two years later Prussia again brought on war, this time against Austria, and once more the other German states came to Prussia's aid. Austria was soon defeated, the old Germanic Confederation was dissolved, and a new Prussian-dominated confederation was formed, in which Austria did not participate.

In 1870 Prussia instigated a war with France. For the third time in six years the other German states co-operated in the conflict, and within a few months the French were defeated. As a result of the Franco-Prussian War the German states were politically united into the new German nation under the sovereignty of the Prussian king. As war booty, Germany received from France the border province of Alsace, together with a part of neighboring Lorraine.

The history of German unification under Prussian leadership illustrates the roles played by both economic unity and by co-operation for a common cause in the process of achieving political cohesion. Somewhat analogous situations have existed in the unification of other political units, notably the thirteen American colonies, the Italian states, and the units of Indonesia, and a similar process may in time occur among the Benelux states. The existence of a common language and culture among the German states was an important element in unification, as was also the presence of determined leadership in the form of Prussia.

Expansion of the United Nation. During the decades following its unification Germany worked to build up its economic strength in Europe and to expand its political and economic power abroad. Industrialization proceeded at a rapid rate, and the population increased from 41 million in 1871 to 65 million in 1914. Growth in German agriculture, foreign trade, and armaments kept pace with these other increases.

Overseas, Germany moved rapidly to develop a colonial empire in Africa and the Pacific. By the last quarter of the nineteenth century other European powers were expanding their colonial holdings in Africa and the Pacific, and by the time Germany entered the race for territories much of the more valuable land had already been claimed. During the 1880's German settlements were established in Africa, and gradually Germany's claims were recognized over Southwest Africa, the Cameroons, Togoland, and German East Africa (most of which now comprises Tanganyika). In the Pacific Germany annexed the northeastern shore of New Guinea, as well as the Bismarck Archipelago and the northern Solomons. In less than a decade and a half after its formation as a unified state Germany had developed the third largest colonial empire in the world at that time. Later acquisitions in the Pacific included western Samoa, the Marshall Islands, the Carolines, and the Marianas.

Territorial Changes at the Versailles Conference

In 1914 Germany, Austria-Hungary, and the other Central Powers entered World War I against France, Britain, and their allies. Four years later the Central Powers surrendered. Germany's defeat put a temporary stop to the nation's expansion and led to a major reapportionment of the areas under German control (Table 3).

Table 3

EUROPEAN TERRITORY LOST BY GERMANY AFTER WORLD WAR I

	Area (in sq. mi.)	Population (Census of 1910)
Alsace-Lorraine	5,607	1,874,014
Saar Basin (under League of Nations for 15 years)	744	713,105*
Belgium (Eupen and Malmédy)	400	60,003
Poland	17,816	3,854,971
Memel	1,026	141,238
Danzig	739	330,630
Denmark (Schleswig—northern zone) . .	1,542	166,348
Czechoslovakia (part of Upper Silesia) .	122	48,446
Total	27,996	7,188,755

*Census of 1922.

From Isaiah Bowman, *The New World*, p. 273. Copyright 1928 by World Book Company. Used by permission.

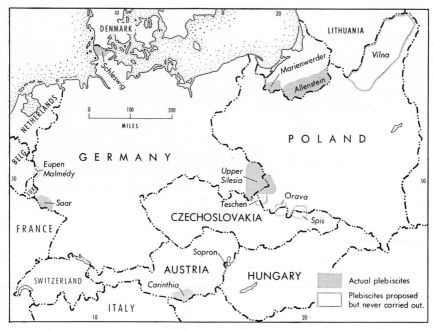

Figure 46. Plebiscites in Europe After World War I. The Eupen-Malmédy plebiscite was only partially carried out. (After Wambaugh, *Plebiscites Since World War I*, Carnegie Endowment for International Peace, 1933. Used by permission.)

The task of redefining the German borders was complicated by three major factors: (1) the distribution of German peoples adjacent to the border areas; (2) the complex history of German territorial control in central Europe; and (3) the economic ties within the border regions which were liable to destruction through drastic boundary alterations. A majority of the population inhabiting the areas detached from Germany were German in culture and national sentiment. In addition, over 3 million Sudeten Germans, living under Austrian sovereignty before World War I, were included in the new nation of Czechoslovakia. Many of these also had strong pro-German sympathies. Nearly 28,000 square miles of territory, containing just over 7 million persons, was separated from Germany at the end of World War I. Many of Germany's complex territorial problems in 1919 were settled by plebiscite (Figure 46).

The German-Polish Borders. The area ceded to Poland by Germany in 1919 returned the German-Polish border to approximately its location in 1772, at the time of the first partition of Poland. In the area along the Baltic coast border delimitations were particularly difficult, for on the one hand most of the inhabitants here were German, while, on the other hand, the new Polish nation insisted that it have access to the Baltic Sea. This

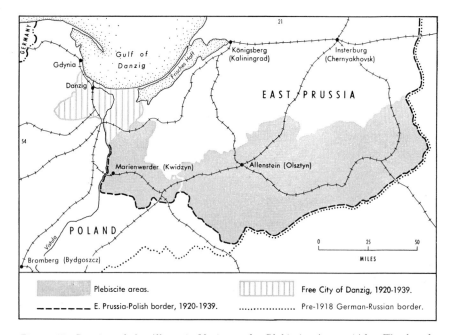

Figure 47. Danzig and the Allenstein-Marienwerder Plebiscite Areas. (After Wambaugh, *Plebiscites Since World War I*, Carnegie Endowment for International Peace, 1933. Used by permission.)

conflict of self-determination versus economic needs was eventually settled by Germany's retention of East Prussia as an eastern outlier along the Baltic, by the creation of a Polish Corridor to the sea between East Prussia and the rest of Germany, and by the establishment of the German-inhabited port of Danzig (lying within the Polish Corridor) as a Free City under League of Nations administration. In the Allenstein-Marienwerder area of southern East Prussia (Figure 47) a plebiscite was held in 1920 to determine the wishes of the local people. The predominantly Protestant population voted to remain with the Germans rather than join Catholic Poland. To the northeast of East Prussia, Memelland, a German-speaking area on the Baltic, was eventually annexed by Lithuania (see page 234).

Despite the concessions made to ethnic and economic claims in this part of Europe, frictions arising from the complicated political pattern grew stronger with the passage of time. Many Germans looked down on the Poles as a culturally inferior group, and waited hopefully for the day when western Poland would be reincorporated into Germany. The Poles in turn, having just emerged from nearly a century and a half of German control, resented past German injustices as well as present frictions, and they feared the possibility of German attempts to regain the lost areas.

Danzig, a city of 400,000 inhabitants at the mouth of the Vistula River, was cut off from its former hinterland, and even after the final delimitation of the German-Polish border the people of Danzig continued their agitation for reunion with Germany (Figure 47). Largely because of the hostility of these peoples, Poland began construction in 1921 of a rival port, Gdynia, located a few miles northwest of Danzig on the Polish-held portion of the Baltic coast. After the port's completion Danzig's commercial activities practically ceased. Because of the economic distress here the Free City during the 1930's was an important center for the Nazi party, with its demands for renunciation of the Versailles Treaty and the return to Germany of its prewar territories.

Hitler exploited the discontent of the Germans in Danzig and the Polish Corridor in his demands on Poland for return of these areas. At the beginning of World War II German forces occupied western Poland, which was subsequently annexed to the Reich. Toward the end of the war, however, Soviet forces, moving westward across Poland, forced the Germans from this area. In 1945 the German-Polish border was shifted westward to the Oder-Neisse line, and the Germans living to the east of this line were repatriated. Thus the boundaries of Poland were extended considerably farther west than they had been prior to Hitler's invasion of 1939.

In Upper Silesia, at the southern end of the German-Polish border, problems arose over boundary delimitations through what was basically a unified economic region. Although there was talk of awarding the entire area to Poland, German spokesmen argued that without at least a part of Upper Silesia their nation's economic future would be in jeopardy. Yet if division were agreed upon there remained the task of drawing the boundary so as to include as many persons as possible within the country of their choice, while at the same time avoiding undue strains on the area's economy and on the maintenance of border functions.

A plebiscite was held in a part of Upper Silesia in 1921. Despite the fact that a majority of the inhabitants here were Poles the results showed 700,000 votes for union of the plebiscite area with Germany and about 470,000 for annexation to Poland. The pro-German victory in this predominantly Polish area demonstrated the fact that here, as in other parts of western and central Europe, economic considerations often outweighed cultural factors in influencing political choices. In this case Germany would eventually revive its economic power, while Poland's economic future was considerably less certain. The final German-Polish border decided upon by the League of Nations split the plebiscite area, leaving 572,000 Poles in Germany and 350,000 Germans in Poland (Figure 48). Since the end of World War II the entire Upper Silesian area has been included within Poland.

The German-Danish Border. The territorial problems between Ger-

Upper Silesia plebiscite area.

International Boundaries 1921-1939.

Boundaries of Teschen area.

Final Polish-German border in plebiscite area.

Coal Basin.

Figure 48. The Upper Silesia Plebiscite Area. (After Bowman, *The New World*, World Book Co., 1928. Used by permission.)

many and Denmark at the end of World War I involved the Schleswig-Holstein area. Taken from Denmark in 1864, Schleswig-Holstein received a large influx of German settlers, so that by 1919 the ethnic character of its population had changed considerably from what it was in the mid-nineteenth century. Danish claims to Holstein itself were considered too weak by League of Nations officials to justify a plebiscite, but it was decided that to the north, in Schleswig, a vote would be taken. The province was divided into two parts for the plebiscite: the people of the northern portion decided three to one in favor of joining Denmark, but those in the south elected to stay with Germany. Despite Danish protests the province of Schleswig was divided (Figure 49).

When Nazi Germany annexed Denmark in 1940 northern Schleswig was returned to German control, but five years later the Danes reannexed it. In this fairly homogeneous agricultural area boundary delimitation along ethnic lines is difficult. Barring large-scale population transfers, the complex ethnic pattern here seems likely to continue. Thus at some future date it may again erupt into a territorial dispute between the two nations.

Other Territorial Changes. The history of territorial change along Ger-

Boundary of Denmark
1864-1920.

Southern boundary of Zone I
(Present frontier).

Southern boundary of Zone II.

German-Danish border prior to 1864.

Danes

Frisians

Mixed Danes
and Germans

Germans

*Figure 49.   The Schleswig Plebiscite
Area.* (After Bowman, *The New World*,
World Book Co., 1928. Used by per-
mission.)

many's western borders is discussed in Chapter 6. The Saar was detached
from Germany for fifteen years and placed under the administration of the
League of Nations, and the Eupen-Malmédy area along the German-Bel-
gium border was joined to Belgium (see page 145). In addition to the
losses in Europe, Germany was stripped of all its overseas possessions.
These were divided among the victorious Allied powers as mandates under
the League of Nations (Table 4).

Expansion of Germany Under Hitler, 1935–39

During the first decade and a half following World War I an attempt
was made to develop a successful democratic government in Germany. The
failure of this attempt was the result of many factors, including Germany's
continued economic difficulties. The economic structure had suffered heavily from the war and from the readjustments which followed it, and, unlike

Table 4

DISTRIBUTION OF GERMAN COLONIES AFTER WORLD WAR I

Colony	Mandate Power	Class of Mandate
German East Africa (Tanganyika)	Great Britain	B
Ruanda-Urundi	Belgium	B
Cameroons	France, Great Britain	B
Togoland	France, Great Britain	B
Southwest Africa	Union of South Africa .	C
North Pacific islands	Japan	C
German New Guinea and nearby South Pacific islands	Australia	C
Western Samoa	New Zealand	C
Nauru	Joint Administration: Great Britain Australia New Zealand	C

conditions which existed after World War II, there was no large-scale foreign aid for defeated enemies during the 1920's. In 1933, at the depth of the world-wide depression, Adolph Hitler became the German chancellor and capitalized on the popular discontent in the nation. He embarked on a program to revive Germany's national power, and was determined to strengthen the nation internally and to expand its territorial holdings. His efforts, like those of Frederick the Great, Bismarck, and Kaiser Wilhelm II, were aided by the blind following of many of the German people. Through skillful use of mass propaganda Hitler and his National Socialist (Nazi) Party were able to win continued support of the German people for their internal and external policies.

The success of Germany's efforts at territorial aggrandizement up to September, 1939, was due in part to an absence of determined opposition from other major world powers. Italy after 1936 was Germany's ally and was engaged in its own program of expansion, while the Soviet Union was only beginning to emerge from its period of isolation after two decades of internal crises. The Western democracies (Great Britain, France, the United States) were for various reasons unwilling to commit themselves to military force to stop the Germans. The United States was pursuing a policy of neutrality toward Europe's problems, while Britain and France, recovering from the depression, were beset with internal difficulties. Even in the face of German aggression many British and French leaders were unwilling—up until 1939—to attempt negotiating a mutual assistance pact with Russia, for they feared communism as much or more than Naziism. There were, of course, a number of officials in Britain, France, and the United States who saw the danger inherent in Germany's moves, but they were unable to effect

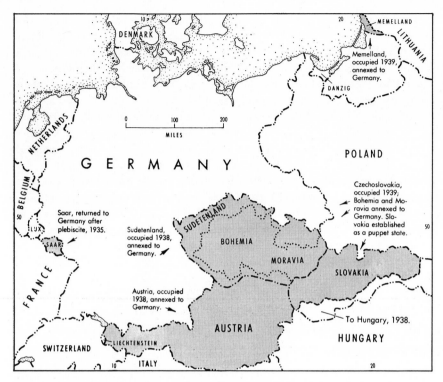

Figure 50. Expansion of Germany Under Hitler Before World War II.

basic policy changes in order to bring pressure to bear against the Nazis. A primary disadvantage of a democratic government is that government leaders are often unable to move swiftly in the face of potential danger, because of the reluctance of the public, which has not been conditioned to the danger, to support drastic steps.

Germany's first territorial acquisition under Hitler occurred in 1935, when the people of the Saar voted nine to one for the return of German control (Figure 50). The following year Germany began to remilitarize the Rhineland, the area between the Rhine River and the western border, which had been permanently demilitarized by the Versailles Treaty. No active opposition to this move on the part of the Allied powers was encountered, and Hitler felt encouraged to continue his renunciations of the Versailles terms. In February, 1938, German military forces occupied Austria. This bold venture to establish a German-Austrian *Anschluss* was carried out despite opposition on the part of many Austrians, who considered the German act one of conquest rather than unification.

By constant utilization of the Pan-German theme, the Nazis were able to stir up discontent among German groups residing in other European countries. In the fall of 1938, after a bitter propaganda campaign, Germany annexed the Sudeten area of western Czechoslovakia with its more than 3 million German inhabitants. By this time demands were also being made of Poland to restore to Germany the Polish Corridor and Danzig with their large numbers of German-speaking peoples.

Despite Nazi claims at the time of the acquisition of Sudetenland that all of Germany's territorial ambitions were now realized, the Germans within a few months moved to annex new areas. In March, 1939, Hitler occupied the remainder of Czechoslovakia, except for the easternmost province—Ruthenia—which Hungary seized. Memelland, on the Baltic coast, was then taken back from Lithuania, and by June the enlarged German nation contained a population of 86 million people. Within a few weeks of the Czech occupation the German government had stepped up its propaganda campaign for the return of western Poland to Germany. The British and French, determined at last to halt Germany's territorial aggrandizement, supported Poland in its refusal to comply with Nazi demands. On September 1, 1939, German forces invaded Poland, and two days later, in fulfillment of their obligations to the Poles, Britain and France declared war on Germany.

Territorial Problems Since World War II

At the end of World War II Germany, a defeated nation, was divided into occupation zones, and a cease-fire line was delimited between Soviet forces in the east and those of the United States, Britain, and France in the west. This line, drawn as a temporary border, followed no particular pattern of physical or historical boundaries. Local political areas were split by the border, villages and towns were separated from their hinterlands. Inability on the part of the great powers to agree on the nature and function of an all-German government led to the hardening of this cease-fire line into a political boundary, and eventually into a sector of the Iron Curtain, across which virtually no traffic moves. Such a dividing line has worked considerable hardship on the people of the border areas, and illustrates clearly the difficulties attendant to ill-conceived boundaries drawn across a unified physical, cultural, and economic region. The border between East and West Germany is among the postwar divisions which are unique in that their effectiveness has relatively little to do with local conditions. Like the border between North and South Korea, this is something of a "super-international" line, reflecting the boundary between global ideologies. Disputes in this border area, instead of being confined to local political administrations, may have world-wide implications.

In 1949 the German Federal Republic (West Germany), comprising the three western occupation zones, came into existence, with its capital located at Bonn. In the same year the German Democratic Republic was established in the Soviet occupation zone, with its capital in East Berlin.

In addition to internal political division, Germany suffered several territorial losses at the end of the war, as shown in Table 5. These losses totaled over 51,000 square miles of territory, containing a predominantly German-speaking population of about 10½ million. Most of the people living in the areas lost to Poland and the U.S.S.R. have been forced to emigrate to Germany; thus the Germans in the future will no longer have claims to those areas on the basis of ethnic ties.

Table 5

GERMAN TERRITORIAL CHANGES FOLLOWING WORLD WAR II

*A. Territory Lost by Germany**

	Area (sq. mi.)	Population
To Poland	44,215	9,000,000
To Soviet Union	6,100	500,000
To the Netherlands	26	13,000
Saar	991	943,000

B. Territorial Division of Germany

	Area	Population (1950)
West Germany (German Federal Republic) .	94,634	49,842,624
East Germany (German Democratic Republic)	42,392	18,259,523

C. Economic Comparison of post-World War II German Areas in Terms of 1938 Production (figures represent percentages of national total)

	Coal	Iron & Steel	Food
West Germany	74	67	43
East Germany	3	3	30
Polish- and Soviet-controlled eastern territories .	17	11	25
Saar	6	19	2

*The Germany of 1935–38, after the return of the Saar. The Saar was again returned to Germany in 1957.

Berlin. Berlin, located ninety-five miles within the Soviet zone, was divided in 1945 into four occupation zones under the authority of a committee comprising the four Allied commanders. By 1948 this committee had ceased to function because of Cold War friction. West Berlin, comprising the British, French, and American zones, has an area of 188 square miles and a population of about 2,000,000 (Figure 51). It is governed as a single unit, and although represented in the legislature of the West German republic, it is not actually a state of the republic, but a separate political entity.

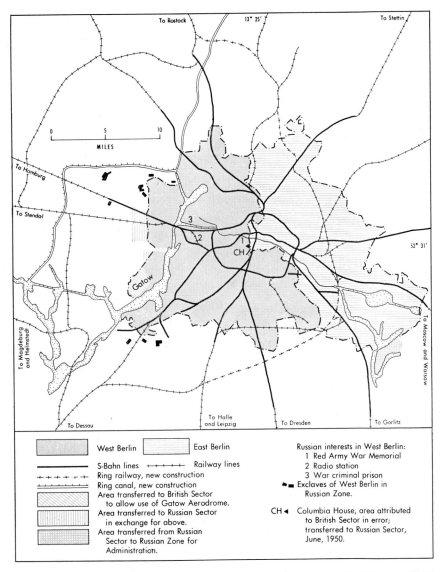

Figure 51. The Division of Berlin. (After Robinson, *The Geographical Review*, XLIII (Oct., 1953). Courtesy of American Geographical Society.)

The problems connected with the maintenance of a Western outpost deep within Soviet territory were amply demonstrated by the airlift of 1949–50, when all surface communications between West Germany and West Berlin were cut off by the Soviets and supplies had to be brought in by air. In normal times a fixed number of freight and passenger trains is permitted over the rail line from Helmstedt in West Germany to West Berlin; also an *autobahn* connecting the same cities is kept open and some barge traffic is permitted between West Germany and Berlin. In addition, three air corridors twenty-miles wide are kept open between Berlin and West Germany. Only over these airways has traffic remained unimpeded throughout the occupation.

Economic problems revolve about the ability of West Berlin to sustain itself through the export of goods and services. Approximately one-half of the city's expenses are covered by these; the rest must be met by grants from the West German government and from the United States. East Berlin, on the other hand, is adjacent to East German territory, and thus can function normally. Along with economic problems is the problem of refugees from East Berlin to the West. These people must either be cared for in West Berlin itself, or flown to other areas of West Germany.

As an island of Western-controlled territory within the Soviet satellite bloc, West Berlin offers both assets and liabilities to the West. Its principal assets are its role as a symbol of resistance to Soviet power in eastern Europe and its value as a listening post within the satellite area. The liabilities are, first, the difficulty of supplying West Berlin with food, coal, and other commodities when normal surface travel from West Germany is cut off, and, second, the problems of economic viability within this heavily populated enclave. The West is committed to remaining in West Berlin indefinitely. As a result, the pattern of political control will continue to be one of the most unusual and potentially dangerous of any which exists throughout the world.

Austria

Location, Size, and Shape

Austria's location in central Europe has been of great importance to the nation's development. Major north-south and east-west transportation lines pass across the area, and Austria has served as an historic marchland protecting central and western Europe against attacks from the east and southeast. The Romans established Vienna as a fortress guarding the Danube route, and later Charlemagne developed the Austrian area as a defense zone against hostile forces to the southeast. In the sixteenth and seventeenth centuries Vienna was besieged by the Turks moving up the Danube valley; the city's successful resistance to these invaders prevented Mohammedan control from spreading west of the Vienna basin. The Brenner, Tauern, and Semmering passes in Austria are major links in the north-south routes between the Mediterranean Basin and the lands to the north of the Alps. These routes are traversed by important rail lines, as are the east-west routes through Austria connecting Switzerland and southern Germany with the Danube basin.

Despite its nodal position Austria suffers from certain disadvantages. The nation has no seacoast and must depend on foreign ports, such as Trieste and Hamburg, for its overseas trade. Culturally and economically Austria maintains close bonds with three of its neighbors—Germany, Hungary, and Italy—yet geography and history have combined to keep it politically and economically separated from each of the three. Language and economic ties bind it with Germany; Hungary, with its foodstuffs and potential markets, is a former political and economic partner; Italy, in which many former Austrian citizens live and through whose territory passes one of Austria's principal links with the sea, has historically been an enemy of the Austrian state. Instead of representing a focus of power in central Europe Austria has often been forced to accept the role of buffer area between the major power blocs which surround it.

The area of Austria is about 32,000 square miles. The nation borders on seven states—Germany, Czechoslovakia, Hungary, Yugoslavia, Italy, Switzerland, and Liechtenstein—and with all of these except the last two Austria has had conflicts of political control during the twentieth century. At the end of World War I the Austrians lost territory to Czechoslovakia, Yugoslavia, and Italy, while at the same time gaining land from Hungary. Although the German-Austrian border has remained stable for many years, the two countries, as noted earlier, were joined together politically from 1938 to 1945.

Population

Austria's population totals over 7,000,000. The people are predominantly German speaking and Roman Catholic. The Jews, most of whom had been exterminated by 1945, were the most important minority group in the nation prior to World War II. The annual population increase is less than three per thousand, reflecting the low birth rate. Although its population is fairly large when measured against its potential resources, Austria, unlike such areas as Italy and the Netherlands, is not faced with the problem of severe population pressures.

Economy

Austria possesses a variety of minerals and power fuels. Although the amounts of these commodities are not great when compared with some of the reserves of other European countries (France's iron ore, Germany's lignite), Austria's resources are nevertheless of sufficient quantity and variety to provide the basis for an important industrial economy. These resources include iron ore, timber, salt, graphite, lignite, petroleum, and water-power potential. The nation is Europe's second largest producer of petroleum, and although the output is only about forty per cent of Romania's, it fulfills domestic needs and permits some exports as well. Austria also exports timber and electric power, but it must import considerable quantities of coal for local use. Approximately twenty-two per cent of the total area is devoted to agriculture; since World War I Austria has been a food-deficit nation, producing at best only about three-fourths of its total food requirements.

Before World War I Austria (with Bohemia, in what is now Czechoslovakia) served as the industrial and commercial heart of the Austro-Hungarian Empire. With the breakup of the empire the Austrians were separated from prewar markets, food sources, and industrial raw materials. Vienna, with a population of nearly 2 million people, had been the leading city of an area of 51 million persons; in 1919 it became the center of a nation whose total population was only about three times as great as the city's itself.

Following the dismemberment of the empire Austria struggled to develop its resources and to increase its industrial output, but the nation's economy never regained its prewar economic stability. In 1921 the Austrians officially requested an *Anschluss* of their country with Germany, hoping thereby to prevent a collapse of the national economy, but the move was blocked by France, which feared it might produce too great an increase of Germany's power potential. Seventeen years later, when the *Anschluss* did take place, Austria's economic structure became geared with that of Nazi Germany.

After World War II the Austrians were faced with serious economic problems. The ties with Germany were dissolved, and German assets in Austria were seized by the Allied powers.[4] Although in 1946 the United States, Britain, and France returned to the Austrians the industrial facilities which they had previously dismantled, the Soviets permanently removed an estimated twelve per cent of the nation's total industrial equipment. For ten years the Soviets siphoned off most of the wealth of their occupation zone, and by the terms of the 1955 peace treaty the Austrians were forced to supply the U.S.S.R. with $152,000,000 worth of free goods in the ensuing six years, 1,000,000 tons of oil a year (approximately one-third of the nation's oil output) for a period of ten years, as well as an additional 200,000 tons a year for six years in payment for the return of German assets in Austria which the Russians had previously confiscated.

---

[4] Austria's position with respect to war reparations was complicated by the fact that German capital, particularly after the 1938 *Anschluss*, had built up much of the nation's economy. In some cases the Germans had confiscated through technical purchases many former Austrian enterprises. After World War II all German assets in Austria were classed as enemy property, subject to confiscation as war reparations.

Despite these terms Austria's economy is gradually improving. The nation is building up its industrial and agricultural production, increasing its hydroelectric output, and developing other sources of income such as tourism and banking. In years to come the economic viability of Austria will be an important factor in the Cold War, for communism stands ready to capitalize on economic weaknesses within the nation.

Political Features

The Austrians are united by language, religion, and national sentiment. The principal minority group are the Slovenes in the southeast (see page 211). Austria is not a large country, and the effects of regional differences on the attitudes and objectives of the people do not represent particularly strong centrifugal forces. The principal core area, focused on Vienna, the capital city, is located well to the east of the geographic center of the country. There are no other population centers comparable in size or political significance to the Vienna basin.

Austria's boundaries in the south and west are primarily physical in character; in the south, however, they do not correspond to ethnic divisions, for German-speaking peoples are settled south of the mountains in Italy, while farther east Slovene settlements have spread northward into Austria from what is now northern Yugoslavia. On the northwest and west Austria adjoins other German-speaking areas; the removal of the Sudeten Germans from western Czechoslovakia since World War II has meant that Austria's border adjoining Czechoslovakia has become largely a linguistic as well as an ideological one. In the east the Austro-Hungarian border, which for most of its length crosses a level to gently-rolling area, is also an ideological boundary between communist Hungary and democratic Austria.

Problems of Territorial Control

The Austro-Hungarian Empire. Before World War I Austria had an area of 116,000 square miles, and a semicircular shape which stretched from Bucovina and eastern Galicia (both now Soviet territories) westward through Bohemia and present-day Austria, then southeastward along the Dalmatian coast of Yugoslavia. From 1815 to its defeat by the German states in 1866 the nation, as noted earlier, was a member of the Germanic Confederation. In 1867 Austria joined with Hungary in the Austro-Hungarian Empire, an enormous political complex, which contained, in addition to Hungarians and Austrians, such diverse groups as Poles, Italians, Romanians, and various Slavic peoples—Czechs, Slovaks, and Croatians.

Within the Austro-Hungarian Empire centrifugal forces were strong, for many of the subject peoples had developed a high degree of political self-consciousness, not only as a result of ethnic contrasts but also because of differences in physical environments and historical development. As a single customs unit embracing the greater part of the Danube basin, the empire possessed something of an economic *raison d'être,* for there was free movement of goods between the agricultural lowlands and the industrial areas of Austria and Bohemia, as well as a flow of exports through the Adriatic ports of Trieste and Fiume. Even in the economic sphere, however, there existed divisive forces, for economic policies were geared to the benefit of special groups rather than for the great mass of people. By the outbreak of World War I pressures for the division of the Austro-Hungarian Empire had grown increasingly strong.

The Dismemberment of Austria after World War I.   The defeat of Austria-Hungary in World War I completely shattered the empire. Austria and Hungary were separated from one another, and Austria was stripped of seventy per cent of its territory. Prewar Austrian areas contributed to the formation of three new nations—Poland, Czechoslovakia, and Yugoslavia—as well as to the expansion of Italy and Romania.

THE CARINTHIA AND SOPRON PLEBISCITES.   In the Carinthian basin of southeastern Austria and in the Sopron area along the Austro-Hungarian border two plebiscites were held after World War I in connection with Austria's territorial realignment. In Carinthia the dispute involved Austria and Yugoslavia. In the Drava River lowland of southeastern Austria both Austrians and Slovenes were settled. Some League of Nations experts argued against any territorial changes which would split the economic unity of the basin, but a vote was nevertheless taken in the area south of the river, with the results six to four in favor of the continued inclusion of Carinthia in Austria (Figure 52). Following World War II Yugoslavia sought to annex a portion of the Carinthia area, measuring nearly 1,000 square miles and containing a population of about 190,000. No mention was made of a plebiscite, although neutral estimates placed the number of Slovenes in this area at less than twenty per cent of the total population. Despite strong Yugoslav claims the Carinthia basin continued to remain with Austria.

The Sopron plebiscite involved the transfer of Burgenland from Hungary to Austria in 1919. This 1,558-square-mile district, with a largely German-speaking population of 218,000, was a rich agricultural area and an important asset to a food-deficit nation such as postwar Austria. A plebiscite was held in 1920 among the people in the Sopron area in the eastern sector of Burgenland, and the pro-Hungarian vote resulted in the separation of this small area from Burgenland and its retention in Hungary.

SOUTH TYROL.   These two plebiscites did not end Austria's problems, for in the South Tyrol section of northern Italy were 200,000 German-speaking Austrians, residents of what had been a part of Austria up to 1919.

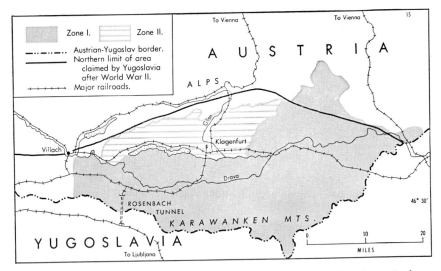

Figure 52. The Carinthia Plebiscite Area. The plebiscite held in Zone 1 was in favor of continued union with Austria. If the vote had been pro-Yugoslav, a plebiscite would then have been held in Zone 2. (After Wambaugh, *Plebiscites Since World War I,* Carnegie Endowment for International Peace, 1933. Used by permission.)

The Tyrol was an historic "pass" region, lying across one of Europe's most important north-south routes from southern Germany and the Inn valley of Austria south through the Brenner Pass into Italy (Figure 53). From South Tyrol strategic passes connect northward with the Austrian Tyrol and east with the Drava valley, as well as south with the North Italian Plain. From 1363 to 1919 the South Tyrol was an Austrian glacis extending south of the main crest of the Alps.

Following World War I no plebiscite was held among the inhabitants of South Tyrol to determine their wishes. Italy's northern boundary was moved to the main crest of the Alps (in this section to the Brenner Pass), thereby including former Austrian territory in the Italian regions of Alto Adige and Trentino. Under Italy's Fascist government (1923–43) attempts were made to Italianize South Tyrol, first, by transferring large numbers of Italians to the area and, second, by interfering with the customs and economy of the German-speaking inhabitants. In governmental positions and in public services Germans were replaced by Italians. The use of German in the schools was forbidden, street names and public signs were changed to Italian, and Germans were forbidden to engage in various cultural activities, such as the wearing of traditional costumes or membership in German social clubs. With the gradual industrialization of South Tyrol, Germans were generally excluded from employment in the new industries and power projects which developed after 1923.

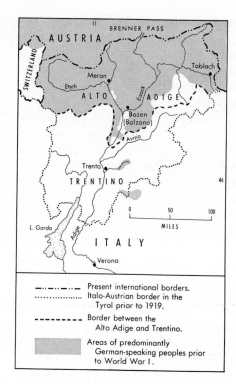

Figure 53. The South Tyrol. (Based on Marinelli, *The Geographical Review,* VII (March, 1919). Courtesy of American Geographical Society.)

In 1939, a year after the Austrian union with Germany, the governments of Germany and Italy agreed to a plebiscite to be held among the German-speaking persons of the South Tyrol to determine whether they wished to be repatriated to Germany or remain in Italy. Approximately 185,000 persons, or seventy per cent of the voters, elected to return to Nazi Germany, while some 80,000 others voted to stay in Italy. About forty per cent of those who voted to return to Germany were actually repatriated before World War II halted the operation. Many of the returned Germans were subsequently settled in those sections of eastern Europe which were overrun by German armies in the opening years of World War II, but by 1945 most of them were back in Germany itself. Some of the former Tyrolese attempted to return to the South Tyrol after the war, but the Italian government refused permission on the grounds that these people when given the opportunity had chosen German rather than Italian sovereignty.

In 1946 Austria put forth claims to the northern province (Alto Adige) of South Tyrol. Although even the Italian government admitted that a plebiscite in this area would show a majority of the inhabitants favoring reunion with Austria, neither the Western powers nor the Soviet Union actively supported Austria's claims, and the area remained with Italy. The

Italians eventually agreed to grant local autonomy to the Tyrol, to respect the German culture there, and to readmit most of the former German-speaking inhabitants who had left in the years 1939–43.

Since 1946 the German language has again been permitted in the South Tyrol schools, and discrimination against the German-speaking peoples there has largely disappeared. However, in granting local autonomy to South Tyrol, Italy has included the area administratively with the province of Trentino to the south; thus the German-speaking people are greatly outnumbered by the Italians. Finally, the Austrian government contends that Italy, although encouraging emigration of Italians to South Tyrol, has still refused to admit all but a few of the German-speaking people who voluntarily left the Tyrol in the early 1940's. The territorial dispute here has not become a major source of conflict between Italy and Austria, but there is potential friction which could be intensified should Italo-Austrian relations deteriorate at some future date.

Austria Since World War II. Because of the *Anschluss* with Germany, Austria was forced to collaborate with the Germans during World War II. In 1945 the country was occupied by troops of the victorious powers and was divided into four occupation zones (American, British, French, and Russian). Vienna, like Berlin, was established as an enclave in the Soviet zone and placed under four-power administration.

Although foreign troops were to remain in the nation for over ten years, a national Austrian government was set up in 1945 with jurisdiction over the entire country. The political union with Germany was completely dissolved. Along Austria's southern borders problems of boundary rectifications arose with respect to South Tyrol and Carinthia, but, as already noted, political control was not changed in either area.

The military occupation of Austria was scheduled to end with the signing of an Austrian peace treaty. Despite repeated efforts by Austrian, British, American, and French representatives to conclude a treaty, however, the Soviet Union refused for a number of years to agree to a restoration of Austrian sovereignty. Finally, in 1955 the Soviets acquiesced to a treaty on condition that Austria become a permanently neutral nation, be forbidden to join Germany in any future political or economic union, and make important economic concessions to the U.S.S.R. (see page 209).

Austria's future development is restricted by a number of factors. Ideological differences block the creation of any type of Danubian federation, in which Austria might once again become associated with Hungary and other states of the Danube basin. Unification with Germany has been specifically prohibited. The legacy of past differences with the Italians and the lack of strong economic bonds between Austria and Italy preclude the development of particularly close ties here. Although it is now a neutralized state, Austria does not enjoy Switzerland's long history of neutrality and its climate of stability, which has served to attract foreign economic activities. As a result the Austrians face serious problems in their efforts to evolve a stable economic and political system in what once again has become an exposed position to dynamic and potentially hostile forces to the east.

GERMANY AND AUSTRIA IN THE WORLD POWER ALIGNMENT

Germany and Austria are located at the border between Soviet-controlled eastern Europe and noncommunist western Europe, and are therefore of great strategic importance (Figure 54). The neutralization of Austria, for example, has meant that foreign troops are no longer permitted in that country. Thus NATO supply routes between West Germany and Italy can no longer use the Brenner Pass, but must run 400 miles to the west through France.

In both Austria and West Germany future developments will be of great importance to world power alignments. Small but vocal communist parties are present in each nation, ready to exploit popular discontent against adverse economic or political conditions. The communization of either state would constitute a westward extension of Soviet control, and would jeopardize the stability of all of noncommunist Europe. Germany and Austria thus represent something of a power balance in Europe today—a unique position, particularly for the Germans, who but a few years ago unconditionally surrendered to the victorious Allied nations.

German Reunification

In the years since World War II one of Europe's most pressing problems has been the search for a permanent settlement of Germany's territorial limits and form of government. The continued division of what was recently one of the leading powers of the world creates a potentially dangerous situation, particularly in view of the split between Germany's conquerors and the desire of the Soviet Union and the West to withhold the resources of their respective areas from one another.

The Soviet Union would probably never agree to a reunited Germany unless there were a guarantee that Germany would not again be in a position to attack the U.S.S.R. West Germany's inclusion in the anti-Soviet NATO alliance does little to allay Soviet fears in this respect. The Western powers, on the other hand, would not agree to a reunited Germany unless there were a provision for free nation-wide elections—in which case the Communists would probably emerge as a minority political party even in East Germany.

Even if an all-German government were re-established, a number of major problems of political control would still remain in central Europe. A

Figure 54. Germany and Austria.

reunited Germany might very likely exert pressure on Poland for the return of the former German territories east of the Oder-Neisse line. Likewise, a free democratic Germany would exert a powerful pull on the Soviet satellite states, and in time might succeed in weakening and perhaps eliminating altogether Soviet control west of the Russian border.

Another problem associated with German reunification is the fact that a reunited Germany would possess the strongest national economy in Europe west of the U.S.S.R., and would be able to exploit economic difficulties in both the Soviet and non-Soviet blocs. Moreover, there is no real guarantee that a reunited Germany will not eventually become a major anti-Soviet power, or, on the other hand, that it will not succumb to communism and ally its vast power potential with that of the Soviet sphere.

BIBLIOGRAPHY

HARTSHORNE, RICHARD. "Geographic and Political Boundaries in Upper Silesia," *Annals of the Association of American Geographers,* XXIII, No. 1 (March, 1933), 195–228.

A detailed and carefully documented boundary study. One of the outstanding pieces of research of its kind in political geography.

HOFFMAN, GEORGE W. "The Survival of an Independent Austria," *The Geographical Review,* XLI, No. 4 (October, 1951), 606–22.

A concise regional study of Austria after World War II.

————. "The Political Geography of a Neutral Austria," *Geographical Studies,* III (January, 1956), 12–33.

A consideration of Austria's economic and political situation, particularly as a result of the 1955 peace treaty.

MEYER, HENRY CORD. "Mitteleuropa in German Political Geography," *Annals of the Association of American Geographers,* XXXVI, No. 3 (September, 1946), 178–95.

A discussion of how political geographic thought in Germany and Austria was warped by pressures of exaggerated nationalism. Carefully documented.

ROBINSON, G. W. S. "West Berlin: The Geography of an Enclave," *The Geographical Review,* XLIII, No. 4 (October, 1953), 540–58.

A detailed study of the geography of West Berlin and its relationships with East Berlin and the Cold War.

SAUCERMAN, SOPHIA. *International Transfers of Territory in Europe.* Washington: U. S. Government Printing Office, 1937.

Detailed statistics on all transfers of territory which took place in Europe following World War I.

VAN VALKENBURG, SAMUEL. "The Rise and Decline of German Lebensraum," in *New Compass of the World,* ed. WEIGERT, STEFANSSON, and HARRISON. New York: The Macmillan Company, 1949, pp. 205–19.

Valuable population statistics are included in this article on Germans living in Europe outside Germany's borders up to and including the end of World War II.

WAMBAUGH, SARAH. *Plebiscites Since the World War.* Washington: Carnegie Endowment for International Peace, 1933.

Detailed treatment of the various plebiscites which took place in Europe following World War I, as well as consideration of disputes where plebiscites, although suggested, were never held.

WEIGAND, GUIDO C. "Effects of Boundary Changes in the South Tyrol," *The Geographical Review,* XL, No. 3 (July, 1950), 364–76.

A well-knit survey of South Tyrol, particularly since World War I. Contains important population figures for the area.

9

EASTERN EUROPE

● Eastern Europe[1] is one of the great buffer areas of the world. Across this important region a great number of armies and migrating peoples have moved, each leaving its imprint upon the cultural landscape. Thus, in addition to physical diversity, particularly in its central and southern portions, eastern Europe also contains a wide variety of ethnic groups as well. The political pattern in turn has been characterized by complexity and by frequent change, as ethnic groups have struggled for self-rule, as states have vied with one another for territory, and as major powers bordering on eastern Europe have expanded or contracted their control in this area.

Physical Elements

Surface Configuration. Eastern Europe, as defined here, stretches through nearly thirty degrees of latitude from the Arctic coast of Finland to the northern borders of Greece (Figure 55). North of the Carpathians along the Czech-Polish border eastern Europe consists of plains and low hills. Except for the Scandinavian Shield of Finland and the uplands of southern Poland, few parts of this northern sector rise above 1,000 feet in elevation. Between the Carpathians and the Baltic coast of Poland lies the historic

---

[1] Eastern Europe here comprises the tier of states located between the Soviet Union and the central European states of Germany, Austria, and Italy, with the Arctic Ocean to the north and the borders of Albania, Greece, and Turkey to the south. Within the region thus described are approximately 573,000 square miles of territory and some 96,000,000 persons. Estonia, Latvia, and Lithuania, although treated here as a part of eastern Europe, are now actually included within the borders of the Soviet Union.

Figure 55. Eastern Europe: Physical Features.

"invasion gateway" to Russia—the route followed by Napoleon, Hitler, and other would-be conquerors of the Russian state. Because of the relative uniformity of surface configuration north of the Carpathians, there are no effective physical barriers to mark national boundaries; settlement patterns are often intermixed with one another, and few national units have managed to survive for more than a short time here.

In southeastern Europe surface configuration is more diverse and there is a variety of mountain and basin areas. The largest of the basins is the Hungarian Plain. This region is drained by the Danube and its tributaries, and includes not only Hungary itself but also portions of Yugoslavia, Romania, southern Czechoslovakia, and eastern Austria. Since 1945 the Soviet Union, by means of its control of the former Czech province of Ruthenia, has also had a foothold in the Hungarian Plain.

Downstream from the Hungarian Plain the Danube drains the lowlands of Wallachia and Moldavia in Romania. These fertile regions, which slope away from the mountain arc of central Romania, form the nucleus of the Romanian state. They also lie on the historic transit route between southeastern Europe and southern Russia and, like the North European Plain, have been the scene of many invasions and settlements.

The Bohemian basin of Czechoslovakia and the Transylvanian basin of west central Romania are also important areas of settlement and economic development. Other principal lowland areas of southeastern Europe are the Maritsa valley of Bulgaria, the Vardar valley of southern Yugoslavia, the Drava valley in northern Yugoslavia, and the Morava valley of central Czechoslovakia. In addition to their function as settlement and economic areas each of the basins of southeastern Europe has formed the nucleus for the development of political areas. Thus Hungary has developed on the Hungarian Plain; Bohemia—and later the Czech nation—focused on the Bohemian basin; while Serbia developed largely about the Vardar valley extending southward from the Danube. The political partitioning of eastern Europe after World War I resulted in the inclusion of several lowland nuclei within individual states, as the Bohemian basin and the Morava valley in Czechoslovakia, and the Wallachia-Moldavia lowland and the Transylvanian basin in Romania. The strong sense of regionalism, however, which had been developed in these separate areas, continued even after political unification, and often represented a powerful divisive force within the east European states.

One of the significant aspects of the political geography of southeastern Europe has been the conflicts for control of the various passes and lowland routes leading to and from the basin areas. There are several important "gates," for example, to the Hungarian Plain; among them are the Vienna Gate from the northwest, the Sava Corridor in northern Yugoslavia, the Vardar-Morava route leading north from the Aegean, the Iron Gate where the Danube cuts through the Transylvanian Alps along the Romanian-Yugoslav border, and a number of passes through the northern mountain rim, including the Yablonitsa Pass in the northeast, the Moravian Gate leading to Polish Silesia, and the Elbe Gate between Bohemia and Germany.

Natural Resources. Eastern Europe has several areas in which soil fertility is extremely high and in which climate, slope, and drainage combine to produce nearly optimum conditions for agriculture. Countering these, however, are large areas in which the physical environment prevents, or greatly limits, agricultural production.

In mineral and power resources the area is relatively rich. Romania has oil and natural gas. Hungary has bauxite and some oil. Yugoslavia has a wide variety of minerals, including chromite, bauxite, copper, mercury, and iron ore, as well as coal and some oil. Czechoslovakia and Poland both have coal and iron ore. Czechoslovakia also contains uranium, while Poland has important deposits of lead and zinc. In addition there is considerable hydro-electric-power potential, particularly in the countries of southeastern Europe.

Only recently has extensive utilization of most of the mineral and power resources in eastern Europe been started. Romania's oil and the coal and iron ore of Czechoslovakia and Poland were the major commodities developed prior to World War II. Since 1945 both Yugoslavia and the Soviet satellite states have placed increasing emphasis on industrial development; as a result, the agricultural, mineral, and power resource-base of eastern Europe is coming to assume great importance to the over-all power status of this part of the world.

Cultural Groups

The major cultural groups in eastern Europe are shown in Table 6. The actual numbers in each group are for the most part only approximations, for there has been a considerable movement of populations in eastern Europe since 1939. The great variety of peoples emphasizes the corridor location of the area, through which many groups have moved during the past two thousand years. Migrations of peoples westward from the grassy steppes of Asia have been countered by movements eastward on the part of Scandinavian groups, Germans, and Mediterranean peoples. In recent centuries eastern Europe has been a zone of conflict between Germanic and Slavic peoples, with the boundaries between them continually shifting from east to west.

Since 1918 there have been a number of major population changes. Turks, Bulgars, Greeks, and Macedonians were involved in mass movements during the early 1920's, and Turkish groups have continued to be repatriated from Bulgaria since that time. The slaughter or exile of Jews in Poland, Czechoslovakia, and other east European countries before and during World War II removed at least 3,000,000 persons from the area. In 1939 German groups were repatriated from the Baltic states, and in 1945 they were sent to Germany from Poland, Hungary, Czechoslovakia, Romania, and Yugoslavia. Many Latvians, Lithuanians, and Estonians have been killed or exiled since the Soviet absorption of the three countries in 1940. There have been other population shifts since World War II, such as the repatriation of Hungarians from southern Czechoslovakia and Italians from Yugoslavia. Boundary changes have also affected the ethnic composition of east European states.

Table 6

MAJOR CULTURAL GROUPS IN EASTERN EUROPE[a]

Country	Approximate Number	Percentage of Total Population	Cultural Characteristics (language in parentheses)
Finland (1950)			
Finns	3,680,000	90	Finno-Ugrian (Finnish); Protestant
Swedes	350,000	9	Nordic (Swedish); Protestant
Karelians	85,000	0.2	Finno-Ugrian (Karelian)
Lapps	3,000	—	Origin not known (Lappish)
Estonia (1940)			
Estonians (Esths)	1,134,000[b]	100	Finno-Ugrian (Estonian); Protestant
Latvia (1940)			
Latvians (Letts)	1,994,506[b]	100	Nordic (Latvian); Protestant
Lithuania (1940)			
Lithuanians	2,879,070[b]	100	Nordic (Lithuanian); Roman Catholic
Poland (1950)			
Poles[c]	25,000,000	100	Slavic (Polish); predominantly Roman Catholic, also Eastern Orthodox
Czechoslovakia (1948)			
Czechs[d]	8,100,000	65	Slavic (Czech); predominantly Roman Catholic
Slovaks	3,130,000	25	Slavic (Slovakian); Eastern Orthodox
Hungarians	450,000	4	Magyar (Hungarian); Roman Catholic
Germans	200,000	1.5	Nordic (German); Protestant
Ruthenians	115,000	1	Slavic (Ruthenian); Eastern Orthodox
Poles	85,000	0.7	See above
Hungary (1950)			
Hungarians	9,300,000	93	See above
Germans	475,000	5	See above
Slovaks	75,000	0.8	See above
Yugoslavia (1953)[e]			
Serbs	7,275,000	43	Slavic (Serbo-Croat); Eastern Orthodox
Croats	5,775,000	34	Slavic (Serbo-Croat); Roman Catholic
Slovenes	1,175,000	7	Slavic (Slovenian); Roman Catholic
Macedonians	750,000	4	Slavic (Macedonian); Eastern Orthodox
Hungarians	500,000	3	See above
Albanians	500,000	3	Dinaric (Albanian); predominantly Eastern Orthodox
Albania (1951)[f]			
Albanians	1,200,000	100	Dinaric (Albanian); about 65% Moslem, also Eastern Orthodox and Roman Catholic
Greece (1951)[f]			
Greeks[g]	7,000,000	93	Mediterranean (Greek); Eastern Orthodox
Albanians	500,000	6.5	See above
Macedonians	80,000	0.1	See above

Table 6 (continued)

MAJOR CULTURAL GROUPS IN EASTERN EUROPE[a]

Country	Approximate Number	Percentage of Total Population	Cultural Characteristics (language in parentheses)
Bulgaria (1952)			
Bulgars	6,700,000	93	Predominantly Slavic (Bulgar); Eastern Orthodox
Turks[h]	500,000	7	Altaic (Turkish); Moslem
Romania (1948)			
Romanians	13,625,000	86	Predominantly Slavic (Romanian); Eastern Orthodox
Hungarians	1,500,000	9	See above
Germans	350,000	2	See above

[a] Compare this with Table 8. Figures in the Percentage column do not necessarily total 100, because of small minority groups which may not be listed.

[b] Figures cited are pre-World War II. The number of Baltic peoples still living in these countries is not known.

[c] Since 1939 the approximately 2,500,000 Polish Jews have been killed or have left the country, and over 9,000,000 Germans have been repatriated. Border shifts and population exchanges have also removed Ruthenian, White Russian, and Lithuanian minorities.

[d] 450,000 Ruthenians, included in the Czech nation prior to 1945, were transferred with the province of Ruthenia to the Soviet Union at the end of World War II. Approximately 3,000,000 Germans and 200,000 Hungarians have been repatriated since World War II.

[e] The 500,000 Germans who once lived in the northeastern lowlands of Yugoslavia have been repatriated, as has a majority of the 4,800 Italians who lived in the Adriatic coastal areas.

[f] Albania and Greece, although not discussed in this chapter, are listed here to complete the cultural description.

[g] Approximately 350,000 Turks and 185,000 Bulgars living in Greece after World War I were repatriated.

[h] Nearly 250,000 Turks living in Bulgaria at the end of World War II were forced to emigrate to Turkey in 1950.

Sources: The Statesman's Yearbook; The Columbia Encyclopedia; H. L. Kostanick, *Macedonia: A Study in Political Geography.*

The transfers of minorities and of territories, particularly since World War II, have resulted in a greater cultural unity in most of the east European countries than existed at the end of World War I. In Poland, for example, the Poles in 1920 numbered sixty-eight per cent of the population; now they number close to one hundred per cent.

Within the complex cultural patterns of eastern Europe the factor of weakness in diversity is clearly recognizable in the struggles of small national units to remain independent and to keep their borders intact. Of the several major groups only the Poles number over 20 million, and only the Romanians and Hungarians (scattered throughout four countries) over 10 million. As a result all these states lack the population requirement for a strong power status. To secure a position of strength the countries of eastern Europe have had two alternatives: alliance with one another in a regional bloc, or the acceptance of military and economic support from Germany or the U.S.S.R.

Economic Features

Throughout most of eastern Europe agriculture still forms the dominant economic base, despite recent communist efforts to speed industrial development. Although the soil is inherently fertile and agriculture is dominant in the general economy, the average yields per acre are generally lower than in western Europe. This is the result of more backward agricultural techniques and less investment per acre in fertilizers. The average per capita income in eastern Europe is considerably lower than that in the West. The educated middle class in most countries represents a small minority of the total population. One political effect is that democracy has never gained much headway in eastern Europe. During the interwar years only Czechoslovakia and Finland were successful in maintaining democratic governments for more than a short space of time.

Since the absorption of most of eastern Europe within the Soviet bloc, the U.S.S.R. has attempted in three ways to alter the economic basis of the area: (1) by forced collectivization of farms; (2) by pushing industrialization; and (3) by orienting the economy to the Soviet Union. The presence of a large landholding class throughout much of eastern Europe, representing something of a holdover from feudalism, was a cause of peasant unrest, particularly during the late nineteenth and early twentieth centuries when new political and social ideas began to permeate the area. The communist program, with its emphasis on land redistribution, won considerable popular support among the landless farmers. In their first steps after the communization of eastern Europe the communists broke up the large estates and distributed land to the peasants, after which they worked to collectivize the peasant holdings in order to gain greater political and economic control over the farmers and to increase the total agricultural production. The peasants in varying degrees have resisted collectivization, and the total agricultural production of some parts of Soviet-controlled eastern Europe is lower than it was before 1940.

Although industrialization throughout eastern Europe has proceeded at a much faster rate since 1945 than it did prior to World War II, the area still has a long way to go before it will approach western Europe in the production of heavy industrial goods or consumer products. Czechoslovakia and the Silesian district of what has become southwestern Poland had important industrial economies even before World War II. The communists have large-scale plans for industrialization of other satellite areas as well, in order to aid the Soviet Union in its own economic and military build-up and to provide for a higher standard of living of the peoples in Soviet-controlled eastern Europe, thereby lessening the chances for popular discontent against the communist regimes. Industrialization has also advanced rapidly in Yugoslavia since the end of World War II, but here again, because of the limits of capital and of certain raw materials and the lack of an important prewar industrial base, the total output continues to be relatively small.

Finally, the orientation of eastern Europe's economy to that of the

Soviet Union has meant that the U.S.S.R. is now in a position to benefit from any exportable surpluses from the area (except from Finland and Yugoslavia, which are nonsatellite states), with a resultant strengthening of the Soviet economy (see page 250).

Political Features

The political diversity of eastern Europe is clearly shown by the existence of a large number of states, by the centrifugal forces which are present in many of the countries, and by the territorial problems which have been so characteristic of this part of Europe. The legacies of past conflicts and of former political units are much in evidence here, as they also are in other parts of the continent. Many of the boundaries correspond to historical lines, and contested areas, such as Transylvania and Southern Dobruja, have had histories of political vacillation which are equally as complex as some of the west European regions.

Forces of unity and diversity in eastern Europe have not followed the same patterns of development as in western Europe. Following World War I the area was divided into ten independent states, many of them containing two or more important ethnic groups within their borders. For two decades these states struggled with the problems of economic development and of internal cohesion; some of them also engaged in increasing their territories at the expense of their neighbors. Under such conditions united military and political action on the part of the eastern European countries was virtually impossible, and they eventually fell prey to the expanding power of Germany, Italy, and Russia. Since World War II there have been but seven national units in eastern Europe—five of them satellite states of the U.S.S.R.

The establishment of most of eastern Europe as a Soviet satellite area has, of course, greatly diminished the divisive forces existing there. There is little room in the Soviet system for the operation of centrifugal forces within satellite states, nor for boundary disputes between these countries. The complete elimination of nationalist pressures is a difficult, if not impossible, task, yet one which the Soviets, at least in their early years of control in this area, appeared determined to accomplish. One of the most significant political aspects in eastern Europe is the degree of unity on both national and international levels which can be maintained here by the U.S.S.R. The long-range effectiveness of Soviet control in eastern Europe will be measured in part by the future development of centrifugal forces within and between the states of this area.

DEVELOPMENT OF THE PRESENT POLITICAL PATTERN

The origins of the present political pattern in eastern Europe go back to the nineteenth century. The slow disintegration of the Ottoman (Turk-

Table 7

TERRITORIAL CHANGES IN EASTERN EUROPE AFTER WORLD WAR I

1. Territorial Division of the Austro-Hungarian Empire

Political Entity	Area (sq. mi.)	Per Cent	New Sovereignty
Austria	115,832	100.0	
	30,844	26.6	Austria*
	84.988	73.4	Countries listed below:
	30,670	26.5	Poland
	30,366	26.2	Czechoslovakia
	10,815†	9.3	Yugoslavia
	9,106	7.9	Italy
	4,031	3.5	Romania
Hungary (Kingdom of Hungary comprising Hungary proper, Fiume, and Croatia-Slavonia)	125,641	100.0	
	35,893	28.6	Hungary
	89,748	71.4	Countries listed below:
	39,586	31.5	Romania
	24,578	19.6	Yugoslavia
	23,801	18.9	Czechoslovakia
	1,558	1.2	Austria (Burgenland)
	220	0.2	Poland
	5	—	Italy

2. Russian Territorial Losses‡

Political Entity	Area (sq. mi.)
Finland	130,094
Estonia	17,463
Latvia	25,262
Lithuania	20,395
Poland	101,471
Bessarabia (to Romania) . . .	17,143

3. Bulgarian Territorial Losses

Political Entity	Area (sq. mi.)
Greece	2,332
Yugoslavia	888

* Austria also received Burgenland (1,558 sq. mi.) from Hungary in 1919.
† Also Bosnia-Hercegovina (19,758 sq. mi.).
‡ Russia also lost 10,128 sq. mi. to Turkey in 1918.
Source: Sophia Saucerman, *International Transfers of Territory in Europe* (Washington: U. S. Government Printing Office, 1937), pp. 6, 53, 100. Used by permission of the author.

Figure 56. Territorial Division of the Austro-Hungarian Empire After World War I. In addition, Fiume and its immediate environs passed from Hungarian to Italian control in 1924. (Based on Saucerman, *International Transfers of Territory in Europe*, U. S. Government Printing Office, 1937. Used by permission.)

ish) Empire led to the creation of new and relatively weak states in south-eastern Europe—Montenegro, Greece, Serbia, Romania, Bulgaria, and Albania—thereby forming something of a power vacuum into which major powers sought to extend their control. With the defeat of Germany, Austria-Hungary, Bulgaria, Turkey, and Russia in World War I most of the immediately-adjacent antagonists were eliminated at least temporarily from the power struggle in eastern Europe, leaving only Italy, Britain, and France, together with the nations within the area, as major contestants for control.

Between the Two World Wars

By the terms of the treaties ending World War I the political map of eastern Europe was almost completely redrawn (see Table 7). Serbia

and Montenegro disappeared as separate political entities, and the new
states of Finland, Estonia, Latvia, Lithuania, Poland, Czechoslovakia, and
Yugoslavia were created. Romania gained territory at the expense of Hungary, Austria, and Russia; and Bulgaria lost eastern Thrace to Greece as
well as some small territories to Yugoslavia (Figure 56).

During the 1920's and early 1930's, while Germany, Italy, and the
Soviet Union were absorbed in their own internal problems, the political
pattern of eastern Europe remained unchanged except for border areas in
Poland and Lithuania. During this time no one state was in a position to
embark on a program of territorial expansion against its neighbor, but
after the mid-1930's both Germany and the Soviet Union loomed as threats
to the existing political pattern in this area. By the fall of 1938 the Germans
had begun to expand their borders eastward, and eventually they were
joined in this process of aggrandizement by both the Soviets and the Italians
(Figure 57). Ultimately the countries of eastern Europe became embroiled
in World War II.

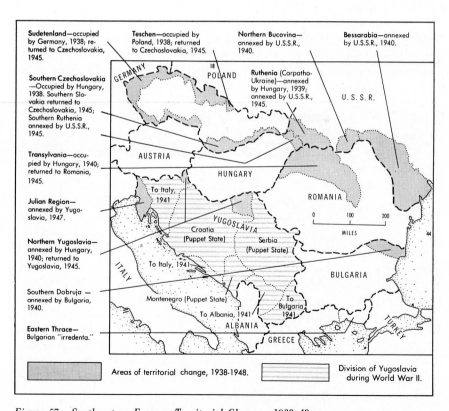

Figure 57. Southeastern Europe: Territorial Changes, 1938–48.

Since 1945

The defeat of Germany and Italy in World War II removed them as immediate contenders for power in eastern Europe. Soviet forces occupied most of the area and Soviet power became firmly established here. Estonia, Latvia, and Lithuania had been absorbed into the U.S.S.R. in 1940. After the war the Soviets annexed territory in eastern Finland, Poland, Czechoslovakia, and Romania (see Table 10). Pro-Soviet communist governments were subsequently established in Poland, Czechoslovakia, Yugoslavia,[2] Hungary, Romania, Bulgaria, and Albania. Eastern Europe was thus set up by the Soviet Union as a broad buffer area against the West. In a future world conflict this area may serve as a defense zone for the U.S.S.R., in which much of the fighting and destruction would take place rather than within Russia itself. In the absence of war this zone forms an area in which Western and Soviet territories and influence come into closest contact with one another, and as such it is a region of potential political and cultural tension.

In the sections which follow the individual states of eastern Europe will be considered in the the light of territorial developments since World War I, with particular emphasis on post-World War II problems. In this way greater insight may be gained into the complex political pattern of the region and its role as a buffer area between great powers.

POLITICAL AREAS OF EASTERN EUROPE

Finland

Finland—and also Yugoslavia—is something of an anomaly in eastern Europe, in that it was not occupied by Soviet forces during World War II and has remained outside of the Soviet satellite bloc since that time. Finland's continued independence is due in part to the stubborn character of the Finnish people, who agreed to surrender to the Russians in 1944 only on the grounds of continued national survival, and who subsequently refused to support the local Communist Party in its bid to acquire control of the national government.

The Finns, whose ancestors migrated to northeastern Europe from Asia by the eighth century, are unlike the Slavic peoples to the east and the Scandinavians to the west. With their own language and culture they are a distinct ethnic group, occupying something of a buffer position between Sweden and Russia. Prior to 1809 Finland was for many years a possession of Sweden, and from 1809 to 1919 it was joined to the Soviet Union. Following World War I Finland was one of the tier of independent states which was created along Russia's western border.

---

[2] In 1948 the Yugoslav communist government broke with the Soviets.

The Finnish nation has few resources except forests, water power, **and** fish. Climate and soil limit the land in agriculture to but seven per **cent** of the nation's total area. Population is concentrated largely along the south-ern and western coasts. Helsinki, the capital, is also the largest city. **Most** of the over 4,000,000 Finns are united by language, religion, and **national** sentiment; this strong sense of nationalism has been one of the most **impor-**tant factors contributing to Finland's continued independence since 1919. In addition to the Finns there is an important Swedish-speaking minority (totalling about nine per cent of the population), which lives along **the** west coast of Finland. Since World War I relations between Sweden **and** Finland have generally been friendly, and this minority has not posed **a** threat to Finland's national unity. The principal threat has come from **the** east, where the Soviets have twice pressed for reannexation of a part **of** the territory of their former possession.

Despite its record of political and economic development and of **neu-**trality in foreign affairs during the interwar years, Finland was invaded **by** the Soviet Union in 1939 and was defeated after a short war. As a **result**

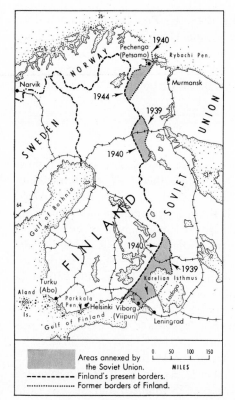

Figure 58. Finland's Territorial Losses to the Soviet Union, 1940–44. The **Pork-**kala Peninsula was returned to **Finland** in 1956. (After Van Valkenburg, "Euro-pean Jigsaw," *Headline Series* No. **53,** Foreign Policy Association, 1945. **Used** by permission.)

the Russians gained valuable territory along the Finnish border, including the Karelian Isthmus, northwest of Leningrad, within which was located Vyborg, Finland's second city (Figure 58). In an effort to regain these lands Finland joined Germany in 1941 in the attack on the U.S.S.R. Again Finland was defeated, and in 1944, after its second surrender, the nation was forced to cede additional land to the Soviets, including territory in the Petsamo area in the north which contained Finland's valuable nickel deposits (for a listing of Finnish losses in World War II see Table 10). After the two defeats 450,000 refugees from areas ceded to the U.S.S.R. fled to Finland, placing a tremendous strain on the nation's already disturbed economy. Although the communists within Finland sought to capitalize on the nation's economic and political problems and to overpower the democratic government (as they did in Czechoslovakia), the Finns resisted the pressure and thereby prevented their country from becoming a Soviet satellite state.

Since World War II Finland has maintained as neutral a position as possible with respect to the Cold War. The nation has paid off in full the heavy war reparations demanded by the Russians, but the Soviet Union remains a major trade partner and Soviet economic ties with Finland are stronger than those of the West. In 1948 the Finns were compelled to sign a treaty of mutual assistance with the U.S.S.R., providing for joint defense in the event of enemy attack on either nation. Under adverse conditions the Finns have been remarkably successful in maintaining an independent democratic nation in the northern portion of this historic east European buffer area.

The Baltic States

The three Baltic states—Estonia, Latvia, and Lithuania—had short and troubled histories of independence before they were reabsorbed into the Russian nation. Created from Russian territory at the end of World War I the Baltic states illustrate well the principle that population differences alone are not sufficient grounds for the establishment of independent units, unless (a) the territorial integrity of the new states is guaranteed by major powers and (b) sufficient attention is given to the nations' potentialities for developing a sound economic base. Estonia, Latvia, and Lithuania not only suffered from economic depression and a lack of trained personnel to carry out the tasks of government during their two decades of independence, but their strategic location between Russia and the Baltic coast was almost certain to result in reabsorption into the U.S.S.R., without an effective safeguard of independence on the part of the Western powers.

The boundaries of the Baltic states as set up in 1919 corresponded fairly closely to the cultural pattern, except in southern and western Lith-

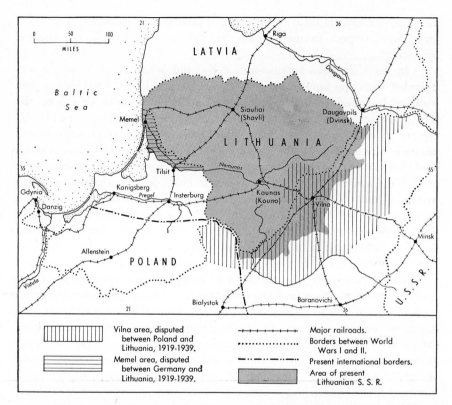

Figure 59. Lithuania: Territorial Problems Between World Wars I and II. (Details of Vilna area after Lord, *Foreign Affairs*, I (Jan., 1923). Copyright by Council on Foreign Relations.)

uania where Poles, White Russians, and Germans were included in the new nation. Some Lithuanian groups were also left within Poland. The three Baltic states were essentially agricultural, although before 1914 the Latvian port of Riga had been an important outlet for Russian foreign trade and there was some industrial development here and in the Estonian city of Tallinn. German landowners played major roles in the economies of the Baltic states, particularly in Latvia and Estonia; and even after Germany's surrender to the Allies in 1918 these persons continued as important groups in the newly created nations.

Vilna and Memelland. At the end of World War I the new country of Lithuania found itself involved in territorial controversies over the city of Vilna (Vilnyus) along the frontier with Poland and over Memelland on the Baltic coast (Figure 59). These disputes are of politico-geographic interest, since they illustrate both the difficulties involved in delimiting a mutually satisfactory boundary in a complex ethnic area, and the fact that an unarmed international organization is powerless to enforce its authority, even with respect to small states, in the face of determined national resistance.

In the Vilna area Lithuanians, Poles, and White Russians were intermingled with one another, and it was impossible in 1919 to draw a true cultural boundary separating them. During the process of delimiting the Polish-Lithuanian boundary both nations claimed the Vilna territory (11,500 square miles in area), the Poles on the basis of population composition[3] and the Lithuanians on the grounds that Vilna was their historic capital and their largest and most beautiful city. After four years of bitter debate and of military campaigns in the area, the Poles, whose military power was stronger than that of the Lithuanians, officially incorporated the Vilna territory into the Polish state. In the face of Polish resistance the League of Nations was unable to carry out a plebiscite or even to effect a mediation between Poland and Lithuania, and all relations between the two neighboring states were completely suspended for many years.

The dispute over Memelland, a 1,026-square-mile area on the Baltic coast north of the Nemunas (Neman) River, involved primarily Lithuania and Germany. Of the 150,000 inhabitants of Memelland about 25,000 were Germans, the rest Lithuanians. By the Treaty of Versailles Germany ceded Memelland to "the Principal Allied and Associated Powers," and while the Vilna controversy was raging the transfer of Memelland to Lithuania was delayed by the League of Nations. Finally, in January, 1923, when Poland annexed Vilna, Lithuania, in defiance of the League, occupied Memelland and declared the area to be a part of the Lithuanian state.

By their refusal to co-operate in settling territorial disputes nations often place themselves in positions in which united military and political action become impossible. The resultant weakening of their resistance to potential aggressors often means that in time these border disputes become academic. In 1939 Memelland was forcibly annexed to Nazi Germany; six years later both Memelland and Vilna were incorporated into what had become the Lithuanian S.S.R. of the Soviet Union.

The Collapse of the Baltic States. The strategic position of the three Baltic countries in relation to Soviet defense became increasingly important with the growth of German power under Hitler. In the fall of 1939 the Soviet Union demanded that the Baltic states change the composition of their governments and make them friendly to the U.S.S.R. The Soviets also insisted that Russian air and naval bases be established within the borders of the Baltic states as defense against possible German attack. Later, as a result of Russian pressure, the nearly 140,000 German-speaking inhabitants

---

[3] Of a total population of 1,600,000 in the Vilna area the Polish census of 1919 (which in detail is open to question) listed fifty-four per cent of the inhabitants as Poles, twenty-one per cent as White Russians, eight per cent as Jews, and seven per cent as Lithuanians.

of the Baltic states were repatriated to Germany, thus ending over five centuries of German influence in that area. The three nations were unable to resist Soviet demands, and pro-Soviet governments were installed. In July, 1940, Estonia, Latvia, and Lithuania were officially incorporated as republics within the Soviet Union. In an effort to destroy any semblance of nationalism, the Russian government reportedly uprooted a large proportion of the Baltic peoples from their homes and resettled them deep within the Soviet Union.

Poland

The problems of maintaining the political independence of an ethnic group located between powerful neighbors are well illustrated by the tragic history of Poland. To the north of the area originally inhabited by Poles is the Baltic Sea, along which large German concentrations existed until 1944. To the south are the Carpathians, which form both a physical and cultural boundary. The plains of Poland merge into Germany in the west and into Russia in the east (although the Pripet Marshes offer something of a "natural" border in White Russia). This lack of physiographic obstacles not only hinders defense and boundary delimitation, but also influences settlement patterns. In the west Germans and in the east Ruthenians, White Russians, and Lithuanians were intermixed with Poles in complex settlement patterns along the borders of the major bloc of Polish-speaking peoples (Figure 60).

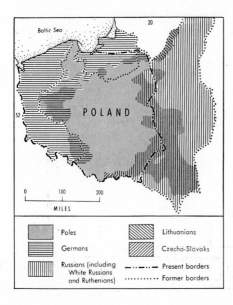

Figure 60. Ethnic Patterns in Poland After World War I. Map based on 1918 figures. (Adapted from Bowman, *The New World*, World Book Co., 1928. Used by permission.)

Territorial Problems of the Polish State. When Poland was formed at the end of World War I from Russian, German, and Austrian territory two principal factors were taken into consideration: (1) the nation should include areas inhabited by Polish populations, and (2) it should have access to the Baltic Sea. In its northern and central sections the Polish-German border followed the linguistic boundary fairly closely. In the southwest territorial control in Upper Silesia was eventually settled by plebiscite (see page 199), with Poland receiving most of the coal, lead, and zinc resources. The final delimitation of Poland's western border left over 900,000 Germans in Polish territory and nearly 600,000 Poles within Germany (see Table 8).

Table 8

TERRITORIAL AND POPULATION STRUCTURE OF POLAND, CZECHOSLOVAKIA, AND YUGOSLAVIA FOLLOWING WORLD WAR I

Poland (1921 population, 27,000,000)

Area (sq. mi.)	Per Cent	Former Sovereignty	Ethnic Group	Percentage Breakdown into Ethnic Groups
149,958	100.0		Poles	68.0
101,223	67.5	Russia	Ruthenians	14.0
30,723	20.5	Austria	Jews	10.0
17,809	11.9	Germany	Germans	3.5
203	.1	Hungary	White Russians	3.5
			Others (incl. Lithu- anians)	1.0

Czechoslovakia (1921 population, 14,000,000)

Area (sq. mi.)	Per Cent	Former Sovereignty	Ethnic Group	Percentage Breakdown into Ethnic Groups
54,206	100.0		Czechs	50.0
30,304	55.9	Austria	Slovaks	16.0
23,781	43.9	Hungary	Ruthenians	4.0
121	.2	Germany	Germans	23.0
			Magyars	5.0
			Others	2.0

Yugoslavia (1921 population, 12,000,000)

Area (sq. mi.)	Per Cent	Former Sovereignty	Ethnic Group	Percentage Breakdown into Ethnic Groups
95,576	100.0		Serbs	50.0
30,573	32.0	Austria	Croats	22.0
24,578	25.7	Hungary	Slovenes	9.0
888	.9	Bulgaria	Macedonians	4.0
34,194	35.8	Serbia	Magyars	4.0
5,343	5.6	Montenegro	Germans	4.0
			Albanians	3.5
			Others	3.5

Statistics on territorial structure from Sophia Saucerman, *International Transfers of Territories in Europe* (Washington: U.S. Government Printing Office, 1937). Used by permission of the author. Statistics on population from *Statesman's Yearbook.*
See Table 6 for post-World War II population figures.

The problem of Poland's access to the sea was complicated by the presence of a large German population along the Baltic. East Prussia was awarded to Germany in 1919; the German-inhabited port of Danzig and its immediate hinterland was made a Free City, under administration of the League of Nations; and a Polish Corridor, averaging twelve to fifteen miles in width, was created between Germany and the Danzig-East Prussian border. (See page 198 for a further discussion of this area.)

The delimitation of Poland's eastern boundaries was as great a complication as the delimitation of those in the west. In the face of population patterns, natural resources, and strategic demands, historical boundaries which had existed a century and a half before had little significance in determining new political borders. At the Paris Peace Conference a British expert, Lord Curzon, was called upon to aid in fixing the new Polish-Russian border. The resulting "Curzon Line" was drawn to conform as closely as possible with the distribution of Poles and Russians. In the spring of 1920 the Poles, dissatisfied with the Curzon arrangements, invaded western Russia. After considerable vacillation of military lines, the Polish-Russian boundary was fixed by the Treaty of Riga (1921) somewhat east of the Curzon Line, and over 4,750,000 White Russians and Ruthenians were included in the new Polish state.

The difficulty over Vilna has already been discussed. A final territorial problem involved the new Polish-Czech border in the former duchy of Teschen, where a small disputed area proved to be a source of considerable friction between the neighboring states. The Teschen district, with an area of 853 square miles, contained coal deposits and industrial facilities and was an important rail center as well (Figure 61). Both Poland and Czechoslovakia claimed it, but eventually it was divided, Czechoslovakia obtaining the coal and the railroads and Poland most of the city of Teschen and a majority of the industrial facilities. Spis and Orava, two small areas to the east of Teschen, were also divided. Approximately 80,000 Poles were included within Czech territory, and during the Munich crisis of 1938 Poland capitalized on Czech weakness and occupied all of the Teschen area. The international repercussions of the Teschen dispute were more important than the area itself, for they contributed to the general disunity of the east European area at a time when united action might have preserved the independence of the various states.

With conditions of disputed control along practically all its borders the new nation of Poland represented a complex politico-geographic area, whose independence had been achieved mainly as a result of the collapse of both its powerful neighbors, Germany and Russia. Lacking effective support from other major powers, Poland's independence was jeopardized as soon as these two nations regained power. With its population of 27 million, its coal, lead, zinc, petroleum, timber, and agricultural land, and its grow-

Figure 61. The Teschen Area. (After Bowman, *The New World*, World Book Co., 1928. Used by permission.)

ing industrial strength, Poland struggled to become a strong national unit between 1920 and 1939. Centripetal forces within the nation were strong. Warsaw, the capital and leading city, was located near the geographic center of the state, and communication was easy between it and other core areas, such as the Vilna region to the northeast, Poznan to the west, and the Krakow and Silesian districts in the southwest. Despite differing histories of past political allegiance, the Polish majority was bound together by ties of national sentiment, as well as by language and religion. The nation, however, was plagued by large minorities and by the growing pressures from Germany and the Soviet Union to recover their lost territories.

The Destruction of Polish Independence. In September, 1939, western Poland was invaded and conquered by the Germans, eastern Poland was occupied by the Russians, and the nation was divided between the two states. In June, 1941, German armies swept eastward across Russian-held Poland in the opening of the invasion of the U.S.S.R.; three years later the Russians were driving them back across the Polish plains. The collapse of Germany in May, 1945, and the occupation of both eastern Germany and Poland by Soviet troops ended any hopes the Poles might have had for a revival of independence after the war.

Efforts by the United States and Britain after World War II to re-establish the prewar Polish republic were frustrated by the Soviets, who installed a communist administration in Warsaw, so that by 1946 Poland had become a full-fledged Soviet satellite state. At the Yalta Conference (February, 1945) the Russians claimed the Curzon Line as a basis for the Polish-Russian border. Since the Western powers had accepted this line in 1919 as one dividing Russians and Poles, they were in no position to oppose Soviet demands a quarter century later. To the Soviet Union Poland ceded nearly 69,000 square miles and a population of about 11 million, including over 5 million Ruthenians and White Russians and 4 million Poles. The Poles, however, were eventually repatriated to Poland. With the ceding of this eastern territory Poland lost some of its best agricultural and forest land, as well as most of its oil reserves, to the Russians.[4]

Other Polish border lands were also affected by postwar changes. German East Prussia was divided between Poland and the Soviet Union, the Russians gaining the port of Königsberg (renamed Kaliningrad). The Polish-German boundary was moved westward from the 1939 location to the Oder and Neisse rivers. By this move Poland gained 44,215 square miles of territory, including the German portion of the Upper Silesian industrial area, the port of Stettin, the Free City of Danzig, as well as considerable agricultural land. Over 9 million Germans living in the areas which became Polish were forced to leave their homes and to become refugees in Germany itself. Finally, Poland was forced to return southern Teschen to Czechoslovakia. As a result of these territorial changes, Poland's area of 120,359 square miles was but 80 per cent of the country's size prior to World War II.

The establishment of the Soviet satellite system in eastern Europe has at least temporarily ended Poland's boundary problems, for the state's territorial integrity is backed by the power of the U.S.S.R. Likewise, the mass exchange of upwards of 13 million persons has resulted in the creation of ethnic unity in Poland and the removal of minorities from within its borders, a step which would seem to eliminate further friction. German reluctance to accept the Oder-Neisse line as the eastern border with Poland is the greatest potential threat to the present Polish political area. If Germany regains its normal power position in central Europe this boundary will undoubtedly be challenged. Despite this threat, however, the Poles violently expressed their resentment against Soviet rule in 1956, and succeeded in winning some measure of freedom from Moscow's direct control.

Czechoslovakia

The Czech state presents an outstanding example of centrifugal forces operating within a national unit. At the time of its establishment in 1919

---

[4] In 1951 Poland and Russia exchanged territories, amounting to about 260 square miles, in the southern portion of their common border. This gave Russia control of territory containing a link in the Lvov (Lemberg)–Kovel railroad in the area east of Lublin, while Poland received an oil and natural gas area southeast of Przemysl.

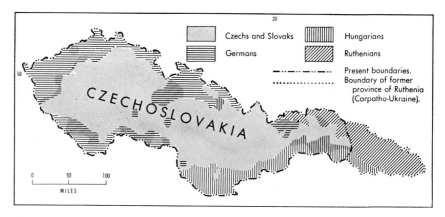

Figure 62. Ethnic Patterns in Czechoslovakia After World War I. Map based on 1918 figures. (Adapted from Bowman, *The New World*, World Book Co., 1928. Used by permission.)

on territory of the former Austro-Hungarian Empire, Czechoslovakia was a long, narrow country in which the obstacles of distance and surface configuration prevented easy communication between the three major Slavic groups—Czechs, Slovaks, and Ruthenians. The Czechs were concentrated in the Bohemian basin, the Slovaks were settled largely in the Morava valley, while the Ruthenians were in the Carpathian uplands and in the valleys which opened southward to Hungary (Figure 62). Each of these groups had its own language and religion, and feelings of national unity were not sufficiently developed to act as a strong unifying force among them. The national capital was at Prague, the former Bohemian capital and center of Czechoslovakia's principal core area. Prague's disadvantage as a capital city, however, lay in its location in the western part of the state. With a poorly-developed circulatory system Czechoslovakia had many divisive forces operating within its borders.

The formation of the Czech nation, like that of other east European states in 1919, was based theoretically on the principle of self-determination for ethnic groups. Economic and military factors, however, also figured prominently in the determination of the Czech borders: as a result Slovaks and Ruthenians were included with the Czech majority rather than being given their own independent states, and several foreign minorities were also incorporated within the territory of Czechoslovakia. At the time of the nation's establishment about thirty per cent of the population consisted of foreign minorities—principally Germans, Magyars, and Poles (Table 8).

Despite the limitations of the population structure, of shape, and of poor communications, Czechoslovakia remained a democracy with a comparatively high standard of living during its interwar independence. Developing its resources of coal, iron ore, timber, and agricultural land, as well as its skilled labor force, it became the leading industrial nation of eastern Europe, specializing in iron and steel, shoes, glass, and beer. The Czech government was careful to avoid discrimination against its foreign minorities. However, the country lay in the path of German expansion, and in the late 1930's, despite its record of internal achievements, Czechoslovakia was eventually destroyed because of its minority problems and the lack of military support from the Western powers in the face of German pressure.

The Gradual Destruction of Czech Independence. Early in 1938 Nazi Germany in its drive for territorial conquests began to foment discontent among the more than 3 million Sudeten Germans living in Czechoslovakia, descendants of settlers who migrated to the area during and after the thirteenth century. Although these people had been well treated by the Czech government, propaganda was built up around the "repressions" they were supposedly undergoing, and the German government sought to "liberate" the oppressed minority by annexation of the territory they inhabited. The Czechs prepared to resist the Germans by force if necessary, and looked for support to France and Britain, their powerful allies. But at Munich in September, 1938, the French and British agreed to Germany's territorial demands on Czechoslovakia in exchange for a promise by Hitler of "peace in our time." The shattered Czechs not only saw Germany annex the Bohemian rimland; but they were also forced to cede the southern rim of Slovakia to Hungary and southern Teschen to Poland on the grounds of the ethnic composition of these areas. Six months later the remainder of Bohemia and Slovakia were occupied by the Nazis without the formality of explanation, while Ruthenia was seized by Hungary.

The dismemberment of Czechoslovakia in 1938–39 illustrates what may be termed the "jackal" principle of territorial aggrandizement—that is, if a nation proves itself unable to resist territorial encroachment it may become the victim of territorial losses to several of its neighbors. This process sometimes occurs after a nation has suffered defeat (for example, China after the Opium War in 1842, Russia after World War I, and Yugoslavia in World War II), or, as with Czechoslovakia and Romania, it may take place in time of peace.

At the end of World War II, Czechoslovakia was occupied by Soviet troops. Germany, Hungary, and Poland returned the areas they had seized, but the Russians demanded and received the eastern province of Ruthenia (4,921 square miles) on the grounds that the Ruthenians were in reality Ukrainians and should be under Soviet control (Figure 57). In another territorial change, Czechoslovakia received from Hungary 30 square miles of territory on the south bank of the Danube opposite Bratislava for an industrial expansion of this city. At that time the Czechs had not forgotten the prewar annexations by Germany, Hungary, and Poland, nor the "sell-out" at Munich by France and Britain, and despite the loss of Ruthenia to the Soviets relations with Russia were friendly in the early postwar years. The Communist Party in Czechoslovakia was the nation's largest, having polled thirty-eight per cent of the votes in the 1946 national elections. In February, 1948, the Communists effected a complete *coup d'état,* ousted the democratic government, and made Czechoslovakia a satellite state of the U.S.S.R.

Hungary

The people of Hungary never became reconciled after World War I to the territorial losses which their country had suffered. They therefore seized the opportunity offered by Hitler during the 1930's to extend their borders at the expense of their neighbors, thereby compounding the international tensions existing among the eastern European states prior to World War II. The aggressive attitude of the Hungarians proved to be a decided asset to Nazi Germany in its drive for power in southeastern Europe in the years preceding World War II.

The Hungarians are a non-Slavic ethnic group, which since the ninth century has occupied the center of the fertile Danube plain. Before World War I Hungary was joined politically with Austria, but following the war the Austro-Hungarian Empire was broken up and the size of the Hungarian portion reduced by over seventy per cent. To its neighbors Hungary lost its best agricultural land, its mines, and most of its timber, as well as control over the upper courses of the rivers which cross the Hungarian lowlands. The new frontiers cut rail and highway lines; and in the absence of international action joint projects for irrigation, power, and flood control in the Danube basin became impossible. The economic unity of the area was completely destroyed. Besides its agricultural land the postwar Hungarian nation had few resources left to it except bauxite, a small amount of oil, and salt. Cut off from Austria, its economic partner, Hungary found itself stripped of Ruthenia, Slovakia, Transylvania, and those areas which became part of northeastern Yugoslavia. The final delimitation of the nation's borders in 1920 resulted in the separation of over 2,500,000 Hungarians (or Magyars, as they are sometimes called) from Hungary itself (Figure 63).

The much-reduced Hungarian state was a closely-knit political unit, in which most of the people were united by language, religion, and national sentiment. Several hundred thousand Germans formed the only important minority group. Upland areas did not interfere with the transportation systems throughout the country. Budapest, the capital and leading city, was unrivalled in political and economic power by any other region. With its

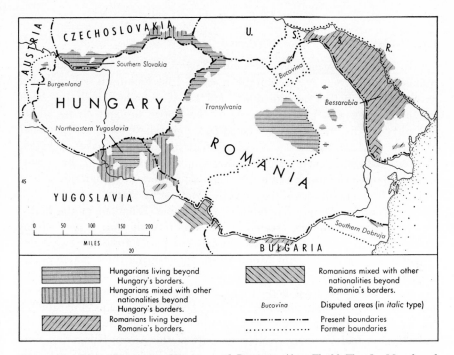

Figure 63. Ethnic Patterns in Hungary and Romania After World War I. Map based on 1918 figures. (Adapted from Bowman, *The New World*, World Book Co., 1928. Used by permission.)

strong internal unity Hungary waited for the day of retribution when it could reannex its lost borderlands.

In 1938 the Hungarians shared in the dismemberment of Czechoslovakia, reannexing about 750,00 Magyars in this move. In the following year Ruthenia was occupied, and in 1940 the Germans forced Romania to return northern Transylvania with its Magyar and German minorities to Hungary. For their help in the conquest of Yugoslavia, the Hungarians in 1941 received two sectors in the northeastern plains region of that country.

In the closing months of World War II Hungary was overrun by Soviet forces, and a Moscow-oriented Communist Party gradually assumed control of the country. The areas which Hungary had seized from its neighbors were returned to their former owners, and by 1946 Hungary had become firmly welded to the Soviet satellite bloc. Many Hungarians, however, continued to remain outside the national borders, thus presenting the possibility of future Hungarian expansionist drives. The uprisings of 1956 clearly demonstrated the powerful forces of opposition to Soviet control in this non-Slavic country.

Yugoslavia

In its politico-geographic structure Yugoslavia has certain aspects in common with two other east European states. Like Finland it has remained outside of the Soviet satellite orbit, and like Czechoslovakia it has been troubled in the past by complex centrifugal forces brought on by ethnic and physical diversities. These centrifugal forces have been compounded primarily of four factors: (1) diversity in language, alphabet, religion, and national sentiments; (2) difficult communications due to the mountainous character of much of the country; (3) important foreign minorities; and (4) frequent border disputes with neighboring states.

The Yugoslav State. Yugoslavia—the former Kingdom of the Serbs, Croats, and Slovenes—was created at the end of World War I, partly from territory of the Austro-Hungarian Empire and partly from the two independent states of Serbia and Montenegro. In 1919 the three major Slavic groups—Serbs, Croats, and Slovenes—together accounted for about eighty-one per cent of the total population. There were differences not only of language, religion, and alphabet among these three groups, but also of historical development. Before the formation of the Yugoslav state Croatia and Slovenia had for many years been part of the Austro-Hungarian Empire, while Serbia had been under the rule of the Turks from the fourteenth to the early nineteenth centuries and then independent. Education and technical training among the Croats and Slovenes had been more highly developed than in Serbia, thus contributing to the mutual antagonism between the numerically superior Serbs on the one hand and the Croats and Slovenes on the other.

The delimitation of the Yugoslav borders in 1919 resulted in controversies with Italy, particularly in the Trieste and Fiume areas (see page 175), and with Austria (see page 211). In both instances Yugoslavia failed to get the territory it desired. In the northeast the final borders with Hungary and Romania were drawn so as to include 450,000 Hungarians, 500,-000 Germans, and 200,000 Romanians in the new nation. In the south over 500,000 Macedonians and more than 400,000 Albanians, together with Turks and Bulgars, came under Yugoslav sovereignty (Table 8).

Yugoslavia consists of five major regions—the northeastern plain (a part of the Danube lowlands), the Vardar-Morava valley, leading southward to the Aegean, the central (Dinaric) upland, the Adriatic coast, and the mountain and hill areas of the north. The northeastern plain is inhabited largely by Serbs, together with Hungarian and Romanian minority groups. Here is located Belgrade, the national capital and center of the nation's principal core area. Serbs also occupy the northern portion of the Vardar-Morava valley, while in the southern part of this lowland are the

Macedonians, another Slavic group with their own language and culture (see page 252). In the central uplands are Croats, a third Slavic group, whose language is the same as that of the Serbs, but whose alphabet and religion differ. The Serbs are Greek Orthodox, while the Croats are Roman Catholic. Finally, in the northern part of Yugoslavia are the Slovenes, also Slavic and Roman Catholic, with the same alphabet as the Croats, but with their own distinctive language. Albanians live in the southern part of the central uplands, and there is a small Turkish minority in the southeast. Italians, Germans, and Jews, who once formed additional minorities in Yugoslavia, have largely disappeared since World War II.

Economic and strategic considerations were important in the formation of the Yugoslav state, as they were in the creation of Czechoslovakia. Yugoslavia is well supplied with mineral resources—chromite, bauxite, copper, mercury, and iron ore—although most of these have yet been only partly utilized. About one-third of Yugoslavia's petroleum requirements is met by local production. The nation also has low-grade coal and abundant water-power potential. At the time of Yugoslavia's formation its economy was still at a low stage of development and transportation facilities were poor. Only since World War II has there been a marked development of the nation's mineral resources, improvement of land utilization techniques, and appreciable expansion of industrial activities. With its 98,766 square miles of territory, its population of over 17,000,000 persons, and its varied resource base, Yugoslavia may in time become one of the economically strong nations of eastern Europe.

Yugoslavia's Development as a Nation. From 1919 to 1941 Yugoslavia struggled to develop internal unity and to strengthen its economy. The ruggedness of the terrain, the lack of contact with the Adriatic because of mountains and poor transportation facilities, the general backwardness of the economy, and finally the political upheavals within the government itself all combined to prevent Yugoslavia from developing into a strong national unit during the interwar years. The Croats desired a federal political structure in order to prevent political domination by the Serbs who comprised over forty per cent of the national population, but the Serbian concept of a centralized administration formed the basis for the nation's government. There were movements for an independent Croatian republic, but no permanent political unit developed, and in spite of continued rivalries between the various groups, Yugoslavia remained a nation intact until June, 1941, when it was invaded and conquered by Germany and its allies. Following its defeat Yugoslavia disappeared as a separate entity, its several parts apportioned out among Germany, Italy, Hungary, Bulgaria, and Albania as direct territorial annexations or as puppet states (Figure 57).

In 1945 Yugoslavia regained its prewar political shape. Eventually about 3,050 square miles of former Italian territory was incorporated into the nation. Postwar Yugoslavia was set up as a federation of six autonomous units—Serbia, Croatia, Slovenia, Bosnia-Hercegovina, Macedonia, and Montenegro—but political control still remained firmly centered within the national communist government. The emphasis on national unity rather than on regional differences is a potent force working to overcome the various divisive pressures which existed in Yugoslavia from 1919 to World War II. Although the nation was originally within the Soviet orbit, Tito broke with Moscow in June, 1948, and the Yugoslav government, while still communist in form, has since maintained its own independence.

Yugoslav resistance to the U.S.S.R. is compounded of various factors. Unlike Hungary, Romania, and Bulgaria, Yugoslavia does not occupy an exposed position, while diversity of relief has fostered relatively isolated, closely-knit cultural groups, whose spirit of resistance to foreign control is strongly developed. Yugoslavia had its own national army in the closing months of World War II and the country was not occupied by Soviet forces. Moreover, its continued independence from Soviet control was partly due to the determined leadership of Marshal Tito. Yugoslavia stands out as a symbol of resistance to Soviet imperialism in that it is the only nation of eastern Europe which, after having passed under the control of the Moscow communist government, has completely regained its independence.

Bulgaria

Bulgaria, like Hungary, is a nation which has suffered territorial losses and which has anxiously awaited the time when it could recover its former lands. Most of the boundary problems in southeastern Europe during the twentieth century have been associated directly or indirectly with Bulgarian territorial aspirations.

The original Bulgars migrated to the area from Asia in the seventh century A.D., but with repeated incursions by other groups they came to lose much of their original identity. The modern Bulgar language is a Slavic tongue, and modern Bulgarians are often considered to be Slavs.

The inhabitants of Bulgaria form a fairly compact ethnic group, united by language and religion. The principal minorities are in the northeast, where there are Turks and some Romanians. Although there are some agricultural plains, particularly in the central portion of the country, much of Bulgaria is composed of low, forested mountains trending in an east-west direction. The country lacks industrial resources, and the level of its agricultural production is low when compared with that of areas in western and central Europe. In per capita income Bulgaria ranks among the lowest of any of the states of the continent. The mountains have not only influenced settlement patterns in Bulgaria, but have also made communications between the various parts of the country more difficult than is the case in

Hungary or Poland. The capital and leading city, Sofia, lies in a basin in the western portion of the mountains. The political effects of this physical diversity and off-center location of the capital have, however, been more than offset by the strong feelings of national unity among the Bulgars.

The Bulgarian people were under the control of the Turks from the fifteenth century until 1878, when the northern part of the nation became independent. In the following thirty-five years the present central and southern sections were also acquired by the Bulgar nation. During World War I Bulgaria fought on the losing side, for which it was forced subsequently to yield territory to its neighbors. By the Treaty of Neuilly (1919) Bulgaria lost some small areas along its western border to Yugoslavia, but more important, it was forced to cede eastern Thrace to Greece, thereby cutting off Bulgaria's access to the Aegean Sea. Although the Bulgars were later offered the port of Dedeagach (Alexandroupolis) on the Aegean as a free port, they declined to accept the gesture.

When the memory of military defeat dies and national pride is rekindled, nations often strive to regain political prestige by agitating for the return of lost territory. Bulgaria was no exception. Bulgarian terrorists operated in Yugoslav and Greek Macedonia during the interwar years (see page 252), and in 1940 Bulgaria became a willing ally of Nazi Germany, hoping thereby to regain its national prestige. However, the territories it acquired in 1941 at the expense of Yugoslavia and Greece were returned to those states at the end of the war. On the other hand, Southern Dobruja, an area bordering the Black Sea which was taken from Romania during World War II, remained with Bulgaria after 1945. The region is peopled largely by Bulgars and Turks, and has been a scene of disputed sovereignty since before World War I.

Although Bulgaria did not declare war on Russia, it was occupied by Soviet forces in 1944 as the German armies were forced westward. Within two years a Soviet puppet government was established and Bulgaria passed within the Soviet sphere. Control of Bulgaria puts Russian forces within less than twenty miles of the Aegean coast and about eighty-five miles of the Turkish Straits.

The Evacuation of Turks from Bulgaria. A potent communist weapon against noncommunist countries is the expulsion of thousands of minority peoples from communist states, thereby placing a tremendous strain on the economy of the noncommunist areas which must receive them. These refugees are generally compelled to leave behind practically all of their possessions, to which the communist state then falls heir. In 1950, 250,000 Turks, or about one-third of the total Turkish population in Bulgaria, were ordered from the country by the Bulgarian government. These people were transported to the Turkish border and Turkey was forced to accept the refugees, many of whom had few ties with modern Turkey except those of language and religion, and to provide food, shelter, and eventually employment for them. In time the other half million Turks in Bulgaria may also be expelled.

The forced evacuation of minorities can under certain conditions stabilize international borders and remove troublesome elements, as in the Czech Sudetenland. Such mass evacuations, if they are to be carried out in an orderly and humane fashion, require careful planning between the sending and receiving nations, and provisions for compensation to the evacuated groups. The use of a quarter-million destitute refugees as a political weapon indicates the extremes to which the Soviet Union and its satellites will go in order to burden nations outside the Soviet bloc.

Romania

Romania, like Poland, is located between militant neighbors—in this case the Soviet Union and Hungary—and its various borders have vacillated back and forth with the political fortunes of these states. Like Poland, it has also looked to the nations of western Europe for support in its efforts to maintain its territorial integrity; at times, however, this support has been ineffective and Romania has suffered important losses.

Among the original settlers of Romania were Roman colonists, and the Romanian language is a Romance tongue. As in Bulgaria, the constant flow of diverse groups through the area has profoundly altered the characteristics of the inhabitants, so that the present Romanian is a mixture of many ethnic strains. Romania passed under Turkish rule in the sixteenth century; not until 1866 did the nation gain complete independence.

Romania is cut by the Carpathian mountain chain which trends northwest-southeast through two-thirds of the country, then swings west as the Transylvanian Alps. East of the mountains is the plateau of Moldavia, and to the south is the Wallachian lowland. These two areas, inhabited largely by Romanians, form the core area of the nation. Bucharest, the capital and largest city, is located in the Wallachian lowland.

To the east of Wallachia is Bessarabia, with its Romanian, Russian, Bulgarian, and Turkish population. To the northeast is Bucovina, an area of mixed Romanian-Ruthenian-German population, which adjoins Bessarabia and controls the eastern approaches to a portion of the Carpathians. To the west is the basin of Transylvania, long the scene of disputed sovereignty between Romania and Hungary. In this basin are approximately 2,800,000 Romanians, 1,500,000 Hungarians, 500,000 Germans, and 300,000 others. Finally, in the southeast, control of Southern Dobruja has frequently been contested by Romania and Bulgaria. Thus both terrain and ethnic differences represent powerful centrifugal forces in Romania (Figure 63).

Territorial Changes Since World War I. At the end of World War I Romania, which had sided with the Allies in the conflict, found itself in possession of all four of its border areas—Bessarabia, Bucovina, Transylvania, and Southern Dobruja. With an area of 122,000 square miles and a population of over 12,000,000, Romania was the largest nation in southeastern Europe. Within its borders were valuable resources, including oil, gas, timber, and fertile soils. The development of these resources, however, was not far advanced except for petroleum, and the standard of living here was low.

With the rise of Russian and German power in the 1930's Romania's boundaries were threatened. In June, 1940, the Soviet Union demanded and received Bessarabia and northern Bucovina from Romania. The primary cause of these demands was the Soviet desire to establish a defense zone against Germany. Even though Bucovina had never been a part of Russia, the population of the northern part was largely Ruthenian rather than Romanian, and the area represented a connecting link between Bessarabia and Russian-controlled eastern Poland. Two months later northern Transylvania was returned to Hungary at Germany's insistence. Hungary was by now a German ally, and this territorial move foreshadowed the expansion of German power into southeastern Europe. Similarly, the Bulgarian annexation of Southern Dobruja in September, 1940, was a further German-inspired move, for Bulgaria was also a German military ally. Thus Romania, in its buffer position, became the victim of great-power rivalries. The nation was forced to co-operate with the Axis powers in the war on Russia, and in 1944 Romania was occupied by the Red Army.

The post-World War II history of Romania is similar to that of most of the other east European states. Two years after its occupation by the Soviets it became a satellite state of the U.S.S.R. Transylvania had been returned by the Hungarians to Romania at the end of World War II, but Southern Dobruja, Bessarabia, and northern Bucovina—all of them annexed in 1940—were not reunited with Romania. The power of Britain, France, and other Western countries after World War II was unable to restore Romania's territorial losses or to prevent its incorporation within the satellite system.

CONTRIBUTIONS OF THE SATELLITE STATES TO THE U.S.S.R.

The contributions to the Soviet Union of the seven European satellite states[5]—Albania, Bulgaria, Czechoslovakia, East Germany, Hungary, Poland, and Romania—can be considered under the following headings: strategic location, population, natural resources, agricultural and industrial production, armaments and armed forces. Since these states exist in a dependent status to the U.S.S.R., they are in a position to assist the Soviet Union in any extension of its present economic, military, and political power.

---

[5] Because of their close economic and political associations with the other satellites, Albania and East Germany, although technically not in eastern Europe as defined here, are included in this section.

Strategic Location. The combined area of the satellite countries is 393,000 square miles. This area provides defense in depth along Russia's western borders (the "gateway" to the Heartland). With the exception of northern Norway and northeastern Turkey, NATO territory is now removed from the Soviet Union by a wide "buffer zone" through which Soviet forces could fall back in the face of enemy pressure. Soviet military power is in a strong position with regard to the southern shore of the Baltic, to Denmark and West Germany, Austria, Yugoslavia, and Greece. The Russians control the eastern shore of the Strait of Otranto, and thus pose a threat to Allied activities in the Adriatic and central Mediterranean. Russian forces are also close to the Aegean (through Thrace) and to the Turkish Straits.

Population. The population of the Soviet satellite area is over 90,-000,000, providing reserves for both labor and armed forces—assuming, of course, that centripetal pressures within the area remain strong. Some of these people are miners or industrial workers with specialized training and technical skills, engineers or scientists, but the great majority are farmers. When added to that of the Soviet Union this satellite population increases the total for the Soviet bloc to close to 300,000,000.

Natural Resources. In addition to good agricultural lands, the satellite states have other valuable resources, including oil (Romania, Hungary), coal (Poland, Czechoslovakia), bauxite (Hungary), uranium (Czechoslovakia), and iron ore (Czechoslovakia, Poland). The large areas of fertile agricultural land probably represent the satellite area's greatest natural resource. Czechoslovakia's uranium may be of great value to the U.S.S.R., for the major efforts which the communists have made to develop the Czech deposits would imply that within the Soviet Union uranium is in short supply.

Agricultural and Industrial Production. The Soviet satellite area has long been noted as an important agricultural region. Prior to World War II important exports included wheat, corn, and meat. Theoretically, these surpluses could go now to the Soviet Union, where food production is falling behind the needs of the growing population, but actually agricultural production in some of the satellite states since 1945 has been insufficient to do much more than meet domestic demands.

The satellite countries contain two important industrial areas, Polish Silesia and western Czechoslovakia, although the communists are working to increase the industrial output in other areas as well. Steel production from the satellite states amounted to over 13 million tons in 1955. Other important manufactures include chemicals, machinery, textiles, armaments, and electro-technical supplies. These manufactures are used to strengthen the economies of the eastern European countries as well as that of the Soviet Union.

Armaments and Armed Forces.   Among the industrial resources now available to the U.S.S.R. are the armament plants of the satellite states, including the famous Skoda works of Czechoslovakia, once the foremost armament producer of the Austro-Hungarian Empire. These armament plants are now operating at capacity in order to equip the armies of the satellite countries. It is estimated that there are over one million men in the combined armies of the satellites. Some military experts question the effectiveness of these troops in an offensive war, but agree that they would fight in defense of their homelands and with the Soviet Union, if they were convinced that by so doing they could profit economically or politically.

The extent and value of these contributions are, of course, dependent upon future Soviet-satellite relations. The uprisings in Poland in 1956 led to an apparent weakening of Soviet control in that country and the creation of a more independent communist regime in Warsaw—somewhat analogous to the situation in Yugoslavia. The Hungarian uprisings of 1956, on the other hand, were met by fierce Soviet resistance, thereby emphasizing the myth of independence in this country. The long and bitter struggle by the Hungarians against the Soviet forces served to point out the underlying hatred for the U.S.S.R. existing throughout the satellite area, and the necessity for perpetual Soviet vigilance and force in this area if the unity of eastern Europe and the Soviet Union is to be maintained.

THE MACEDONIAN QUESTION

A special territorial problem, which involves four southeast European nations, is that of Macedonia, the area centered on the Vardar valley from Skopje, Yugoslavia, to Salonika, Greece, and extending east and west to include easternmost Albania and southwestern Bulgaria (Figure 64). Mace-

Figure 64. Macedonia. (After Kostanick, "Macedonia: A Study in Political Geography," Doctoral dissertation, Clark University, 1948. Used by permission.)

donia thus occupies a strategic location in control of the southern portion of the historic Vardar-Morava lowland route from the Aegean Sea to the Danube basin.

The area of Macedonia is about 26,000 square miles, of which fifty per cent is in Greece, forty per cent in Yugoslavia, just under ten per cent in Bulgaria, and a small fraction in Albania. Greek influence had spread into the area by the fourth century B.C., and later Macedonia was part of the Roman Empire. In the seventh century Slavs settled here, and shortly after the Bulgars also colonized the area. At various times from the ninth to fourteenth centuries it was part of both the Bulgarian and Serbian empires; then in 1371 it was conquered by the Turks and remained under Turkish control until 1913.

The Macedonian question has been one of the most persistent and perplexing territorial problems in eastern Europe. During the past half-century historical, ethnic, economic, and strategic claims have been put forth at various times by the four contesting countries (Yugoslavia, Greece, Bulgaria, and Albania), and disputes over political control have been an important source of friction between the neighboring states. Serbia, and more recently Yugoslavia, claimed the area on the grounds that the Macedonian Slavs are essentially Serbian in speech, while the Bulgars insisted that the Macedonian tongue closely parallels Bulgarian. Actually, the Macedonian language represents something of a transition between Serbian and Bulgarian. Both nations have also pressed historical claims (dating back to before 1371) and "strategic needs," based on vague requirements for national security. The Greeks have at times claimed Macedonia on the grounds that Greek culture was there first, and that southern Macedonia is predominantly Greek in culture. Albania has based its claims on the presence of 100,000 Albanians in the general area of Macedonia.

Besides the claims of the four nations are, of course, those of the Macedonians themselves, many of whom have long desired independence (as have other ethnic groups politically divided between two or more states, such as the Armenians, Basques, and Kurds), while others favor a political role within one of the existing nations. Thus the claims and desires of the various countries and peoples in this area add up to an extremely complex territorial situation, the solution of which would appear to be almost impossible within the framework of the traditional concept of national control.

Following World War I large transfers of population were made in the Macedonian area, with the result that political patterns came to correspond fairly well with ethnic boundaries. Of 1,500,000 persons in Greek Macedonia, all are Greek except for 80,000 Macedonian Slavs; in Bulgarian Macedonia the 250,000 persons are almost entirely Bulgarian; while in Yugoslav Macedonia there are about 750,000 Macedonian Slavs and 100,000

Albanians.[6] Although Bulgaria was thus excluded from control over the Macedonian peoples, the nation did not abandon hope for future sovereignty in the area. A Bulgarian-supported "International Macedonian Revolutionary Organization" was responsible for waves of terrorism in non-Bulgarian Macedonia, particularly between the two World Wars, in an effort to undermine political authority and ultimately to win territory for Bulgaria itself.

In December, 1944, warfare broke out between communist guerrillas and the Greek army in northern Greece. After two years of fighting Greece brought the case before the United Nations. A U.N. commission found that the three Soviet-dominated neighbors (Albania, Yugoslavia, and Bulgaria) were giving assistance to the guerrillas. In 1947 American military aid was granted to the Greeks, and the guerrilla threat gradually subsided. This aspect of the "Macedonian problem" differed from earlier ones in that the three satellite states had no quarrel with one another over possession of Macedonia, but were using this territorial problem as a means of extending communist control into Greece.

Tito's break with Moscow in 1948 removed some of the Macedonian threat to Greece, since nonsatellite Yugoslavia could not be used as a base for Soviet-inspired hostilities. Agitation in Greek Macedonia can still be directed from Bulgaria and, to a less extent, from Albania, but since 1948 a strong centralized Greek government and an effective military force have succeeded in preventing serious trouble along the northern borders. In Yugoslav Macedonia Tito's government has expended large amounts of time and money in developing the area and in uniting the Macedonian Slavs within the nation. From all reports these activities have met with considerable success.

BIBLIOGRAPHY

CAMPBELL, JOHN C. "The European Territorial Settlement," *Foreign Affairs,* XXVI, No. 1 (October, 1947), 196–219.

Maps and descriptions of the territorial settlements at the end of World War II involving Italy, Romania, Bulgaria, Hungary, and Finland.

DOMINIAN, LEON, *The Frontiers of Language and Nationality in Europe.* New York: The American Geographical Society, 1917.

Although much of the material is outdated, this book remains one of the classic studies of language patterns in Europe. Excellent maps and descriptions of pre-World War I conditions throughout the continent.

---

[6] In mountainous areas such as this settlement patterns are often complex. Within Greek and Yugoslav Macedonia are also Romanian shepherds (Vlachs) who move seasonally with their flocks, and in Yugoslavia some Turkish groups still remain. The small area of Albanian Macedonia is practically uninhabited.

DUCHACEK, IVO. "The Strategy of Communist Infiltration: Czechoslovakia, 1944–1948," *World Politics,* II, No. 3 (April, 1950), 345–73.

Describes in some detail the expansion of Soviet territorial control.

HARTSHORNE, RICHARD. "A Survey of the Boundary Problems of Europe," in *Geographic Aspects of International Relations,* ed. C. C. COLBY. Chicago: The University of Chicago Press, 1938.

Actually considers border disputes throughout all of Europe following World War I. Contains a table giving a tentative evaluation of conflicting claims in each dispute, based on the association of the area with the claimant states—an interesting experiment, which can be adapted to other parts of the world as well.

———. "The United States and the 'Shatter Zone' of Eastern Europe," in *Compass of the World,* ed. WEIGERT and STEFANSSON. New York: The Macmillan Co., 1947, pp. 203–15.

A discussion of the general problems of political control.

SAUCERMAN, SOPHIA. *International Transfers of Territory in Europe,* Washington: U. S. Government Printing Office, 1937.

Detailed statistics on all transfers of territory which took place in Europe following the Balkan wars of 1912–13 and World War I.

TEMPERLEY, HAROLD. "How the Hungarian Frontiers Were Drawn," *Foreign Affairs,* VI, No. 3 (April, 1928), 432–48.

Interesting discussion of the problems of political control in eastern Europe following World War I.

10

THE SOVIET UNION

● The Soviet Union, or the Union of Soviet Socialist Republics (U.S.S.R.), ranks with the United States as one of the two great power centers of the world. Its area is the largest of all countries, and its population is surpassed only by those of China and India. The nation's central location in the Eurasian land mass, its rich resource base and growing economic might, and its role as the center of the world communist movement are factors which also contribute to the great strength of the Soviet state. Internally the U.S.S.R. is faced with the problem of welding its diverse ethnic groups into a strong national unit. Externally it is confronted with a variety of opposing forces, many of which have arisen as a result of Soviet moves for territorial aggrandizement since the summer of 1939. Because of the dynamic nature of its foreign relations, and because of the great power potential which it possesses, the Soviet Union represents a force of primary importance in the pattern of territorial control throughout the world.

Physical Elements

The location of the U.S.S.R. in the Heartland of Eurasia is, of course, of great significance to its power potential. To the west lie the nations of Europe, with their large populations and their great industrial development. To the south are the oil resources of the Middle East and the Suez land bridge to Africa, as well as peninsular India and southeast Asia, with their great concentrations of people and natural resources. To the east lie China, with its 600,000,000 inhabitants, and Japan, with its population and

economic strength. Thus Russia is centrally located with respect to much of
the people, resources, and economic development of the Eastern Hemisphere. Because of this location, it is often in a position to exert powerful
influences on economic and political developments within the great belt of
nations which borders it on three sides.

The physical elements of a state are important both as assets and as
liabilities to national development. For the U.S.S.R. the effects of these
elements may be measured in terms of economic strength, defense, and internal unity and diversity.

Economic Strength. As a result of Russia's northern continental location its climate is an important limiting factor to agricultural and commercial development. Long, severe winters exist throughout much of the nation,
and there are large areas of arid or semiarid conditions, particularly in the
south central parts. Approximately two-thirds of the U.S.S.R. is normally
too cold for agriculture and another one-sixth is too dry. Commercially
Russia's climate has meant that the nation has few ice-free ports and that
many of the rivers are frozen during several months of the year. Much of
Russia's history of territorial expansion since the late seventeenth century
has been interpreted in part as a quest for warm-water ports on open water
bodies, although explanations may also be found in other economic and
political drives, such as desire for security, for national prestige, for control of resources, and (since 1918) for the spread of communism.

Areas of steep slope and of infertile soils and poor drainage also place
limitations on agriculture. East of the Yenisey River in Siberia and along
the southern borders of the nation much of the land is mountainous. Large
sectors of European Russia and of western Siberia, however, are flat to
gently-rolling, and within this region there are extensive areas in which the
soils are of moderate to high fertility. The belt of fertile chernozem soils
in the U.S.S.R. is probably the largest of any nation in the world.

Geologic findings have indicated that the Soviet Union has within its
borders a considerable supply of practically every major mineral except tin.
In addition, it has large reserves of coal and petroleum. Certain ferro-alloys,
particularly molybdenum, tungsten, and vanadium, are lacking, but the
last two are thought to be available from Communist China.

Forests and water resources are two other physical aspects of Soviet
economic strength. Russia has one of the greatest forest reserves in the world,
although the small annual rate of growth in the northern areas, combined
with their inaccessibility, restricts the potential value of much of these vast
forested areas.

Many of the great rivers of Russia are navigable for considerable distances, but three of the largest (Ob, Yenisey, and Lena) flow north to the
Arctic Ocean, while the Volga discharges into the Caspian Sea, from which
there is no outlet. In addition to transportation, Soviet rivers are important

for water power and irrigation. The rivers of the central and eastern Siberian uplands are particularly valuable for their hydroelectric potential, while the Volga in European Russia and the Amu and Syr rivers in southern Siberia are used extensively for irrigation. The U.S.S.R. and China have arranged for the joint development of the Amur River in the Far East for transportation and hydroelectric power. One of the major Soviet engineering projects being developed is the diversion of the waters of some of the northward-flowing rivers to the southern steppes and deserts, where they can be used for irrigation projects.

Size, climate, and surface configuration also affect surface transportation facilities in Russia. From Brest on the western border to Vladivostok on the Pacific it is over 6,000 miles by railroad, and for a nation which has only recently entered the Industrial Age distances such as this can pose tremendous problems in the development of transportation systems. The difficult climate and terrain have slowed the progress of railroad-building in northeastern Siberia, where for years the Soviets have been working on a northern extension of the Trans-Siberian Railroad to the Pacific.

Defense. Russia's size, climate, and physical borders are important assets in terms of national defense. Because of the great area of the nation (about 8,600,000 square miles) Russian armies have been able to fall back in the face of invading forces without being conquered or destroyed, as they did before Napoleon in the nineteenth century and Nazi Germany in the twentieth. The severe Russian winters have also been a defense factor, for the military operations of the invaders have been severely limited by the cold. In the Air Age large size permits greater dispersion of bombing targets; at the same time, however, it also means longer borders to defend against air attacks.

The defense value of the mountain regions and water bodies surrounding Russia was an important factor in Mackinder's concept of the Heartland area. From the eastern end of the Black Sea to Vladivostok on the Pacific the Soviet Union's borders are marked almost continuously by mountains, and they are also generally removed by considerable distances from large population centers in neighboring states. From the Black Sea north to the Arctic terrain barriers are much less effective, and it is here in the east European lowland that Russia has suffered the most from invasion. Water bodies, such as the Black and Baltic seas, have provided protection for Russia only if the country has had military control of these areas. The assault on Crimea during the nineteenth century, for example, illustrated the danger of foreign control of the surrounding water bodies, and the Soviet Union, particularly since World War II, has made strenuous efforts to assure itself of naval and air supremacy in the waters which surround it.

Russia's central location is important in terms of both defensive and offensive operations. Eleven nations have territory adjoining the Soviet

Union.[1] Japan is separated by less than ten miles from the Soviets in the Kuril Islands, and the American territory of Alaska is but two miles from the easternmost island of Siberia. Although physical barriers exist between the Soviet Union and its neighbors to the south and east, the existence of so many countries along the borders of the Soviet Union could represent a serious threat to Russian security in the event that all or most of them were united in military action against the U.S.S.R. It was this possibility that underlay Spykman's thesis of the predominance of power in the Rimland area of Eurasia. Added to this list of potential enemies is Anglo-America, separated from Russia by the Arctic wastes, but close to it in terms of air operations.

For Russia, as formerly for Germany, this ring of surrounding nations may also offer possibilities for territorial aggression—assuming that these states are not united militarily in defense against such a move. The weakness of disunity has been amply demonstrated by repeated Soviet successes in expanding into adjoining states, such as Finland, the Baltic states, Poland, Manchuria, and Japan.

Internal Unity and Diversity. Russia's size and shape have contributed greatly to the centrifugal forces in the nation, first, because of the difficulties of politically uniting such a vast area and, second, because between the Black and Caspian seas the nation extends across a strong natural boundary—the Caucasus—to include an area whose climate and population differ in many respects from those of the rest of the U.S.S.R. It is in this Transcaucasian area, containing the republics of Georgia, Armenia, and Azerbaijan, that some of the strongest opposition to Moscow's control has developed, particularly since 1917.

In European Russia, north of the Caucasus, and in western Siberia the lack of landform diversity has been a contributing factor to political unity. Climatic conditions change slowly, and diversity of agricultural and commercial interests is not so strong here as in areas such as eastern United States. In central and eastern Siberia and in the southern Siberian border regions, however, distance, surface configuration, and even climate do constitute important centrifugal forces. Following World War I, for example, there was a move to set up a separate state in the Maritime Province along the Pacific. Resistance to Moscow's authority has also been encountered many times among the mountain peoples along the borders of China and Afghanistan. The government's answer to these moves has been to improve the circulatory systems here, not only railways and highways, but also educational facilities, motion pictures, political rallies, and other communication media to indoctrinate the inhabitants with a sense of national loyalty to the Russian state.

---

[1] Recent Soviet claims to the eastern panhandle of Afghanistan would bring the Russians to the borders of Kashmir, adding one more political unit to the list of those touching the U.S.S.R.

Population

The population of the Soviet Union is an important power factor in terms of size, age breakdown, and the increasing degree to which the people are becoming educated and trained. The use of women in the labor force and army is much more widespread than in the United States and western Europe, and thus adds further to the available supply. This large population, of course, represents a centrifugal force within the nation, particularly since the ethnic characteristics differ, and the distribution pattern is such that large sparsely-settled areas separate the major populated regions. One of the major tasks of the Communists has been to foster local cultures in order to reduce dissension within the vast nation, while at the same time preventing the formation of strong divisive political forces.

In 1956 the population of the U.S.S.R. was reported by the Soviet government as being 200,200,000[2]—a figure nearly one-quarter greater than that of the United States. The birth and death rates in the U.S.S.R have dropped considerably since the 1920's, reflecting the higher standard of living, the increased urbanization, and the greater effectiveness of health measures. In 1926 the birth and death rates were 47 and 20.3 per thousand respectively; in 1955 they were 25.6 and 8.4, indicating a drop in the rate of population increase in Russia over a thirty-year period from 26.7 to 13.2 per thousand. Thus in 1955 the annual population increase amounted to about 2,650,000 persons.

In terms of age breakdown the Soviets benefit from the fact that there is a large number of persons in the 18–45 age group—the age group with the greatest production and military potential. Kulischer[3] puts this figure at 85 million, or 43 per cent of the total, in comparison with 63 million (42 per cent) in the United States. A further breakdown of age groups reveals that there are 16 million men in Russia in the 18–25-year-old group (the prime military ages), as against 9 million in the United States. It is estimated that in 1960–61 there will be 19 million men in this group in Russia, after which the number will gradually decline. The young virile population in the Soviet Union is reflected by the continuing high birth rate, the challenge to traditionalism, and the emergence of a "pioneer" spirit among many of the Russian people.

The population of the U.S.S.R. comprises a large number of ethnic groups. Approximately fifty per cent are Great Russians, over eighteen per cent are Ukrainians or Little Russians, and just under five per cent are White Russians (Belorussians), making a total Slavic majority of about

---

[2] The 1956 handbook *National Economy of the U.S.S.R.* is the first complete statistical summary of the Soviet Union published by the Soviet government. In it many previously estimated facts (including those on population) were officially revealed.

[3] Eugene M. Kulischer, "Russian Manpower," *Foreign Affairs*, XXXI, No. 1 (October, 1952), 67–79.

seventy-three per cent. Within this Slavic majority, however, the political unity tends to obscure certain divisive elements. Ukrainians and, to a lesser degree, White Russians have in the past sought independence from Moscow and the Great Russians, and in the present communist state centrifugal forces in the Ukraine still appear in the resentment of many Ukrainians to Moscow's control. The non-Slavic groups, listed in Table 9, are generally too small in number to offer serious competition to the political dominance of the Slavs.

Table 9

SOVIET POPULATION STRUCTURE ACCORDING TO
ETHNIC GROUPS

Major Groups	Per Cent of Total
Slavs	73
Great Russians	50
Ukrainians	18
Belorussians	5
Moslems	9
Kazakhs	4
Uzbeks	2.5
Tatars	2
Kirghiz	*
Tadzhiks	*
Turkmens	*
Caucasians	3
Georgians	1
Azerbaijanis	1
Armenians	1
Baltics	2
Lithuanians	1
Latvians	*
Estonians	*
Others	13
(Within this category are Jews and Moldavians (1 per cent each), together with a large number of smaller groups, including Karelians, Bashkirs, Mongols, Tuvinians, and Tungus.)	

*Less than 1 per cent.
Approximate Soviet population (1956): 200,200,000.
Adapted from Theodore Shabad, *Geography of the USSR*
(New York: Columbia University Press, 1951).

The many differences of language, religion, and customs among the peoples of the Soviet Union represent significant elements of potential disunity. The U.S.S.R. is divided politically into 15 Soviet Socialist Republics (S.S.R.'s) each one based—in theory—upon cultural differences. Within each republic the local language, religions, and customs are retained (providing they do not lead to political separatist movements). The Soviets use the theme of cultural liberalism as a propaganda weapon, but in reality the government's attitude toward such groups as the Jews or the Baltic peoples has been anything but liberal. Many cultural groups in the Soviet Union, for example, the Jews, Bashkirs, Tatars, and Tuvinians, have failed to receive political recognition in the form of separate republics, although some have been included in autonomous units within the major republics.

The attitude of the Soviet government toward religion has often varied. The Russian Orthodox Church is by far the largest in the nation, and because of its national affiliations is permitted to operate relatively freely. The 20 million Moslems are also permitted religious freedom, but toward the Jews, the Armenians, and the non-Orthodox Christians government policy has ranged from considerable liberalism (particularly during World War II) to strong interference. Since 1945 the Russian Jews have been the victims of two vicious anti-Semitic movements.

The population distribution in the Soviet Union has changed significantly since the mid-1920's. At that time the population was concentrated largely in European Russia, in a triangle whose base ran along the western border from Leningrad to the Black Sea and whose apex was roughly in the central Ural Mountains. With the development of the Soviet Five Year Plans and the gradual industrialization of the nation, great numbers of people have moved away from this triangle into the grasslands of western Siberia, the Maritime Province, the Kuznetsk Basin of central Siberia, the Kazakh steppes, and in the areas close to the borders of southern Siberia. The Lake Baykal region, centering on Irkutsk, and districts north of the Arctic Circle have also increased greatly in population since the start of the first Five Year Plan. The Soviet government has encouraged these population movements in order to organize more effectively the national territory and to permit greater utilization of resources. Increased intermingling of ethnic groups throughout Russia will also have the effect of lessening the regional differences between various peoples. Associated with this dispersal has been a great growth of the urban population, in response largely to industrialization efforts and to the attraction of higher living standards in the large cities.

Economic Structure

The rapid economic growth of the Soviet Union, measured by any one of several indices, has been an outstanding development of the past few decades. In 1928 the U.S.S.R. produced 4 million tons of steel, placing it fifth among the industrial nations of the world; twenty-five years later this figure had risen 850 per cent to 38 million tons, and the Soviet Union was in second place among world producers. The goal for 1960 has been placed at 60 million tons. In coal output the figure for 1928 was 35 million tons, for 1953, 320 million tons, and the goal for 1960 is 500 million tons. Statistics for oil output, railroad mileage, and textile production indicate a similar expansion.

The economic advances made by the Russians during the past quarter-century are attributable in part to the Five Year Plans, in which the whole economic program of the Soviet Union for the ensuing half-decade was determined in advance. Production goals were set, and the requirements of industry, agriculture, commerce, and the military were worked out in such a way as to insure maximum efficiency. The first plan lasted from 1928 to 1933, and has been followed by a series of additional ones.

Industry. The U.S.S.R. possesses in considerable quantities the prime requirements for industrial growth—raw materials, power, labor, capital, technical know-how, and markets. The availability of raw materials and of power facilities has already been noted, as has also the fact of Russia's huge population, particularly in the 18–45 age group, which provides a large labor pool for the nation.

The flow of capital is controlled by the government, whose economic power for over a quarter-century has been geared primarily to industrial expansion. Much of the capital for industrialization was obtained from the farmers, whose products were purchased by the government at low prices and then resold to consumers at high prices—the difference providing an important source of government revenue. Technical training in Russia has been extended to many people, and concerted efforts have been made to enhance the status of the technical class. The U.S.S.R. is turning out approximately 50,000 trained engineers each year, thereby building up a large supply of skilled workers for its industrial expansion. Finally, the market potential in Russia is tremendous for armaments and heavy manufactures, as well as for consumer goods. As a result industrial growth can presumably continue for a long time before any saturation point in the market is reached.

The effects of Russia's industrial growth on its power potential are of course extremely significant. During World Wars I and II the industrial strength and flexibility of the United States proved to be a decisive factor in Allied victory. In any future world conflict Soviet industrial strength will also be an extremely formidable weapon.

A significant aspect of Soviet industrial development has been the gradual dispersal of industries (Figure 65). Much of the impetus for this dispersal occurred during World War II, when the Donets Basin—then Russia's foremost industrial area—was threatened by the German armies advancing eastward across the southern Ukraine. Much of the Soviet industrial plant was moved to the central and southern Urals, and cities such as Sverdlovsk, Chelyabinsk, and Magnitogorsk became important industrial producers. Following World War II this area continued to increase its output, and in addition other sectors of Russia also were developed as indus-

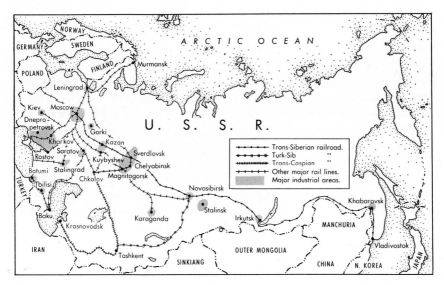

Figure 65. The Soviet Union: Major Railroads and Industrial Areas. Note the dispersal of industrial areas throughout much of the nation.

trial centers. Among these were the Kuznetsk Basin, 1,200 miles east of the Urals; the Amur valley in the Far East; Karaganda in the Kazakh steppe; Transcaucasia; the Murmansk district across the border from northern Finland; Tashkent in southern Siberia; and the Irkutsk region near Lake Baykal. This dispersal of industries has affected population distribution, transportation needs, and the vulnerability of the Soviet Union's productive means to enemy air attack.

Agriculture. In the process of Russia's planned economic development, industrial expansion has received a higher priority than agriculture. Moreover, communism has proved itself better equipped to organize industrial than agricultural workers, and as a result agricultural production in Russia has failed to register significant growth since 1928. During the first Five Year Plan the Soviet government began the process of collectivization, gradually abolishing private holdings and setting up large collective farms, on which the workers receive a share of the profits, or state farms, where the workers are paid a fixed wage. The resistance of the farmers to these measures was accompanied by widespread suffering. During the winter of 1932–33 several million persons, principally in the Ukraine, died of starvation because of famine conditions and government measures to stamp out peasant resistance to official agricultural policies.

In an effort to provide for the great increase in population, the Russian government has been working on a number of large-scale agricultural projects. One is to increase the mechanization of agriculture, a process for which parts of Russia are well suited, particularly sectors of the Ukraine and western Siberia. A second is to improve agricultural methods by providing training and advice to the farmers. A third is to bolster farmer incentive by increasing the prices received by him for his produce, to permit more private gardens, and to impart enthusiasm through closer party discipline. Soviet economic development has involved great sacrifices from the working groups. Of these the farmer has probably suffered the most in the past quarter-century.

Still another method for increasing food production has been to bring additional land under cultivation through irrigation, drainage, and the utilization of areas with low precipitation and short growing seasons. Government leaders hope eventually to bring 70 million new acres under cultivation. Low agricultural production represents a major weakness in the Soviet economy, and a difficult problem to solve, yet one which, if unresolved, may cause widespread resentment and unrest on the part of the mass of the Russian people.

Transportation and Commerce. In transportation Russian progress since 1925 has been steady but not spectacular. By 1955 rail mileage had increased four times over what it had been thirty years before, but the total was still small for an industrial nation of the size of the U.S.S.R. The Trans-Siberian Railroad is being double-tracked, and a new line is under construction north of Lake Baykal to connect central Siberia with the Pacific coast. Several international rail lines link Russia with its eastern European satellites. On these lines the gauges are being broadened to conform with the Russian width, thereby permitting more efficient transportation between the U.S.S.R. and these areas. There are also rail connections between Russia and other adjacent states, including Finland, Turkey, Iran, Outer Mongolia, and Manchuria.

Railroads form the strategic arterial system of the nation, but they are supplemented by highways and canals. Among the most important of the latter are the Volga-Don Canal at Stalingrad, linking the Volga system with the Black Sea; the Baltic-White Sea Canal, running northeast from Leningrad; and the Moscow-Volga Canal. The improvement of canals and canal equipment permits increased use of Soviet waterways (except during winter months), thereby helping to take the pressure off the railroads. The Russian air network has also been greatly expanded in order to handle both passengers and freight. Despite these advances, however, the Soviet transportation system is still underdeveloped, particularly east of the Urals. In any future conflict inadequate transportation lines would be a serious handicap to Soviet military operations.

In order to reduce the strain on its transportation system the U.S.S.R. has undertaken a nationwide program for economic regionalization, in which several economic regions have been established, each of which is to become as self-sufficient as possible. Although this compartmentalizing applies particularly to critical industries, there are also efforts to achieve limited self-sufficiency in agriculture, particularly in dairy products, meat, and feeds. Such a regional program may have political as well as economic repercussions, for by reducing the economic interdependency of the various parts of the nation a potential situation is created in which forces for political independence might also come into play.

Since the end of World War II the Soviet Union has not been a major nation in international trade. This has been the result partly of the government's efforts to achieve national self-sufficiency, and partly of the embargo on trade in various "strategic" commodities, imposed on the Soviet bloc by the Western nations. In 1954 the total Soviet foreign trade was valued at 6.2 billion dollars, compared with 25.4 billion for the United States and 17.3 billion for the United Kingdom. The Soviet Union looks upon foreign trade—including that with the satellite states and China—primarily as a source for raw materials (for example, rice and rubber), machinery, transportation equipment, and consumer products ranging from butter to refrigerators. The Russians have relatively few commodities available for export, except pulpwood, fish, and furs, and to pay for imported commodities they often must export gold or some products which they may need at home, such as oil, cotton, or grains.

The Russians have at times utilized international trade for political purposes: (a) by exporting food and other needed commodities to countries, such as India and Iran, in time of crisis, thereby winning friends for the U.S.S.R.; (b) by "dumping" oil on the world market at below the price established by Western exporters; and (c) by capturing markets from Western exporting nations by the conclusion of various types of bilateral agreements. Some of the bilateral agreements are associated with Soviet "foreign aid," through which certain goods and services are extended to less-developed countries in exchange for long-term agreements covering exports to the U.S.S.R. Estimates made in 1956 indicated that the Soviet Union had extended over one billion dollars worth of this type of credit to other states (as Egypt, Afghanistan, and Burma), thereby tying much of the export facilities of these countries closely to the U.S.S.R.

Political Features

The U.S.S.R. consists of fifteen republics which, although theoretically independent, are actually under the strict political control of the Moscow government (Figure 66). The facade of independence in the republics is formalized by the representation of two of them—Ukraine and Belorussia —in the United Nations. Of the fifteen republics the Russian Soviet Feder-

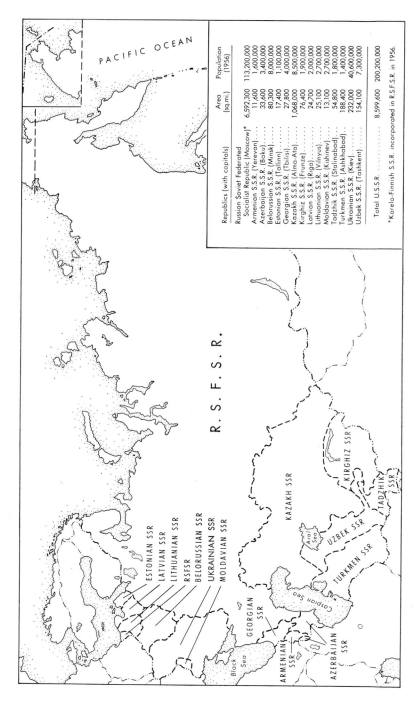

Republics (with capitals)	Area (sq.mi.)	Population (1956)
Russian Soviet Federated Socialist Republic (Moscow)*	6,592,300	113,200,000
Armenian S.S.R. (Yerevan)	11,600	1,600,000
Azerbaijan S.S.R. (Baku)	33,600	3,400,000
Belorussian S.S.R. (Minsk)	80,300	8,000,000
Estonian S.S.R. (Tallinn)	17,400	1,100,000
Georgian S.S.R. (Tbilisi)	27,800	4,000,000
Kazakh S.S.R. (Alma-Ata)	1,068,000	8,500,000
Kirghiz S.S.R. (Frunze)	76,400	1,900,000
Latvian S.S.R. (Riga)	24,700	2,000,000
Lithuanian S.S.R. (Vilnyus)	25,100	2,700,000
Moldavian S.S.R. (Kishinev)	13,100	2,700,000
Tadzhik S.S.R. (Stalinabad)	54,800	1,800,000
Turkmen S.S.R. (Ashkhabad)	188,400	1,400,000
Ukrainian S.S.R. (Kiev)	232,000	40,600,000
Uzbek S.S.R. (Tashkent)	154,100	7,300,000
Total U.S.S.R.	8,599,600	200,200,000

*Karelo-Finnish S.S.R. incorporated in R.S.F.S.R. in 1956.

Figure 66. The Soviet Union: Political Divisions.

ated Socialist Republic (R.S.F.S.R.) is by far the largest in area and population. Among the units at lower administrative levels are the *autonomous republics, krays* (territories included only in the R.S.F.S.R.), *autonomous oblasts, okrugs,* and other subdivisions, each representing a particular ethnic group or groups.

A study of the internal political structure of the Soviet Union offers a broad field of investigation for students of political geography. The boundaries of the republics are often subject to change, not only because of shifts in Russia's external borders, but also because of realignments of the nation's internal administration, such as the transfer in 1954 of Crimea (Krym) from the R.S.F.S.R. to the Ukraine, or the absorption of the Karelo-Finnish

Table 10

SOVIET TERRITORIAL GAINS SINCE 1939

Area and year of annexation	Area (sq. mi.)	Population
*Finland (1940)**		
Karelian Isthmus	10,570	486,365
Four islands in the Gulf of Finland	19	2,935
Salla sector (central Finland) .	3,010	5,550
Rybachi Peninsula (1944) . .	45	9,401
Petsamo (Pechenga) district .	4,288	c. 10,000
Total	17,932	514,251
Estonia (1940)	17,463	1,134,000
Latvia (1940)	25,262	1,994,506
Lithuania (1940) (excluding Vilna area)	20,395	2,879,070
Germany (1945)		
Northern East Prussia	6,100	830,000
Poland (1945) (including Vilna area)	68,667	10,900,000
Czechoslovakia (1945)		
Ruthenia (Carpatho-Ukraine) .	4,921	725,000
Romania (1940)		
Northern Bucovina	2,195	650,000
Bessarabia	17,143	3,000,000
Afghanistan (1946)		
Kushka area	c.1,000	—
Tannu Tuva (1946)	64,000	65,000
Japan (1945)		
Southern Sakhalin	13,935	332,000
Kuril Islands	3,944	17,550
Total gains	262,957	23,041,377

*The Porkkala Peninsula, near Helsinki, leased to the Soviets as a naval base after World War II, was returned to Finland in 1956.

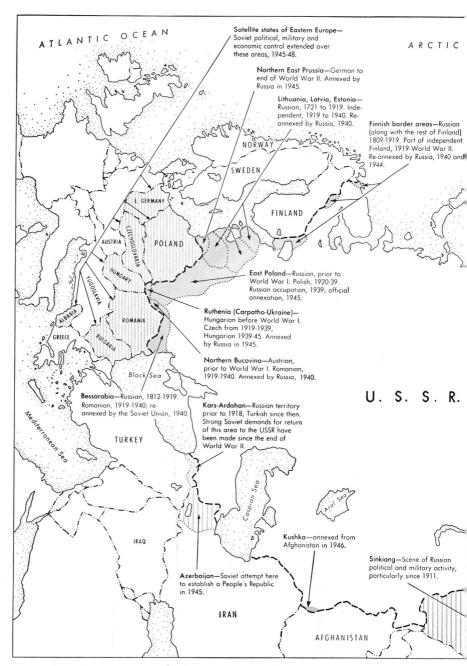

ATLANTIC OCEAN

ARCTIC

Satellite states of Eastern Europe— Soviet political, military and economic control extended over these areas, 1945-48.

Northern East Prussia—German to end of World War II. Annexed by Russia in 1945.

Lithuania, Latvia, Estonia— Russian, 1721 to 1919. Independent, 1919 to 1940. Reannexed by Russia, 1940.

Finnish border areas—Russian (along with the rest of Finland) 1809-1919. Part of independent Finland, 1919-World War II. Re-annexed by Russia, 1940 and 1944.

NORWAY

SWEDEN

FINLAND

E. GERMANY

CZECHOSLOVAKIA

AUSTRIA

POLAND

HUNGARY

YUGOSLAVIA

ALBANIA

GREECE

ROMANIA

BULGARIA

East Poland—Russian, prior to World War I. Polish, 1920-39. Russian occupation, 1939; official annexation, 1945.

Ruthenia (Carpatho-Ukraine)— Hungarian before World War I. Czech from 1919-1939, Hungarian 1939-45. Annexed by Russia in 1945.

Northern Bucovina—Austrian, prior to World War I. Romanian, 1919-1940. Annexed by Russia, 1940.

Black Sea

U. S. S. R.

Bessarabia—Russian, 1812-1919. Romanian, 1919-1940; reannexed by the Soviet Union, 1940.

Kars-Ardahan—Russian territory prior to 1918, Turkish since then. Strong Soviet demands for return of this area to the USSR have been made since the end of World War II.

TURKEY

Mediterranean Sea

Caspian Sea

Aral Sea

IRAQ

Kushka—annexed from Afghanistan in 1946.

Sinkiang—Scene of Russian political and military activity, particularly since 1911.

Azerbaijan—Soviet attempt here to establish a People's Republic in 1945.

IRAN

AFGHANISTAN

Figure 67. The Soviet Union: Border Areas.

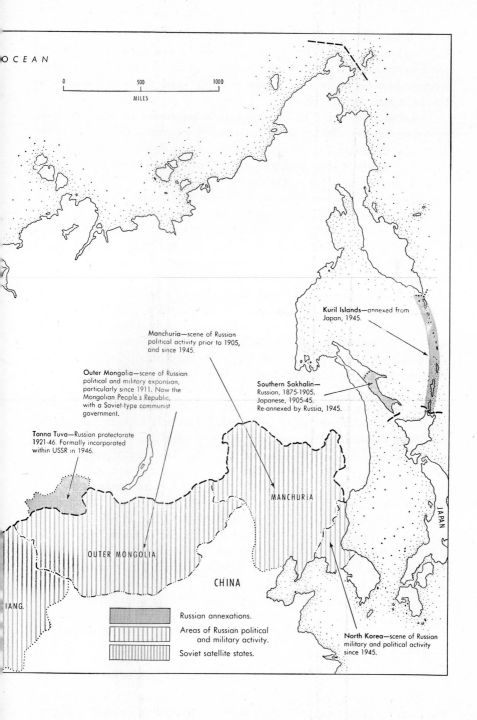

OCEAN

0   500   1000

MILES

Kuril Islands—annexed from
Japan, 1945.

Manchuria—scene of Russian
political activity prior to 1905,
and since 1945.

Outer Mongolia—scene of Russian
political and military expansion,
particularly since 1911. Now the
Mongolian People's Republic,
with a Soviet-type communist
government.

Southern Sakhalin—
Russian, 1875-1905.
Japanese, 1905-45.
Re-annexed by Russia, 1945.

Tanna Tuva—Russian protectorate
1921-46. Formally incorporated
within USSR in 1946.

MANCHURIA

JAPAN

OUTER MONGOLIA

CHINA

IANG.

Russian annexations.

Areas of Russian political
and military activity.

Soviet satellite states.

North Korea—scene of Russian
military and political activity
since 1945.

S.S.R. within the R.S.F.S.R. in 1956. From a careful study of boundary shifts within the republics one can gain considerable insight into the relationships between economic and political regions, the contests for power between Moscow and the provincial capitals, and the centrifugal forces existing within the nation.

Moscow, the capital and leading city of the Soviet Union, is centrally located with respect to European Russia, but is geographically removed from the area east of the Urals. As the historic seat of Russian power, Moscow exerts a great sentimental pull, although for nearly two centuries St. Petersburg (now Leningrad) was the capital city. Peter the Great moved the capital to St. Petersburg in order to benefit from contacts with Western countries, but in 1918 Moscow again became the seat of government, thus symbolizing a reorientation of Russian policy after the fall of the Czar.

Since August, 1939, the Soviet Union has annexed a total of almost 263,000 square miles (Figure 67), containing a population of over 23 million persons, of which about forty per cent belong to non-Slavic groups (Table 10). In addition, the nation has developed a satellite area in Europe totalling nearly 393,000 square miles in area with a population of well over 90 million. The satellite states, although directly subject to Moscow's control, are technically independent (all but East Germany are represented in the United Nations), which absolves the Russians from accusations of imperialism in the historical sense of the term.

Unlike the Germans of past decades, the Russians have never engaged in many theoretical justifications for aggrandizement, such as the nation's "organic borders" or its "place in the sun." The only Russian justifications have been constant reiterations of the requirements for national security, and an occasional "rigged" plebiscite, as in the Baltic states and Ruthenia. Even the theme of Pan-Slavism is of little value, for except in Yugoslavia there are no large Slavic groups left in Europe beyond the borders of the Soviet satellite bloc.

Officially the Soviet Union has no colonies. The Kuril Islands and Sakhalin are administered as a part of the R.S.F.S.R., whose territory also includes eastern Siberia. With no colonies the Russians are in a position to pose as the champions of peoples in dependent areas. This process of incorporating new areas into the political structure of the nation, rather than considering them as dependent units, is an interesting variation of the traditional imperialism, and one which has blinded many people, particularly in dependent or recently-independent areas, to the realities of Soviet imperialist policies.

THE TERRITORIAL DEVELOPMENT OF RUSSIA

The evolution and expansion of the Russian state to its present size and extent is a complicated history of the interaction of internal and external forces. Since the fifteenth century Russia has undergone a gradual process of territorial growth, which has been particularly successful under its communist administrations. In order to present some of the basic factors of this territorial development in condensed form, the history of Russia can be arbitrarily divided into three phases: (1) the establishment of the Russian state and its expansion prior to 1900; (2) territorial losses to 1919; (3) the Soviet Union since World War I.

The Establishment of the Russian State and Its Expansion Prior to 1900

The history of the Russian people can be traced back to the first centuries of the Christian era. At that time Slavic groups occupied an area northeast of the Carpathians between the Vistula and Dnieper rivers. Under the pressure of invading groups the Slavs began to spread out after the second century. A western group moved across Germany as far as the Elbe[4] and southwestward into Slovakia and Bohemia; the eastern Slavs moved eastward to the Dnieper and Don valleys, and northward to the vicinity of the present city of Moscow; and the southern Slavs migrated into the Balkan Peninsula. The Slavic peoples were prolific, and from their several branches came the Poles, Czechs, Bohemians, Moravians, Slovaks, Ruthenians, Serbs, Croats, Slovenes, and Macedonians, as well as the three Slavic groups of present-day Soviet Russia—the Great Russians, Ukrainians, and White Russians.

The Russian people were under Tatar control from the early thirteenth to the latter part of the fifteenth century, when the Grand Duke of Moscow succeeded in establishing an independent political unit. During the next four and a half centuries Moscow's borders were gradually extended in all directions, particularly during the reigns of Peter the Great (1682–1721), Catherine the Great (1762–96), and Alexander I and II during the nineteenth century. The history of Russian expansion is shown graphically in Figure 68. The absence of strong political units within Russia to compete with Moscow, the continued military and cultural development of the Russian state, the steady growth of its population, and the skill of Russian leaders in capitalizing on the weaknesses of neighboring states were important factors in the expansion of the nation from 15,000 square miles in the fifteenth century to $8\frac{1}{2}$ million square miles by the mid-twentieth. The centralization of political and military power in the capital, despite the country's great distances and inadequate transportation, has meant that at no time in Russia's history since 1462 has there been a serious challenge from some other part of the nation to the political control of the central government.

---

[4] The Wends, a group of western Slavs living near Berlin, have kept some of their ancient customs and continue to speak a distinct Slavic dialect to this present day.

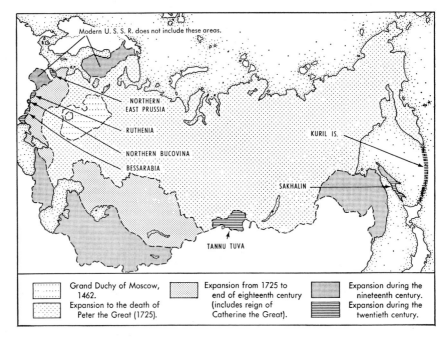

Figure 68. Territorial Expansion of the Soviet Union.

The vast areas of sparse population in central Asia were important to Russia's territorial growth, particularly during the nineteenth century when the nation moved its borders southward and eastward until stopped by opposing pressures from Britain, China, and Japan. Alaska, Russia's one holding in the Western Hemisphere, was sold to the United States in 1867. Along the western and southwestern boundaries, however, the process of territorial expansion was considerably slower, because of strong opposing forces from such nations as Sweden, Germany, Austria-Hungary, and Turkey.

Territorial Losses to 1919

The process of territorial growth was temporarily halted during the early twentieth century, first, by the military defeat by Japan and, second, by Germany. In 1904 Japan launched an attack against Russia in the Far East in order to eliminate Russian power in this area. As a result of its defeat Russia was forced to cede the southern part of Sakhalin Island to the Japanese and to abandon its attempts to establish a power sphere in Manchuria (see page 451).

Less than a decade later Russia entered World War I on the side of

Britain and France, but was again defeated, this time by Germany in 1917. By the Treaty of Brest-Litovsk, signed with Germany and its allies in March, 1918, Russia lost heavily in the west and southwest. Seven states were detached from Russia and created into an east European buffer zone. These states—Finland, Estonia, Latvia, Lithuania, White Russia, Poland, and Ukraine—were to be German-oriented in their foreign affairs, and Germany was to have strong influence in their over-all national development. In addition, the Kars-Ardahan region along the Russo-Turkish border was joined to Turkey (see page 183).

It is interesting to note the similarities between the terms of this agreement and those of the Versailles Treaty with regard to Russia's western borders. Germany's surrender in November, 1918, nullified the Brest-Litovsk Treaty, but the victorious Allies, fearful of Russia's new communist regime, favored the isolation of Russia as much as possible. By the Versailles Treaty Finland, Estonia, Latvia, Lithuania, and Poland were confirmed as independent states, although without German supervision and control.

In the southwest the province of Bessarabia was annexed by Romania and the Russo-Turkish border, as delimited in the Brest-Litovsk Treaty, remained unchanged. Most of the territorial gains made by Russia in eastern Europe during the two preceding centuries were thus removed.

The Soviet Union Since World War I

The development of the Soviet state since World War I can be summed up in three phases: internal political consolidation, reacquisition of lands lost after World War I, and expansion into new areas. The first period lasted until 1939, the second from 1939 to 1941, and the third has taken place since 1941.

During the first period (1918–39) Russia's borders remained fairly stable.[5] For fifteen years after the end of World War I there was little contact between Russia and other nations of the world. Within the Soviet Union, meanwhile, political activities were confined largely to overcoming all significant opposition to the new Communist regime. By 1933 the Soviet Union was again playing an important role in world affairs, and as the menace of fascism increased in Europe during the late 1930's political leaders, particularly in France and Great Britain, began to look to the Soviet Union as a possible ally in resisting Germany's territorial expansion. However, misunderstandings and distrust between the democratic Western governments and the Soviet Communist regime precluded any East-West military alliance. In August, 1939, after the German dismemberment of Czechoslovakia, the

---

[5] In 1921 the western border with Poland was established. During the same year Tannu Tuva became a Russian protectorate, and Outer Mongolia moved within the Soviet sphere of influence (see page 435).

Soviet Union concluded a nonaggression pact with Germany, principally to gain time for further developing Soviet defenses against the possibility of an eventual German invasion.

The second phase of postwar Russian history opened in September, 1939, when German forces invaded Poland. The Poles fell back in the face of the attack, but after seventeen days of resistance the defenders found themselves overwhelmed, as Soviet forces invaded from the east. Once again the Polish nation was partitioned, this time between Germany and Russia, and Russia's border was moved west to the Bug River. Two months later the Soviets invaded Finland, and after a short war Finland was defeated and forced to cede territory along its eastern border to the Russians (see page 232). The U.S.S.R. was thus able to improve its northwestern defenses, particularly around the city of Leningrad. In June, 1940, Russia presented Romania with a twenty-four-hour ultimatum which resulted in the return of Bessarabia and the cession of northern Bucovina, and in the following month the three Baltic states of Lithuania, Latvia, and Estonia were annexed by the Soviets (see page 235).

Thus in ten months the Russians had succeeded in reoccupying much of the territory in eastern Europe which was lost to them after World War I, and in erecting a defense zone against the Germans. Like the dismemberment of Czechoslovakia in 1938–39, here was an example of the "jackal" theory of territorial aggression, for the Soviet advance into eastern Europe did not begin until after Germany had inaugurated its penetration of this area in 1939. The historical process of great-power rivalry in eastern Europe was also clearly demonstrated. Despite the detailed work of Allied and League of Nations officials after World War I, local territorial problems in the east European area were completely submerged in the race for territory between the Soviet Union and Germany in 1939–40.

The third phase—that of Soviet expansion into new territories—began in 1944, as Soviet forces, after falling back in some areas nearly 1,000 miles in the face of the German attack, now drove the Germans westward across the Russian border and occupied what later became the satellite states. Eventually, the retreat of the enemy forces across eastern Europe provided the Soviets with the opportunity to occupy all the nations of that vital area except Greece, where United States and British forces were brought in by sea, and Yugoslavia and Albania, where local partisan forces liberated the areas. Finland remained free of Soviet occupation through the terms of its surrender agreement in 1944. With the gradual collapse of Germany and its allies there were no armies in eastern Europe to challenge the Soviet advance, and the westward expansion of Russian-occupied territory was halted only upon contact with other Allied forces advancing eastward from France and north from Italy. Within a short time Soviet-occupied eastern Europe, together with Yugoslavia and Albania, where local communist groups gained political dominance, came under the *de facto* political control of the Soviet Union.

The point of contact of Soviet and Western forces occurred roughly along a line running from Stettin on the Baltic south to Trieste. Russian armies were given the honor of "liberating" Berlin, Prague, and Vienna, and the American forces which had entered Czechoslovakia were withdrawn across its western border. In Germany and Austria cease-fire lines were laid down between Soviet and Western armies, and the countries were divided into military occupation zones. In Germany the cease-fire line eventually came to mark the border between West Germany and Communist-dominated East Germany.

At the end of World War II the Russians advanced their borders in Finland, in the former territory of East Prussia, and in Czechoslovakia (see Chapter 9). The Finns were also forced to lease the Porkkala Peninsula in the Gulf of Finland to the Soviets as a naval base. This area was returned to Finnish control in 1956. In addition the Soviet Union succeeded in establishing an east European satellite empire to the west of its borders, composed of states controlled by Moscow-oriented communist governments. In Central Asia Tannu Tuva, the Russian protectorate, was completely absorbed within the Soviet Union in 1946, and Soviet power was also extended into Outer Mongolia and western Sinkiang (see Chapter 16). In the Far East the U.S.S.R., which had declared war on Japan a few weeks before that nation's surrender in 1945, gained control of all of Sakhalin Island and of the Kuril Islands northeast of Japan. Thus the Soviet Union emerged from World War II as the dominant nation of Eurasia. Most of its potential enemies had been seriously weakened by the war, and the Soviets moved into a powerful position with respect to Europe, central Asia, and the northwestern Pacific. Much of the history of international relations since World War II has revolved about the readjustments of the states of the world to the new power status of the U.S.S.R. (see Table 10).

Obviously the establishment of Soviet control over many non-Soviet areas carries with it the danger of centrifugal tendencies in these areas, and it is this danger, particularly in the satellite states of eastern Europe, which has forged one of the weakest links in the Soviet bloc. One important factor has been the morale of many of the peoples in eastern Europe as a result of their reduced standard of living under Soviet control. Several devices have been employed to weld the recently-acquired areas to the Soviet Union, including an emphasis on Soviet language and culture, establishment of firm economic bonds, removal of potentially hostile elements, particularly among the middle class, and propaganda campaigns which play on the fears of the satellite peoples against their historic enemies in non-Soviet Europe. These devices serve as centripetal pressures, designed to counteract such centrifugal forces as national sentiment, hatred of the Rus-

sians, and resentment of communism and the confiscation of private property. These smouldering centrifugal forces, however, occasionally erupt into
violence, as in the East Berlin riots of 1954 and the Polish and Hungarian
uprisings of 1956.

SOVIET PRESSURES ALONG THE IRON CURTAIN

Since the establishment of the Soviet bloc in its present form, various
Soviet expansionist pressures have continued to be exerted along the borders
between this bloc and non-Soviet areas. These pressures have been associated
with the trend toward the extension of Soviet territory outward into adjacent areas, and appear in several forms or combinations of forms.

(1) *Direct support for communist minority groups seeking political
control.* The support given to communist guerrilla forces in Greece, to the
North Koreans before and during their invasion of South Korea, and to
the Chinese Communists prior to their victory over Chiang Kai-shek's forces
are all illustrative of this form of pressure. Military support has in the past
also been given to antigovernment forces in the Chinese province of Sinkiang.

(2) *Demands for boundary changes.* These demands reflect the move-
ment outward of Soviet borders, and since 1945 they have involved Turkey,
Iran, and Afghanistan. From Turkey Russia has sought the return of the
Kars-Ardahan area. In Iran Russia claims six small boundary areas. In
Afghanistan Soviet demands culminated in an agreement in June, 1946,
which provided for the rectification of the Afghan-Soviet border, with Russia
gaining uncontested control of the Kushka area. More recently, unofficial
Soviet claims have been made for the eastern Afghan panhandle between
Russia and Pakistan.

(3) *Propaganda for political unification of divided areas.* This has
been demonstrated in both Germany and Korea, where the communists
occupy a part of the area and where pressure exists for the re-establishment
of political unity, particularly from within the divided sectors. Capitalizing
on this pressure, the Soviets have offered to permit unification, but only
under conditions which would lead to the eventual establishment of communist governments in the reunified nations.

(4) *Establishment of cultural bonds with border peoples in order to
weaken political unity.* A major objective of Soviet cultural activities in
Azerbaijan has been to lessen Tehran's control over the area. Similarly in
Armenia (where Soviet activities have been less direct than in Azerbaijan)
Russia has sought to disrupt the unity of the Turkish nation and, if possible,
establish Soviet control in Turkish Armenia.

(5) *Attempts to disrupt normal economic and political operations.*
This type of pressure accompanies military activities (South Korea, Greece),
but it also may take the form of restrictive devices, such as the blockade of
West Berlin, or of local communist-inspired strikes and riots, as in Iran.

(6) *Extension of Economic Aid.* The Soviet economic offensive against neighboring states has taken the form of advancing large amounts of foreign aid—as, for example, to Afghanistan—and then applying economic pressure to orient the country's policies toward those of the Soviet Union.

(7) *Intimidation with Soviet military power.* To a certain extent this type of pressure has been exerted all along the Soviet borders, but with varying degrees of success. In Finland the pressure has been relatively effective; in Norway, West Germany, Austria, Greece, Yugoslavia, Turkey, and Japan it has been less so. The specter of Soviet power can be a potent force against small nations—particularly those which have not joined in military alliances with powerful noncommunist nations.

BIBLIOGRAPHY

CRESSEY, GEORGE. *How Strong is Russia?* Syracuse: Syracuse University Press, 1954.

A discussion of the various factors of the Soviet Union's power potential.

EAST, W. GORDON. "The New Frontiers of the Soviet Union," *Foreign Affairs,* XXIX, No. 4 (July, 1951), 591–608.

A summary of conditions along the Soviet borders since the end of World War II.

HARRIS, CHAUNCY D. "Growing Food by Decree in Soviet Russia," *Foreign Affairs,* XXXIII, No. 2 (January, 1955), 268–82.

The problems faced by the Soviet government in its efforts to increase food production.

SHABAD, THEODORE. *Geography of the U.S.S.R.* New York: Columbia University Press, 1951.

A regional geography of the Soviet Union, with special emphasis on internal political features.

———. "Political-Administrative Divisions of the U.S.S.R., 1945," *The Geographical Review,* XXXVI, No. 2 (April, 1946), 303–12.

Discussion and detailed map of administrative divisions and subdivisions of the Soviet Union. Also chart of changes in area and population, 1940–45.

———. "The Soviet Concept of Economic Regionalization," *The Geographical Review,* XLIII, No. 2 (April, 1953), 214–23.

The causes and results of this Soviet program.

SHIMKIN, DMITRI B. "Economic Regionalization in the Soviet Union," *The Geographical Review*, LXII, No. 4 (October, 1952), 591–614.

A detailed description of the economic regions within the U.S.S.R. Contains maps and detailed charts of the program.

TEAL, JOHN J., JR. "Europe's Northernmost Frontier," *Foreign Affairs*, XXIX, No. 2 (January, 1951), 263–76.

Relations between the Soviets and their neighbors along the northwestern border, northern Norway, and Spitsbergen (Svalbard).

WILES, PETER. "The Soviet Economy Outpaces the West," *Foreign Affairs*, XXXI, No. 4 (July, 1953), 566–81.

An interesting hypothesis of future Soviet power. Although some of the conclusions are open to debate, this article should be read by all persons interested in Cold War problems.

11

THE ARAB WORLD

● The desert regions of southwest Asia and northern Africa constitute one of the world's principal zones of tension. Here at the junction of three continents are located the spiritual centers for nearly half the peoples of the globe, over sixty-five per cent of the world's estimated petroleum reserves, and the sea link between the Mediterranean and Indian Ocean basins. Here also are over a dozen and a half separate states in various stages of political evolution. Because of its location, resources, and religious importance the Arab World is one of the historic prize areas of the globe, for the control of which men have struggled since the beginning of recorded history.

Recent political developments within the Arab World are of great importance to global power relations. Under pressures from local nationalism, European political control has been gradually disappearing, although even in now-independent areas the legacies of European colonialism still remain in the fragmented political structure, the foreign military bases and alliances, and the prominent European position in local economies. Since 1945, however, United States and Soviet influences have substantially increased here, and the region now represents a major focus of conflict between Soviet and anti-Soviet power spheres.

Several geographical names have been applied to this part of the world. W. B. Fisher[1] suggests that the term Near East lost its significance with the end of the Ottoman Empire, and that Middle East has several ambiguous definitions. In addition to a core area of Syria, Lebanon, Israel, Jordan, and Iraq, the term Middle East generally includes Iran, Egypt, Cyprus, and

---

[1] "Unity and Diversity in the Middle East," *The Geographical Review*, XXXVII, No. 3 (July, 1947), 414–36.

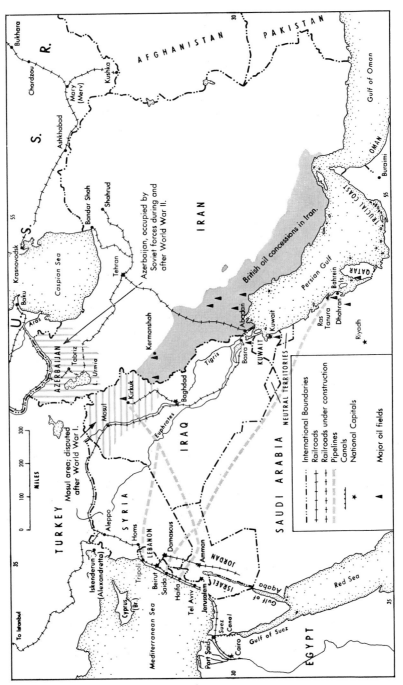

Figure 69. The Middle East.

the Arabian Peninsula. It may also include Turkey, Afghanistan, Libya, and countries to the south of Egypt.

In this chapter another term, the "Arab World," is used. The Arab World here includes the region from the Iran-Iraq border west to the Atlantic shores of Morocco, and from the southern boundary of Turkey south through the Arabian Peninsula, Egypt, and the Sudan. The non-Arab nation of Israel is thus within this area. In north central and northwest Africa the northern borders of French West Africa and French Equatorial Africa are generally considered as the southern limit of the Arab World (Figure 69). A special section on Iran is included at the end of this chapter; otherwise Iran is considered only in connection with the oil developments in the Persian Gulf area.

Physical Elements

The location of the Arab World is of great significance to an understanding of the political forces operating in this region. Extending over 3,000 miles from west to east, it straddles the major transportation routes southwards out of Europe, and the question of political and military control in the area is of importance to the British lifelines to the Indian Ocean-southern Asia area and the French lifelines to northern and western Africa. The Suez Canal reduces the sea distance from Europe to southern Asia and eastern Africa by thousands of miles, and Cairo has become one of the great air terminals of the Eastern Hemisphere, serving both north-south and east-west links between the three continents.

In terms of Cold War activities the location of the Arab World is also significant. Because of its position with respect to Europe and the U.S.S.R. this area has figured prominently in Western plans for the "containment" of Soviet power. On the other hand, it is also important in Soviet plans for outflanking the containment moves and for interfering with communication links between western European powers and the countries of Africa and southern Asia.

The North African-Asian desert belt stretches 4,000 miles from India westward to the Atlantic shores of Morocco. Some areas within this belt receive adequate moisture for agriculture either from mountain slopes intercepting rain-bearing winds or from rivers flowing across the desert lowlands. Lowland areas close to the Mediterranean coast in Israel, Lebanon, and Syria, and to the west from Tunisia to the Atlantic also contain belts of moderate precipitation. In the hills of Syria and northern Iraq, western Jordan, southern Morocco, western Yemen, and southwestern Arabia are other areas of ample moisture for crop cultivation. In Egypt's valley of the Nile and along the Tigris-Euphrates system in Iraq the fertile soil, level land, and year-round water supply combine to produce nearly optimum agricultural conditions. To the south of Egypt the Sudan extends into the tropical rain forests of central Africa.

Water supplies are unevenly distributed, giving rise to widely-scattered regions of population settlement; these are often separated from one another by long distances of sparsely-inhabited area. Many persons of the Arab World are nomadic, moving frequently in search of pasturage and water for their flocks. To such persons the existence of international boundaries in the areas through which they move usually mean very little. Tribal loyalties are often stronger than state or national loyalties, and armed conflict between tribal groups is a common feature of many parts of the Arab World.

Most of the minerals and power resources are concentrated within a relatively few areas. Oil is present in the Persian Gulf region; iron ore, phosphate, and manganese exist in the western portions of North Africa; Egypt has some iron-ore reserves; and Israel has potash. The Nile and the Tigris-Euphrates rivers possess water-power potential, as do such well-watered mountain areas as those in northern Algeria and in Morocco. Much of the area has not been adequately mapped, so that the extent and variety of resources are imperfectly known. The general scarcity of minerals and power fuels throughout large areas of the Arab World, however, has been a factor contributing to the shortage of investment capital in all but a relatively few areas.

Population Factors

The inhabitants of the Arab World are for the most part Arabic-speaking Mohammedans (or Moslems), although there is a number of important minority groups. The Mohammedans themselves are divided into two main branches—the Shiites, who reside in many sections of Iraq and along the southeast coast of Arabia, and the Sunnites (by far the larger branch) in the other parts of the area. Within the Arab World, where religion plays such an important role in the lives of the people, this division, roughly analogous to the Catholic-Protestant division in Christianity, represents a force for cultural and political diversity, particularly in Iraq where the numbers of Sunnites and Shiites are believed to be about equal. There are also smaller Moslem sects, such as the Druses and Alawi of Syria, which contribute further to religious disunity. In addition, there are Christian groups in all countries, as well as Jews, predominantly in Israel but also in most of the Arab states.

Egypt contains over 20,000,000 persons, or about one-third of the total population of the Arab World. Algeria, Morocco, Sudan, and Saudi Arabia have between 5,000,000 and 10,000,000 persons each, while the remaining states have less than 5,000,000 each. It must be remembered, however, that most of the states have relatively small areas suitable for agriculture. Thus, despite what may seem to be small population totals (except for Egypt),

there are high average population densities in terms of arable land throughout most of the Arab World. The population is increasing rapidly as a result
of continuing high birth rates and gradually lowering death rates. In Egypt
the birth rate in 1951 was forty-five per thousand, compared with forty-three
in 1920, while the death rate during the same period dropped from twenty-
six to nineteen. The nation's population increased over fifty-three per cent
in three decades (1920–50). In Iran the population total rose an estimated
twenty-nine per cent in ten years (1941–51). During the same decade Syria's
population increased twenty-three per cent and Morocco's nineteen per cent.

Population distribution throughout the Arab World is extremely irregular, with large concentrations along river courses and on well-watered coastal
plains, and with great expanses of practically uninhabited land. The bulk
of the population inhabits those regions enumerated on page 281, in which
water can be obtained from precipitation, from rivers, or from wells. There
is also a number of oases, such as the Fezzan in central Libya and Riyadh
in Saudi Arabia, where settlement has developed in response to water supply. Population distribution, of course, has had political repercussions both
within and between states. Most of the major population concentrations
have formed the foci for the development of individual political units. In
some states there is more than one important concentration, a factor which
contributes to the existence of strong centrifugal forces.

Economic Conditions

The economy of the Arab World is essentially an agricultural one, in
which the poverty of the great mass of the people is reflected in the low
average incomes which prevail here. In 1953, for example, the annual per
capita income in Saudi Arabia was estimated to be $40, in Iraq $85, and
in Egypt $112, compared with $708 in France for the same year and $1,911
in the United States. Only in Egypt and Israel has there been a definite
growth of a middle class.

The following quotation sums up the economic conditions existing
throughout most of the Arab World:

"The basic cause for the poverty of the countries of the Arab
[World] lies in the semi-feudal structure of their economy. This
economy is predominantly agricultural, as shown by the fact that
over two-thirds of the population derive their livelihood directly
or indirectly from the land. . . . The backwardness of the agrarian
structure limits agricultural productivity and so keeps down the
living standard of the majority of the people. . . . The semi-feudal
structure . . . manifests itself in the existence of large landholdings
owned by a small number of landlords who are mostly absentee
owners and who constitute a rentier class drawing comfortable in-

comes from the land but taking little or no interest in its utilization. . . . Besides the class of absentee landlords there is the class of poor share-tenants and landless agricultural workers who cultivate the land and constitute the great majority of the rural population. The share-tenants, who are usually burdened with debts contracted at excessively high interest rates, have no incentive to improve the land."[2]

Many of the nations of the Arab World must rely on food imports to satisfy domestic demands, and there are relatively few agricultural exports except cotton from Egypt, citrus fruits from Israel, wheat and wine from Algeria, and dates from Iraq. The impact of commercialized agriculture upon a subsistence economy has presented difficulties in several areas, notably in Egypt, where many farmers now raise cotton as a cash crop. Most of the cotton is exported, and in return for the low prices the farmers receive for their sales, they must purchase high-priced manufactured articles as well as seed and fertilizer. Oftentimes dependence on a cash crop has only further increased their poverty and also has led to serious depletion of the soil.

Except for Israel and Egypt, where much of the earlier traditional social and economic system has been overthrown, there has been little industrialization within the Arab World. Lack of investment capital has been an important factor limiting the development of industries. Throughout most of the Arab World any surplus capital which is accumulated is likely to be siphoned off by powerful individuals or groups for their private use, so that little finds its way into public improvements, social welfare, or industrial growth.

Because of rigid social systems and a shortage of educational and technical training facilities, much of the human resources of the Arab states are not being adequately utilized. The training of civil servants, the establishment of an effective electoral system, even the maintenance of law and order in time of crisis, are difficult problems for most of these states. One of the tragic circumstances of history is that some of the countries of the Arab World, whose greatest need is for peace and internal development, are still involved in warfare and political tensions, burdened by thousands of refugees, and with many of the normal trade patterns disrupted through international dissension.

Political Features

The modern political pattern in the Arab World is of recent origin, for even at the beginning of the twentieth century the Ottoman Empire still controlled much of the area, while France and Britain held sovereignty

[2] Charles Malik, "The Near East and the Search for Truth," *Foreign Affairs,* XXX, No. 2 (January, 1952), 248, 249.

over most of the remainder. Since that time two world wars and the rise of Arab nationalism have greatly altered this pattern. The limits of many of the political units were established at the end of World War I. Political fragmentation in the Arab World was partly the result of conflicting great-power interests, particularly British and French, which led to the partitioning of the former Turkish territories. Transjordan, for example, was a largely artificial creation by the British which lacked a strong *raison d'être,* a significant core area, or the resources necessary for the development of a viable economic structure. Between 1918 and 1956 twelve states became independent, eleven of them Arab and one Jewish.[3]

Many of the boundaries in the Arab World are antecedent in nature, for they were delimited through regions in which settled areas did not exist. Considerable use has been made of straight-line boundaries. In some areas, particularly on the Arabian Peninsula, the exact—or even approximate—location of boundaries has never been fixed. Few of the boundary lines have been demarcated, and throughout much of the desert areas little attempt is made to guard them against illegal crossings.

Despite the empty areas through which many of the boundaries pass, and the general lack of valuable resources in boundary zones, there have been quite a few border disputes in the Arab World since the end of World War I. Two controversies involved the delimitation of Turkey's southern border after World War I. Turkey and Britain disputed the location of the Turkish-Iraq border in the oil-rich Mosul area, while France and Turkey were involved in the delimitation of the Turkish-Syrian border, particularly around the port of Alexandretta. Both of these disputes are discussed later in this chapter. Israel's border conflicts have posed a major threat to peace in this part of the world since 1948. Still another dispute centers in the Buraimi Oasis in the southeastern Arabian Peninsula, where Saudi Arabia and Britain have conflicting claims of sovereignty over an area with rich oil deposits. In addition to these disputes, local controversies often exist —particularly over water rights—along the many poorly-defined boundaries.

Elements of Unity and Diversity

Within the Arab World there exists a wide and often conflicting variety of unifying and divisive elements. Among the Arab peoples there is what Charles Malik refers to as a feeling of "mystical unity."[4] The political effects of this sense of unity are difficult to determine, although in time of crises it can apparently be a potent force for united action on the part of the member states of the Arab League.[5]

---

[3] Syria, Lebanon, Jordan, Iraq, Egypt, Libya, Saudi Arabia, Sudan, Yemen, Tunisia, Morocco, and Israel.
[4] Malik, *op. cit.,* p. 240.
[5] Formed in 1945 to include Syria, Lebanon, Jordan, Iraq, Egypt, Saudi Arabia, and Yemen; Libya (1953) and Sudan (1956) later became members.

The tangible results of unity in the Arab World may be measured in two respects—the adoption of common policies toward world problems, and the reduction of boundary functions. These results apply only to the Arab states themselves and not, of course, to Israel. Although common policies have developed among some of the Arab areas with regard to relations with the communist bloc, Britain, and the United States, only in their hostility to Israel has there been any unanimity of approach to foreign affairs on the part of all the Arab governments. As far as boundaries are concerned, the Arab countries have held closely to the political patterns of preindependence days. Steps have been taken toward reducing economic barriers between states, particularly between Syria and Lebanon, but in general the forces of local nationalism have been too strong to permit the unification of the Arab states. Proposals for a Greater Syria, embracing Syria, Lebanon, Jordan, and Iraq, although possessing considerable economic validity, have never been seriously considered by the respective governments, while in northeastern Africa, Sudan has rejected any suggestions that it be politically united with Egypt. Only in Morocco, where the former Spanish and French zones have been merged, has there been a major unification of territories in the Arab World.

Forces of disunity within and between the Arab states are often as strong or stronger than those of unity. In several states strong centrifugal pressures exist which may threaten national cohesion. In Libya the widely-separated centers of population may eventually bring about a political partitioning of the country. In Sudan and Morocco the presence of diverse ethnic groups represent potentially divisive forces. On the international level Egypt's bid for leadership of the Arab bloc has been challenged by Iraq, and differences in outlook between these countries are further reflected in Iraq's adherence to a defense alliance against the Soviet Union, while Egypt (along with Syria and Yemen) accepts armaments from the communist countries. Dynastic rivalries also create tension. The Hashemite family, to which the heads of Jordan and Iraq belong, has been the bitter enemy of the ruling house of Saudi Arabia, since in the 1920's Ibn Saud drove the Hashemites from power in Arabia. An additional source of friction might arise should one of the Arab states cease to exist as a political entity. Such a situation could develop in Jordan, as a result of the complete withdrawal of British power there (see page 299). If the state should no longer function as an independent unit, there could be a contest involving Egypt, Syria, Iraq, Saudi Arabia, and possibly Israel for control of the Jordanian territory.

DEVELOPMENT OF THE ARAB NATIONS

The Decline of Turkish Power and Expansion of European Control. The history of the Arab World dates back thousands of years, but for the purposes of analyzing the present political pattern the changing aspects of territorial control in the area will be considered only since the beginning of the nineteenth century. For three hundred years prior to that time Turkish control of the Arab lands had remained virtually unchallenged. The maritime powers of western Europe saw little profit to be gained from the Middle East, and rather than battle the Turks for control of the barren land they had turned to other continents in search of empires.

The establishment of European control in the Arab World during the nineteenth and early twentieth centuries produced a complex history of conflicting power forces. Expanding westward from India in the early part of the nineteenth century, Britain became the first of the European nations to secure areas of permanent political control in this part of the world. Commercial and political treaties were signed with the local sheiks and sultans of southern Arabia, and the port of Aden, lying close to the mouth of the Red Sea, was annexed as a British colony; thus with the opening of the Suez Canal in 1869 between the Mediterranean and the Red Sea, Britain was provided with a new and well-guarded lifeline to her Eastern possessions. A few years later the island of Cyprus in the eastern Mediterranean was leased to Britain by Turkey, and in 1882 British troops occupied Egypt, in order to put down serious riots which were sweeping the country and to protect European lives and property. The country eventually became a British protectorate, and Port Said, at the northern end of the Suez Canal, was established as an important British naval base, thereby further safeguarding Britain's lifeline to the East.

To the south of Egypt nearly a million square miles of territory were also added to the British Empire in the closing years of the nineteenth century, when British and Egyptian troops gained control of the Sudan. The Sudan controls the headstreams of the Nile, its Red Sea coast can be used for naval bases between Suez and Aden, and at the time of its annexation it served as a check on French territorial ambitions in east central Africa. In 1899 a British-Egyptian condominium was set up over the Sudan, whereby the two governments shared in its administration.

While Britain was expanding its power in the eastern Mediterranean-Red Sea area, French influence was being established in western North Africa. In 1830 French forces landed on the Algerian coast across the Mediterranean from France, and began a drive inland to subjugate all of North Africa. The coastal lowlands afforded considerable opportunities for agriculture, and much of the better land in Algeria was taken over by French settlers. To the east of Algeria the state of Tunisia was administered by a native ruler. Although nominally a part of the Ottoman Empire, Tunisia by the mid-nineteenth century enjoyed virtual independence. In 1881 France forced the ruler to accept the establishment of a French protectorate over his country, so that, although he retained nominal powers, actual control in Tunisia passed to the French resident-general and his staff.

In northwestern Africa French interests during the nineteenth and early twentieth centuries conflicted with those of Britain, Spain, and Germany. Only through various compromises was France able eventually to establish undisputed control of the area of French Morocco. At the end of the nineteenth century Britain withdrew its claims here in exchange for French withdrawal from the Anglo-Egyptian Sudan, Spain was granted a strip of Moroccan territory in the northwest facing the Spanish coast, and Germany abandoned its demands in northwest Africa after territory had been transfered from French Equatorial Africa to the German Cameroons. Territorial compromises such as these were characteristic of the political partitioning of all of Africa during the late nineteenth and early twentieth centuries.

Morocco was ultimately divided into three zones in 1912. Most of the area became a French protectorate under the nominal control of the native sultan. About five per cent was constituted as Spanish Morocco—Spain's only possession in the Arab World. Ceuta, a coastal enclave in Morocco under Spain's direct sovereignty, was developed as a Spanish naval base close to the Strait of Gibraltar. Control of the city of Tangier, located at the northwestern tip of Africa, became a source of international controversy, since the harbor is on the southern shore of the Atlantic approach to the Strait of Gibraltar. Finally, in 1925 Tangier and the territory adjacent to it was established as an international zone. With an area of 225 square miles and a population of 150,000 the zone was placed under the control of a committee composed of the consuls of eight European nations. Tangier, the only international area of its kind in the world, represented a unique arrangement for control of an area disputed among several states.

Another European power to acquire territory in the Arab World was Italy. This nation was late in its drive for colonies, and by the time it began to expand most of the territory in Africa had already been claimed by other European states. In 1911 Italian troops landed at Tripoli on the North African coast; simultaneously the annexation of Turkey's province of Libya was announced in Rome. War with Turkey followed, but within a year the Italians were victorious and Libya was subsequently recognized as an Italian colony.

By 1914 the Turks had lost all territorial holdings in North Africa, as well as in much of the southern and eastern parts of the Arabian Peninsula. The British, pursuing a policy of "marginal control," had concentrated their power in key areas within their territorial possessions, maintaining relatively small but mobile military units and administering wherever possible through local rulers. To Britain the Arab World was important primarily because of its military value in protecting the sea routes to India and the Far East. France, Italy, and to a less extent, Spain were interested in their possessions as settlement areas. Many Frenchmen had moved to North Africa, but the

Italian government, both before and after World War I, was less successful in its colonization efforts in Libya. The Italian people had little interest in permanent settlement in Africa, and Libya had much less to offer as a settlement area than did the French North African territories. The Germans, although controlling no territory in the Arab World, sought to extend their influence in the area through cultural and economic contacts with the Arabs, including the proposed and partly constructed Berlin–Baghdad Railway. As centrifugal forces grew stronger in what remained of the Ottoman Empire both before and during World War I, various European states began making preparations for expanding their control in the Arab World.

World War I and the Palestine Dispute. During World War I Turkey joined Germany and the other Central Powers against France, Britain, Italy, Russia, and their allies. Early in the fighting the British began a campaign to enlist the aid of Arab groups in the struggle against the Turks. As an incentive for their co-operation the British held out the promise of eventual Arab independence once Turkey was defeated. In 1915 Sir Henry Mac-Mahon, British High Commissioner for Egypt, wrote to the sherif of Mecca, promising British support for Arab independence in the Middle East. Sir Henry was forced to recognize the existence of historical French interests in Syria and Lebanon, and he therefore stated that the future independence of those areas lying west of the districts of Damascus, Homs, and Aleppo could not be guaranteed by the British government at that time.

British commitments were accepted by the sherif and his associates, and Arab forces were soon battling against the Turks. However, the British government made another commitment in the Middle East, this one to the Jews. In the years preceding World War I several thousand Jewish immigrants came to settle permanently in Palestine in the hopes of establishing a Jewish homeland here. As reward for Jewish contributions to the war effort the British government in 1917 issued the Balfour Declaration:

> His Majesty's Government view with favour the establishment of
> a National Home for the Jewish People . . . in Palestine.

To the Arabs the Balfour Declaration was in direct contradiction with the promises made to them in the MacMahon letter. Palestine lies west of the Damascus-Aleppo line, but also to the south of Syria. The MacMahon and Balfour declarations became a source of British embarrassment during the next thirty years, and the dispute eventually erupted into the Arab-Jewish War of 1948–49.

The High Point of European Power, 1919–1939. Turkey's defeat in 1918 heralded a complete political realignment in the eastern part of the Arab World. Britain and France, the leading European states in the Allied coalition of World War I, became the dominant powers in this part of the world and shared between them the territorial spoils of the old Ottoman

Empire. The area south of Turkey itself, between Egypt and Iran, was divided into five small political units—Syria, Lebanon, Palestine, Transjordan, and Iraq. This political partitioning seriously weakened any potential unity which the Arab peoples might have experienced after liberation from Turkish rule.

It was felt by the Allied officials that independence for these Arab states should eventually come about, but only after an indefinite "training period." These countries were deemed ill-prepared immediately after World War I for the responsibilities of self-government. Therefore, they were set up as Class A mandates of the League of Nations, with Britain and France as administering powers. Under the terms of the mandates, the Arab countries were to be governed during the interim period before independence by the European nations under the supervision of a League of Nations commission. Palestine, Transjordan, and Iraq were set up as British mandates, and Syria and Lebanon became French mandates.

No provisions were made for the establishment of mandates on the Arabian Peninsula, for much of the area had not been under Turkish control before the war and, except for Aden, the peninsula was then considered to be of little economic value. The regions of Nejd, al-Hasa, Hejaz, and Asir were later combined into the independent kingdom of Saudi Arabia. Unlike events in other parts of the Arab World, this unification took place through internal means (the military campaigns of Ibn Saud) rather than as a result of action by foreign powers. Except for some of its coastal areas the Arabian Peninsula has always been relatively isolated from foriegn control. Centrifugal forces here are illustrated by the existence of two Saudi Arabian capitals—Riyadh, the political capital, in the desert, 250 miles inland from the Persian Gulf, and Mecca, the religious capital, in the west.

In addition to Saudi Arabia the peninsula contains a number of small political units. Yemen, a mountainous area on the southwestern coast, has been independent since 1925. The port of Aden and the territory around it is a British colony, and much of the southern Arabian Peninsula consists of the British-supervised Aden Protectorate. Kuwait in the northeast is an independent state under British protection, as are the Bahrein Islands in the Persian Gulf. In the southeast are the sheikdoms of Qatar, the seven sheikdoms of Trucial Oman, and the sultanate of Oman (or Muscat and Oman). Political patterns in this area are in a state of frequent change: even the number of these small political units varies according to the fortunes of local wars, although in recent years attempts have been made to stabilize political and military conditions here in order to facilitate oil exploration and development.

Along Saudi Arabia's northeastern border two Neutral Zones were established after World War I. The word "neutral" is a misnomer, for the zones are actually condominiums, controlled in the one case by Iraq and

Saudi Arabia and in the other by Kuwait and Saudi Arabia. The Neutral Zones, like the former Anglo-Egyptian Sudan, are compromises of territorial claims. In the Kuwait-Saudi Arabian area oil is now being developed.[6]

To the north of the Arabian Peninsula the territorial dispute between Turkey and Britain over the determination of Iraq's northwestern border has already been noted. The Mosul area here is part of the Tigris-Euphrates valley (Mesopotamia) and contains some of the country's most promising oil resources. With a mixed Arab-Turkish-Kurd population, the Mosul region was tied economically more closely with Iraq than with Turkey at the end of World War I, although the Turks claimed—possibly with some justification—that a plebiscite in this area would have shown a predominance of the population favoring continued Turkish control. Britain was interested in obtaining the Mosul area for Iraq, first, in order to strengthen its friendship with the Iraq government and, second, because of British claims to the oil resources there. In 1926 the final boundary was delimited, awarding practically the entire area to Iraq.

The Beginnings of Arab Independence

The gradual establishment of independence in the Arab World was the result of three principal factors: (1) the terms of the mandate agreements, which called for eventual self-rule, (2) local pressures for an end to foreign control, and (3) changing policies and conditions within the European countries themselves. In many cases, of course, independence resulted from a combination of two or even of all three of these elements.

During the period between the two World Wars Britain was the only European nation to grant independence to Arab states—Egypt in 1922 and Iraq in 1932—and even here, the withdrawal of British political control was accompanied by military treaties, whereby Britain was permitted to maintain bases and use the resources of the two countries in time of war. Britain also retained a strong economic position in Egypt and Iraq.

The French did little in the way of advancing self-government for their two mandates, Syria and Lebanon. Through their insistence on special political and economic privileges for French citizens in these two areas, the French created considerable antagonism among the Syrians and Lebanese, and thereby accentuated the local demands for independence. Shortly before World War II the French government further alienated the people of Syria by permitting Turkey to annex the coastal district of Alexandretta (now called Iskenderun). French authorities maintained that the district's population was predominantly Turkish in character, and despite France's

---

[6] See Alexander Melamid, "The Economic Geography of Neutral Territories," *The Geographical Review*, XLV, No. 3 (July, 1955), 359–75. The original condominiums set up in 1922 were with Nejd, which later became the core region of the new state of Saudi Arabia.

obligations under the League of Nations to protect Syria against loss of territory, the transfer was agreed to in 1939. Iskénderun is now the third largest Turkish port.

In other parts of the Arab World there was little progress toward self-rule between the two World Wars. All the dependent areas were governed according to the economic and political policies of the various mother countries, with the result that during this period regional differences between the states were accentuated and the possibilities for Arab unity diminished.

World War II and the Postwar Changes

When World War II broke out in September, 1939, the Arab World became of great strategic importance to the contesting powers. The defeat of France in June, 1940, and Italy's entrance into the war on the side of the Germans were serious threats to Britain's position in the Middle East. To the British the Arab World was of great value because of its oil supplies, its position with respect to reinforcement lines from India, Australia, and New Zealand, and its role as a base for resisting German pressures south and southeast from occupied Europe. After 1943 the Arab World also served as a staging area for the reinvasion of Europe. To the Germans the Arab World also was a source for much-needed oil supplies, as well as a base for operations against southern Russia and British supply lines from the East. However, the Germans were never able to win military control of this area. Finally, to the peoples of the Arab World, many of whom were more concerned with independence demands than with Axis aggression, World War II appeared as both a continuation of foreign exploitation of their resources and location and as an opportunity to further their own political goals.

Since World War II several major changes of sovereignty have taken place in the Arab World. Syria, Lebanon, Libya, Transjordan, Israel, Morocco, Tunisia, and the Sudan have achieved independence, and the British have evacuated the Suez Canal Zone. The gradual decline of European power here has been further accentuated by such actions as the Egyptian nationalization of the Suez Canal, by anti-British moves in the former mandate of Transjordan, by the adoption of neutralist policies with regard to the Cold War by some of the Arab states, and by the abortive invasion of the Suez by British, French, and Israeli forces. In the sections which follow the changes of sovereignty in the Arab World since World War II will be considered in detail.

The Partition of Palestine and Creation of Israel. The steady influx of Jewish immigrants into Palestine after the establishment of the British mandate in 1920 increased the Jewish proportion of the population from sixteen per cent in 1922 to twenty-four per cent in 1947. In general the Jewish arrivals were better educated than the local Arab inhabitants. Outside funds were solicited by the World Zionist Movement to be used in the settlement of Palestine. The hard-working immigrants developed land reclamation projects, new farming techniques were instituted, and Palestine's agricultural production rose substantially during the quarter century following World War I.

Resentment between Jews and Arabs in Palestine continued to rise. During the interwar years the Jews gained ownership of nearly all of the country's agricultural and commercial enterprises. In 1939 in response to Arab demands the British placed restrictions on future Jewish immigration, limiting the number of immigrants to 15,000 per year. By 1945 thousands of European Jews, who had survived the horrors of fascism and war, were desperately eager to reach Palestine, where future security and hope awaited them. While the British navy attempted to intercept ships laden with illegal immigrants, Zionist and Arab underground organizations in Palestine were conducting campaigns against one another and against the British.

A United Nations Palestine Commission eventually was established with the task of seeking a just and equitable solution to the problem. The Commission's recommendation was for partition of Palestine into three Jewish and three Arab sectors. The future of Jerusalem, holy city to Jews, Arabs, and Christians alike, was left for subsequent discussions. In November, 1947, this partition plan was approved by the United Nations General Assembly. Jewish leaders accepted the U.N. partition plan, but the Arabs denounced it bitterly. In May, 1948, Britain surrendered its mandate, and British forces withdrew completely from the area. Fighting immediately broke out between the Jews and Arabs, the latter supported by the armies of Jordan, Egypt, Syria, Lebanon, and Iraq. More than 600,000 Arab civilians living in the Jewish sectors of Palestine evacuated their homes and retreated behind the Arab lines.

In the months which followed the Arab attack the Jewish armies were able not only to stand up against the Arab forces but also to drive them back in many sectors. In the spring of 1949 separate armistice agreements were signed between the Jews on the one hand and the several Arab states on the other. Hostilities ended and military truce lines were set up. At that time the Jews controlled an area about 2,200 square miles greater than that which had been awarded them in the 1947 partition scheme.

The new Arab-Jewish border followed the old Palestine frontier throughout much of its length. One exception was in eastern Palestine, where a 2,300-square-mile area west of the Jordan-Dead Sea line remained in Arab hands, and another in the extreme west, where the Egyptians retained a coastal strip about eight miles in width (Figure 70). The six-zone concept of the U.N. Palestine Commission disappeared, and all the Jewish territory was now contiguous. The temporary cease-fire boundaries have remained as permanent political features of the landscape. In Jerusalem

Figure 70. *Israel.* (After Alexander, *World Politics*, VI (April, 1954). Courtesy of Princeton University Press.)

the Jews controlled the New City, while the Arabs retained the old part with its religious relics, including Gethsemane, the Church of the Holy Sepulcher, and the Jewish Wailing Wall.[7] Bethlehem was also in Arab hands.

The erratic political pattern in the former Palestine area has caused a number of potentially dangerous situations. Like the "iron curtain" across Korea, the military cease-fire line has formed a closed boundary across what used to be a unified region, with resultant hardships to the peoples and economies of the border areas. Violence has broken out repeatedly between Jews and Arabs across the border, and a United Nations commission has supervised the border functioning and, where possible, negotiated between Jews and Arabs in an effort to control the border warfare.

Assuming the 1949 borders of Israel become permanent, several out-

---

[7] The United Nations in 1949 passed a resolution calling for the internationalization of Jerusalem under a U.N. commission. Neither the Jews nor the Arabs would acquiesce to this proposal. The Jews announced that Jerusalem was the legal capital of Israel, while Jordan proceeded to annex eastern Jerusalem, as well as the other Arab-held portions of Palestine, and to make them integral parts of the Kingdom of Jordan. After a year of fruitless negotiations the United Nations admitted it was unable to implement the 1949 decision.

standing problems remain to be solved. First, there is the matter of the Arab refugees who once lived in what is now Israel.[8] The Arabs have insisted that before peace negotiations can take place these people must be returned to their former homes. The Jews have contended that such repatriation is impossible, since the refugees left their homes voluntarily in 1948 hoping to return with the victorious Arab armies, and that because of the influx of Jewish immigrants to Israel since 1948 there is no room left for the readmission of these former Arab inhabitants.

A second problem is that of water scarcity. Any long-term proposal for the increase of agricultural areas in Israel and the neighboring Arab states (thus providing among other things for the resettlement of Arab refugees) is related to this problem. The most promising source of water for Israel and western Jordan is the Jordan River and its tributaries. Most of the headwaters of the Jordan actually rise in Syria and Lebanon; they unite in the Huleh Marsh area of northern Israel to form the major stream, which flows south partly in Israeli territory, partly along the Israeli-Jordan border, and in its southern sector entirely within the territory of Jordan (Figure 70). The utilization of the waters of the Jordan system could best be accomplished through some form of international agreement between the Jews and the Arabs, but since the Arabs refuse to negotiate with Israel such agreement is impossible, and both groups are preparing plans for separate irrigation and power developments within their own areas.

A third problem involves the economic position of Israel, as additional Jewish immigrants continue to arrive. The Israeli nation is committed to the support of all Jews, yet there are limits to the number of persons who can be adequately cared for by a nation with less than 8,000 square miles of territory and few natural resources. Hundreds of millions of dollars have already been advanced to Israel by Jews living in other parts of the world, particularly by those in the United States and western Europe, and one of the major sources of Israel's strength is the financial and political support it receives from the approximately 10 million Jews living outside its borders. The nation must eventually become self-supporting, however, if it is to be a strong national unit in this part of the world. Since Israel's creation all efforts to improve the country's economic position have, of course, been handicapped by the economic blockade imposed on Israel by the Arab states.

Another problem concerns the Gulf of Aqaba, extending south from Israel to the Red Sea. Jordan, Egypt, and Saudi Arabia also border on the gulf, and thus it is an international waterway. However, the only navigable channel between the gulf and the Red Sea is through the Strait of Tiran, a three-mile-wide waterway, both sides of which are controlled by Egypt.

---

[8] Natural increase (and the addition of "refugees" who actually never lived in the territory which is now part of Israel) has swelled the number of Arab refugees to close to 900,000. The U.N. Relief and Works Agency has been caring for these displaced persons in refugee camps located in the Arab states bordering Israel.

In 1949 Egypt established fortifications along the strait, and prevented Israeli shipping from using the waterway in passing to and from the port of Elath in southernmost Israel. Blocking an international waterway is contrary to the generally accepted rules of international law, but here, as in the case of Israeli shipping passing through the Suez Canal, Egypt resisted all efforts by the United Nations to bring about a relaxation of restrictions on passage by Israeli vessels.

Syria and Lebanon. French claims to predominance in Syria and Lebanon were based largely on France's historical role as protector of Christianity in this part of the world. Lebanon, occupying a well-watered mountain area along the Mediterranean coast has a population of 1,400,000, which is over fifty per cent Christian. Because of its importance as a commercial and financial center, Lebanon is a relatively prosperous country, and has long maintained close ties with the European nations. Beirut, its capital and leading city, is an important harbor, and two other Lebanese ports serve as Mediterranean outlets for pipe lines from oil fields in Iraq and Saudi Arabia.

Syria, on the other hand, is a much poorer country. Like Lebanon, it has no mineral or petroleum wealth. In addition, it has no good harbors along the Mediterranean, having lost Beirut to Lebanon and Alexandretta to Turkey. The bulk of its 4,000,000 inhabitants is settled inland from the coast along a north-south axis running from Aleppo, close to the Turkish border, to Damascus, the capital, in southern Syria. Both cities are approximately equal in size—a significant centrifugal factor, since each is an important regional center. The population is largely Mohammedan, and includes two important minorities—Turks, who live in northern Syria, and the Druses, a group numbering about 100,000 who inhabit a mountain area in south Syria, and often engage in armed conflict against the Damascus government.

French control in both Syria and Lebanon was marked by strife and rebellion. The Syrians, among other things, resented the political partitioning of their country: by the separation of Transjordan, Palestine, and Lebanon from what had been the prewar Turkish province of Syria, by the subdivision of postwar Syria into theoretically autonomous regions, and finally by the loss of Alexandretta.

No definite steps were taken by France prior to World War II to terminate the mandates in Syria and Lebanon. In 1941 France, then under a pro-Axis administration, officially withdrew from the League of Nations. The governments of Syria and Lebanon announced that as a result of this withdrawal they were no longer to be considered as French mandates. At the end of World War II the independence of these countries was officially acknowledged by France, and French political and military power was thereby eliminated from the eastern Mediterranean.

By the mid-1950's strong Soviet influence was apparent in Syria. Arms from the communist bloc were being delivered to the Syrians, economic ties had been strengthened between the two areas, and a left-wing government had come into office in Damascus. A power vacuum had existed in Syria since the withdrawal of the French, and Soviet activities here have posed a potential threat to the position of the Western nations in the Middle East. Were Syria to align its foreign policy with that of the Soviets, Turkey would be outflanked, and aircraft based in Syria would be in a position to threaten Iraq, Jordan, Lebanon, Cyprus, and the United States naval base at Iskenderun. The oil pipe line from Iraq could be permanently cut, and raiders from Syria could easily cross the border into Israel. Thus the future of Syria is important to the geopolitical plans of the Soviet Union, Britain, and the United States.

Libya. The newly independent state of Libya is of little value economically, but it is of great strategic importance in the Arab World. Libya borders the Mediterranean for over one thousand miles, and also adjoins Egypt, Tunisia, and Algeria. As a result political and military developments in Libya have had strong repercussions in other parts of North Africa.

This former Italian colony is a desert nation of 1,150,000 inhabitants with three widely-scattered centers of population, each forming the nucleus of a large administrative division: Tripolitania in the west along the Mediterranean coast, with Tripoli as its center; Cyrenaica nearly four hundred miles to the east, also on the Mediterranean coast, with Benghazi its main population center; and the distant oases of Fezzan, four hundred miles south of Tripoli. Over seventy per cent of the population (including most of the Italians) lives in Tripoli, twenty-five per cent lives in Cyrenaica, and less than five per cent inhabits the southern area. The existence of two important core areas is, of course, a factor of considerable significance to political cohesion within the state.

During World War II British forces occupied portions of northern Libya while French forces were in the Fezzan. Following the war the British proposed a ten-year interim period during which Libyans could be trained for independence, but this proposal was blocked in the United Nations by other countries (particularly France, Egypt, and the Soviet Union), which were jealous of Britain's power in the area. No workable solution could be found for a trusteeship status for the area (among other things it was feared that under a trusteeship arrangement Soviet power might be able to establish itself in North Africa), and thus Libya was eventually granted independence by the United Nations.

In the brief time between the United Nations decision for Libyan independence (November, 1949) and the actual start of self-rule Libyan authorities were faced with the problem of obtaining trained personnel for the necessary government posts. The Emir of Cyrenaica was eventually chosen as king by the national assembly, and the cities of Tripoli and Benghazi were designated as twin capitals, with the parliament meeting alternately in each city. In December, 1951, Libya became an independent nation.

Libya's poverty is even greater than that of Tunisia or Egypt. Over ninety per cent of the country's inhabitants are illiterate. There is no defense force; Libya's independence must be guaranteed by American, British, and French forces. The United States operates the Wheelus Air Base in northwestern Libya, near Tripoli, the only American-controlled air base in this part of the Arab World. The British have an important naval and air base in northeastern Libya in the Tobruk area. The French also maintain forces in the country. The revenue from these bases represents an important source of income for the Libyan government. Libya's budget is also aided by subsidies from the British Treasury, and Britain thus continues to maintain influence here in North Africa.

Independence for a disputed area (in contrast with condominiums, neutral zones, and United Nations administration) is an unusual method for solving problems of political control. A decision to establish independence may, of course, fail to take into account the inability of the inhabitants to maintain effective independence due to a lack of internal organization, economic stability, or military power. In the light of the intense nationalist efforts in such areas as Indochina, Indonesia, and Tunisia, it seems ironic that Libya should have received independence almost as if by default.

Jordan. Jordan—formerly the British mandate Transjordan—is one of the poorest of the Arab countries. The eastern and southern portions are desert, and only in the western uplands is there sufficient precipitation for agriculture and extensive grazing. Phosphate is the only important mineral resource. Prior to 1948 the population of about 400,000 was concentrated largely in the western sector, centering on the capital city of Amman. The British mandate was ended in 1946, at which time the area became independent. British bases were retained here, and Britain was granted the right to utilize Jordan's territory in time of war. In return, the state's annual deficit was to be met by payments from the British Treasury.

In 1949, as a result of the Israeli war, Jordan acquired an additional 2,300 square miles of the former Palestine mandate, containing approximately 400,000 persons. At the same time Jordan also received over 450,-000 Arab refugees, so that the nation's population actually trebled within a short space of time. The acquisition of the eastern section of Jerusalem and other regions of eastern Palestine has been an economic asset to Jordan; while, on the other hand, the refugees (whose number in 1956 was given at 499,000) are a drain on its economy. Foreign help will be needed to provide for the permanent settlement of these refugee peoples in Jordan and the other Arab states. The presence of these diverse groups in Jordan has constituted a powerful centrifugal force within the country, since the cultural, economic, and political interests of these people differ widely from those of the majority of the inhabitants of pre-1948 Jordan.

Early in 1957 the Jordanian government announced it would terminate its economic treaty with Britain. The annual subsidy made to Jordan by the British would be provided by Egypt, Saudi Arabia, and Syria. Thus, British influence, which already had been seriously weakened by the "nationalist" trend in Jordan, appeared destined to disappear almost entirely. Here, perhaps even more than in Syria, the resulting power vacuum could destroy the national existence of the state, unless some other power, such as the United States, succeeds in effectively bolstering the Amman government.

The Territorial Problems of Egypt. Since the end of World War I the Egyptian people have gradually established control over the area and resources of their country. In 1922 the British protectorate was ended, although Britain continued to maintain certain rights in Egypt, including that of stationing troops there. Eighteen years later British forces were withdrawn from the country after the conclusion of a treaty which permitted them to remain in the Suez Canal Zone and gave Britain the right to reoccupy Egypt in time of war. This right was exercised during World War II. Although the Egyptians did not declare war on the Axis powers until the spring of 1945, their country was used as a base of operations by Britain and its allies from 1939 to the end of the war by virtue of this Anglo-Egyptian military treaty.

During the decade following the war Egyptian nationalism manifested itself in the abrogation of the Anglo-Egyptian military treaty, and in pressuring the British to evacuate their military forces from the Suez Canal Zone and to terminate their political control in the Anglo-Egyptian Sudan. In 1956 the Egyptians nationalized the Suez Canal. The details of these events involving the Sudan and Suez are considered on page 312.

The pressure of population on Egypt's meager resources has already been noted. With a shortage of minerals (iron ore is the only important resource) and petroleum, and a rapidly increasing population total, Egypt faces a difficult economic future. One of the proposed projects for alleviating Egypt's land problem has been the construction of a high Aswan Dam on the Nile, 400 miles upstream from Cairo, at a cost of $1,300,000,000. The dam would provide for the irrigation of 2,000,000 acres, an increase of nearly one-third of Egypt's cultivated area, and would also be an important source of hydroelectric power. Two problems, however, are associated with this project. First, there is the need for funds to finance the dam; second, permission for its construction must come from Sudan, since the dam would back up water 100 miles across the Sudanese border, inundating the town of Wadi Halfa and the agricultural lands to the south of it. It was in order to obtain funds for the dam from canal tolls that the Egyptian government nationalized the Suez waterway in 1956.

The Sudan.   The controversy which arose between Egypt and Britain after World War II over control of the Anglo-Egyptian Sudan is of politico-geographic interest, since it illustrates the conflict of power forces here in northeastern Africa. During the discussions which took place between British and Egyptian officials two solutions appeared to be the most feasible for the Sudan: first, complete independence for the area or, second, political unification with Egypt. The reduced power position of Britain in this part of the world was evident, for in either case the British stood to lose their share in the control of the Sudan, with its area of nearly one million square miles.

Egypt's claims to the Sudan were based primarily on conquest, ethnic ties, water rights, and the need for additional land for settlement. In addition, Egypt was interested in obtaining a position of power in northeastern Africa. Egyptian forces conquered the Sudan in 1821, and Egypt controlled the area for sixty-four years. A majority of the population is of Arabic origin and Mohammedan. The two main sources of the Nile, although rising outside the borders of the Sudan, flow for a long way through Sudanese territory before crossing the border into Egypt. Since ninety-six per cent of Egypt's population lives in the Nile Valley, the Egyptian government is naturally concerned over the control of the upper reaches of the river. Finally, if the Sudan were joined politically to Egypt it might offer potential areas for the settlement of Egyptians, thereby relieving the population pressure in Egypt, which amounts to over 2,200 persons per square mile of arable land.

There were other factors, however, which served to weaken Egyptian claims. First, although the Egyptians once controlled the Sudan, they were forced out by local uprisings in 1885, and it was the British who did the bulk of the fighting which subdued the area from 1898 to 1917. Second, about thirty per cent of the Sudanese are pagan or Christianized Nilotic peoples rather than Arabs, and have almost no cultural ties whatever with the Egyptians. Finally, even the Sudanese Arabs would oppose large-scale immigration of Egyptians into their country. The British thus felt that it would be unfair for the Sudanese to be forced against their will to join politically with Egypt. Eventually British and Egyptian representatives agreed to grant the Sudan local self-government, and in January, 1956, after native Sudanese leaders had registered their opposition to union with Egypt, the independent state of the Sudan came into existence (see Figure 71).

Like Libya, the Sudan faces enormous internal problems as an independent state. In the absence of adequate transportation, education, and health facilities, of trained personnel, and of a sound economic base, the process of political development may take many years to accomplish. The poorly-trained Arabs and the primitive peoples of the south must be united into a single, cohesive political unit, otherwise the southern sector may break away from the rest of the state and perhaps join the Negro country of

Uganda. A future division of the Sudanese nation into two physical-ethnic units might prove to be a sound move, for the old Anglo-Egyptian Sudan was an artificial creation with little justification as a single political unit.

Relations between the Sudan and Egypt are, of course, complicated by the problems of the Nile. Despite the refusal of the Sudanese to permit the inundation of part of the Nubian Valley as a result of the proposed Aswan Dam, the Egyptian government has gone ahead with its plans for construction. Likewise, the Sudanese wish to reopen the question of the distribution of Nile waters between the two countries. By the terms of the 1929 treaty Egypt gets twelve times as much water as the Sudan, and the latter feels that as a sovereign state it is entitled to a greater share.

The Suez. While they were withdrawing from the Sudan the British also made plans to evacuate the Suez Canal Zone, in order to appease local nationalist aspirations. Constructed in 1869, the 105-mile long waterway greatly reduces the sea voyage from western Europe to the Indian Ocean and Far East. From London to Kuwait on the Persian Gulf, for example, is 7,488 miles via the Suez and 13,437 miles around South Africa; and the distances to Singapore are 9,392 and 13,314 miles respectively. The Suez Canal handles over 100,000,000 tons of cargo a year, more than twice that of the Panama Canal. Of this tonnage about sixty-five per cent consists of oil and oil products, most of it bound from the Persian Gulf area to Europe. Ownership of the canal rested with the Suez Canal Company, an international organization in which French interests controlled a majority of the stock, while the British government owned about forty per cent. In the Constantinople Convention of 1888 nine states (not including Egypt) laid down the principle of freedom of navigation for all vessels through the waterway in peacetime and in war.

Not only is the canal a vital link in seaway communications between Europe and the Indian Ocean basin, but it also crosses the land connection between Africa and Asia. Thus, British military strength in the Suez Canal area was centrally located with respect to the Arab areas to the east, northeast, west, and south. The evacuation of British forces from the Suez Isthmus removed a major focus of European power in the Arab World.

In October, 1954, an agreement was concluded between British and Egyptian authorities, providing for the gradual withdrawal of all British forces from the Suez Canal Zone. The agreement which was to last for seven years, further stipulated that, in the event of a hostile attack on Turkey or any of the Arab states, Britain could reoccupy its Suez bases and remain there until hostilities ended, and that Egypt would keep installations in the Canal Zone "in efficient working order and capable of immediate war action." Thus the British, who previously had abandoned Palestine as a major base, were forced to leave the Suez area as well and concentrate their Middle East forces on Cyprus. Although the Suez Canal was to become by treaty the property of the Egyptians in 1968—99 years after its completion —the Egyptian government announced the nationalization of the canal twelve years before this date, thus following a trend established by Iran in 1951, in which European holdings in this part of the world are gradually being taken over by the Arab countries themselves (see also page 312).

Morocco. The former protectorate of Morocco—including both the French and Spanish areas—became an independent state in 1956. With a population of over 9,000,000 (including some 400,000 Europeans, most of whom are French) Morocco has a large area of cultivable land, as well as phosphate, iron ore, manganese, coal, and hydroelectric resources. The population pressure on the land is not excessive, and the area offers good possibilities for further economic development.

There are several important centrifugal forces in this country. The African population is divided between the Arabs, located largely in the plains areas, and the Berbers, who inhabit the mountains. Because of the concessions granted to them by the French, some of the Berber chieftains remained loyal to France during times of Arab resistance to French control. Rabat, the Moroccan capital, is a coastal town, and is surpassed in size by Casablanca, Marrakech, and Fès. To the rivalry between these regional centers may eventually be added a major contest for power between the Berber and Arab peoples.

The country's location both on the western Mediterranean and on the Atlantic places it in a strategic military position. Following World War II the United States constructed four large air bases in Morocco. Permission for these bases was, of course, secured from France. If the Moroccan government adopts the neutralist policies of Egypt and other Arab states, the availability of these bases to the United States may end. Moreover, as a result of its incorporation of the former Spanish protectorate, independent Morocco occupies the southern shore of the Strait of Gibraltar. Here again, the future policies of the Moroccan government with regard to defense installations will be important to the power position of Western nations in this part of the world.

Less than twenty per cent of the population can read or write, and France for many years contended that these people were unready to assume the responsibilities of self-rule. Nevertheless, in late 1955 local uprisings in Morocco became so intense that the French were forced to recall from exile Morocco's former sultan (who had been deposed by the French for being too nationalistic) and to consent to an ending of Morocco's protectorate status.

The repercussions of independence for French Morocco affected the other dependent areas of North Africa as well. The French protectorate over Tunisia was also ended, as was Spain's protectorate in northwestern Morocco. Ceuta, Spain's naval station on the African side of the Strait of

Gibraltar, was not included in the transfer of sovereignty to the Rabat government, nor were the port of Melilla, east of Ceuta, and three small off-shore islands. Spain also continues to control the enclave of Ifni, a part of Spanish West Africa, on Morocco's southwest coast, and the Southern Zone of Morocco—another part of Spanish West Africa—whose integration into independent Morocco is yet to be negotiated. International control was terminated in Tangier, and the city included within the Moroccan state. Moreover, in Algeria the French have been faced with mounting disorders, as Arab groups—encouraged by the ending of the protectorates in Morocco and Tunisia—have increased their agitation for self-rule (see also page 311).

Tunisia. In contrast with Morocco Tunisia is a poor country, with a population of about 3,700,000 and with an agricultural area which is greatly limited by climate and surface configuration. Tunisia's population includes over 300,000 Europeans, divided almost equally between Frenchmen and Italians. The Europeans here, as in Algeria and Morocco, have tended to settle on the best agricultural lands, leaving the poorer sections for the Arab population. Agricultural practices among the Arabs are often backward, and much of the land is in need of redevelopment. Iron ore, phosphate, lead, and zinc are the principal mineral resources, but their estimated total value is far less than that for the mineral reserves in Morocco. With its rising population, Tunisia, like many other Arab states, faces difficult problems ahead in its economic structure.

Education and training in Tunisia have advanced well beyond the level in Morocco, and among the African population here there do not exist the strong centrifugal forces which are present between the Arabs and Berbers of Morocco. In 1957 Tunisia abolished the office of the bey or native ruler, and adopted a republican form of government. This trend away from monarchical rule in the Arab World may eventually spread to other countries as well, such as Morocco, Libya, and Saudi Arabia.

Algeria. Algeria, with its population of 8,200,000 Arabs and 1,200,000 Frenchmen, is, like Tunisia, overpopulated in terms of housing, education, and employment opportunities for the local population. The country derives economic strength from its wheat, minerals, and hydroelectric power, but these advantages diminish in face of the rapidly-growing population and the lack of capital for development of industry and agriculture.

The birth rate among the Arabs in Algeria of forty-one per thousand (1951) is twice as high as among the Europeans. The Arabs, although theoretically citizens of France, do not enjoy full political privileges equal to those of the French. Poor economic conditions and a lack of faith in France's integration plans have led to bitter riots and guerrilla warfare in Algeria. The French have long looked upon Algeria as an integral part of the homeland, and the French residents of the area have strongly resisted movements by the French government toward greater degrees of Algerian autonomy. However, here, as in Tunisia and Morocco, local pressure may ultimately force major concessions from Paris.

THE PERSIAN GULF OIL AREA

To the west and north of the Persian Gulf is located one of the major oil-producing areas of the world, consisting of southwestern Iran, Iraq, and the eastern part of the Arabian Peninsula.

The first discovery of oil in this area was made by a British company in 1908 in western Iran. By 1914 this region had become an important oil producer, and a pipe line had been constructed between the oil wells and Abadan, where a refinery had been built and from which overseas shipments could be made. By this time the search for oil had also begun to the west of Iran in what is now northern Iraq. Between 1918 and 1939 oil production in the Persian Gulf area expanded rapidly. In both Iran and Iraq revenue from the oil companies came to play a major role in national finances. During the 1930's oil exploration was undertaken along the Persian Gulf coast of the Arabian Peninsula, while to the north the Iraq fields were connected by pipe line with the Mediterranean coast in order to facilitate their exploitation. During World War II oil production in the Persian Gulf area was an important asset to Allied military operations, particularly in the Middle East.

Hundreds of millions of dollars have been poured into the oil-rich Arab states, and from the expanded impact of Western culture upon these countries a whole new set of sociological and political problems has emerged. The contrasts between the rich and the poor have been accentuated as a result of the oil revenues, many Arabs have received educations in Western nations, and in countries such as Kuwait much of the new wealth has been directed toward improvements in health, education, and other social services. Several of the Arab states are now in a position to purchase sizable quantities of military equipment from foreign powers.

With the increased oil activities Arab leaders have demanded a greater share in the wealth from oil operations. In 1951 the Anglo-Iranian Oil Company was nationalized, and in other oil-producing states Arab officials have frequently pressed foreign oil companies for higher production quotas and increased profits, which, if not forthcoming, might result in further nationalization movements.

By the end of 1956 the Middle East accounted for approximately twenty per cent of the world oil production (see Table 11 for production by countries). Much of the oil is sent in crude form to refineries in other parts of the world, although the bulk of Iran's production is refined at Abadan, and there are smaller refineries near Dammam in Saudi Arabia and on Bahrein Island. To facilitate transportation the Trans-Arabian Pipe-

Table 11

WORLD CRUDE OIL PRODUCTION, 1956

Continent and Country	Average Daily Production (actual barrels)	Year's Production as per cent of World Total
North America	7,869,585	47.26
Canada	459,352	2.75
Cuba	1,555	0.01
Mexico	257,377	1.55
United States . . .	7,151,301	42.95
South America	2,826,961	16.98
Argentina	85,669	0.52
Barbados	—	—
Bolivia	8,727	0.05
Brazil	8,560	0.05
Chile	9,153	0.06
Colombia	120,219	0.72
Ecuador	10,027	0.06
Peru	50,191	0.30
Trinidad	78,415	0.47
Venezuela	2,456,000	14.75
Europe	1,992,508	11.97
Albania	4,500	0.03
Austria	61,202	0.37
Czechoslovakia . . .	3,301	0.02
France	22,923	0.14
Germany, West . . .	67,607	0.41
Great Britain . . .	1,366	—
Hungary	13,973	0.09
Italy	10,109	0.06
Netherlands	20,355	0.12
Poland	4,098	0.03
Romania	226,301	1.35
U.S.S.R.	1,550,374	9.31
Yugoslavia	6,000	0.04
Africa	32,929	0.20
Algeria	743	—
Egypt	30,055	0.18
Morocco	2,131	0.02
Asia, Total	3,926,394	23.59
Asia, Middle East . . .	3,445,500	20.70
Bahrein	30,033	0.18
Iran	542,732	3.26
Iraq	637,077	3.83
Israel	500	—
Kuwait	1,086,298	6.52
Neutral Zone . . .	32,787	0.20
Qatar	124,044	0.75
Saudi Arabia . . .	986,128	5.93
Turkey	5,901	0.03
Asia, Far East	480,894	2.89
Burma	5,169	0.03
India	6,396	0.04

Table 11 (continued)

WORLD CRUDE OIL PRODUCTION, 1956

Continent and Country	Average Daily Production (actual barrels)	Year's Production as per cent of World Total
Pakistan	5,921	0.04
China	30,055	0.18
Indonesia	283,306	1.70
Japan	6,257	0.04
New Guinea	7,063	0.04
Sakhalin	19,126	0.12
Sarawak-Brunei . . .	117,536	0.70
Taiwan (Formosa) .	65	—
Australia-New Zealand .	14	—
Total World	16,649,391	100.00

Source: *World Oil*, Vol. 144, No. 3 (February 15, 1957), 214. Used by permission.

line (Tapline), over 1,000 miles in length, was constructed across northern Saudi Arabia, linking the American-controlled fields on the Persian Gulf with the Lebanese port of Saida (Sidon) on the Mediterranean.

Ownership of the oil companies in the Persian Gulf area is shown in Table 12. British influence is powerful in Kuwait, Bahrein, in the southeastern Arabian Peninsula, and to a less extent in Iraq and Iran. The United States has close relations with Saudi Arabia, primarily as a result of American control of the oil company in that state. The United States maintains an air base at Dhahran on the Persian Gulf. The base is not militarized, but United States military aircraft are permitted to use its landing and refueling facilities.

Because of its great oil wealth Saudi Arabia has come to occupy a significant position in international politics in this part of the world. In contrast with the poverty existing in most of the Arab countries, the Saudi Arabian government receives several hundred million dollars annually in oil royalties, only a small percentage of which is spent on public improvements and on domestic health and education projects. The government has generally followed the Egyptians in neutralist policies toward the Cold War, in attempts to reduce British influence in this part of the world, in rivalry toward Iraq, and, of course, in hostility to Israel. Thus, on the one hand, Saudi Arabia derives great wealth from United States-managed oil operations, while on the other it pursues a course of action which is often inimical to the interests of the United States and of Britain.

The development of oil resources on the Arabian Peninsula has resulted in a boundary controversy between Saudi Arabia and two small states along the Persian Gulf. These states are Abu Dhabi, one of the Trucial States, and Muscat (Oman), an independent sultanate. The dispute involves the

Table 12

OWNERSHIP OF MAJOR OIL COMPANIES

IN PERSIAN GULF AREA

(*Percentages*)

British Petroleum Company

British Government	51.55
Burmah Oil Company	24.95
Individuals	23.50

Iraq Petroleum

British Petroleum	23.75
Royal Dutch Shell	23.75
Cie. Française des Petroles	23.75
Standard Oil (N.J.)	11.875
Socony-Mobil Oil Company	11.875
C. S. Gulbenkian	5.00

Kuwait Oil

British Petroleum	50.00
Gulf Oil Company	50.00

Arabian-American

Standard Oil (Cal.)	30.00
Texas Company	30.00
Standard Oil (N.J.)	30.00
Socony-Mobil Oil Company	10.00

Bahrein Oil

Standard Oil (Cal.)	50.00
Texas Company	50.00

Iranian Consortium

British Petroleum	40.00
Royal Dutch Shell	14.00
Standard Oil (N.J.)	7.00
Standard Oil (Cal.)	7.00
Socony-Mobil Oil Company	7.00
Gulf Oil Company	7.00
Texas Company	7.00
Cie. Française des Petroles	6.00
American Independent Oil Cos.	5.00

Source: Pratt and Good, *World Geography of Petroleum* (New York: American Geographical Society, 1950), pp. 177–78; and *The New York Times*.

location of Saudi Arabia's boundaries with respect to the Buraimi Oasis, an area containing valuable oil reserves. If the oasis is located within the territory of Saudi Arabia, the Arabian-American Oil Company will develop the oil; if it is not, the Iraq Petroleum Company, in which the British are strongly represented, will carry out the exploitation. Boundaries in this area have never been clearly delimited, and the case has since been referred to the International Court of Justice. One of the interesting aspects of the case has been the British complaint that the Saudi Arabians have been spending enormous sums of money bribing local chieftains in this area to switch their allegiance from the ruler of Abu Dhabi and the sultan of Muscat to the king of Saudi Arabia. The British feel that if they lose control of the Buraimi Oasis their whole position with respect to the Persian Gulf states—including Kuwait—will be severely threatened. As a result they are determined to do all in their power to prevent the expansion of the boundaries of Saudi Arabia to include this area.

The Israeli-Arab controversy has had reverberations in Middle Eastern "oil politics," since Saudi Arabia and Iraq both belong to the Arab League, whose members are still technically at war with Israel. The governments of the United States and Britain were forced to weigh their relationships with both the Jews and the Arabs against the background of Western interests in the oil of the Arab states and of the important strategic location of the Arab areas in terms of the Cold War. With the outbreak of hostilities in Israel, the pipe line from Kirkuk, Iraq, to Haifa, Israel, was permanently closed. Since Iraq has refused to reopen this line, Israel has had to import more expensive oil from overseas, which has further aggravated its economic difficulties. Moreover, since 1948 all projected routes for pipe lines from the oil areas to the Mediterranean coast have carefully avoided Israeli territory.

Iran

Iran lies beyond the limits of the Arab World as defined here, but it is considered in this chapter because of its role in the oil developments and because of its geographic location.

Forces of Unity and Diversity. Iran consists of a vast plateau, divided by numerous highland areas into a series of cultivable basins, and a few coastal lowlands. The terrain offers no central unifying area for the nation; rather there are several core areas. Most of Iran is desert or semidesert, and communications between the capital, Tehran, and other population centers are poor. The movement of people and of ideas throughout much of the country is not well-developed, and Tehran's control is weak in many provincial areas.

From a cultural point of view there is remarkable unity throughout Iran on the basis of tradition and religion. It is this cultural unity, more than any other factor, which has preserved Iran as a cohesive political unit. Unlike the inhabitants of most other Moslem states, the Iranians belong largely to the Shiite sect. Major minority groups among the total population of over 20 million include some 2 million Azerbaijanis and 800,000 Kurds in the northwestern part of the nation, as well as over 500,000 other persons belonging to various tribes throughout Iran, whose languages differ from that of the majority of Iranians. Tribal leaders still exercise considerable control over their people, and only recently has Tehran's authority become strongly felt in these non-Iranian-speaking areas.

Foreign Control in Iran. At the beginning of the twentieth century Iran, then known as Persia, was a weak but independent state. The principal external pressures exerted on it at this time were from Great Britain and Russia, the former moving northward from the Arabian Sea-Persian Gulf area, and the latter pressing south from the Caspian Sea region and its long border with Iran. British military power was also stationed in India, along Iran's eastern border. In 1907 the British and Russian governments agreed to establish zones of influence in Iran, thus developing the country as a buffer between the power spheres of the two nations. Although the foreign spheres of influence in Iran were abandoned after World War I, a Soviet-Iranian agreement was concluded in 1921, whereby Russia was permitted to send armed reinforcements to Iran in case that country should be invaded by a third power and used as a base for aggression against the Soviet Union.

During World War II Soviet forces occupied northern Iran to protect military supply lines running north to the U.S.S.R. from the Persian Gulf. By agreement with the Iranian government foreign occupation troops were to leave the country within six months of the end of World War II, but in the spring of 1946 Russian forces were still in Azerbaijan Province in northwestern Iran. Inhabited largely by Turkic-speaking peoples, Azerbaijan (area 41,000 square miles; population 2¾ million) is one of the best-watered parts of Iran, and thus an important agricultural area. Past relations between Azerbaijan and Tehran have not always been friendly, and the Soviets, during their period of occupation, sought to establish an autonomous people's republic in the area with close ties to the U.S.S.R., where there is also an Azerbaijani population. In the face of strong pressure from the United Nations, the Soviets finally withdrew their forces from Iranian Azerbaijan in May, 1946, and the movement for a people's republic here quietly collapsed.

The Kurds. The Russians also fostered an independence movement among the Kurds, a cultural group of about 2½ million people spread out over five nations—Iran, Iraq, Syria, Turkey, and the U.S.S.R. The Kurds, united by the common use of the Kurdish language, are primarily nomadic tribesmen, living in the mountain masses southeast of the Black Sea and adjoining areas to the south. Because of their relative isolation and their military traditions, they have managed to retain considerable independence of action in their rugged homeland, regardless of the power or powers nominally controlling the territory in which they live. A delegation allegedly representing the Kurds appeared before the Versailles Conference in 1919 and the San Francisco Conference in 1945, seeking an independent Kurdish state to be created from parts of Turkish, Syrian, Iraqi, and Iranian territory. The political demands of the Kurds appealed to the Soviets after the occupation of Azerbaijan in 1941, and the Russians assisted the Kurdish nationalists, hoping thereby to weaken Iran, Iraq, and Turkey in the areas close to the Soviet frontier.

The Oil Crisis in Iran

Iranian nationalism, which reached a climax in the 1951 nationalization of the Anglo-Iranian Oil Company, eventually resulted in widespread economic and political difficulties for the country. In response to what they termed the illegal seizure of the company, the British established a world-wide boycott of Iranian oil. Since profits from the sale of oil normally represented about forty per cent of Iran's national revenue, the boycott created enormous financial hardships for the nation. Because of internal political and economic problems the Iranian Communist (Tudeh) Party became the strongest political group in the country.

By 1953 strikes and riots were a frequent occurrence, and the nation appeared to be in danger of a communist-inspired revolution. Yet if a major communist uprising took place, British and American forces could not intervene (even at the invitation of the Iranian government) without risking Soviet armed intervention by right of the 1921 Soviet-Iranian agreement. In August, 1953, an army-led revolt resulted in the establishment of a pro-Western government in Tehran, and gradually the danger of a communist revolt subsided. An arrangement was worked out to compensate the British for their loss of investments in the Anglo-Iranian Oil Company, the boycott was lifted, and eventually Iran concluded military agreements with Britain and the United States. A consortium was formed to handle Iranian oil production and international sales (see Table 12). Iran, however, still faces internal problems, which have been brought on by the extreme poverty of most of its people, the presence of a strong landholding class which opposes major land-reform programs, and the existence of a strong, though illegal, Communist Party, ready to capitalize on popular discontent at the earliest opportunity. Because of the nation's location and resources, its political future is a matter of great concern to all the major world powers.

Problem Areas

1. Israel's Borders

The continued Arab hostility toward Israel has posed a serious threat to world peace. The Arab states have refused to concede the permanent existence of the Jewish state. They have remained officially at war with Israel, intermittent fighting has continued along the Israeli borders, and there has been an international arms race in this part of the world, as both Israel and the Arab countries prepare for the possible outbreak of full-scale warfare. As a result of the Israeli-Egyptian conflict of 1956, United Nations forces are deployed along the borders of the Gaza strip, as well as on the west shore of the Strait of Tiran, thereby enabling Israeli shipping to enter and leave the Gulf of Aqaba.

Perhaps the most difficult aspect of this problem is the attitude of the Arab states in refusing to negotiate with Israel for a lasting territorial settlement and to make plans for the permanent solution of the refugee problem. The Israeli government has been forced to allot a large proportion of its budget to defense, since the nation must remain in a state of permanent military preparedness. With their locational importance and their control of oil resources, the Arab states are in a strong bargaining position with respect to the Cold War. Thus Israel, having won the military campaign of 1948–49, still faces many serious problems in safeguarding its existence in the midst of hostile Arab states.

2. France's Declining Position in North Africa

France's power position in North Africa has been greatly reduced since the end of World War II. Among the factors contributing to this decline have been (1) France's defeat and occupation during the war, (2) the rise of independence in other parts of the Arab World, and (3) the steadily-mounting costs of French colonial administration in North Africa.

The ending of the French protectorates over Morocco and Tunisia has already been noted. The French position with regard to these areas is that they shall remain tied to France by bonds of "interdependence"—that is, France will continue to give economic and other forms of assistance, in return for which the two governments will co-operate with the French in defense and foreign affairs. One of the practical effects of interdependence as conceived by France is that French forces will continue for a time to occupy portions of the former protectorates. Among the reasons why the French have insisted on maintaining their military position in these areas is that from Morocco and Tunisia French troops can help to combat local rebellion in the neighboring state of Algeria.

The concessions to nationalism which France has already made in Morocco and Tunisia may eventually be followed by other moves which will further weaken French control in North Africa. Greater degrees of self-rule may become necessary in Algeria, France may in time be compelled to withdraw its military forces completely from Morocco and Tunisia, and Moroccan officials have already suggested extending the countries' borders southward into French West Africa, on the basis of the historic claims of the old Moroccan Empire. Economic necessity, however, will continue to bind the two former protectorates to France, for, despite the many sources of friction with the Paris government, both states are urgently in need of financial aid.

3. The Suez Crisis

The nationalization of the Suez Canal by the Egyptian government in the summer of 1956 has already been noted. In October–November, 1956, the Suez area was invaded by the forces of Britain, France, and Israel, in an effort to bring to a head such problems as the future status of the canal, the continued violation of Israel's borders by Egyptian raiders, and the steady drift of the Arab states away from Western influence. In the face of United States pressure and Soviet threats, the invading armies halted after a brief campaign, and the existing Egyptian government—whose anti-Western actions had provoked the invasion—remained in power. The foreign troops were eventually withdrawn, and a United Nations force was sent to occupy the areas which they had evacuated, although the conditions of occupation and the duration of time the troops were to remain in Egypt were not made clear at the time of occupation.

The invasion of Suez raised a great many questions concerning future power relations in the Arab World. One effect of the invasion was that Egypt abrogated its 1954 treaty with Britain for the defense of the Suez area in time of war. The British have also lost their rights to military bases in Jordan and the government of Yemen, apparently anticipating the withdrawal of British power from this part of the world, has engaged in armed attacks against some of the northern states of the Aden Protectorate. Conversely the position of the Soviet Union has grown stronger in this part of the world. The flow of Soviet arms to Arab states has apparently increased, economic ties have grown stronger between the Arab and communist areas, and there is a danger of communist-type governments developing in certain of the Arab countries. Countering this has been the commitment of increased United States military and economic aid in this part of the world.

At the time of the invasion the Egyptians blocked the Suez waterway by sinking ships in the channel. Approximately one-half of Europe's normal oil requirements are brought by tanker through the Suez; another twenty per cent are transported by pipe lines from Iraq to the Mediterranean coast and then by tanker to Europe. The Iraq pipe lines were cut by Arab nationalists during the Suez fighting, and with the canal blocked most of Europe's oil imports from the Persian Gulf region were brought by ship around Africa. In view of the shortage of tankers for this long haul, Europe's oil imports were seriously curtailed as a result of the military action in Egypt, and the price of oil for the European states was increased. This was a severe blow to the economies of these countries, necessitating increased oil shipments to Europe from the Western Hemisphere. At the same time some of the Middle Eastern governments were deprived of very important revenues from their oil operations. These, then, are some of the world-wide repercussions resulting from the interference with shipping through the Suez Canal.

BIBLIOGRAPHY

ALEXANDER, LEWIS M. "The Arab-Israeli Boundary Problem," *World Politics*, VI, No. 3 (April, 1954), 322–38.

Historical and geographical background of the conflict along Israel's borders.

FISHER, W. B. *The Middle East*. New York: E. P. Dutton & Co., Inc., 1950.

An excellent regional geography of the area.

MELAMID, ALEXANDER. "The Buraimi Oasis Dispute," *Middle Eastern Affairs*, VII, No. 2 (February, 1956), 56–63.

The problems and events associated with this controversy.

————. "Political Geography of Trucial Oman and Qatar," *The Geographical Review*, XLIII, No. 2 (April, 1953), 194–207.

A comprehensive description of the political areas along the southern Persian Gulf coast. Contains a detailed map of the area.

MONTAGNE, ROBERT. "Modern Nations and Islam," *Foreign Affairs*, XXX, No. 4 (July, 1952), 580–93.

A description of some of the basic forces and problems associated with the new states of the Arab World.

PRATT, WALLACE E., and GOOD, DOROTHY. *World Geography of Petroleum*. New York: American Geographical Society, 1950.

A basic text on the petroleum industry with a special section on the Middle East.

SIEGFRIED, ANDRE. "The Suez: International Roadway," *Foreign Affairs*, XXXI, No. 4 (July, 1953), 605–19.

A detailed account of problems of territorial control in this area.

WESTERMANN, WILLIAM LINN. "Kurdish Independence and Russian Expansion," *Foreign Affairs*, XXIV, No. 4 (July, 1946), 675–87.

A political history of Kurdish attempts to win independence.

WHITTLESEY, DERWENT. "Lands Athwart the Nile," *World Politics*, V, No. 2 (January, 1953), 214–42.

A concise politico-geographic study of the Nile basin.

12

CENTRAL AFRICA

● Central Africa is the last major area of colonialism left to the nations of western Europe. Within this region of great resources complex forces of unity and diversity are evident in the physical and ethnic environments and in the complicated and gradually-changing pattern of territorial control. Boundaries delimited in the early periods of African colonialism have come to be sources of conflict, as mineral and power resources are utilized and as various native groups begin to develop political consciousness. In central Africa, as in Asia, nationalism has been a rapidly-growing force, particularly since World War II. The process of readjusting the patterns of political control to fit the changing needs and aspirations of the people of Africa is the most significant politico-geographic factor of this area.

Six nations share colonial control in Africa: Belgium, Britain, France, Italy, Portugal, and Spain. Some of the aspects of European sovereignty in central Africa were considered in Chapter 5, especially the changing relationships between the African territories and the European states from the point of view of the latter. In this chapter the relationships will be treated from the African point of view.

According to the limits defined in Chapter 11, central Africa adjoins Morocco, Algeria, Libya, and the Sudan on the north. On the south it borders the Union of South Africa and its mandate, Southwest Africa. The region thus delimited has an area of approximately 7,500,000 square miles and a population of some 140,000,000 persons. By 1957 it contained three independent and twenty-eight dependent political units.

Physical Features

Central Africa stretches from approximately 15° north latitude to 25° south latitude; it therefore lies almost entirely within the Tropics. With respect to other continents, central Africa is relatively isolated. Major world trade routes generally avoid the central African coasts, since the sea route from Europe or Anglo-America to southern Asia and the Far East is considerably longer around southern Africa than through the Mediterranean and the Suez Canal. The relative isolation from Europe which it possesses because of location and the protective barrier of the Sahara, together with its resource wealth, makes central Africa an important area in terms of world power relationships. The region could provide a strong defense area for the Western nations should all or a large part of Europe be overwhelmed by Soviet power. Conversely, central Africa in hostile hands would be a potent threat to the nations of western Europe and the Western Hemisphere, because of the loss of resources and investments, and because enemy power in central Africa could threaten the South Atlantic and Brazil, as well as the Indian Ocean area and southwestern Asia.

The surface configuration of central Africa consists for the most part of a plateau, 2,000 to 4,000 feet in elevation, although there are many local variations of this. Lowland areas include the Congo River basin (averaging 1,000–2,000 feet), the narrow Atlantic and broader Indian Ocean coastal plains, and extensive areas of less than 1,000 feet elevation along the Guinea coast, west of the Cameroons mountains. Mountain areas, rising above the plateau, consist of the highlands of Ethiopia, the uplands of southern Kenya, Tanganyika, Nyasaland, and the Rhodesias, and the mountains of Ruanda-Urundi, Cameroons, and Belgian Congo. Within the Tropics such uplands generally have temperatures more like those in mid-latitude areas, and many of these mountain regions offer important settlement areas for Europeans. Examples of the range of average mean monthly temperatures at sea level can be found at Lagos, Nigeria, 78°–83°, Mombasa, Kenya, 75°–82°, and Lourenço Marques, Mozambique, 74°–82° (as compared with New Orleans, 54°–84°). Characteristic upland temperatures are at Livingstone, Northern Rhodesia (3,000 feet), 64°–81°, Elizabethville, Belgian Congo (4,500 feet), 60°–75°, and Addis Ababa, Ethiopia (8,000 feet), 59°–66°.

The natural resources of central Africa are of considerable value. Heavy precipitation and relief combine to give this region the greatest hydroelectric-power potential of any area in the world. Petroleum is virtually nonexistent, but there are coal deposits in Southern Rhodesia, Nigeria, and Tanganyika. The list of minerals is impressive: gold, copper, tin, chromium, cobalt, uranium, and manganese, as well as lead, zinc, vanadium, and diamonds, are produced in quantity. Iron ore is located in the Rhodesias, Liberia, French

Guinea, and Sierra Leone. Much of central Africa has never been mapped geologically, and new mineral resources will undoubtedly be discovered in future years. Another important feature of the area's mineral wealth is that many of its resources, such as uranium, manganese, cobalt, and tin, are in great demand in the industrialized countries of the world. Agriculturally, central Africa is also important. Throughout much of the region the growing season is twelve months in length (although some areas experience seasonal drought), and the agricultural potential is high, particularly if capital becomes available and new farming practices are adopted.

Economy

Despite the variety of natural resources which exist in central Africa, economic development has been slow throughout much of the area. In most regions subsistence agriculture remains the basic way of life, and with the increasing pressure of population there is a growing problem as to the ability of the land to support the indigenous population. Mechanization of agriculture is not always feasible because of the nature of the soil and the dangers of soil erosion and loss of fertility. Thus many of the farming practices which have proven useful in mid-latitude areas cannot be applied in central Africa, and new techniques must be developed if the per capita productivity in subsistence farming areas is to be maintained.

Much of the commercial agriculture has been undertaken by Europeans, although in the Gold Coast, Nigeria, and, to a less extent, in other western areas native capital and labor have been responsible for considerable economic growth. In eastern Africa—particularly in Uganda and Tanganyika—native groups are likewise engaged in the growing of commercial crops, such as coffee and cotton. In these areas, and along the Kenya coast, there have also been large investments of Asiatic capital, both in agriculture and commerce. Most of the trade of the central African countries has been with overseas areas. The relatively small amount of intra-African trade has helped to perpetuate the sense of political diversity among the peoples of this part of the world.

Industrialization in central Africa is only starting to develop and is confined principally to the Rhodesias and the Belgian Congo. Shortages of capital and power facilities have hindered the growth of all but the most basic types of industries. As a result the countries of central Africa are forced to import the major share of their manufactured articles—a situation which seems destined to continue even after the achievement of independence by many of the areas. The impact of Westernization has increased the market for processed goods, and the continued dependence of central Africa on foreign areas for these commodities may have repercussions not only in trade patterns but also in the spread of political influence.

As the world demand for Africa's minerals increases, and as capital and transportation facilities make possible greater production, the area's commercial importance will continue to grow. Likewise, with new advances in scientific soil improvement and insect pest eradication, new regions will be opened to commercial agriculture and new crops will be developed. Central Africa faces difficult problems in its efforts to raise substantially the average per capita income of its people. Economic and political advancement must go together. However, the paradox exists that as African territories achieve self-rule and their policies, particularly with regard to private investments, become more susceptible to fluctuation, foreign investors become reluctant to commit themselves heavily in these areas.

Population

The population of central Africa may be divided roughly into four groups—natives, Europeans, Arabs, and Asiatics (Table 13). The natives, numbering about 139 million, comprise by far the largest group. Professor Stamp[1] subdivides them into three principal types: the Guinea and Sudanese Negroes of the western and central portions of the continent, roughly between the Sahara and the equator; the Bantu Negroes in the central and southern parts; and the non-Negroid peoples of Ethiopia, Eritrea, and the Somalilands, as well as northern Nigeria and parts of French West Africa.

The whites number over 600,000, and represent the controlling economic and political groups in practically all of the countries. The approximately 90,000 Arabs are concentrated principally along the east coast, in Zanzibar, Kenya, and Tanganyika. The Asiatics, who total about 250,000, are mostly Indians, whose forebears came to Africa as contract laborers, and who are concentrated along the east coast (Tanganyika, Kenya, Zanzibar, and Mozambique), as well as in Uganda and Angola.

Although large areas still have a low population density, a significant factor of central Africa's population is the rapid increase in the number of native peoples. Here, as in other parts of the world, the impact of Western culture has resulted in a gradual lowering of the death rates; birth rates, on the other hand, remain high. Some representative native birth rates are: Southern Rhodesia, 46.2 per thousand (estimated 1950); Northern Rhodesia, 59.0 (estimated 1950); and Ruanda-Urundi, 42.9 (estimated 1949). As the native population climbs, the pressure on central Africa's resources, particularly agricultural resources, will increase. Soil erosion and exhaustion will continue to limit production, and unless native agricultural techniques are improved, and the over-all basis of central Africa's

[1] L. Dudley Stamp, *Africa: A Study in Tropical Development* (New York: John Wiley & Sons, Inc., 1953).

Table 13

POLITICAL UNITS AND PEOPLES IN CENTRAL AFRICA

Unit	Area (sq. mi.)	Population		
		Natives	Whites	Others
Independent States				
Ethiopia (incl. Eritrea)	475,800	16,000,000 (1953 est.)	25,000	
Ghana (incl. former Brit. Togoland)	91,840	4,119,000 (1948)	6,770	
Liberia	43,000	2,500,000 (1953 est.)		
British Empire				
Bechuanaland	275,000	297,000 (1946)	2,300	1,800 (Asiatics)
British Somaliland	68,000	650,000 (1953 est.)	100	
Gambia	4,003	277,000 (1951–52)	300	
Kenya	224,960	5,550,000 (1952)	40,000	98,000 (Indians); 24,000 (Arabs)
Nigeria (incl. Brit. Cameroons)	373,236	31,625,000 (1952–53)	5,200	
Northern Rhodesia	290,300	1,890,000 (1951 est.)	37,200	3,600 (Indians and Colored*)
Nyasaland	48,442	2,392,000 (1952)	4,000	5,250 (Indians)
Sierra Leone	27,924	2,000,000 (1951 est.)	1,000	2,000 (Indians)
Southern Rhodesia	150,327	2,010,000 (1951 est.)	140,000	10,300 (Indians and Colored*)
Tanganyika	362,674	7,400,000 (1948)	17,900 (1952)	56,500 (Indians— 1952); 13,000 (Arabs)
Uganda	93,981	4,918,000 (1948)	3,450	35,200 (Indians); 1,500 (Arabs)
Zanzibar (incl. Pemba)	1,020	200,000 (1948)	300	44,560 (Arabs); 15,900 (Indians)
French Union				
French Cameroons	169,500	3,064,000 (1952)	13,200	
French Equatorial Africa	969,000	4,413,000 (1952)	21,900 (1951)	
French Somaliland	8,500	55,600 (1952)	2,400	6,000 (Arabs)
French Togoland	21,200	1,029,000 (1952)	1,400	
French West Africa	1,831,100	17,300,000 (1951)	62,200	
Madagascar	227,950	4,372,000 (1952)	66,400	17,000 (Asiatics)
Portuguese Empire				
Angola (and Cabinda)	481,350	4,072,000 (1950)	45,000	28,000 (Mixed*)

Table 13 (continued)

POLITICAL UNITS AND PEOPLES IN CENTRAL AFRICA

Unit	Area (sq. mi.)	Population		
		Natives	Whites	Others
Mozambique	297,731	5,680,000 (1950)	49,000	16,000 (Mixed*) ; 9,150 (Indians) ; 1,500 (Orientals)
Portuguese Guinea	13,948	504,000 (1950)	2,300	4,600 (Mixed*)
São Tomé and Príncipe	372	54,700 (1950)	1,200	4,300 (Mixed*)
Belgian Empire				
Belgian Congo	904,991	11,789,000 (1952)	81,900	
Ruanda-Urundi	20,916	4,006,000 (1952)	5,100	2,000 (Indians)
Spanish Empire				
Spanish Guinea (incl. Fernando Po)	10,830	210,000 (1950)	4,400	
Italian Empire				
Somalia	198,275	1,250,000 (1950 est.)	4,600	

*The terms "colored" and "mixed" refer to persons of white-native ancestry.
Source: Population figures from *The Statesman's Yearbook,* 1954. Unless otherwise noted, the figures for "Whites" and "Others" are for the same year as those for "Natives."

economy becomes more varied, the increasing population will create far-reaching economic, political, and social problems.

One important aspect of central Africa's population structure is the increased mobility which has taken place as a result of improved circulatory systems. Because of this greater freedom of movement tribal authority has been weakened and there has been a general drift of people to the cities or to mining areas. The trend toward urbanization has, among other things, affected the labor supply, for in some farming areas there is a shortage of workers, while in many cities there is widespread unemployment among the African population.

POLITICAL DEVELOPMENT

Exploration and Early White Settlement

The modern history of central Africa dates back to the fifteenth century and the voyages of the Portuguese along the Atlantic coast in search of a new route to the Indies. By the middle of the century Portuguese seamen had passed south of the Sahara barrier and explored the Guinea coast. By 1500 permanent settlements had been established on the Gold Coast, Vasco da Gama had rounded the Cape of Good Hope and discovered the

sea route to India, and by the Treaty of Tordesillas (1494) Portugal had
been granted title to all newly-discovered lands east of 50° west longitude—
an area which included all of central Africa. At this early date the nations of
northwestern Europe had not yet developed their maritime facilities to the
point where they were ready to undertake expeditions to the central African
coastal region, so that Portugal had a relatively free hand in the early exploration and development of the area. A string of forts was established on
the Guinea coast to guard the Portuguese trade in gold, ivory, and slaves,
while other settlements were located further south on the west coast (in
what is now Angola) and on the east coast (Mozambique and Kenya).
Portuguese colonial interests, however, were directed more toward Brazil
and the Far East than toward central Africa, and little effort was made to
halt the gradual expansion in this area of other European states during and
after the seventeenth century. In 1618 the British established a fort at Gambia in west Africa, and soon settlements were also developed along the
Guinea coast by Holland, France, Denmark, and the German state of Bran-
denburg-Prussia. In 1642 France also established a fort on the island of
Madagascar to protect its trade routes to the East.

The chief objectives of the European powers in central Africa from the
mid-seventeenth to mid-nineteenth centuries were (1) to develop the lucra-
tive trade in slaves, gold, and ivory, particularly along the western coast,
and (2) to safeguard their sea lanes to the Indies. The European development of the African coastal areas continued slowly during the eighteenth and
nineteenth centuries, and little effort was made to investigate the interior
of the continent, either for commercial exploitation or for the establishment
of political control. The lack of major indentations in the coast, of good
harbors and of navigable waterways extending inland into the continent, the
obstacles of tropical forests and hostile tribes, the absence of readily-available
riches, and finally the greater opportunities for wealth in the New World and
the Orient combined to discourage European penetration into central Africa
until four centuries after the first settlement of the coasts.

Nineteenth-century explorers, notably Livingstone and Stanley, finally
acquainted European governments and businessmen with the wealth of central Africa. "When European industrialization had developed a need for
raw materials that yearly grew more active, when vacant spaces in the Pacific, the Far East, and southern and western Asia had been allocated, with
South America a politically closed world on account of the Monroe Doctrine,
Africa was the only large free realm in which political power and colonial
trade could yet be won together."[2] Not until 1870 did the political division of
central Africa finally get under way, and within thirty years practically the
entire area had been partitioned.

---

[2] Isaiah Bowman, *The New World* (New York: World Book Company, 1928), p. 637.

Colonial Expansion—1870 to World War I

In a survey such as this the details of the territorial division of central Africa cannot be considered except in general terms. There were various motives for the rapid movement to acquire territories in the late nineteenth century. Among these were commercial exploitation, desire for national prestige, attempts to suppress the illegal slave trade, missionary activities, and jealousy over the expansion of territorial control by rival powers. The race for territorial expansion was at first a rather haphazard affair, with numerous and conflicting claims, but at the Berlin Conference of 1884–85 the European powers agreed to regularize their imperialism in order to avoid serious clashes. The treaty which was drafted at the conference made no mention (other than to denounce slavery) of the rights of the Africans themselves, but it drew up a code of ethics for territorial expansion by providing that no nation was to establish a new claim in Africa without first notifying the other powers, that recognition of territorial claims must depend on effective occupation, and that all disputes were to be settled by arbitration.

The territorial scramble in central Africa during the late nineteenth century involved France, Germany, Italy, Belgium, Portugal, and Britain. Spain, the seventh colonial power in Africa, merely retained the small possessions it had acquired in the early years of overseas explorations in the Gulf of Guinea area and to the north along the Atlantic coast. France, having suffered defeat at the hands of the Germans during the Franco-Prussian War (1870–71), wished to regain its national prestige, and from their bases along the Atlantic and Guinea coasts the French pressed inland to acquire control over what are now French West Africa and French Equatorial Africa. France also established a base on the lower Red Sea coast as a nucleus for what later became French Somaliland.

The German states were unified in 1871, but until the mid-1880's the German government had little interest in acquiring colonies in central Africa, because of the difficulties and expense involved and the general lack of knowledge about the area's potentialities. After the Berlin Conference, however, the Germans began moving rapidly to secure their nation's "place in the sun." Treaties were signed with native rulers along the Guinea coast, in Southwest Africa, and in the eastern sector of the continent, which placed these areas under German protection and set up commercial establishments to develop Africa's resources.

Italy, unified in 1870, soon became interested in Africa as an area for colonial expansion. By the 1880's, however, the Italians found that most of the desirable coastal areas had already been occupied by other powers, and they were forced to content themselves with territories having little economic value. In 1882 Italy established a foothold in Eritrea on the Red Sea coast, and seven years later Italian Somaliland on the Indian Ocean was also claimed. Attempts to move inland and conquer the native state of Ethiopia ended in military defeat at the hands of the Ethiopians in 1896.

Belgium's colonial activities in central Africa came about through the personal interest shown in this area by Leopold II, the Belgian king. In 1878 Leopold established the International Association of the Congo, an organization over which he exercised dominant control and which eventually became the agency for the establishment of the Independent State of the Congo. Non-Belgian interests in the Congo were bought out by Leopold in 1887, and for twenty-one years this area of over 900,000 square miles was held as virtually the private property of the Belgian monarch. The brutal treatment of the Congolese, together with other excesses in the administration of this area, finally led a reluctant Belgian government to annex the area as a colony in 1908.

Portugal also partook of the new imperialist spirit in the closing years of the nineteenth century, In Portuguese Guinea on the northwest African coast and on the islands of São Tomé and Príncipe in the Gulf of Guinea Portugal strengthened its colonial holdings. Farther south the Portuguese attempted to link their west- and east-coast possessions (Angola and Mozambique) by a strip through the central part of the continent, but their plans were thwarted by the activities of Cecil Rhodes (see discussion below).

Britain was the nation which eventually established the most extensive colonial holdings in central Africa. In addition to possessions along the western coast (Gambia, Sierra Leone), dating back to seventeenth-century settlements, the British after 1870 expanded their power in the Gold Coast and Nigeria in the face of opposing claims by France and Germany. Commercial exploitation was the primary motive here, as well as to the south in Rhodesia, where Cecil Rhodes, the empire-builder from South Africa, enlarged the holdings of the British South Africa Company to the upper Zambezi basin, and thus drove a wedge of British territory between Portugal's east- and west-coast possessions.

In the northeastern sector of central Africa British interests were concerned primarily with protecting the Suez-Red Sea route to India, and to this end Britain viewed with concern the expansion of Italian, French, Egyptian, and, later, German power into this area. In 1884 the British established the protectorate of British Somaliland to guard the southern entrance to the Red Sea. Six years later a protectorate was also established over the Island of Zanzibar (and the nearby island of Pemba) off the coast of what has become Tanganyika. British control in the east African territories of Uganda and Kenya came belatedly in the 1890's, only after the British East Africa Company had aroused public opinion against German expansion northward from German East Africa, thereby forcing the British government to establish protectorates over the two areas.

The protectorate process represented a remarkably effective method of gaining political control, and it was employed throughout most of central Africa. Local native chieftains, who themselves possessed power over certain territories, were persuaded, generally in exchange for gifts or favors, to accept the protection and advice of a particular European government. Thus the Europeans were often able to obtain colonies without the necessity of military conquests. The ease of territorial expansion in central Africa has been unmatched on so vast a scale in modern times. In a politico-geographic sense this was the final era of "free land" anywhere on the globe, except for the Antarctic continent.

By 1900 only two central African areas—Ethiopia and Liberia—remained independent of European control. Neither one was considered to be of great economic value. The independence of Liberia, which owed its existence to the United States, had been recognized by several European states during the mid-nineteenth century. American interest in the area undoubtedly contributed to the reluctance of the European powers to annex the country. Ethiopia owed its continued independence primarily to its physical inaccessibility and the military prowess of its armies, which had defeated the invading Italian forces during the 1890's.

Developments after World War I

After Germany's defeat in World War I its colonies were distributed among the victorious Allies. Important military campaigns had been waged in central Africa during the war, and some of the subsequent changes in political control reflected the military conquests of the Allied forces. In western Africa German Togoland was divided into mandates of Britain and France, while farther east German Cameroons was also divided, Britain receiving a mandate over the western portion, France over the central area, while the eastern Cameroons was joined to French Equatorial Africa. French Togoland and Cameroons were administered by France as separate areas; the British, on the other hand, included their portions of Togoland and Cameroons within the administrative structure of the Gold Coast and Nigeria respectively, a step which later gave rise to movements for permanently including these areas within the two larger territories. In southern Africa the Union of South Africa was awarded a mandate over Southwest Africa. Britain also received a mandate over German East Africa (Tanganyika), with the exception of Ruanda-Urundi in the northwest, which was mandated to Belgium, and the tiny Kionga Triangle in the southeast, which as a result of a boundary adjustment, was ceded to Portugal.

The African mandates were classed as "B" mandates, with the exception of Southwest Africa, which was designated a "C" mandate. B mandates were described as "principally . . . communities administered by a mandatory

power that is able to guarantee freedom and public order and equal opportunities for trade under specially devised governments and regulations,"
while a C mandate was "sparsely settled . . . administered according to
the laws of the mandatory power as an integral part of its territory, subject
to safeguards in the interests of the population."

The establishment of the League mandates was for the most part a re-
shuffling of colonial empires, but international conscience had advanced
somewhat during the thirty-five years since the Berlin Conference, and some
attempts were made to provide for the well-being of the native inhabitants
of the former German areas. Despite the demands for outright annexation
of the German possessions made by the Union of South Africa and, to a
less extent, by other Allied nations, the League insisted on the creation of
a mandate status for each area, and it required that the mandatory powers
submit annual reports on conditions within the areas over which they had
jurisdiction.

Since 1919 the political pattern of central Africa has remained relatively stable. Italian territorial ambitions during the 1930's led to the conquest of Ethiopia from bases in Eritrea and Italian Somaliland, but following Italy's defeat in World War II Ethiopia again became independent. The
former Italian-held Eritrea was federated with Ethiopia in 1952.

In 1947 the League of Nations mandates were changed to trusteeship
territories of the United Nations, although the administering powers remained the same,[3] and in 1950 Italian Somaliland also became a U. N.
trusteeship territory under Italian administration. The trusteeship system
differs from that of the League mandates in that United Nations delegations
can visit the trust territories to investigate conditions there, and representatives of native groups in the territories can appear in person before the
United Nations. Consequently, a considerable increase in political activity
has taken place in the trusteeship territories since 1945. Two other changes
in the political pattern of central Africa since the end of World War II were
the merger in 1954 of the three British territories of Northern Rhodesia,
Southern Rhodesia, and Nyasaland into the Federation of Rhodesia and
Nyasaland, and the establishment of the independence of the Gold Coast
(renamed Ghana)—to which British Togoland was added—in 1957.

THE POLITICAL PATTERN OF CENTRAL AFRICA

The political pattern of the mid-twentieth century in central Africa is
one of considerable complexity. Although there have been few recent boundary disputes, earlier struggles for territorial control are reflected in the enclaves, projections, and foreign-controlled islands existing throughout the

---

[3] The Union of South Africa refused to recognize this change in political status, and has continued
to administer Southwest Africa as a mandate.

area. Many boundaries follow rivers, lakes, or straight lines. Of the great river systems—the Congo, Niger, Zambezi, and upper Nile—only one, the Congo, lies for the most part within (or bordering) a single political unit. Thus the utilization of rivers for power, navigation, and irrigation is often complicated by the political pattern.

Three factors have been of major importance in the political partitioning of central Africa: (1) control of the coast, (2) access to rivers and lakes, and (3) control of territory containing known or suspected mineral reserves. A study of the pattern of control in the area will reveal many instances where one or more of these factors was important in boundary delimitation. Many of the political divisions have been made with little reference to physical or cultural patterns, and as a result considerable diversity exists within some of the national units. The inclusion of the northern semiarid districts within the boundaries of Nigeria, for example, has meant that a large Moslem minority in the north exists alongside the pagan and semi-Christian majority in the central and southern parts to threaten the area's political cohesion. On the other hand, the division of Togoland into French and British areas has worked hardships on the Ewes, one of the principal tribes of this area, who are now divided between two countries (see page 343).

Despite the relative stability of the political structure in central Africa since the end of World War I, there exist strong pressures for changes in sovereignty and for boundary corrections in the interests of cultural and economic needs. Coastal enclaves such as Spanish-held Río Muni and the Portuguese Cabinda interfere with the economic development of large inland areas. Poor circulatory systems and the inclusion of competing core areas within one country give rise to strong centrifugal forces, particularly as these countries approach self-rule. Thus three principal types of forces for change are operating in central Africa: (1) independence drives, (2) moves for unification of national units, and (3) pressures for partition, as a result of ethnic, political, or economic differences.

Independence drives may be of two types—the desire for self-rule on the part of the white minority (Southern Rhodesia) or of the African majority (Ghana). In the former situation the nonwhites may resist the independence move, since they feel that less discrimination is probable under the mother country's colonial office than if local whites were given complete freedom of action.

Moves for the unification of national units are generally prompted by the desire for greater economic and political strength. These centripetal moves may originate with or gain much of their strength from the controlling European power. On the other hand, centrifugal forces within the African states (brought on by regional differences, divergent native policies, or the competition of local political officials) often raise strong opposing pressures to unification efforts. Among the recent examples of unification have been the federation of Eritrea with Ethiopia and the formation of the Federation of Rhodesia and Nyasaland. In 1956 the people of British Togoland voted to merge their country with the Gold Coast, while the Union of South Africa has completed a *de facto* annexation of Southwest Africa.

Forces for political partitioning are strong in both the eastern and northwestern sectors of central Africa. In Uganda native kingdoms still retain much of their independence; there has been some pressure in Buganda, the largest of these kingdoms, for a division of Uganda and the establishment of an independent Buganda state. In both Ghana and Nigeria powerful forces have developed for separating the northern and central sectors from the southern coastal areas. In Kenya and the Rhodesias, where a small, concentrated white minority exercises political authority, it is possible that the nonwhite areas may eventually seek to separate themselves from the white-controlled administrations and become African-dominated states.

The changes of territorial control in central Africa must be viewed against the background of changing conditions both here and in other parts of the world. The increased development of central Africa's circulatory systems, the gradual detribalization of the natives, the economic expansion, and finally the growing political interests of the Africans all contribute to the transitional character of the region. As the pattern of political control is adjusted to the needs and aspirations of the African inhabitants the pressures of global ideologies grow stronger. Thus the Africans are faced with three alternatives in their future economic and political development: (1) a continuation of their ties with Western ideas, (2) an acceptance of the communist way of life and the forging of bonds with the Soviet bloc, or (3) isolation from both groups, and the development of typical African concepts and techniques. Whichever course or combination of courses is selected, it is obvious that the relative isolation which central Africa has in the past experienced has now ended.

POLITICAL AREAS IN CENTRAL AFRICA

For the purposes of this discussion central Africa may be divided into five sectors: the *northeastern sector*—Ethiopia, Eritrea, the Somalilands; the *eastern sector*—Uganda, Kenya, Tanganyika, Zanzibar; the *southern sector*—Mozambique, Madagascar, the Federation of Rhodesia and Nyasaland, Bechuanaland, Angola; the *western sector*—Belgian Congo, French Equatorial Africa, Cameroons, Spanish Guinea; the *northwestern sector*—Nigeria, French Togoland, Ghana, Liberia, Sierra Leone, Portuguese Guinea, Gambia, French West Africa, Spanish Sahara. It is not intended that each of the political units of central Africa be treated in detail; rather, certain ones will be emphasized in order to illustrate the basic problems of territorial control in this area.

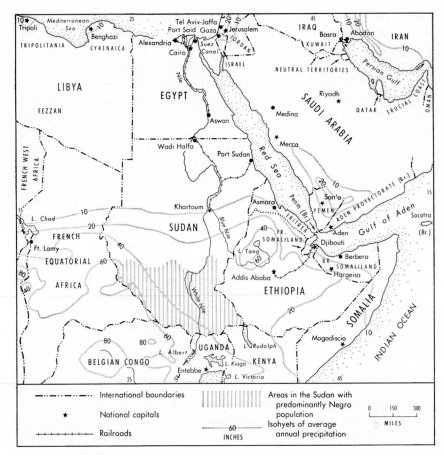

Figure 71. Northeast Africa and the Arabian Peninsula. Note the north-south transition in climate, particularly in the Sudan and French Equatorial Africa.

The Northeastern Sector

This region may be divided physically into two parts: the well-watered highlands of northern and central Ethiopia and of central Eritrea, and the semiarid hills and coastal plains in the remainder of the sector (Figure 71). No important mineral development has taken place in this area and the general level of the economy remains very low.

Ethiopia is an empire, divided administratively into twelve provinces. The capital is located at Addis Ababa, at an elevation of over 8,000 feet. About half the population of Ethiopia are Coptic Christians (the Coptic Church is an autonomous Eastern faith which recognizes the Bishop of Alexandria as its patriarch), and there is a large Moslem majority in the northern part of the country. With its agricultural possibilities, its hydroelectric potential, and indications of coal and considerable mineral wealth (including gold, silver, and iron ore), Ethiopia possesses a resource base which, if adequately developed, could place it in a strong economic position.

The country has had a long history. Political unification, however, took place toward the close of the nineteenth century, at the time when the British, French, and Italians were establishing footholds along the coasts of the Red Sea and Indian Ocean. The result was that Ethiopia emerged as a unified independent state, cut off from the sea by European colonies. With its great physical and ethnic diversity and its lack of a strong circulatory system, Ethiopia was a loosely-knit political area, whose emperor, acknowledged as the "King of Kings," exercised only nominal control over much of the territory.

During the 1930's the Italian fascist government became interested in expanding Italy's empire as a symbol of Italy's growing power and prestige. On the pretext of moving in to "civilize" Ethiopia, Italy invaded and conquered the country in 1936, but five years later, during World War II, British forces drove out the Italians and restored Ethiopia's independence.

After World War II the disposition of Italy's two colonies, Eritrea and Somaliland produced a series of compromises between the claims of the interested powers and local groups. In Eritrea the population is divided between Coptic Christians (with historical and cultural ties with Ethiopia) in the central highlands and the Moslem peoples in the northwest and along the Red Sea coast. At the end of World War II the Christians desired union of Eritrea with Ethiopia, while the Moslems, fearing they would be submerged in a non-Moslem state, favored independence or some type of federation, at least of the Moslem-inhabited areas, with the Sudan. Unwilling to split Eritrea along ethnic lines, the United Nations in 1948 ruled that the area should be federated with Ethiopia as an autonomous state, with Ethiopia responsible for defense, foreign affairs, and finance, and in 1952 this federation became effective. The acquisition of the Eritrean Red Sea littoral strengthened Ethiopia's economic and strategic position. A powerful Ethiopian state might in time exert pressure for the inclusion of the three neighboring Somaliland territories within its borders as well.

The rivalry over Italian Somaliland, principally among Britain, France, Egypt, and the U.S.S.R., resulted in a stalemate over the future status of the area, with its one million and a quarter persons. Somalia, as the area is now officially termed, is an extremely poor region with arid to semiarid climate. The principal economic activities are cattle raising and some irrigated agriculture. Despite the area's impoverished economic situation, the United Nations eventually ruled that, like Libya, it should become independent, although the date of self-rule was delayed to 1960 and during the intervening period Italy was named as administering power. Inasmuch as

Italian contributions amount to approximately one-half of Somalia's annual budget, the country may face serious economic and political problems, unless it continues to be under the protection of a more powerful state, or unless the dream of the Somalis comes true and oil is discovered in their land.

The Eastern Sector

The British territories of Uganda, Kenya, and Tanganyika occupy a part of Africa which in general lies at elevations of over 4,000 feet. Only along the coast, in a strip varying from 50 to 200 miles in width, is there low relief (less than 1,500 feet), and with it the heat and humidity associated with tropical climates. In southern Kenya, and to a less extent in the other two possessions, elevations rise to 6,000 feet and over. At Nairobi, Kenya (elevation 5,450 feet), the average mean monthly temperatures vary between 59°F. and 65°F., approximately the temperatures of Britain in spring and summer. In the twentieth century thousands of Europeans have immigrated to east Africa, particularly to Kenya, transferring their own culture to Africa and staking out certain areas as reserves for European development. The conflict between the whites and the natives for control of agricultural lands in the Kenya highlands has been one of the most serious politico-geographic problems in central Africa.

Economic developments in the three British possessions differ considerably. Uganda, a protectorate, has copper deposits and iron ore, as well as water-power potential. The Owen Falls Dam on the upper Nile, opened in 1954, will have an ultimate output of 150,000 kw. and be one of the largest hydroelectric projects in central Africa. There is little land in Uganda above 4,000 feet, and the "modified equatorial" climate has not attracted large-scale settlement by Europeans. Actually, there is an official ban on European ownership of land. The natives engage in the production of agricultural goods for export (coffee, cotton, and tobacco), although here, as in the other two territories, the business of processing and exporting these commodities is largely in the hands of Indians.

Kenya also has iron ore and hydroelectric-power potential, but the principal economic wealth in this country is from the agricultural production of the southern highlands, where extensive white settlement has taken place. In Kenya land has been reserved for both white and native settlement, and the color bar, which is largely absent in Uganda and Tanganyika, is strong here. Considerable capital has been poured into Kenya's rail, highway, and port facilities, and the region has become of considerable economic value to Britain.

Tanganyika possesses diamonds, gold, coal, and water-power potential. Although there is considerable land above four or even five thousand feet, particularly in the north adjacent to the Kenya highlands, Tanganyika has failed to attract large numbers of white settlers. By the terms of its trustee-ship agreement Tanganyika cannot become a "white man's country" in the sense that the Kenya highlands are, for the rights of the nonwhite population (including both native Africans and Indians) are better protected. Transportation and other facilities are not as developed here as in Kenya, partly because the trusteeship status has made the British government and private investors less willing to expend capital in the country.

The Land Problem in Kenya. In the highlands of southern Kenya racial tension, leading to widespread acts of terrorism, has resulted from the conflict between white and native interests. At altitudes generally above 5,000 feet lands reserved for white settlement are located in the midst of native agricultural holdings (Figure 72). Although comprising but a small fraction of the total highland area of southern Kenya, the white reserves generally consist of good agricultural land, and, perhaps more important, much of the land is unused—reserved for future farmers.

The first European farmers arrived in Kenya in the early 1900's. Land was acquired from various tribes in the Kenya highlands, among them the Kikuyu, who occupied areas close to the capital city, Nairobi, and whose reserves here became intermeshed with those of the Europeans. Although only about 100 square miles of the European reserves ever belonged to the Kikuyus, the people of this tribe, now numbering over 1,000,000, have been the

Figure 72. Kenya: Land Distribution. (After map in *Focus*, III (June, 1953). Courtesy of American Geographical Society.)

principal fomenters of trouble for the whites. The white farmers have engaged in scientific farming, producing coffee, grains, tea, and cattle, while most of the natives, with their primitive land-use practices, have contributed to soil erosion and exhaustion. Average densities per square mile are far higher on native than on white reserves.[4] The native population in Kenya has increased rapidly (more than doubling since World War I), and on his crowded overworked land the African could not help but notice the discrepancy between the land resources available to him and those reserved for the European.

A few of the Kikuyus were educated at European universities. Many of them work for the Europeans in Kenya, and their close association with the whites and their knowledge of the tools and techniques of the white culture made them formidable opponents. A secret society, the Mau Mau, was formed among the Kikuyus, dedicated to throwing the white man out of Kenya. Beginning in 1952 an undeclared war engulfed the Kenya highlands, as the murder and destruction wrought by the Mau Mau against the whites and against fellow Kikuyus who refused to join in the struggle was met by stern countermeasures on the part of the British.

By 1956 the combination of strong military action and increased opportunities for native education and economic and political betterment had succeeded in practically eliminating Kikuyu terrorism. The British have inaugurated an extensive program for bringing the Africans into greater contact with Kenya's expanding economy, thereby enabling them to obtain better wages and a higher standard of living. Among the steps taken are instruction of the African in modern farming methods, increased native participation in local government, and large-scale rehabilitation programs for Kikuyus imprisoned during the armed conflict. The success of the British in Kenya may provide a blueprint for colonial policy in other parts of the continent, where native resentment against the concentration of wealth and power in the hands of the whites is strong.

Racial Problems in the Eastern Sector. There are a considerable number of Indians and Arabs in this part of the continent. The Indians number about 230,000, and approximately fifty per cent are in Kenya. These Indians —mostly Hindus—have come to occupy an intermediate position in the social scale between the Africans and the whites. They are concentrated for the most part in urban areas, and many are engaged in commerce and white-collar jobs, such as clerks and professionals. Because of the economic power of the Indians they are resented by whites and Africans alike. However, the Indians, like the Africans, are victims of color discrimination; the difference in the position of the two groups is that the Indians have a homeland nation to turn to for support and thus represent a potent political force in

---

[4] Derwent Whittlesey gives the figure of 285 per square mile as the average density for the Kikuyu Reserve. See "Kenya, the Land and Mau Mau," *Foreign Affairs*, XXXII, No. 1 (October, 1953), 88.

the area. There is a certain analogy between the position of the Indians in this part of Africa and that of the Chinese in southeast Asia, or of the Jews in pre-World War II Europe. In each case a minority group, some members of which are quite wealthy, occupies an intermediate position between the large number of people who are poor and the small rich upper class.

The over 80,000 Arabs are mainly concentrated in Zanzibar and Pemba, and along the Kenya coast. During most of the nineteenth century the sultan of Zanzibar ruled a large area of the mainland in this eastern sector, but with the extension of German and British power after 1880 his territorial holdings here were gradually removed. The Arabs have not been affected by the racial problems which exist in this sector, but, like the Indians, they represent a potentially powerful political force which could be important in any large-scale racial conflict.

The East African Federation Plan. Uganda, Kenya, and Tanganyika have been gradually strengthening their economic bonds. The three territories are united in a customs union, so that no tariffs exist on the movement of goods across their common borders. In 1948 an East Africa High Commission was established with authority over certain activities in the three countries, such as transportation, postal and telegraph services, and customs and excise. Thus in effect a limited federation already exists here. The creation of the Federation of Rhodesia and Nyasaland in the southern sector of the continent has, however, prompted speculation and planning for a formal political association of the three territories. Local economic and political differences are strong, and a political unit such as this would probably come into existence largely as a result of pressure from London in the interests of economic and administrative efficiency.

Kenya is governed as a colony, except for a ten-mile-wide coastal strip in the southeast, which is a protectorate. Within the colony the interests of the whites are carefully protected. Uganda is a protectorate, with a small white minority whose economic and political interests result in relatively little conflict with the natives. The country includes four native kingdoms (Buganda, Bunyoro, Ankole, and Toro), together with the lands of lesser tribes, and it stands as an example of indirect rule, in which the chiefs are strengthened by the British in their positions of traditional authority, and in which their power to rule is derived largely from the loyalty of their subjects rather than from the mandate granted to them by the colonial state. In Tanganyika, a United Nations trusteeship territory, where racial problems have been kept to a minimum, there is a white minority of about eighteen thousand, engaged largely in agriculture in the highlands along the Kenya border and in the southwest, as well as a fairly prosperous African agricultural group raising crops for export. In east Africa, as in the Federation of Rhodesia and Nyasaland, political unification would work against the various independence movements. In addition, the different racial policies in an east African federation might in time create serious friction unless considerable local autonomy were granted to each of the several units.

The Southern Sector

The belt of territory extending across Africa from approximately 10° south latitude to the northern borders of Southwest Africa and the Union of South Africa is, for the most part, a continuation of the central African upland, with elevations of 3,000–5,000 feet, entrenched rivers, and occasional highland areas above the plateau, particularly in Nyasaland, sections of the Rhodesias, and central Angola. Most of the area is drained eastward by the Zambezi system, which empties into the Indian Ocean in Mozambique. Because of the prevailing winds and the existence of a cold current along the west coast, the western portion of this area (Angola, Bechuanaland, western Northern Rhodesia) is arid or semiarid. The eastern part, on the other hand, receives considerable precipitation. There has been far greater mineral development here than in the eastern sector of central Africa: copper, lead, asbestos, chrome, coal, and iron ore are valuable commodities, particularly in the Rhodesias.

As late as 1885 the interior of this southern sector between the Congo Free State and the Limpopo River (now the northern border of the Union) remained unsettled and unclaimed by the Europeans. In the following decade, however, practically all the territory was divided politically among the European powers. Concessions for mineral development in what later became the Rhodesias were granted to Cecil Rhodes in 1888 by Lobengula, king of the Matabele, and with this wedge British authority was gradually established in the upper basin of the Zambezi. Bechuanaland became a British protectorate in 1890, in order to protect the route from the Cape Colony north to the Zambezi, and Nyasaland was also annexed as a British protectorate in the following year. Many years were to pass before precise boundaries were worked out between the British and Portuguese territories, but by 1895 the general political pattern of this area had been established, and a British-controlled corridor extended north from Capetown to Tanganyika.

Racial Problems. The relationships between racial groups in the southern sector of central Africa differ in certain respects from those in the east. The Indian population is not nearly as large and does not constitute a significant political force, while the Arab element is practically nonexistent. Within the territories of Portugal and Britain there is considerable variation in governmental racial policy.

The Portuguese, in their efforts to develop a true European culture in their African possessions, are slowly working to bring an end to racial discrimination. In Mozambique, for example, where nearly 50,000 whites constitute about one per cent of the total population, only four per cent of the area has been set aside as white reserves. In other areas of Mozambique the Portuguese government is undertaking irrigation and land reclamation projects and is opening the region to settlement by both Europeans and natives, the only major condition being that the natives must agree to follow European-approved agricultural practices on the improved land. Similar developments are being carried out in Angola, an area of transition in climate and vegetation between the desert of Southwest Africa and the equatorial rain forest of the Belgian Congo.

Portugal's colonial policies must be considered in the light of its traditional conservatism toward native advancement, as well as recent shortages of capital and trained personnel to carry out the ambitious *assimilado* program. The actual difficulties confronting the African in his efforts to achieve Portuguese citizenship, the small number which has been assimilated, and the lack of funds for resettlement and land development have meant that, despite the high purposes embodied in Portugal's plans, the progress of improvement of the African's status in Mozambique and Angola has been a slow one.

Bechuanaland and Nyasaland are British protectorates, in which, because of the relative absence of Europeans, there is little racial conflict. In Nyasaland some 4,000 Europeans are concentrated in the Shiré Highlands south of Lake Nyasa, and are engaged primarily in plantation agriculture. The remainder of the country is rather densely populated with natives, many of whom remain little affected by the European culture. Northern Rhodesia is a British protectorate, which has never attracted large-scale white immigration, partly because of the warm climate (few places are much over 3,000 feet in elevation), the prevalence of disease, particularly malaria, and the relative isolation of the area. In the northwest, however, a sizable white settlement has grown up about the important copper mines, while to the south, at Broken Hill, the mining of lead and zinc has attracted additional Europeans. Altogether there are about 40,000 whites in Northern Rhodesia, and since their major interests are not agricultural, the problem of white and native reserves has never become an acute one. On the other hand, friction exists between white and native miners, since the average wages for the former are considerably higher than for the latter, and relatively few opportunities exist for native advancement in the mining industries. There is an African trade union, and the Africans have gone out on strike to secure better working conditions. A labor agreement in 1955 broke the monopoly position of the white miners' union and opened the way for important advancements by nonwhite workers. Trends such as these are in direct contrast with the position of African labor in the mines of the Union of South Africa.

In Southern Rhodesia, a self-governing British colony, 140,000 Europeans constitute about six per cent of the total population. Since only the whites have the vote, they alone exercise political power, and there is a greater degree of color discrimination here than in other parts of the southern sector. With its iron ore and coal resources Southern Rhodesia has experienced a modest industrial development. However, agricultural activity in this country is far more important to the whites than it is in Northern Rhodesia and Nyasaland, and Southern Rhodesia, like Kenya, has been faced with the difficult problem of protecting the interests of both white and native farmers. Portions of Southern Rhodesia have been set aside as native reserves, and the whites are divided among themselves on the question of future native policy—whether to continue the "liberal" trend toward the Africans or to adopt more of the restrictive measures which are practiced in the neighboring Union of South Africa.

About 240 miles off the Mozambique coast lies the French island of Madagascar, a predominantly plateau area with a population of about 4½ million. Madagascar has little mineral wealth (graphite is the principal mineral export), but its agricultural potential is considerable. The island exports coffee, meat, hides, and spices. The French are seeking to avoid the problems of native land ownership, which the British have experienced in their African territories, even at the cost of a slow development of Madagascar's agricultural resources. Although the process of assimilation of the natives into the European way of life is steadily going forward on the island, most of Madagascar remains a relatively primitive area, in terms of both economic and political development.

The Federation of Rhodesia and Nyasaland. In 1954 Nyasaland and the two Rhodesias were formed into a loose political unit, in which such functions as customs duties, currency, and railways were unified. Within this federation Nyasaland and Northern Rhodesia retained their political status of protectorates, and Southern Rhodesia that of a self-governing colony. A federal parliament was established in Salisbury, Southern Rhodesia, but its duties were limited largely to the economic sphere. Many local problems, including white-native relations, remained within the domain of the individual units.

The primary aims of the federation were to attract greater investment in the new political area and to prepare the region for eventual independence. The impetus for political unification of the three territories came in part from the government in London, which was interested in strengthening the economic basis of its possessions, and in part from local groups in southern Africa. The whites in Nyasaland, faced with serious economic conditions in their protectorate, favored federation in order to bolster the area's position, while the whites of Northern Rhodesia, fearing a decline in the price of copper, were anxious to broaden their territory's economic base by an alignment with the agricultural and industrial economy of Southern Rhodesia. On the other hand, native groups in both Nyasaland and Northern

Rhodesia opposed federation because they feared their present protected status would be replaced by more restrictive policies and that they might lose their land and be crowded on native reserves. In 1964, after a ten-year "inaugural" period, the federation's constitution will be reviewed for the purpose of providing greater centralization of authority at Salisbury.

Regional Economic Developments. In central Africa, as in other parts of the world, political progress is closely associated with economic progress. For example, before the African natives can assume a status of equality with the whites there must be a substantial increase in their average per capita income, schools and other social facilities must be provided, and the natives must be made to feel they have a stake in the future of their area. To achieve this the economy of Africa must be developed far more than it now is, and to this end regional economic developments are important forward steps.

The economic future of the Federation of Rhodesia and Nyasaland depends in part upon accessibility to the sea. Within recent years the Portuguese have undertaken considerable development of rail and port facilities in Mozambique in order to prepare it as an outlet for the mineral and agricultural exports of the federation. Mozambique is better located to service this area than are the ports of the Union of South Africa. Moreover, the transportation systems of the Rhodesias have also been improved and have been linked more closely with those of the Portuguese territory. Lourenço Marques, in southern Mozambique, has a good harbor and has been connected by rail with Southern Rhodesia and through it with Northern Rhodesia, while the port of Beira, four hundred miles to the north of Lourenço Marques, will concentrate on the overseas trade of Nyasaland. Such regional economic co-operation in Africa may lead to the increased development of resources and greater opportunities for political and social advancement for both the European and native peoples.

The Western Sector

Within the western sector of central Africa the two major political units are the Belgian Congo and French Equatorial Africa. Both are more than 900,000 square miles in area, and both for the most part have humid tropical conditions of climate and vegetation, although the northern section of French Equatorial Africa extends also into semiarid grasslands. The Belgian Congo has about 12 million inhabitants, including over 80,000 Europeans, while the respective figures for French Equatorial Africa are roughly one-third as large. The shortage of native labor in French Equatorial Africa has hindered economic development—particularly plantation agriculture—and the construction of roads, railroads, and port facilities, while in the Congo deficiencies in the labor force are made up by importations from Ruanda-Urundi. Finally, French Equatorial Africa has practically no developed minerals except manganese (although indications are that valuable deposits exist), and such items as wild rubber, ivory, and palm oil make up the principal exports. The Congo, however, is one of the great mineral-producing areas of the world—copper, radium, uranium, cobalt, diamonds, gold, tin, and silver—as well as an exporter of palm oil, coffee, cocoa, tea, and cinchona.

Physical, cultural, and economic differences between the two areas are paralleled by political dissimilarities. French Equatorial Africa remains a French colonial territory, in which relatively few attempts are made to "Europeanize" the Africans, despite France's avowed assimilation policy. The tropical lowlands have been and probably will continue to be largely undeveloped, while the economic activities carried on in the drier areas to the north, such as cotton production, are handicapped by isolation. In the Belgian Congo, however, not only has considerable economic development taken place, particularly since the end of World War I, but the Belgian government has evolved a somewhat unique political system for handling the problems of racial policy and self-government. The Belgians hold that the Africans must be trained and educated before they can have a voice in governing themselves, and the government is making efforts through the establishment of schools and the elimination of color bars in economic activities to achieve the goal of native advancement as rapidly as possible. In the meantime the white minority in the Congo is not allowed to control the area's destinies; rather, political power is being firmly retained in Brussels, until such time as all persons in the Congo are ready for enfranchisement. The Belgians look upon the Congo and the Congolese as an economic investment, in which case it is clearly to the interests of the mother country to develop the area's physical and human resources to their greatest degree. However, the slowness of the Belgians to train the Congolese for political responsibilities may present problems in the future, since the increased political activities of native groups in other parts of central Africa has already resulted in demands for greater political participation on the part of the Congolese as well.

In addition to serving as a source for mineral and agricultural products, the Belgian Congo also forms a link in the trans-Africa supply route being developed between the Gulf of Guinea on the west coast and the ports of Mombasa and Dar es Salaam on the Indian Ocean. Such a route would serve as an alternative to the Mediterranean-Suez link between Europe and the East. In wartime troops and equipment from the Atlantic area would be unloaded at ports along the west coast of central Africa, and then sent by air or rail to the east coast, where they would be reloaded for shipment across the Indian Ocean to military bases in the Far East.

In addition to French Equatorial Africa and the Belgian Congo, the western sector of central Africa possesses a complex political pattern of

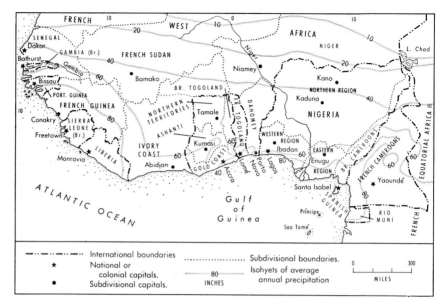

Figure 73. Central Africa—Northwestern Sector. Note the north-south transition of climate, and the orientation of political units toward the coast.

European colonies and trust territories. The Belgian Congo is practically shut off from the Atlantic coast by the Portuguese enclave of Cabinda to the north of the Congo mouth. Farther north the small enclave (Río Muni) of Spanish Guinea is entirely surrounded by French territory. These two areas are survivals of old coastal holdings of the two Iberian states. In 1922 the Belgians were awarded a League mandate over Ruanda-Urundi, an upland area of some 21,000 square miles to the east of the Congo. Formerly a part of German East Africa, this coffee- and cattle-producing area is now a U.N. trusteeship territory, administered as a part of the Belgian Congo. Another former German area is the Cameroons, to the west of French Equatorial Africa, divided in 1919 between France and Britain.

The Northwestern Sector

The northwestern sector of central Africa forms a rather distinct geographic unit, stretching from Dakar on the west to the Cameroons mountains on the east, and from the Atlantic Ocean and the Gulf of Guinea north to the Sahara. In terms of relief, climate, vegetation, and even cultural groups there is a north-south zonation along the southern coast of the "bulge," but the political regions for the most part are aligned east-west, thereby including within these regions a variety of physical features, peoples, and economic activities (Figure 73). Here, perhaps more than in any other part of Africa, political boundaries have been drawn with little regard for cultural or economic unity, with the result that political cohesion within some of the states is proving extremely difficult to achieve.

The early activities of European powers along the west African coast, leading to the political fragmentation of the area, has already been mentioned. As early as 1884 (prior to the Berlin Conference) British claims were established in Gambia, Sierra Leone, Gold Coast, and Lagos (the nucleus of Nigeria), the Germans were in Togoland, the Portuguese in Guinea, and the French in Guinea, Ivory Coast, and Dahomey. Liberia had been an independent state for over thirty-five years. All that remained in subsequent decades was for the European powers to expand their territorial claims along the coast until they adjoined one another and to move the borders inland as far as possible. Eventually much of the interior of the northwestern sector was included in French West Africa, and at five points between Dakar and the Cameroons mountains French territory extends out to the coast thereby isolating most of the non-French possessions from one another.

Progress Toward Self-rule in the British Territories. The northwestern sector is unique among the areas of the continent in the political and economic development which native groups have achieved here. Ghana is independent, while Nigeria and Sierra Leone are moving gradually toward dominion or republic status within the British Commonwealth. In the absence of large-scale white settlement along the Guinea coast (partly because of the generally high temperature and humidity) economic and political development has been pursued largely by the Africans themselves. In each country political leaders exist among the "advanced" native groups which have had some contact with Western culture. In each case, however, these advanced natives represent but a portion of the total population, and their views toward the treatment of the more backward native elements are often less liberal than those of the whites themselves.

Ghana, which consists of a fairly broad coastal plain and an interior upland, is the world's leading producer of cacao, and in addition exports gold, diamonds, manganese, and bauxite. The Volta River, which flows the length of the country, possesses great hydroelectric-power potential. With its power and bauxite resources, the area could establish a flourishing aluminum industry. As a British dependency the Gold Coast was divided into three sections: the Gold Coast Colony, Ashanti, and the Northern Territories. The first was a crown colony, the other two were protectorates. The Gold Coast Colony, in which lies Accra, the capital and leading city, possesses many detribalized natives and the bulk of the educated intellectual Africans. Ashanti, economically important for its cacao production, is still dominated by the tribal chiefs; in the Northern Territories tribal conditions also prevail and there is a large Moslem population.

In 1951 Britain granted the Gold Coast a constitution which guaranteed considerable self-rule. The movement for independence gradually gained impetus, and by 1956 the legislative assembly had reached a position where it officially requested the British to make the country an independent state (to be named Ghana) within the British Commonwealth. The British subsequently set March, 1957, as the date for the inauguration of self-rule. One of the principal problems of independence in the country has been the important issue of centralism versus federalism, that is, should the governmental structure be such that political power is concentrated largely in the Gold Coast Colony, with its voting majority, or should Ashanti and the Northern Territories have wide measures of local autonomy?

The people of Ashanti have been much concerned about a centralized political system, since a large portion of the country's wealth comes from the cacao production of this area, yet much of the federal revenue is spent in the more populated and more Westernized Gold Coast Colony. In the Northern Territories tribal chiefs fear loss of power and a change of cultural patterns under the domination of the Colony. Local autonomy for the northern and central areas has been provided within the political structure of the new state, Ghana, however, faces difficult problems of internal control in the path of national unity.

In Nigeria, progress toward self-rule has been slower than in Ghana, partly because the territory faces even greater obstacles toward national cohesion. Although Nigeria exports agricultural products and has the only coal resources known to exist in the northwestern sector of central Africa, economic development has been slow. With its large population and lack of valuable minerals, the country faces a more difficult economic future than independent Ghana or the Belgian Congo. Nigeria has an estimated population of about 31 million, and, like Ghana, represents a rather illogical collection of cultural groups in one political unit. In the north are over 11 million Moslems, still associated with their local emirates; in the central area are pagan tribes; while in the south, particularly in the southwest, are the more advanced, largely Christian, native groups. Here, in Nigeria, one can find examples of some of the difficulties of indirect rule. The British have traditionally exercised authority through local native chieftains. As the power of these chieftains weakens under the impact of new political movements, a politically-untrained native majority becomes the dominant force in the decision-making processes of the country.

In 1952 Nigeria began a period of "semiresponsible" government as a first step toward eventual self-rule. The country was organized as a federation of three regions—Eastern, Western, and Northern—together with a federal territory, embracing Lagos, the capital. The Western Region, with a greater population of trained and educated Africans, has become the leading unit in the federation. The Northern Region, with nearly eighty per cent of the country's area, contains both Moslem groups and pagan tribes. Although there is some basis for the economic unification of this northern area, there is little cultural cohesion between its two major ethnic types. The Eastern Region, with a majority of primitive native groups, has had little cultural and economic contact with the other two regions. Although some political elements in Nigeria are pressing for rapid progress toward self-rule, the British are unwilling to relinquish their responsibilities until the problems of the northern, central, and southeastern peoples have been worked out. British Cameroons, which borders Nigeria on the east, will undoubtedly be incorporated into Nigeria, once independence is achieved.

A third area in west Africa moving toward self-rule is Sierra Leone, west of Liberia. Established late in the eighteenth century as a settlement for liberated British slaves, the territory now has a population of about 2 million, of whom over ninety-five per cent are illiterate. Tribal authority is still of great significance in all areas except immediately around Freetown, the capital, where the small minority of educated Africans lives. The principal exports are iron ore, diamonds, and palm oil products, but economic and social developments throughout the country have been handicapped by lack of capital. The small, but politically powerful group of educated Africans, responding to recent developments in Nigeria and Ghana, has been demanding self-rule for Sierra Leone, but here, even more than in its other northwest African territories, the British are concerned over the fate of the great mass of uneducated natives, and thus are going slow in the political emancipation of the country.

The flexibility of British colonial policy in Africa is illustrated in this northwestern sector, where territories have achieved or are approaching self-rule despite the fact that in each case over ninety per cent of the people are still illiterate. This condition is in sharp contrast with developments in other British-controlled areas of central Africa, where little or no advancement toward independence has been made during the past few decades. Perhaps the principal cause of the variability of British policy has been the presence or absence of large numbers of British settlers. Thus the London government apparently feels it must protect the interests of the whites—and of the natives who come in contact with them—in such areas as Kenya and the Rhodesias, while in the northwestern sector, where few whites are permanent residents, native rule can be more rapidly achieved.

Britain's one other territory in this part of Africa is Gambia, a long, narrow country extending inland along both sides of the Gambia River. With an area of about 4,000 square miles and a population of around 265,000, Gambia is economically incapable of existing as an independent unit. Less than two per cent of the population is literate. Gambia's one hope for future self-rule would seem to lie in the creation of a British West Africa Federation, embracing the other British territories in northwestern

Africa as well. Because of local differences among these various territories, however, such a federation does not appear likely.

French West Africa. Independence for Ghana and the prospects for Nigeria and Sierra Leone understandably have created some apprehension among the French, who are committed to a colonial policy of assimilation rather than self-government. French West Africa is a federation of eight former colonies—Dahomey, French Guinea, French Sudan, Ivory Coast, Mauritania, Niger, Senegal, and Upper Volta. The capital is at Dakar, on the west African coast. The sprawling area embraces both the humid Guinea coast and the arid west African interior, and, like Nigeria, contains different physical, ethnic, and economic elements within its borders. The boundaries of the British West African territories adjoin French West Africa for many hundreds of miles, and the spirit of independence in the British territories could not but permeate into the French-controlled area. Political repercussions are also evident as a result of independence for the Sudan, Tunisia, and Morocco, especially as circulatory systems in French West Africa become better developed.

Other States of Northwestern Africa. The independent republic of Liberia, located along the Guinea coast, was established during the 1820's by the American Colonization Society as a haven for freed slaves. The present economic, social, and political conditions of the nation illustrate some of the arguments *for* colonial rule of undeveloped areas. Liberia is extremely poor: the 1953 national budget, for example, amounted to $10 million. Roads and railroads are practically nonexistent, and the only major airfield in the country was constructed by the United States for military use during World War II. Political control of Liberia rests in the hands of a small Americo-Liberian minority, probably representing less than two per cent of the total population, plus about twice as many coastal Negroes, who also have come in contact with Western culture.

Health and education facilities are severely limited by Liberia's shortage of capital. Prior to World War II the only major economic development in the nation was in connection with the Firestone rubber plantations. More recently a concession has been granted to the Republic Steel Corporation to mine iron ore in Liberia. In spite of these activities, however, Liberia remains a poor and undeveloped area, although it has one of the longest records of independence of any state in Africa.

Two other regions of the northwestern sector are Portuguese Guinea, a small enclave just south of the British territory of Gambia, and Spanish Sahara, farther north along the Atlantic coast. Although once important as a source of slaves, Portuguese Guinea has now reached a position of relative stagnation, both politically and economically. Spanish Sahara is an arid country, whose principal source of income is its offshore fisheries. It is inhabited largely by pastoral nomads.

Problem Areas

1. The Ethnic and Political Division of Togoland

One perplexing problem in the northwestern sector is that of Togoland, the former German colony, which was divided into British and French trusteeship territories. The long narrow area is the home of an important native group—the Ewes—numbering about a million persons. Before World War I the Ewes were practically united under German rule (although a few of their number were included in the Gold Coast), but the division of Togoland in 1922 split the Ewes between the British- and French-controlled territories and resulted in considerable hardships for this native group (Figure 74). The Ewes have repeatedly protested this artificial division of their people, but to no avail.

The British sector of Togoland was for many years administered as a part of the Gold Coast. With that area moving toward self-rule, British officials permitted a plebiscite to be held in British Togoland to determine

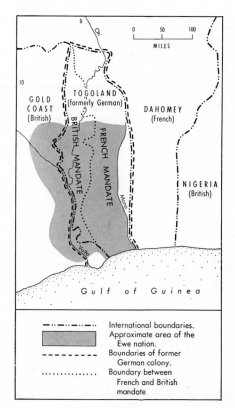

Figure 74. Togoland. (After Fischer, *World Politics,* I (Jan., 1949). Courtesy of Princeton University Press.)

whether the popular sentiment was in favor of permanent inclusion within the new state of Ghana. A 1956 plebiscite, held under United Nations auspices, indicated a consensus in favor of the union. The principal opposition to the move came from the south, where the Ewes face permanent separation from their fellow tribesmen in French Togoland.

The French, whose sector of Togoland is larger, more populated, and of greater economic value than the British sector, desire to maintain the area as a separate unit, rather than unite it with the neighboring territory of French West Africa. In August, 1956, French Togoland was incorporated as an autonomous republic within the French Union and this move was subsequently approved by 71.5 per cent of the Togolese voters in a referendum held in that area. The French government then announced its determination to consider that the trusteeship status of the area has been ended, although the United Nations has refused to agree to this condition, on the grounds that the opposition groups had boycotted the plebiscite, and that the alternatives offered the voters were so worded as to influence their choice.

The political developments in Togoland have pointed up the increased political agitation resulting from United Nations activities in the trusteeship territories. Unlike conditions under the mandate system, U.N. officials are empowered to make on-the-spot observations within the trusteeship territories, and, occasionally, to bring native representatives to the United Nations in New York for reports and consultations. Already there are pressures in French Cameroons for its establishment as an autonomous unit within the French Union, while in Ruanda-Urundi a movement is also under way for a greater degree of self-rule. In Dahomey, French West Africa, demands are being made for autonomy, largely as a result of the new status of French Togoland. In response to these pressures, the French government is gradually revising the basis of its over-all colonial policy from one of assimilation to one of association. Thus, conditions in Togoland are in a sense symptomatic of the changing political pattern in the continent's dependent areas.

2. Independence Movements in Central Africa

For the next few years independence developments in central Africa will probably be confined to the British colonial territories. Nigeria, the Federation of Rhodesia and Nyasaland, and Sierra Leone appear to be the most likely candidates. Somalia, the Italian-administered trusteeship territory, is also destined for independence in 1960.

Another British territory with a potential independence movement is Kenya, where the white minority, disturbed by "overly-lenient" native policies on the part of the British Colonial Office, may agitate for self-rule along the lines of Southern Rhodesia and the Union of South Africa. Something of a native elite is also developing in Tanganyika, and in time this group may ask the British to terminate the trusteeship. In this case the country would probably be run on a "desegregated" basis, with Africans, whites, and Indians participating in the government.

Independence movements in central Africa are predicated upon the existence of either a sizable white population, whose interests have grown apart from those of the mother country and who therefore agitate for self-rule, or else an educated native minority which seeks independence. There would seem to be relatively few central African states outside the British possessions in which independence movements appear probable. The assimilation policies of Portugal and France and the conservative colonial system in the Spanish areas would tend to discourage the rise of independence-minded groups in the territories. Only the Belgian Congo, in addition to the British areas mentioned above, would seem to have possibilities for independence within the foreseeable future, for here an economically powerful native population will be in a position to demand self-rule from the Brussels government.

BIBLIOGRAPHY

BUCHANAN, KEITH. "The Northern Region of Nigeria: the Geographical Background of its Political Duality," *The Geographical Review*, XLIII, No. 4 (October, 1953), 451–74.

A comprehensive treatment of pressures for territorial control in northern and central Nigeria.

PERHAM, MARGERY. "The British Problem in Africa," *Foreign Affairs*, XXIX, No. 4 (July, 1951), 637–51.

A clearly presented discussion of Britain's problems of control over its African territories.

STAMP, L. DUDLEY. *Africa, a Study in Tropical Development*. New York: John Wiley & Sons, Inc., 1953.

A basic regional text for all of Africa. Includes maps and descriptions of the development of territorial control.

WHITTLESEY, DERWENT. "Kenya, the Land and the Mau Mau," *Foreign Affairs*, XXXII, No. 1 (October, 1953), 80–91.

A concise study of the internal territorial problems in Kenya.

———. "Reshaping the Map of West Africa," in *Geographic Aspects of International Relations*, ed. C. C. COLBY. Chicago: The University of Chicago Press, 1938.

The relation of political boundaries to physical and cultural features in west Africa.

WIESCHOFF, HEINRICH A. *Colonial Policies in Africa,* African Handbooks, No. 5. Philadelphia: University of Pennsylvania Press, 1944.

A treatise on the general problems of colonial control. Although the material predates World War II, much of it is still applicable at the present time.

13

RACIAL CONFLICTS IN SOUTH AFRICA

● At the southern tip of Africa lies that continent's most important and most powerful nation. Over one-half of the white residents of Africa live here in the midst of a majority of nonwhites—Negroes, Colored or half-castes, and Indians—who, taken together, comprise nearly eighty per cent of the Union of South Africa's population. Rich, strategic, isolated: these terms characterize the Union. Rich in terms of its reserves of minerals and power fuels; strategic because of its location with respect to the south Atlantic and south Indian oceans, as well as to south central Africa; isolated because of its physical removal from other Westernized nations, because of the trend of its racial policies, and because a majority group of its whites has developed a culture of its own, which is neither British nor Dutch but Afrikaans.

Physical Elements

The Union of South Africa has an area of 472,733 square miles and consists of four provinces—the Cape of Good Hope (or Cape Province), Natal, Orange Free State, and Transvaal (Figure 75). In terms of white population Cape Province and Natal, bordering the coast, have a majority of English-speaking people, while the Orange Free State and Transvaal, in the northeastern uplands, include a predominance of Boers—a name given to the descendants of the original Dutch settlers of South Africa. This population distribution reflects the history of English settlement in the coastal regions during the nineteenth and early twentieth centuries and the migration (trek) of Boers to the interior during the 1830's. There is also a large

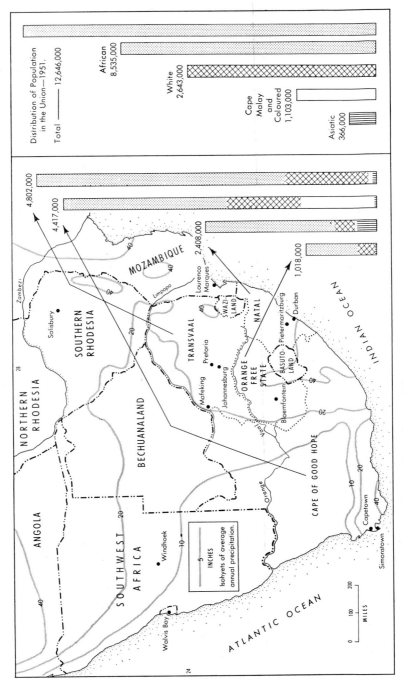

Figure 75. The Union of South Africa and Southwest Africa.
(After map in *Focus*, IV (Oct., 1953). Courtesy of American Geographical Society.)

English concentration in the Johannesburg area of Transvaal, the so-called Rand district, which is the world's greatest gold-producing area.

Within the borders of South Africa there are also two large British-controlled enclaves, Swaziland and Basutoland, which have been established as native reserves. These areas have a combined population of about 800,000, and their economies are tied for the most part with that of the Union.

South Africa's location is of great importance both to the Union itself and to its external relations. Its isolation has enabled the Union to enjoy a certain independence in its national development, as evidenced, for example, by the distinctive Boer culture and by the refusal of the present South African government to liberalize its policies toward the nonwhites, despite the trend in this direction throughout other parts of the African continent. Although the Union was awarded a League of Nations mandate over South-west Africa at the end of World War I, it has consistently refused since 1945 to accede to United Nations' requests to change the area's status to that of a trusteeship territory—another indication of South Africa's independent course of action. In the present era of global interdependence the luxury of national isolation, whether it be of external or internal policies, is one which is becoming increasingly difficult to defend from either a practical or moral point of view. South Africa's position might perhaps be defined as "partial isolation," in that in some respects, such as economic affairs, the country is willing to work closely with other powers, while in other matters it chooses to pursue its own course.

The Union of South Africa consists largely of a plateau, averaging 3,000 to 6,000 feet in elevation, with a narrow coastal plain in the west, south, and east. Capetown is located at about the same distance from the equator as Cape Hatteras, North Carolina. Because of its latitudinal location and the upland character of most of the country, the climate approaches that of mid-latitude areas. Thus South Africa is one of the relatively few parts of the continent which has attracted permanent white colonization on a large scale. Rainfall is a major factor determining settlement. The western half of the state is arid, but in the east grassland plateaus, utilized for sheep and cattle grazing, merge into forested mountains rising to over 10,000 feet. Wheat, corn, and cotton are important products in eastern South Africa, but the nation is not a major food exporter. In minerals the Union is an important producer of gold, diamonds, copper, asbestos, and, to a less extent, manganese and platinum. Uranium ores are also being mined. With its reserves of iron ore and coking coal (as well as some hydroelectric-power potential) South Africa is in the process of developing its heavy industries. Already it is the major industrial power on the African continent and, although agricultural production is restricted by the physical environment and by poor farming practices, the Union's economic potential is a very good one.

Population Structure

Three basic problems exist in the Union which reflect, in part, the country's ethnic complexity: conflict between the Boers and the British, internal relations between the white and nonwhite peoples, and external relations with Great Britain and the Commonwealth. The population in 1953 was divided as follows: 2,750,000 whites, including about 1,750,000 Boers and 1,000,000 British; approximately 8,850,000 Negroes; 1,175,000 Colored; and 390,000 Indians.

The Boers, who comprise about sixty-five per cent of the white population, have historic ties with the Dutch culture, although the Afrikaans language which they speak differs from Dutch. A majority of them are members of the Dutch Reformed Church. There are today few sentimental ties between the Boers and the Netherlands; if anything, the Boers have closer sympathies with the Germans. They are strongly nationalistic, but the concept of their country as many of them envision it is not the South Africa of the past. Rather they see it as a future Boer republic, in which little room is left for Englishmen of any sect, for Roman Catholics and Jews, and for nonwhites, except in the capacity of unskilled laborers. A majority of the Boers are determined to keep the nonwhites indefinitely in a state of political, social, and economic inferiority, although utilizing their labor for white-controlled enterprises. In the mid-twentieth century concepts such as these can have powerful political repercussions.

The British are somewhat divided concerning South Africa itself and the nonwhite population. Some of the more conservative elements still envision the country as a British-oriented area, complete with British traditions and culture; others are ready to concede the trend toward nationalism, but, with a minority of the Boers, they are anxious to retain South Africa's multicultural character, rather than see it develop into an isolationist, anti-British state. With regard to the nonwhites, only the most liberal of the English are ready to move rapidly along the path of racial equality, but the majority of them are opposed to the reactionary policies of the Boers. Any solution, they feel, lies in a slow but steady education and training of the Negroes and a gradual lifting of restrictions for them as well as for the Colored and Indians, with a distant but eventual goal of complete racial assimilation.

A third group in South Africa are the Negroes, whose population is increasing rapidly and by 1963 will probably have reached 10,000,000. The Negroes are the great underprivileged mass in the Union. They have no vote and are represented in the parliament by white officials. Although nearly seventy per cent of the nation's population is made up of Negroes, their representatives in the Senate number 4 out of a total of 89 members and in the House of Assembly 3 out of 159. The Negroes are forbidden to own land outside the native reserves, yet these reserves, comprising but thirteen per cent of the country's territory, have large areas which are unsuitable for cultivation. The Negroes are subject to conscription for labor in the South African mines, and their wages throughout the Union are far below those paid to the whites.

Unlike the situation existing in French Equatorial Africa, where the African society has been left largely untouched, the South African whites have exploited the Negro's labor, but have destroyed his old tribal society (except in parts of the reserves) and have failed to substitute a new social order in its place. At present about forty per cent of the Negroes still live on the reserves under conditions of extreme poverty, about thirty per cent live in the cities where most of them work for the whites, and another thirty per cent are tenant farmers on white-owned farms. Despite these drawbacks, however, South Africa attracts large-scale illegal immigration of Africans, particularly from countries adjacent to the Union, since wages here are higher than in the Rhodesias or the Portuguese territories. In addition, there are hundreds of thousands of legal Negro immigrants in South Africa, who also have been attracted by the wages—especially in industry—and by the health, education, and welfare benefits, which are greater here than in most other parts of the continent south of the Sahara.

The Colored (persons of mixed Negro-white ancestry) occupy a slightly higher social position than the Negroes. Nearly ninety per cent are concentrated in the Cape of Good Hope Province, where they work primarily as servants, craftsmen, and manual laborers. Unlike the Negroes, the Colored were permitted to vote in the Cape Province. Since the approximately 40,000 Colored voters generally voted against the Nationalist Party candidates, the Boer-controlled government has taken steps to establish separate voting rolls for the Colored and for the whites by a law which became effective in November, 1956. The Colored voters, as well as the Negroes, will be represented in parliament by a fixed number of white officials. The government has also undertaken a reclassification of the Union's Colored population, with the result that some have had their official status changed to that of Negro.

The Asiatics in South Africa are the descendants of immigrants who were brought to the area prior to 1913 as indentured laborers to work in the sugar plantations, particularly in Natal Province. Over four-fifths of the Asiatic people in South Africa are still concentrated in Natal, where they find employment as field laborers, small-scale market gardeners, or laborers (mostly unskilled) in industry. In Natal and in the other provinces the Asiatics are also important as peddlers and as proprietors of small businesses. They are denied the right to vote, and are not represented in the South African parliament. Outside of Natal the law forbids Asiatics from owning land, and the Nationalist government has been setting up restricted areas for those Asiatics who live and work in the cities. Immigration quotas now prevent all but a small number of Asiatics from entering the Union. Although not acceptable as whites, the Asiatics, practically all of whom are Indian, have the advantage of support from India itself, while the other nonwhites are without foreign allies.

SOUTH AFRICAN HISTORY

The first Europeans to settle in South Africa were the Dutch, who established a watering station at the Cape of Good Hope in 1652 to service their shipping route to the East Indies. In the decades which followed many settlers came from Holland under the auspices of the Dutch East Indies Company and took possession of the lands about Capetown. The inhabitants they found were aboriginal Bushmen. Not until 1770 did the Europeans clash with the Bantus, a more advanced Negro group, whose members were migrating southward from central Africa. In the ensuing clash of cultures, the Europeans, with their greater technical knowledge and training, eventually triumphed, although the Bantus were neither decimated nor driven away—in contrast to conquered native groups in other parts of the world. The Dutch settlers were stern Calvinists, convinced by their reading of the Scriptures that the whites were destined to rule and the nonwhites to be ruled. Many of their descendants still hold to this conviction today.

In 1814 Great Britain obtained possession of southernmost Africa. In reaction to British control many Boer settlers soon began to move north and east away from the Cape of Good Hope. The climax came in 1836 when 7,000 Boers began a trek to the Transvaal area. During the nineteenth century, while thousands of British colonists were coming to the southern and eastern coastal areas, the Boers subdued the Bantu armies and developed agricultural areas in what are now Transvaal and the Orange Free State. In 1853 the independent South African Republic was established in the Transvaal. The following year the independence of the Orange Free State was also recognized by the British.

Proud of their culture, the Boers had no wish for interference from the British, but their hopes were in vain, for in 1867 diamonds were discovered in the Orange Free State and twenty years later gold was found in the Transvaal. The subsequent efforts of British miners and financiers—among them Cecil Rhodes—to develop these resources led to growing friction with the Boer settlers. In 1880, after Britain had annexed the independent Transvaal republic, war broke out between the Boers and the British. After a few months of fighting the British agreed to restore Transvaal's independence, but after the discovery of the enormous gold deposits in the Witwatersrand (at Johannesburg) the conflict of British and Boer interests grew increasingly severe. The rapid influx of British whites and of British capital into the

Transvaal was countered by increasing Boer resistance, and finally in 1899 the second Boer War broke out. With the British victory in 1902 the two independent Boer republics were abolished. Eight years later these were joined with Natal and the Cape of Good Hope in the Union of South Africa.

The Rise of South African Nationalism

At the time of the establishment of the Union the British inhabitants of the new country were greatly outnumbered by the Boers. Thus a situation existed in which a people who had been defeated militarily might through representative means gain political domination of a country. Equal voting rights were allotted to each of the two white groups, and South Africa became a bilingual area, with legal recognition given to both the English and the Afrikaans languages. The dual nature of South African society was reflected in the establishment of two capitals—one the administrative capital at Pretoria in Transvaal and the other the legislative capital at Capetown. For nearly four decades English was the language generally used in government, education, and economic life, and South Africa was primarily British-oriented in economy and foreign policy. Many Boers, of course, resented the predominant British character of the Union, and a pro-Boer political party —the Nationalists—gradually gained strength in the country. After South Africa's achievement of dominion status in 1926 the British government was no longer able to affect policy directly in South Africa, but statesmen such as Louis Botha and Jan Christian Smuts succeeded for a time in unifying the two European elements in South Africa and piloted a course for the country consistent with the spirit and ideas of the rest of the British Commonwealth.

Before World War II the pressure of Boer nationalism grew increasingly strong. Associated with the greater use of Afrikaans were the formation of secret Boer societies and the appearance of violently pro-Boer papers and periodicals. In 1939 the South African parliament approved the country's participation in World War II by a one-vote margin, and during the war many Boers openly supported the German cause. Finally, in 1948 the moderate United South African Party of Field Marshal Smuts was voted out of office, its place taken by the Nationalist Party, headed by the Boer leader Dr. Daniel F. Malan. Since that time the government has worked to implement its policy of suppression of the nonwhites and of a resurgence of Boer culture. Under the leadership of the Nationalist Party South Africa has undertaken a program of increased racial suppression, with no apparent end in sight except the establishment of a permanent white-controlled police state. South Africa thus represents a variation in modern nationalism, in that British power in the area is being replaced, not by a native nonwhite majority as in other parts of Africa and Asia, but by a non-British white minority, whose policies toward the nonwhites are more reactionary than those of the British.

An interesting question, of course, is why, after nearly four decades of co-operation, did the situation develop which the founding fathers of South Africa feared most—namely, that the Boer majority would turn on the British and jeopardize their cultural and political position in the nation? A latent spirit of Boer nationalism has existed ever since 1902, but why should it erupt so violently under Malan and his successors? Possibly some Boers have been able to identify the British with liberalism in racial matters. The respect many of the Boers had for the Nazis stemmed in part from the latter's racial concepts. Economics also enter into the picture: much of the wealth in the nation is British-controlled, but by the end of World War II many Boers had acquired greater political and economic power. Finally, since the retirement of Field Marshal Smuts from the political scene there have been no strong leaders for the cause of unity among the South African whites. Regardless of the underlying causes, it is apparent that a resurgence of Boer cultural and political institutions has occurred. One question of interest to political geographers is whether this resurgence will eventually alienate the British to the point where they attempt some major move, such as the secession of Natal Province from the Union or a mass "trek" to Southern Rhodesia.

The Apartheid Movement

In the years since 1948 the Nationalist-controlled government has sought to institute a policy of *apartheid* (literally "apartness") as a solution to South Africa's racial problem. Since there is obvious friction between races attempting to exist side by side, the logical step, government officials contend, would be to separate them into areas where they can live with people of their own kind. Such a drastic move would, however, deprive the whites of nonwhite labor (as well as deprive many nonwhites of the means of employment), so that the government has modified the true *apartheid* concept and turned to what might be termed a policy of partial *apartheid*. Under this policy, embodied in the Group Areas Act passed in 1950 by the South African parliament, the Negroes would be encouraged to live in their reserves, where they would have local autonomy, although government inspectors would be permitted to enter and government troops to maintain order if necessary.

In addition to the reserves, restricted areas would be set up in the South African cities in which Negroes live. Wherever possible the restricted areas would be moved well beyond the city limits, so that, except during their working hours, the Negroes would be excluded entirely from white-occupied portions of the city. The establishment of these restricted areas would alleviate population pressure on the reserves. It would also, of course, make available a supply of cheap labor for white-owned industries. Negro laborers would also continue to work in the mines and on white-owned farms; again, in both instances their living quarters would be carefully restricted from those of the whites. Although aimed primarily at South Africa's Negroes, *apartheid* also works to the detriment of the Colored and Asiatics. No special reserves are provided for these groups, but they too are to be restricted to certain areas within the cities.

A proposal put forward in 1956 provided for the establishment of seven Negro reserve areas for the bulk of the country's Negro population. The incorporation of the British High Commission Territories of Basutoland, Swaziland, and Bechuanaland would form the nucleus for these reserves, within which the Negroes could live apart from the whites, although under white jurisdiction. Perhaps eventually the reserves would achieve provincial self-government. In addition, the plan envisions about two million Negroes who would continue to live as "migrant laborers" in restricted areas within the white sections of the nation. Clearly, the policy of *apartheid,* as modified by actual conditions in South Africa, works almost exclusively to the advantage of the whites.

Unfortunately few substitute proposals have originated in South Africa for solving the racial questions. Boers and English alike are united in their fear of black domination. The cultural level of the Negroes and of many of the Colored is abysmally low when compared with white standards, and the task of raising these levels to a point approaching that of the whites appears to many South African leaders as too expensive and time-consuming to be practical. On the other hand, an indefinite continuation of racial suppression contains many elements of potential danger. As fear and unrest among the nonwhites increases so also does government resistance. Law-enforcement measures are becoming increasingly severe against persons of all races who oppose government policies, civil liberties are gradually suppressed, and the nation moves toward a fascist-type regime.

The Triumph of the Nationalists

The strengthening of the Nationalists' grip on South Africa has actually been carried out by constitutional moves. The Nationalist-dominated South African parliament voted to increase the membership of the Senate from forty-eight to eighty-nine (thus giving their party an overwhelming majority in that body) and to expand the Supreme Court from five to eleven members, the new members being appointed by the Nationalists. Thus as the political opposition is gradually rendered ineffective, the Boers, representing less than one-sixth of the total population, are moving into a position of dominance over the Union.

The policies of the Nationalist Party, in addition to antagonizing a majority of the population of South Africa, have had economic repercussions as well. Foreign investments, upon which the nation depended to a considerable extent for its economic development, have dropped sharply since Dr. Marlan took office. Many of his policies—now carried on by his political successors—are viewed as potentially explosive by foreign businessmen, and in order to carry on its economic program the Union has been forcd to rely heavily on domestic capital, some of which is secured through heavy taxation and through forced loans.

The Union of South Africa affords a unique case study in independent action by a national government. The assumption of political power by a minority group, the increased discrimination against nonwhites, and the thwarting of the authority of international organizations are in opposition to trends throughout much of the present-day world. Yet South Africa is not an island cut off from other nations. Its mineral exports, its strategic location, and its growing strength as an African industrial power are factors which tie it closely to them. The future stability of the nation would seem to lie in its capacity to solve its own peculiar problems of location and racial conflict within the broader framework of social and political developments throughout the rest of the world.

Problem Areas

1. Conflicts of Control in Southwest Africa

Southwest Africa is the only post-World War II mandate that has not become a United Nations trusteeship territory. The country, which lies to the north and west of the Union of South Africa, has an area of 325,000 square miles, consisting almost entirely of desert, and a population of 400,-000, of which nearly ninety per cent are nonwhites. Walvis Bay, a South African enclave on the coast, is administered by Southwest Africa and is its leading port. There are some grazing lands in the central sector, and Southwest Africa exports wool, karakul skins, and other pastoral products, and is noted for its diamond and vanadium resources.

Of the 50,000 whites in the area over two-thirds are Boers and some 15,000 are German-speaking. Like most of the Boers the Germans are generally in favor of a policy of white supremacy. Because of its poor economic prospects, Southwest Africa was one of the last of the African areas to be settled by Europeans: colonization was finally begun by Germany in the 1880's. A bitter four-year war raged from 1903 to 1907 between the German army and the local tribes, so that by 1911 the African population had been reduced to less than thirty per cent of what it had been in 1904. The Negro's resentment against the white man was further increased by the extremely harsh treatment meted out by the German colonial administration, particularly after 1911. When the League of Nations selected the Union of South Africa to take on the mandate of the area in 1919, it was generally anticipated that conditions among the Negroes would substantially improve.

Since that time, however, South Africa has failed to carry out the provisions of its mandate. The Union was directed to "promote to the utmost the material and moral well-being and the social progress of the inhabitants." Nevertheless, the system of reserves and conscription of Negro labor as practiced in the Union is also in force in Southwest Africa. The reserves themselves are overpopulated. The country needs industries, irrigation projects, and increased agricultural training for the Africans. Through its exports Southwest Africa has developed a favorable balance of trade, but, rather than utilize this surplus for the betterment of the mandate, the Union employs most of the credits to supplement the economy of South Africa itself—a major factor in the Union's reluctance to report to the United Nations on its administration of the territory.

Since 1945 the Union has governed Southwest Africa as part of its own territory. For a short time South Africa did submit reports on the territory to the U. N. Trusteeship Council, but after the inauguration of Dr. Malan in 1948 even this practice ended. In the following year Southwest Africa was assigned six seats in the South African parliament, and in 1954 the Nationalist Party announced that the mandate over the territory was terminated. The United Nations have specifically refused permission to the Union to annex Southwest Africa, and the International Court at The Hague has handed down an opinion advising South Africa that it is obligated to submit annual reports to the United Nations and that it should not undertake any change in the status of the mandate without United Nations consent. Despite these moves, however, the Nationalist Party has come out in favor of creating Southwest Africa as the fifth province within the Union. Since the former mandate is already a *de facto* territory within South Africa, the eventual announcement by the Nationalist government of its *de jure* status as a part of the Union appears almost inevitable.

2. Relations of the Union with the British Commonwealth

The rise of South African nationalism, particularly since World War II, has raised several problems in connection with the British Commonwealth: (1) will South Africa become a republic? (2) will it force Britain to relinquish control of its naval bases in the area? (3) will it leave the Commonwealth because of friction with other dominions and republics—or with dominions which may soon be created? (4) will it seek to acquire control of the British High Commission Territories of Bechuanaland, Basutoland, and Swaziland?

Boer officials have often talked of ending South Africa's present dominion status and becoming a republic, as have India and Pakistan. The tangible results of such a move would be of small importance (the Queen would no longer be the sovereign head of the nation), but many British inhabitants would dislike the severance of ties with the Crown. The establishment of a republic, however, appears a definite possibility, for the Union would continue to enjoy the various economic advantages of association with the Commonwealth, and yet be able to express even further the determined nationalism of the Boers.

The problem of Britain's major naval base in South Africa was solved in 1955, when control of the Simonstown base, located near Capetown, was turned over to the South African government, with the provision that it could be reoccupied by the British in the event of war, even if South Africa remained neutral. The parallel between this and the British withdrawal from the Suez Canal Zone in 1954 (again with guarantees for wartime reoccupation) illustrates a new trend in British military planning in the face of nationalist pressure.

In Chapter 5 some of the possible points of conflict between the dominions and republics of the British Commonwealth were mentioned. Friction exists between India and South Africa over the treatment of the Indian minority within the Union. The formation of all-Negro dominions in central Africa (Ghana, Nigeria, Sierra Leone) could be anathema to the present Nationalist regime, which holds the African native in such low esteem. Somewhat closer to South Africa's borders is the Federation of Rhodesia and Nyasaland, where English-speaking whites are attempting to maintain political and economic control over a nonwhite population which outnumbers them by more than 65 to 1. The governments of the three states in this federation are seeking to educate and train the Africans for greater responsibility within the new federation, although it is conceded that the process will take considerable time. Proximity to South Africa, however, could have either of two effects. Negro discontent in the Union could spread across the borders to the federation, endangering the "slow but steady" approach to racial equality practiced there. On the other hand, if the federation's policies show signs of success many nonwhites in South Africa might grow increasingly restless with their own restrictions and either emigrate illegally from the Union or resort to violence against the South African whites.

With respect to the British enclaves of Swaziland and Basutoland, the Nationalist government would clearly welcome the chance to gain political control and thus end British influence over the natives in these areas. In fact, in 1952 government leaders announced that the British would shortly be expected to turn over the enclaves, together with Bechuanaland, to South Africa. In the 1910 constitution of the Union of South Africa provision was made for the eventual inclusion of these three areas within the

Union. The British have continuously delayed implementing this provision on the grounds that no action should be taken without first determining the wishes of the local inhabitants. Population densities average forty persons per square mile in the British-controlled areas, while in the Union's Negro reserves it is nearly sixty per square mile, even with only forty per cent of the country's total Negro population residing there. Although many of the Negroes of Swaziland and Basutoland now live in South Africa and find employment there, those who remain in the British territories might, if given the chance, vote against the inclusion of the enclaves within the Union.

BIBLIOGRAPHY

"Apartheid: The Political and Economic Consequences," *The World Today*, VI, No. 7 (July, 1950), 281–89.

A brief but concise discussion of the *Apartheid* movement.

BUCHANAN, KEITH, and HURWITZ, N. "The Asiatic Immigrant Community in the Union of South Africa," *The Geographical Review*, XXXIX, No. 3 (July, 1949), 440–50.

A companion article to that on the Colored community (see below). These studies have valuable maps, charts, and discussions of the racial problems of South Africa.

————."The 'Coloured' Community in the Union of South Africa," *The Geographical Review*, XL, No. 3 (July, 1950), 397–415.

CALPIN, G. H. "South Africa in Afrikaner Hands," *Foreign Affairs*, XXIX, No. 3 (April, 1951), 417–24.

An excellent discussion of the effects of the Nationalists' policies.

"The High Commission Territories and the Union of South Africa," *The World Today*, VI, No. 2 (February, 1950), 83–95.

A comprehensive treatment of the British protectorates enclosed in and adjoining the Union of South Africa.

MOOLMAN, J. H. "The Orange River, South Africa," *The Geographical Review*, XXVI, No. 4 (October, 1946), 653–75.

This article treats a major problem of South Africa's economic potential. The Orange River crosses the semiarid northwest and provides a source for large-scale irrigation.

PATTEN, J. W. "Alternatives to Apartheid in South Africa," *Foreign Affairs,* XXX, No. 2 (January, 1952), 310–27.

Like Calpin's article, this is a general description of conditions in South Africa under the Nationalist administration.

"Southwest Africa and the Union," *The World Today,* VI, No. 11 (November, 1950), 459–69.

A general discussion of the problem of South Africa's control over this former League mandate.

14

THE INDIAN SUBCONTINENT

● In 1947 the subcontinent of India was partitioned into two independent states—India and Pakistan—along the lines of the religious division which exists here. The subcontinent, surrounded on three sides by mountains and on the fourth by the sea, forms a distinct geographic unit, which under British control had been developed as a unified economic and political area. Since the partition, however, millions of persons in India and Pakistan have become refugees, conflicting claims to territorial control have arisen in various parts of the subcontinent, and relations between the two new states have been severely strained. As a result the Indian subcontinent has become one of the outstanding politico-geographic problem areas of the world.

THE GEOGRAPHIC BASIS OF THE SUBCONTINENT

The Indian subcontinent occupies a transitional location in southern Asia between the monsoon nations of southeastern Asia and the desert areas which lie to the west. Many people from India have settled in Burma, Malaya, and other southeast Asian countries, and since 1947 India has occupied a position of leadership in international affairs among a number of the states in this area. Pakistan, on the other hand, with its arid western portion and its large Moslem population, has more elements of affinity with Iran and the Arab World to the west than with the countries which lie to the east of it.

The physical structure of the Indian subcontinent reveals both the unity and the diversity of the area. There are three major surface features: (1) the mountain wall in the northwest, north, and northeast; (2) the block

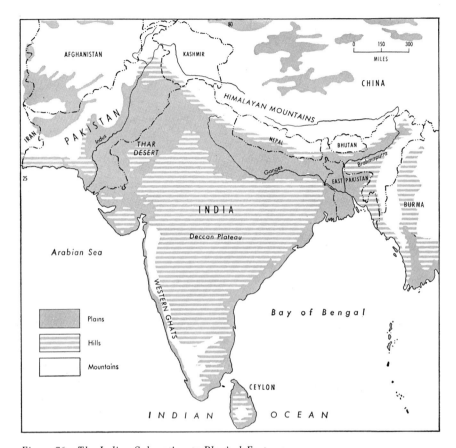

Figure 76. The Indian Subcontinent: Physical Features.

of old resistant rock of the Deccan Plateau in the central and southern portions; and (3) the Indus-Ganges lowland, forming an arc about the northern end of the plateau from the mouth of the Indus River on the Arabian Sea to that of the Ganges on the Bay of Bengal. The mountain wall and the Indus-Ganges lowland are shared by both India and Pakistan. The Deccan Plateau lies entirely within India (Figure 76).

The mountain wall consists of numerous highland structures (including the Himalaya and Karakorum ranges, the loftiest mountain systems in the world) and fertile valleys, which have served as core areas for the development of individual cultural and political units. Relatively few passes exist through the mountain borders: the Khyber and Bolan passes to Afghanistan, the Makran coastal route to Iran, and the Brahmaputra gorge leading to Tibet and southern China. Beyond the highland rim are generally inhospitable areas, notably the deserts of Iran and Afghanistan, the plateau of northeastern Afghanistan and Tibet, and the forested mountain ranges of Burma, all of which have added to India's relative inaccessibility by land.

The Deccan Plateau is a region of considerable physical diversity— coastal highlands, deserts, canyons, and forested hills—which have contributed to the ethnic differences among its population and to the historical development of its political units, such as Hyderabad, Madras, and the Central Provinces. Since 1947 one of the principal tasks of the Indian government has been to weld together the various groups inhabiting the Deccan within the framework of a cohesive national unit.

The lowlands of the Indus-Ganges area exhibit greater physical homogeneity than the other principal physical regions. West Pakistan occupies the major share of the Indus lowland; India controls the Ganges plain, except in the delta area where East Pakistan is located. Thus, despite their elements of physical unity, these lowlands are divided by political borders.

Most of the republic of India is influenced by the summer monsoon, with moderate to heavy rainfall during the summer months. East Pakistan is also affected by the monsoon. In parts of the central Deccan Peninsula (in the lee of the Western Ghats) and in most of West Pakistan semiarid to arid conditions occur. The mountains which border the subcontinent have their own peculiar climates. Natural vegetation reflects the climatic pattern, and ranges from the tropical forests of the west Deccan coast and eastern India to the drought-resistant plants of the western deserts. Soils also vary widely, according to conditions of climate, vegetation, and underlying rock. Among the many varieties of soils is the fertile alluvium of the Ganges flood plain and delta, which supports some of the most densely-populated agricultural areas in the world.

The distribution of minerals and power fuels is uneven, with most of the reserves located on the Deccan Plateau or to the northeast in the general Calcutta area. The Indian state has thus come to possess a majority of these resources. Hydroelectric-power potential exists in the mountain rim, but inaccessibility and lack of good sites for power stations has ruled out much development in these areas. It is also present in some of the well-watered upland areas, such as the Western Ghats and the hills of Assam, and, of course, in connection with the great river systems of the subcontinent.

Although differences in physical features throughout the subcontinent are reflected in regional economic differences, before partition there had gradually evolved in India a pattern of economic unity, based on rail and road nets, irrigation systems, and the movement of goods (cotton, jute, and wool) from agricultural to industrial areas. The distribution of investments became nation-wide, and a potential market of 400,000,000 customers stimulated economic growth. Across this geographic and economic unit a political border was superimposed in 1947.

THE POLITICAL DEVELOPMENT OF THE SUBCONTINENT

The Colonial Period

In spite of the mountain rim which surrounds it on its land sides, the Indian subcontinent was invaded many times by peoples from the northwest before the arrival by sea of the Portuguese at the end of the fifteenth century. Among the invading groups were the Macedonians under Alexander the Great, the Arabs, bringing with them the Moslem faith, and the Moguls under Tamerlane. Sailing east after rounding the tip of Africa, the Portuguese navigator Vasco da Gama reached the coast of India in 1498, and for the next two hundred years India was the scene of commercial—and, to a less degree, political—competition among Portugal, the Netherlands, France, and Britain. By 1800 British sea and land power had triumphed: the Netherlands had been eliminated, and the possessions of Portugal and France had been reduced to a few coastal enclaves.

At the beginning of the nineteenth century British control in India was still administered through the East India Company, a government-chartered commercial organization. In 1858 the British government assumed the responsibilities of administration, and the subcontinent was divided politically into (1) British India, containing about fifty-five per cent of the total area and approximately seventy-five per cent of the population, which was administered as a colonial region; and (2) the Native States and Agencies (numbering 584), which continued to exist as protectorates of the British.

During the 1870's a nationalist movement got under way in India, and by 1900 Indian leaders were agitating for the country's independence. As in other units of the Empire, the British gradually instituted measures granting increasingly greater self-rule for the Indian peoples. The British government, however, insisted that workable arrangements had to be devised to protect the interests of the various cultural groups within the subcontinent before independence could be achieved. The majority of the population was Hindu, but there existed a large Moslem group in the country, as well as Christians, Sikhs, and smaller minority groups. The Moslem leaders were opposed to the creation of a united Hindu-dominated state in which Moslems would be in a definite minority.

Following World War I the political power of the Moslems grew increasingly strong, and in 1940 the Moslem League officially demanded the creation of an independent Moslem state. Two years later the British Parliament offered independence to India, but neither the Hindu nor the Moslem political leaders could agree on conditions for self-government. After many conferences between British, Hindu, and Moslem representatives, a plan was eventually worked out for the partition of India into two states— India, a Hindu nation, and Pakistan, a Moslem one. Finally, in August,

1947, the partition plan went into effect, and two new dominions were created (Table 14).

Table 14

AREA AND POPULATION OF INDIA AND PAKISTAN

(*Pop. (1941) in thousands; area in sq. mi.*)

	Area	Pop.	Density	Moslems	%	Non-Moslems	%
Western Pakistan	306,977	28,258	92	22,328	79.5	5,930	20.5
Eastern Pakistan	54,030	41,845	775	29,381	67.8	12,464	32.2
Total, Pakistan	361,007	70,103	194	51,709	72.7	18,394	27.3
Indian Union	1,138,551	315,480	277	38,965	12.4	276,192*	87.6
Kashmir	82,258	4,022	48	3,074	77.1	948	22.9

*No data available for religious beliefs of 323,000 persons, formerly in French India, now in the Indian Union.

Source: O. H. K. Spate, "The Partition of India and the Prospects of Pakistan," *The Geographical Review*, XXXVIII, No. 1 (January, 1948), 17. Courtesy of the American Geographical Society.

The Division of the Subcontinent

The political partitioning of the Indian subcontinent was an extremely complicated process, for, on the one hand, religion was the essential basis for division, yet, on the other hand, economic and strategic factors also had to be taken into account in the delimitation of the new boundaries. In many areas Hindu and Moslem groups were intermingled with one another, and no workable boundary could be laid down separating them from one another.

The Position of the Provinces. In the course of partitioning, the provinces of what had formerly been British India were assigned to the two states on the basis of the religion of the majority of the population. However, in three cases—Punjab, Bengal, and Assam—the individual provinces were divided.

In Punjab, in the north central part of the subcontinent, the new boundary cut across a unified agricultural region (Figure 77). The Punjab (99,000 square miles, with a population of over 28 million) produced the largest grain surplus of the Indian provinces, and much of its agriculture was dependent on its extensive irrigation system which was fed by the waters of the eastern tributaries of the Indus River. Punjab was also the home of over 5 million Sikhs, and in the partition Sikh territory, including a large number of holy places, was divided. The political division of the Punjab left seventy-five per cent of its Moslem population in Pakistan (as well as 4 million non-Moslems). Most of the canal irrigation works, as well as about seventy per cent of the irrigated land, also was awarded to Pakistan. Control of the waters for the irrigation systems, however, remained in

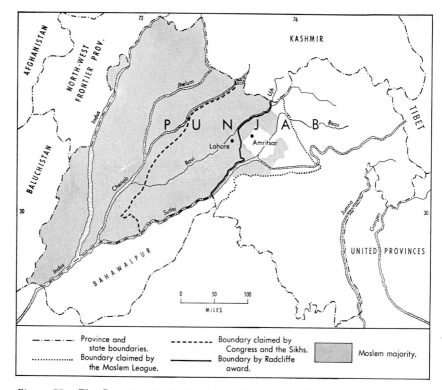

Figure 77. The Partition of the Punjab. (After Spate, *The Geographical Review,* XXXVIII (Jan., 1948). Courtesy of American Geographical Society.)

Indian hands, since the headwaters of the eastern Indus tributaries flow through India. The Radcliffe Award[1] thus split a unified irrigation system, but it granted to Pakistan the basis for its present food surplus.

In Bengal Province (77,000 square miles and 60 million people), located to the east in the Ganges Delta, the partition left approximately seventy-one per cent of the Moslems in Pakistani territory, together with 11,500,000 non-Moslems (Figure 78). The boundary severed communications between Calcutta and the Indian province of Assam east of the Pakistani territory and left practically all the industrial developments in India, while Pakistan won the better agricultural land and most of the jute and rice producing areas. Thus not only was the unified communication network centered on Calcutta divided by the new boundary, but so also was the agricultural-industrial unity destroyed, with India controlling the processing plants (particularly for jute) and Pakistan the raw materials.

---

[1] A name applied to the lines partitioning Punjab and Bengal; so called because of Sir Cyril Radcliffe, chairman of the boundary commissions for both areas.

The division of Assam Province (62,800 square miles, population 8 million) resulted in the inclusion of most of Sylhet District in East Pakistan. With an area of 4,600 square miles, this district, to the northeast of Dacca, contained about 1,700,000 Moslems and 1,000,000 non-Moslems.

The Native States and Agencies. The various Indian states and agencies were given the choice of acceding to either India or Pakistan. Eventually all but four were joined to India. Bahawalpur, Khairpur, the North-West Frontier Agencies, and the Baluchistan States, located in the western part of the subcontinent, acceded to Pakistan. Hyderabad, in the central portion of the Deccan Peninsula, and Kashmir, in the northwestern sector of the

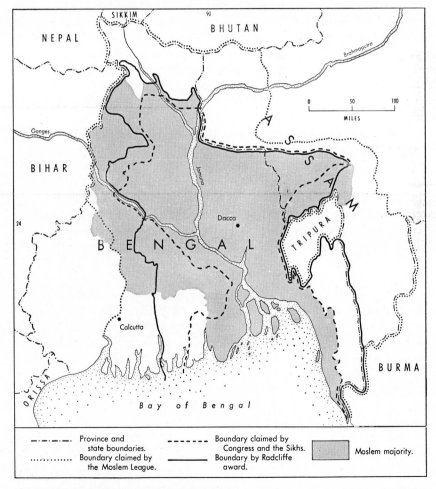

Figure 78. The Partition of Bengal and Assam. (After Spate, *The Geographical Review*, XXXVIII (Jan., 1948). Courtesy of American Geographical Society.)

subcontinent, delayed joining either nation, but in 1948 Hyderabad was occupied by Indian troops and was subsequently joined to India. (For a discussion of Kashmir see page 379.) With the acquisition of Hyderabad, India acquired three-quarters of the prepartition area of the subcontinent and seventy-eight per cent of its population, as well as a majority of its mineral and power resources, while Pakistan, whose two parts were separated from one another by nearly 1,000 miles of Indian territory, received approximately one-quarter of the subcontinent's area and population, as well as those districts which normally produce a surplus of grains, cotton, and jute, but the new nation contained practically no minerals and few power resources.

The Nature of the Indo-Pakistan Boundary. The boundary between India and Pakistan was one of the greatest politico-geographic problem areas the world has ever known. Although this boundary was based primarily on religious considerations, approximately 50 million persons were left on the wrong side of the boundary as a result of its delimitation. Since 1947 an estimated 16–17 million people have crossed between India and Pakistan as political refugees and some 300,000 persons have been killed in border conflicts.

Much of the boundary follows the political borders of prepartition provinces and native states. Two tributaries of the Indus—the Sutlej and Ravi rivers—mark portions of the border in Punjab, and in Bengal the Ganges and tributaries of the Meghna are similarly used. In East Pakistan the river boundaries have given rise to local problems of delimitation, as a result of shifting courses and of inadequate descriptions in the Radcliffe Award. In the northern East Pakistan area are 130 small Indian enclaves (with a total area of thirty-three square miles) and ninety-three Pakistani enclaves (nineteen square miles); approximately 23,500 persons inhabit these various enclaves.[2]

Much of the Indo-Pakistan boundary has yet to be demarcated. Because of continued friction between India and Pakistan since 1947, various restrictions have been imposed on the movements of peoples and products across the borders. Such restrictions magnify the problems of normal economic and cultural contacts in the subcontinent. Settlement patterns and economic activities have gradually adjusted to the existence of the boundary lines, but in many parts of the subcontinent the scars of these superimposed lines are in evidence in road and rail blocks, unused irrigation systems, and deserted farms and villages.

The Causes and Effects of Partition. In view of the magnitude of this political problem, the question might well be asked, was partition necessary, or could India have developed as a united, independent state? Out

---

[2] Figures from P. P. Karan, "Indo-Pakistan Boundaries," *The Indian Geographical Journal*, XXVIII, Nos. 1, 2 (January, June, 1953), 19–23.

of a total Indian population of about 390 million in 1941, about 94 million, or some twenty-five per cent, were Moslems. The Hindus, comprising the bulk of the non-Moslem population, were in favor of a unified nation, and not until 1940 were there official demands by the Moslems for partition. Ninety-four million Moslems in a predominantly non-Moslem nation would represent the largest minority group in the world.

Although religion was often cited as the principal reason behind the Moslem demands, political and economic factors were probably of greater importance. Hindus had taken the lead in the struggle for independence, they were more advanced than the Moslems in education and the professions, and in the national government Hindus would have been in a permanent majority. Moslem business and financial groups feared that they would be in a poor competitive situation with regard to the more entrenched Hindu interests. Factors such as these formed the basis for a tremendous popular movement, which, fanned by religious fervor, succeeded in bringing about the partition of the Indian subcontinent.

INDIA

The Republic of India, faced with a population increase of about 50 million per decade, is hard put to provide even the basic necessities of life for its people. With an area about forty per cent of that of the United States, India has a population two and one-quarter times as great. Its over 380 million persons make it second only to China in size of population. Because of its population, its location, and its economic potential, independent India has become one of the important powers of the world, a leading nation in the rapidly-changing political and economic area of Asia.

The process of modernizing the Indian state has meant that many of the traditional customs and political systems must be changed. For example, the gradual abolition of the caste system will eventually mean that approximately 50 million "untouchables" (persons of the lowest Hindu caste) must be assimilated into the nation's social structure. The population-food supply ratio remains a pressing problem. Some Indian experts favor birth control as a means of easing the strain on India's resources, although such a practice would conflict with the tenets of the Hindu faith. Major changes in India's system of land ownership could lead to a more efficient distribution of crop land among the farmers. Much work has also been necessary in educating the great masses of the Indian people to the responsibilities of self-government and in acquainting them with important issues.

Agricultural Problems and Trends

In order to provide additional food for a growing population, a nation must either expand the area of cultivated land, increase the average yield in areas already in production, or depend on large-scale imports of food to supplement domestic production. In India, where intensive cultivation has been going on for many centuries, much of the potentially arable land is already in crops. Maximum utilization in many agricultural areas is hindered by the shortage of fertilizers, small dispersed farm holdings (a result of inheritance laws), and ignorance of modern farming methods.

In their efforts to obtain fuel for heating and cooking the Indian farmers burn cow dung, which might better serve as fertilizer on the fields, or cut down forests and even small trees and bushes, thereby hastening soil erosion. Food production is further hindered by the failure to rotate crops (and thus prevent soil exhaustion) and by the concentration on cash crops, such as cotton and jute, rather than on grains or vegetables. A final factor is the uncertainty of rainfall in India, where a delay of the summer monsoon can spell crop disaster and famine for millions of people in large areas of the country.

It has been estimated[3] that in 1951, 250 million persons in India were dependent upon agriculture. Of these, 76 million were classed as landless laborers. Among this tremendous group of farmers such political philosophies as communism often have considerable appeal.

The Indian government has been making impressive headway in its battle to overcome the obstacles to increased food production, but it still has far to go before the mass of the Indian population can be assured an adequate diet. Large-scale irrigation projects, increased fertilizer production, technical training for farmers, better distribution of food—these and similar projects requiring capital, skilled personnel, and a change in traditional Indian ways of life must be undertaken if India is to bring the general standard of living of its increasing population in line with that of Western nations. Under the first five-year plan, which ended in March, 1956, 8,000,000 acres of land were put under irrigation. During this same time the Community Development Program sent thousands of trained workers into Indian towns and villages to educate and train the people in modern agricultural techniques.

India has supplemented its domestic production by annual imports of food from grain-surplus areas, such as the United States and the Soviet Union. Because of India's shortage of foreign exchange, a part of these imports has been made possible by the granting of long-term credits to India. As a result of the country's strategic position in world affairs, both the United States and the U.S.S.R. have made important contributions toward alleviating India's food shortages, despite the fact that its government has consistently refused to align itself with either of the power blocs in the Cold War.

---

[3] George Kuriyan, "India's Population Problem," *Focus,* V, No. 2 (October, 1954).

Industrial Growth

In addition to its agricultural resources, India has many of the essentials for industrialization, including minerals, power resources, labor, markets, and transportation. Its minerals include a large reserve of good iron ore, as well as manganese (essential to the production of steel), bauxite (aluminum ore), salt, and mica. The nation has a great water-power potential, of which less than ten per cent is developed, and a relatively small amount of coal. Petroleum is almost nonexistent, along with copper, lead, zinc, and several ferro-alloys. Before partition British capital was responsible for the establishment of a large number of industries in India, including iron and steel, textiles, jute, and food processing, and for the construction of an extensive rail system throughout both India and what is now Pakistan.

By the end of the second five-year plan in 1961 India hopes to have a steel-producing capacity of over 4,500,000 tons. Such a goal requires the building of three new steel plants, and the Indian government here, as in other aspects of its economic development plans, must look to foreign sources for much of its capital. Increasing India's industrial facilities can provide additional employment for the growing population as well as make available more products for the home market.

Internal Political Problems

Centrifugal forces in India are the diverse physical features, the many languages which exist here, and the presence of two great cities, Bombay and Calcutta, which tend to rival one another in power. The capital, located at New Delhi, in the northwest of India, is the center of many transportation routes. The shifting of the seat of government from Calcutta (where the British had originally located it) to New Delhi in 1912 was a symbol of India's gradual independence from overseas influence and power.

One of the great tasks facing the Indian government since 1947 has been to simplify the pattern of the former Native States, in order to form a more efficient national economic and political structure. Local rulers were urged to surrender control over their historic political units and were "pensioned off" by the Indian government, with the result that the number of states in India was eventually reduced to twenty-eight. The resultant savings in local government expenditures and the increase in efficiency of economic operations have reaped considerable benefits to the Indian government.

A new internal political problem has appeared in India in the form of demands for new states to be set up along linguistic lines. Fourteen major languages are spoken in India, but Hindi has been designated as the official tongue (Figure 79). The issue of political divisions on the basis of local languages was considered at the time India attained independence, but

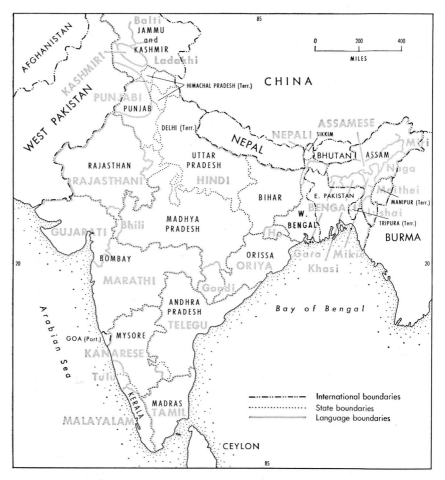

Figure 79. India: Languages and States. (Language data adapted from *Focus,* VI (Feb., 1956). Courtesy of American Geographical Society.)

little was done until 1953, when the government, after considerable pressure, agreed to the creation of a new Telegu-speaking state of Andhra in southeast India, comprised of territory formerly belonging to Madras State.

Recognition of the political rights of 20 million Telegu-speaking persons, has brought demands for similar concessions from other linguistic groups throughout the nation. To the government this linguistic regionalism represents a potential force for national disunity. Less than forty per cent of the population as yet speaks Hindi, and Indian officials are trying to deemphasize the cultural differences among the nation's inhabitants, rather than strengthen them by yielding to demands for linguistic sectionalism. On the other hand, many of the Indian people have a strong sense of loyalty to their particular language, and the government was under great pressure to redraw the political map of the nation, even though by following linguistic patterns in the determination of states it might destroy some of the economic cohesion which existed within the political units as they had been delimited.

After considerable discussion—and occasional outbreaks of violence—the Indian government effected a major revision of the internal political pattern. As of November 1, 1956, the number of states was reduced to 14 (including Kashmir). Hyderabad and 8 other states were abolished, and Bihar, in northeast India, relinquished an important piece of its territory to West Bengal. The government hopes that, by taking both linguistic and economic factors into consideration in the redistribution of states, it can put an end to much of the bitterness which has arisen in India over the problem of its internal political structure.

External Problems

India's relations with Pakistan and other units of the British Commonwealth have been colored by certain problems and by certain objectives. With Pakistan the major disputes concern political control of Kashmir, compensation to the millions of political refugees who have crossed from one nation to the other, and the easing of travel and trade restrictions between the two countries. The political, social, and economic rights of the over 4 million "overseas" Indians have contributed to friction between India and the Union of South Africa, British East Africa, Malaya, Trinidad, and British Guiana, in which Indians form sizable minorities, and in which Indians are involved in white-native conflicts and are generally subjected to various forms of racial discrimination.

As an expression of its national freedom India in 1948 changed its status within the British Commonwealth from that of a dominion to a republic. India's position with respect to Cold War power alignments has been a strong one, since the country has assumed a position of leadership among the so-called "neutral" countries which are committed neither to the Soviet Union and its allies nor to the United States and other Western powers. Maintaining a powerful position in external affairs, however, is dependent upon internal strength, and it is on this problem that the Indian government must continue to concentrate much of its energies. In a sense India and China, the two greatest nations of Asia, are in competition with one another in terms of internal development. China is developing within the framework of communism, India by democratic means. The progress made by these two states under differing ideologies may be an important factor in determining the eventual political and economic philosophies which will be followed by the other countries of southern and eastern Asia.

PAKISTAN

Pakistan is a state in which the various forces of diversity require extremely skillful handling on the part of the national leaders. The country is divided into two parts, differing physically, ethnically, and economically from one another, and separated by a thousand miles of Indian territory. Pakistan is not richly endowed with natural resources. Like India, it has a rapidly-increasing population. Pakistan also is confronted by territorial problems, with India and with Afghanistan.

The division of Pakistan into eastern and western sectors was occasioned by the existence of large Moslem concentrations in and about the delta of the Ganges and in the western portion of the subcontinent. In the establishment of the new dominion, West Pakistan received eighty-five per cent of the total territory and forty per cent of its 77 million people.

Because of the concentration of Moslem power in West Pakistan, this area was chosen as the one in which the national capital would be located. Lahore, in the Punjab, had a central location with respect to the population distribution of West Pakistan, but the city lies close to the Indian border and was therefore considered to be in too vulnerable a position. Karachi, at the mouth of the Indus, was eventually selected as the capital city. Although it is the largest city of Pakistan, it is in an isolated position with respect to both West Pakistan and East Pakistan.

Since partition Pakistan has faced three major problems: (1) how to develop the over-all economy of the country; (2) how to weld East Pakistan and West Pakistan closely together; and (3) how to realize its territorial ambitions in Kashmir.

Pakistan's Economic Structure

West Pakistan is a predominantly arid region, in which there are small reserves of coal, petroleum, and chromium, as well as some salt deposits. The region is drained by the Indus River and its tributaries. Large-scale irrigation works, utilizing the waters of the Indus system, were developed in pre-partition years, largely by British capital. West Pakistan's major economic asset is that it produces high-grade cotton and, in normal times, a grain surplus. In order to capitalize on its agricultural advantage, West Pakistan must continue to increase its irrigated lands, a process requiring both capital and the assurance of available water supply.

East Pakistan is a region of heavy monsoonal rainfall, in which rice and jute are the principal cash crops. With its large population, it is a food-deficit area and must import needed supplies from either West Pakistan or India. There are no known mineral deposits in East Pakistan. Before 1947 the region was tied economically even more closely to India than was West Pakistan, and its economy has suffered more from the political partitioning.

Pakistan's over-all economy is handicapped, first, by the lack of minerals and power facilities within the country and, second, by the complementary nature of the Pakistani and Indian economies. As already noted, the present Pakistan area was an important producer of jute and cotton, which were processed by mills now located in India. Since 1947 trade has been severely disrupted between the two countries. As a result India is developing its domestic sources for jute and cotton, while Pakistan is constructing its own processing mills. The nation does not, however, possess the major requirements for extensive industrialization as India does, and in the coming years the differential of economic power between Pakistan and India will become increasingly great.

Internal Political Forces

Political unity between East Pakistan and West Pakistan has been under severe strain since 1947. Because the national capital is located in West Pakistan, the people of East Pakistan often feel their interests suffer as a result of the distance between them and the seat of political power. Although Pakistan was unified on the basis of religion, the centrifugal forces of language and economic differences serve to divide it. In West Pakistan Urdu is the principal language, while in East Pakistan Bengali, an unrelated tongue, is used. Not until 1954 did the Pakistan government elevate Bengali to the status of an official language, and thus counter the charge that East Pakistan's cultural interests were being neglected. The standard of living in East Pakistan is considerably lower than that in West Pakistan, and the people in the East regard with suspicion any decision made by the Karachi government with regard to prices and controls on such items as rice and cloth, important commodities in the East Pakistan economy.

Only two-thirds of the people in East Pakistan are Moslems, and the ties of religion are thus weaker than in West Pakistan, where over ninety-five per cent of the people are Moslems. Communism has gained a foothold in the East, particularly among the 10 million Hindus who inhabit the area. In the 1954 elections the United Front Party, in which the Communists have considerable strength, won control of the East Pakistan legislature from the Moslem League, the political group which originally formed the Pakistan nation. Leaders of the United Front organization soon began to talk of East Pakistan's "colonial" status and of possible independence for the area. In view of the wide acceptance such views received in East Pakistan, the Karachi government undertook to strengthen the ties between the two areas, notably by recognizing Bengali as an official tongue and developing a broad economic expansion program in East Pakistan.

External Relations

Pakistan's territorial problems with India and Afghanistan are treated later in this chapter. The country's official relation with the British Commonwealth was changed in 1956 when it ceased to be a dominion and became the Islamic Republic of Pakistan. The country has become a military ally of the United States and of other Western powers against possible Soviet aggression. Because of Pakistan's Western military orientation, the United States and Britain have been confronted with a difficult decision with regard to the Kashmir dispute between Pakistan and India. This dispute is very important to both states, and should the Americans or the British openly back Pakistan, India would be greatly antagonized; conversely, support for India might destroy Pakistan's military ties with the West.

Although Pakistan has the greatest population of all the Moslem countries, its location and its foreign policy have combined to keep it from assuming a role of leadership among the Moslem states. Egypt or Iraq are more centrally located with respect to the Moslem peoples than Pakistan. More important perhaps is the fact that many of the states of the Arab World have espoused a neutral approach to the Cold War problems, while Pakistan has openly aligned itself with the noncommunist nations.

CEYLON

The island of Ceylon lies but a few miles off the southeast coast of India, and its interests have been closely tied with those of its large neighbor. One of the important problems facing Ceylon, however, is the presence of a large Indian minority within the country and the prospect of a future influx of Indians from the mainland. With an area of 25,000 square miles and an over-all population of nearly 8,500,000, Ceylon does not approach the population density of parts of southern India. The difference in population densities between Ceylon and India may in time come to be an important factor in the island's relations with India.

Ceylon was not administratively a part of prepartition India, but its independence followed that of India and Pakistan by eight months. The country was established as a dominion, but since 1956 the government has talked frequently about adopting a republic status. Because of its location, Ceylon has long been of importance to British naval operations in the Indian Ocean. Britain maintained a naval base at Trincomalee on the northeastern coast of Ceylon. In 1956, however, the Ceylonese government, following India's neutralist lead, requested that the British evacuate the Trincomalee base, as well as the Katunayaka air base, which was an important staging post for long-distance air travel. As a result, Britain is reviving its air base on Gan in the Maldive Islands, 300 miles southwest of India in the Indian Ocean, for use by long-range aircraft. The Maldives contain about 93,000 Moslem inhabitants and are under British protection. It is unlikely that nationalist pressures will develop here and force the British to abandon their military installations.

Economic Position

Ceylon is an important area for tropical plantation agriculture. Its major export crops include tea, rubber, and coconut products, in exchange for which Ceylon imports approximately two-thirds of its food supply. The island's agricultural potential could be considerably increased by opening up new areas to crops and improving the present yields.

Although there is no coal, water power and iron ore could help to support future industrial development. The commercial significance of the island is augmented by the fact that Colombo, its capital and leading city, is also an important port of call between Suez and the Far East, and its harbor ranks high in terms of tonnage of shipping handled.

Ceylon's Indian Minority

About two million Hindus from India reside in the predominantly Buddhist state of Ceylon. In general the Indians are not popular on the island, and the franchise has been denied to them on the grounds that they are not citizens. Many have entered Ceylon illegally, and quite a few are suspected of procommunist sympathies. About one-third of the Indian population has applied for Ceylonese citizenship, but the Colombo government is reluctant to incorporate such a large minority group within the nation. The solution to this problem would seem to lie in (1) the formulation of a clear-cut policy by the Ceylonese government with regard to requirements and quotas for admitting Indians to citizenship, (2) stricter control measures by both the Indian and Ceylonese governments against illegal immigration from India, and (3) an agreement between India and Ceylon providing for repatriation of a given number of Indians from Ceylon.

The conflict between Indians and Ceylonese is partly reflected in the division of the island's population into some 2½ million Tamil-speaking Hindus and Moslems and 6 million Sinhalese-speaking Buddhists. By 1960 Sinhalese will be the one official language of Ceylon. The Tamil-speaking people want a state of their own in the north under a federal type of government, but it appears unlikely that this wish will be granted.

AFGHANISTAN

Afghanistan, like Iran, is one of the historic buffer areas of Asia. The land-locked country borders the Indian subcontinent on the south and east, the U.S.S.R. on the north, and Iran on the west. It has an area of 250,000 square miles and a population of some 12 million. Despite its isolation as a result of mountains and deserts, Afghanistan is of considerable importance to all three of its neighbors in terms of the conflicting power elements in this part of the world.

Afghanistan has a complex physical structure, resulting in the existence of several core areas. The main range of the Hindu Kush passes through the central part of the country. There is a relatively narrow plain to the north, sloping northward to the Amu Darya (Oxus River), and a broad desert area in the south. Although the majority of the population is united in religion (Sunnite Mohammedanism), it is divided on the basis of language and culture. Among the various groups are the Afghans and Pathans, in the east and south, whose language, Pushtu, is the official language of the nation; the Tadzhiks, of Persian origin, in the Kabul area and to the north; and the Hazaras, descendants of Mongol Tatars, in the central section of the country.

Afghanistan is still relatively backward, with no railroads, few industries, and very little resource development, although it is known to possess a variety of minerals, including gold, iron ore, copper, and asbestos. There are considerable coal reserves, as well as hydroelectric-power potential. One of Afghanistan's great needs is capital for development of its water-power and irrigation facilities. Transportation links are poor between Kabul, the capital and leading city, and other population centers, such as Kandahar in the south central area and Herat in the west. Poorly-developed road systems also connect Kabul with Pakistan and Iran. New highways are being constructed, however, from the Soviet border southward to Kabul and other Afghan cities. In contrast to the mountain barriers separating Afghanistan from Pakistan, the Soviet-Afghan border, to the northeast of Kabul, lies in the flood plain of the Amu Darya, permitting much easier communications between the two countries.

History of Foreign Influence

The modern Afghan nation dates back to the eighteenth century, when the Persians were expelled from the area and the Afghan Empire was established. Frequent warfare between groups within the country, and later between Afghan armies and Russian and British forces, hindered the economic and political development of the nation. During the nineteenth century British efforts to establish a sphere of influence in Afghanistan (and thus protect the northwestern approaches to India) led to the two Afghan wars (1839–42 and 1879–81), as well as to almost constant border warfare in northwest India between British and Afghan forces. In the 1880's Afghanistan consented to British protection, and the Russians in 1907, in exchange for a sphere of influence in Iran, agreed to regard Afghanistan as outside Russia's influence sphere. Afghanistan's role as a buffer state was further emphasized by the extension of the nation's border eastward in a curious projection to the boundary of Sinkiang, thereby separating India and Russia by about twenty-five to fifty miles of Afghan territory (Figure 8).

Following World War I Afghanistan became completely independent of British control, and in order to strengthen its position relative to both Britain and Russia the government looked for assistance and advice to a third power—Germany. German engineers and advisers were active in Afghanistan prior to World War II—a role which American technicians filled for a time following the war. The withdrawal of the British from India in 1947 and the creation of independent India and Pakistan affected Afghanistan's position, for no longer was the country a buffer state between British and Russian power. The decline of British influence was partially compensated by an increase of United States interest, largely through loans and technical aid to develop Afghanistan's economy.

Extension of Soviet Power. Since early 1956 Afghanistan has strengthened its economic ties with the Soviet Union. The boundary dispute with Pakistan eventually led to Pakistan's closing the border and denying to the Afghans the use of Karachi, the major port for Afghanistan's foreign trade. No longer was the nation in a buffer position between opposing forces. By expanding its trade with the Soviet Union and by accepting a Soviet loan of $100,000,000 (nearly five times the country's annual national income), Afghanistan moved within the economic orbit of the U.S.S.R. In the absence of a counterforce (from the United States, India, or Pakistan), the mountain nation may soon come almost wholly within the Soviet sphere.

Problem Areas

1. The Kashmir Dispute

The Vale of Kashmir was once famous as a retreat for members of the British Civil Service in India seeking to escape the heat and rainfall of the summer monsoon. Since 1947 it has been the most serious source of conflict between India and Pakistan. Kashmir—or, more properly, the State of Jammu and Kashmir—comprises the provinces of Jammu (including dependency of Poonch) and Kashmir, as well as the administrative districts of Gilgit and Ladakh (including Baltistan) (Figure 80). It lies in the northwest corner of the Indian subcontinent bordering India, Pakistan, Afghanistan, and China. Kashmir has an area of 82,258 square miles and a population (1941 census) of about four million, of whom over three-quarters are Moslems.

Geographic and Historical Background. Most of Kashmir consists of

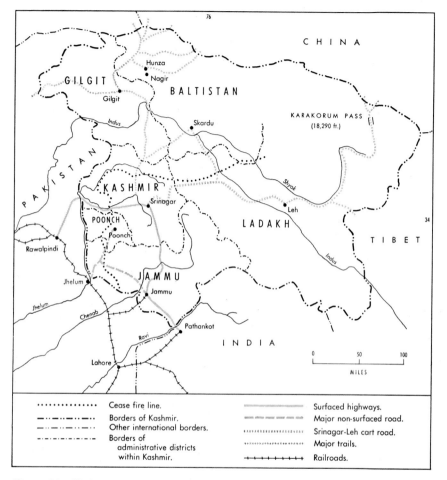

Figure 80. Kashmir. (After Mayfield, *The Geographical Review*, XLV (April, 1955). Courtesy of American Geographical Society.)

uplands, varying in altitude from 3,000–6,000 feet in the southwest to the Karakorum Range in the north, where much of the land is above 15,000 feet. Only in Jammu Province in the extreme southwest, is there a strip of territory with elevations below 3,000 feet. The Vale of Kashmir lies to the north of Jammu at an average elevation of 4,000–5,000 feet. This famous resort area, containing the state's capital, Srinagar, and about forty per cent of its population, is something of a physical and cultural unit, surrounded on three sides by mountains, and with practically all its people united by language and by the Moslem religion. To the south, Jammu, with about one-half the state's population, has a Hindu concentration in the south and

Moslems elsewhere. The remainder of Kashmir, containing less than ten per cent of the total population, is inhabited by mountain peoples, living for the most part in isolated valleys. The Pathans of Gilgit and western Baltistan speak Pushtu and are culturally akin to the peoples of the North-West Frontier Province and eastern Afghanistan, while those of Ladakh are Buddhists whose cultural affinities are with Tibet.

The historical background of the present dispute began in August, 1947, when the governments of the various native states of prepartition India were instructed to decide whether they would join India or Pakistan. In most states the decision was made by the ruling head. In Kashmir, despite its predominantly Moslem population, the ruling house was Hindu. At the time of partition the maharaja of Kashmir did not declare in favor of either nation, but sought to maintain a political status quo. Shortly after the subcontinent's partition riots broke out among Moslem groups in Kashmir against the maharaja's administration, and as fighting spread throughout much of the area Pathan tribesmen from Pakistan entered the state to assist the Moslems. The Kashmir government appealed to India for assistance, and after the maharaja had agreed to accede to India Indian troops were flown into the Vale of Kashmir to quell the rioters. Shortly after regular Pakistani troops were also sent to Kashmir, and fighting between Indian and Pakistani forces went on for over a year. Finally, in January, 1949, a cease-fire line was established as a result of United Nations intervention, leaving two-thirds of Kashmir's area (including the Vale) and four-fifths of its population under Indian control.

Since 1949 Kashmir has remained divided, and all attempts to effect an amicable settlement of this dispute have been unsuccessful. Both India and Pakistan claim the entire area on the basis of ethnic, economic, political, and historical factors. The Kashmir problem has been a major obstacle to the resumption of friendly relations between the two nations, and at times war has appeared imminent. The United Nations has frequently pressed for an all-Kashmir plebiscite to determine the wishes of the Kashmiri people, but such a move has consistently been blocked by India.

Conflicting Claims. The Pakistan government bases its claims to Kashmir on the following major points: (1) the majority of the population is Moslem, and if an impartial plebiscite were held the results would probably be pro-Pakistan; (2) prepartition Kashmir was linked by road and rail with what is now Pakistan, and its normal trade outlets would be with the Moslem nation; (3) Indian control of Kashmir would jeopardize West Pakistan's vital irrigation system and the opportunities for hydroelectric-power development, for the upper Indus River and the headwaters of two of its five major tributaries flow through Kashmir; (4) India's control of Kashmir would threaten Pakistan's national security, because of the lack of natural defenses between southern Kashmir and Pakistan; moreover, Pakistan's control is essential to the security of the North-West Frontier Province against the claims of the Pathan tribesmen (see page 383); and (5) with its military links to the west, Pakistan should control Kashmir in order to defend it against Soviet and Chinese expansion. Countering these are the Indian arguments: (1) the Kashmir government legally acceded to India in 1947; (2) since 1947 India has undertaken an extensive program for developing Kashmir's economy and communications network, and has inaugurated a large-scale land distribution program; both Jammu and the Vale of Kashmir have been linked by road with India, and Kashmir's future economic interests can be better served by India, with its greater markets and industrial facilities, than by Pakistan; (3) Pakistan's claims to the use of river waters for irrigation and hydroelectric-power development can be met by international agreement; and (4) the interests of approximately 1,000,000 Hindus living in Jammu must be protected.

One of the most important aspects of these claims and counterclaims is the availability of water supply. The upper Indus River, containing more water than its five tributaries combined, rises in Tibet, traverses Kashmir amid the towering Himalayas, and does not cross Indian territory in its course southward. One Indus tributary, the Jhelum, drains the Indian-held Vale of Kashmir, but here again the diversion of its waters to India would be difficult due to the mountain barriers. Water may in time be diverted by India from a second Indus tributary, the Chenab, to irrigate the eastern Punjab, but this poses the only threat in Kashmir to Pakistan's water supply. Three other major Indus tributaries rise in India itself, not Kashmir, while the Sutlej rises in Tibet. "Of all the waters of the Indus system, only twenty to forty-five per cent is used in irrigation projects. . . . Pakistan's inclusion of Kashmir in its irrigation arguments is certainly justified in view of possible future developments, but too much emphasis has been put on control of Kashmir as vital to Pakistan's economic existence."[4]

Possible Solutions. Several alternatives exist for the settlement of the Kashmir problem:

1. An all-Kashmir plebiscite, which would require the prior withdrawal of most of the Indian and Pakistani troops. India has refused to evacuate the area in which it has *de facto* control.

2. Retention of the present division (thereby awarding Jammu with its one million Hindus to India), with provisions for a plebiscite in the Vale.

3. Independence for Kashmir, which would probably produce a power vacuum in this vital area.

4. A special United Nations status for Kashmir—or for the Vale—leaving the remainder of the nation as presently divided.

5. Continued division of Kashmir along the 1949 cease-fire line, and

---

[4] Robert C. Mayfield, "A Geographic Study of the Kashmir Issue," *The Geographical Review,* XLV, No. 2 (April, 1955), 191. Mayfield's article is an excellent summary of the Kashmir dispute.

incorporation of the two parts within India and Pakistan respectively. In 1956 Prime Minister Nehru came out in favor of this solution.

Economic activity between India and the Indian-controlled portion of Kashmir has greatly increased since 1949. Large sums of money have been spent to strengthen India's position by orienting Kashmir's economy toward India and by winning the loyalty of the Kashmiri people—both Hindu and Moslem—who may come to realize that it is to their economic interest to remain within the Indian Republic. Pakistan, on the other hand, has made little effort at economic improvement in its portion of Kashmir, since the Karachi government has continued to view the 1949 partitioning of Kashmir as only a temporary situation. In January, 1957, India announced the formal incorporation of Kashmir as a constituent Indian state, thereby adding a new element to the already complex nature of this dispute.

2. The Northwest Frontier

The northwestern portion of Pakistan is a mountainous area inhabited by Moslem tribes, of whom the Pathans form the largest group. These peoples speak Pushtu and are culturally akin to the Pathans to the west, who comprise about forty-five per cent of Afghanistan's population. In 1893, when the Afghan-Indian border was delimited, special political concessions were made to the tribal people in the North-West Frontier Province. When Pakistan was created in 1947 the province was incorporated into the new nation. Since that time there has been frequent fighting in the Khyber Pass area in connection with a movement for an independent Pushtunistan (or Pathanistan), to be composed of 5 to 7 million people, of whom probably less than 2½ million would actually be Pushtu-speaking.

The area envisioned for Pushtunistan would include all of the North-West Frontier Province, as well as northern Baluchistan (including Quetta) and Punjab west of the Indus (Figure 81). With an area of 45,000–50,000 square miles, the new state would control the eastern approaches to the Khyber Pass and would serve as a buffer between Afghanistan and Pakistan. Although Pakistan refuses even to consider the possibility of Pushtunistan, the government of Afghanistan has actively supported the idea, thereby creating considerable friction between Karachi and Kabul. The Afghans claim that the North-West Frontier Province was illegally joined to Pakistan in 1947, and that the rights of self-government should be granted to the Pathans living in Pakistan.

Although there appears to be no possibility that an independent Pushtunistan state will be created, the situation illustrates the problems of political cohesion in the mountain areas of central Asia. The power of the Karachi government is felt scarcely, if at all, in some of the remote Pathan areas of the North-West Frontier Province. The lack of unity between these people

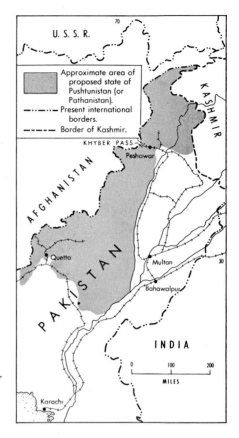

Figure 81. The Afghan-Pakistan Border Area.

and the rest of Pakistan is matched by a similar lack of cohesion between them and the Afghan Pathans to the west of the Khyber Pass. The government of Afghanistan in its propaganda for Pathan unity is in a dangerous political position, for in northern Afghanistan are Uzbeks, whose union with their cultural brothers in Soviet Uzbekistan the Soviet Union could urge with equal logic. The communists, of course, are interested in this dispute between two nations close to the Soviet Union's southern borders, since, like the Kashmir issue, it tends to prevent united action in this area. Pakistan's closing of its border with Afghanistan drove that country into close economic ties with the U.S.S.R. Moreover, the Soviets would be interested in doing what they could to weaken the position of Pakistan, a United States military ally in southern Asia.

3. The European Enclaves in India

At the time of India's independence a question arose as to the political future of the French and Portuguese enclaves which still existed in the subcontinent as relics of the sixteenth and seventeenth centuries. France controlled five separate regions—Pondichéry, Karikal, Mahé, Yanaon, and Chandernagor—with a total area of 196 square miles and a population of about 320,000; while Portugal had three possessions—Goa, on India's west coast south of Bombay, Damão, and Diu—with a total area of 1,537 square miles and a combined population of 638,000. Of these European enclaves, Goa, in which Portuguese sovereignty dates back to 1510, is the most important in size, population, and economic activity. All of the enclaves bordered territory awarded to India.

In 1947 the Indian government demanded that these European enclaves be ceded to India. An agreement was subsequently worked out with the French calling for referendums to be held in the French possessions, but only in Chandernagor did a vote actually take place, with the result in favor of union with India. Chandernagor was subsequently turned over to India. In 1954 the other areas were ceded to India without referendums being held. The French government was apparently under no strong pressure to retain these relics of its former empire, particularly since they were costly to administer and were of little economic or military value to France.

With respect to the Portuguese possessions the Indians have been less successful. Portugal has refused even to consider the transfer of its territories to India, since under the Portuguese constitution all overseas territories are classed as integral parts of Portugal itself, and it is legally impossible to cede them to other powers. Such reasoning holds little appeal to Indian nationalists, who see in the enclaves, particularly Goa, continued vestiges of the hated foreign control to which India was for so long forced to submit. The threats of economic blockades or of "liberation marches" by Indian groups on Goa have had no effect on Portugal's stand.

Portugal's defiance of the march of nationalism in southern Asia has attracted world attention. Neither Portugal nor India wishes a plebiscite to be held, Portugal on the grounds that the alternative of accession to India is not possible and India because a referendum among the over 600,000 Goans would very possibly end in victory for Portugal.[5] Most of the people are Indian, or mixed Indian-Portuguese, and Hindus outnumber Roman Catholics by only a small majority. The standard of living in Goa is higher than in India, and the enclave, with its harbor of Mormugão and its resources of iron ore and manganese, is a relatively prosperous economic area.

Goa is also an important center of Roman Catholicism in the Far East. In its cathedral the remains of the Portuguese missionary St. Francis Xavier are enshrined. The Portuguese, in stating their case for Goa, sometimes refer to the inappropriateness of a Hindu country gaining control of an important Christian shrine. As long as Portugal maintains its stand, India has no way

---

[5] The decision for or against accession to India actually involves only Goa. Portugal's other two enclaves are extremely small.

of acquiring the enclaves short of invasion, a course which would appear unlikely in view of India's efforts to establish a role for itself as international mediator and promoter of peace.

4. The Northeastern Border

Along India's northeastern border are located the small isolated states of Nepal, Sikkim, and Bhutan, while farther east primitive jungle tribes inhabit Indian territory in the Himalaya foothills. There are relatively few routes between these areas and India or between them and Tibet to the north. After the establishment of British political control in India in the mid-nineteenth century, the three border states remained in semi-isolation under the protection of the British, and little effort was made to incorporate the jungle peoples in the eastern foothills within the political and economic life of India.

Since 1947 two events have taken place to affect the isolation of these northeastern border areas. One was the achievement of Indian independence and the substitution of Indian protection for that of the British. The other was the extension of Chinese Communist control over Tibet in 1951. The Communist government, with its penchant for expanding into areas of political weakness, has a potential base for activities along Tibet's southern frontier with India.

The oppressive political systems, which until recently have existed in the three states, together with the extreme poverty of most of the people, have formed the basis for popular discontent, particularly in Nepal, where the local Communist Party is now a powerful political force. At the same time, increased communications to these areas (radio, air service, and improved road facilities) accented the cultural ties which exist between these areas and their northern and southern neighbors. The 300,000 people of Bhutan are predominantly Buddhist and pay spiritual allegiance to the Dalai Lama of Tibet, and the 140,000 people of Sikkim are divided between Hindus and Buddhists. The $8\frac{1}{2}$ million people of Nepal are predominantly Hindu, and thus have religious ties with India, but in the northeastern foothills of the Himalayas the Mongolian characteristics of the people indicate greater cultural affinity with the Tibetans to the north than with the Aryan Indians to the south.

The Indian government is aware of the centrifugal political forces—both actual and potential—existing along the northeastern border, and it is seeking to offset them by strengthening cultural and economic ties between these areas and the rest of India. In this region, as in other parts of the interior of Asia, the degree and effectiveness of political pressures are often impossible to determine, yet it is in this area that patterns of territorial control can be rapidly altered.

BIBLIOGRAPHY

AHMAD, NAFIS. "The Indo-Pakistan Boundary Disputes Tribunal, 1949–50," *The Geographical Review,* XLIII, No. 3 (July, 1953), 329–38.

A short but detailed study of disputes along the boundary between India and East Pakistan after the partition.

BARTON, SIR WILLIAM. "Pakistan's Claims to Kashmir," *Foreign Affairs,* XXVIII, No. 2 (January, 1950), 299–309.

An exposition of one side of this territorial controversy. The arguments are sound, but a pro-Indian point of view should also be consulted.

BRUSH, JOHN E. "The Distribution of Religious Communities in India," *Annals of the Association of American Geographers,* XXXIX, No. 2 (June, 1949), 81–99.

Excellent maps and discussion of religious patterns in India prior to partition.

KORBEL, JOSEF. "Danger in Kashmir," *Foreign Affairs,* XXXII, No. 3 (April, 1954), 482–91.

A discussion of the political history involved in the Kashmir dispute.

MAYFIELD, ROBERT C. "A Geographic Study of the Kashmir Issue," *The Geographical Review,* XLV, No. 2 (April, 1955), 181–97.

A comprehensive survey of the issues involved in this dispute. The article includes maps and is carefully documented.

SPATE, O. H. K. "India and Pakistan," in *The Changing Map of Asia,* ed. W. GORDON EAST and O. H. K. SPATE. New York: E. P. Dutton & Co., Inc., 1950, pp. 119–79.

Regional study of the area, including tables on political and economic features and population.

———. "The Partition of India and the Prospects of Pakistan," *The Geographical Review,* XXXVIII, No. 1 (January, 1948), 5–30.

One of the most comprehensive articles to appear on the partition. Detailed treatment of boundary problems in Punjab and Bengal-Assam. Valuable tables on areas and populations of the various political units.

WILBER, DONALD N. "Afghanistan, Independent and Encircled," *Foreign Affairs,* XXXI, No. 3 (April, 1953), 486–95.

The political history of Afghanistan, particularly since World War I.

15

SOUTHEAST ASIA

● In that part of Asia which lies south of China and east of the Indian sub-continent three basic trends have developed since the end of World War II: the gradual disappearance of European political control, the achievement of independence by several states, and the growing significance of Chinese expansion under the guise of international communism. The area is one in which the physical and cultural environments contain many aspects of diversity, but in which there are also important unifying forces which tend to draw together the peoples and countries which are located here. The political pattern of southeast Asia[1] is in many respects a product of the conflicting forces of unity and diversity in this part of the world.

FORCES OF UNITY AND DISUNITY

The regional unity of southeast Asia is based primarily on climate, economic development, and a history of colonialism. Most of the countries in this area have recently become independent, and they share with one another many problems of national development—including the threat of Chinese expansion. Southeast Asia also contains many elements of disunity, such as landforms, ethnic types, and conflicting colonial interests, which in turn have been reflected in political differences between and within the countries of this area. To these countries the diversities of their physical and cultural

[1] Southeast Asia here comprises Burma, Thailand, Indochina, Malaya, Indonesia, and British Borneo. The name Thailand was officially adopted in 1949, replacing Siam. Indochina, although no longer a single political unit, is used here to designate the former French-controlled area embracing Vietnam, Laos, and Cambodia. Because of their close ties with the Pacific area and with the United States, the Philippines are considered in the chapter on the Pacific Basin.

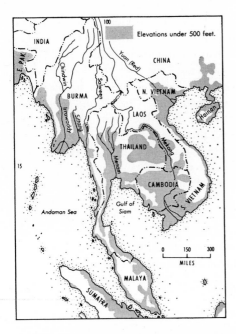

Figure 82. Southeast Asia: Physical Features.

environments present major obstacles to regional collaboration.[2] As a result, progress toward coping with common social, economic, and political difficulties has been delayed, and the ever-present dangers of internal revolt and the spread of communist control are thereby increased.

Physical Features

The climate of southeast Asia is an important unifying element. Most of the region is influenced by the tropical monsoon, with its alternating wet and dry seasons. Bamboo and palm trees are characteristic vegetation forms, and the cultivation of paddy rice and the development of tropical plantation agriculture are economic responses to this climate. Variations in the climatic pattern exist primarily in upland areas, or along northward- and eastward-facing coasts where the season of heavy rainfall is the reverse of that which exists throughout most of southeast Asia.

The sea also offers a kind of physical unity, since it tends to bind islands and coastal regions together economically, culturally, and politically. Examples of this unifying trend are to be found in the spread of Islam throughout the coastal areas of Malaya and Indonesia during the fifteenth century, and the political unification of the Indonesian archipelago by the Dutch three hundred years later.

---

[2] See Jan O. M. Broek, "Diversity and Unity in Southeast Asia," *The Geographical Review,* XXXIV, No. 2 (April, 1944), 175–96, for an excellent discussion of this problem.

In contrast to these unifying elements are the landforms and soils. The terrain of southeast Asia is compartmentalized into relatively small lowlands, separated by blocks of rough hill country or mountain cordilleras (Figure 82). The principal plains on the mainland are located on the deltas of great rivers, which have their sources within the heart of the Asian continent: the Irrawaddy and Salween of Burma, the Menam (Chao Phraya) of Thailand, and the Mekong and Yuan (Red) rivers of Indochina. Although the narrow river valleys afford poor routes into the interior, the broad deltas which have been formed by each of these rivers, except the Salween, contain major population concentrations and represent focal points for political and economic activities. The rugged terrain of the mainland area also extends south through the Malay Peninsula and out onto the islands of Indonesia. The diversity of soil fertility is associated in part with the uneven distribution of volcanic activity, so that even in lowland areas there may be wide differences in soil types. These physical elements naturally affect population distribution. Areas of concentrated settlements are often separated from one another by sparsely-inhabited territory, in which national governments may exercise little or no effective control.

Population Features

The ethnic complexity of southeast Asia is a result of the many waves of peoples—coming both from the Asian mainland to the north and northwest and by sea from the west—which have passed through and across this area. In addition to the major population types, such as Malays, Thais, Burmese, Annamese, Laotians, and Cambodians, there is a great number of smaller ethnic groups, which, because of their isolated locations, have managed to maintain their cultural individuality. There are also three important "foreign" peoples in southeast Asia: the Chinese, the Indians, and the Europeans.

The patterns of language and religion are shown in Figures 83 and 84. The white population of southeast Asia, and those nonwhites dealing directly with them, generally speak the languages of the present or former colonial powers. The Chinese often use their native dialects, and many of the Indians speak Tamil. The Malay language group predominates throughout much of southeast Asia, yet within this framework many variations occur. In Indonesia, for example, there are some twenty-five different languages. Religious diversity is evidenced by the presence of Mohammedanism, Buddhism, Christianity, and many other sects. Differences in language and religion, of course, reflect the great diversities of cultural interests—diversities which have often been magnified by certain states (for example, China, India, Thailand) in an effort to further the interests of their respective "national" groups in southeast Asia, often at the expense of other peoples in this area.

Population distribution is also an important factor for political diversity

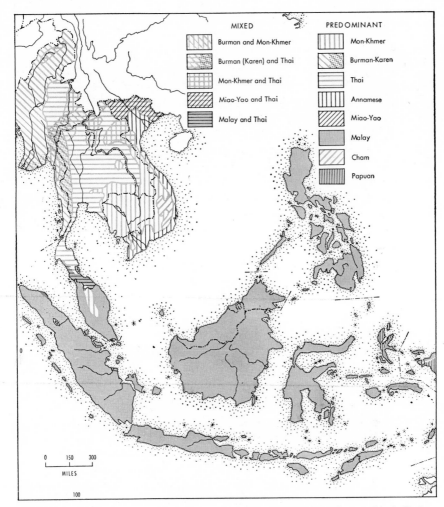

Figure 83. Languages in Southeast Asia. (After Broek, *The Geographical Review*, XXXIV (April, 1944). Courtesy of American Geographical Society.)

in southeast Asia, for in most of the countries there exist two or more core areas. In addition, many people are settled in small towns and villages which, because of the poor transportation facilities, are practically inaccessible to effective political control from the national capital. This isolation, of course, is heightened by the ethnic differences between inhabitants of provincial areas and those of the urban centers, and by the continuing armed warfare which has been carried on in some of the more inaccessible areas, particularly in Burma, Indonesia, Malaya, and parts of Indochina since the end of World War II.

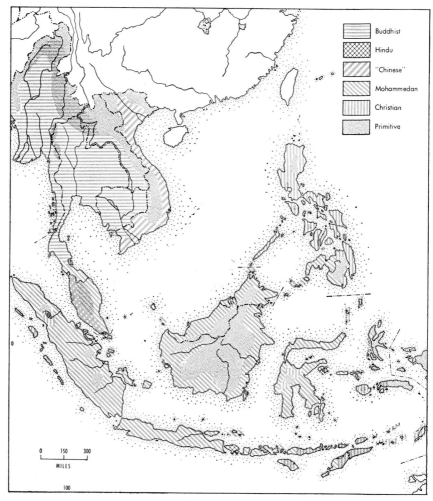

Figure 84. Religions in Southeast Asia. (After Broek, *The Geographical Review*, XXXIV (April, 1944). Courtesy of American Geographical Society.)

Economic Features

Climate and land utilization in southeast Asia have produced great similarities of economic activities and interests throughout much of the region. Agriculture forms the predominant basis of the economy, supplemented in some areas by mining and in a few large cities by commerce and light industries. The national economies have been geared primarily to the export of agricultural and mineral raw materials to the industrialized nations of the world. The realization of common goals, however, has been at least partially blocked by competing—rather than complementary—economies. During their years of colonial control here the British, Dutch, and French oriented the economic structures of their possessions toward the respective mother countries, and little trade was carried on regionally.[3] With the advent of independence, this economic orientation to foreign markets has continued. Communication lines, particularly railroads, tend to focus on the commercial centers of each individual state rather than to cross international boundaries. The only important transportation links between countries are coastwise and interisland shipping, and, particularly since World War II, the growing international air routes.

Political Features

The political pattern of southeast Asia reflects its history of foreign control (Figures 85 and 87). The Europeans were responsible not only for the political partitioning of the area but also for the unification of various groups into national units, as in Burma, Indochina, Malaya, Indonesia, and the former Straits Settlements. The pressures of colonialism beyond its borders also represented a cohesive force in the independent state of Thailand. Political unification had varying effects among the countries of southeast Asia: in general it meant greater economic development, although at the same time differing ethnic groups were brought together within one political unit, which resulted in the creation of strong centrifugal forces. In the case of Burma not only were various peoples included within one country, but prior to 1937 Burma itself was joined administratively to India, a fact which was bitterly resented by many of the Burmese.

The political structures of the colonial areas reflected the desire for administrative efficiency on the part of the European states. The French organized Indochina into four protectorates—Cambodia, Laos, Tonkin, and Annam—and one colony, Cochin China. In creating Tonkin, Annam, and Cochin China the French gave political recognition to geographic divisions in eastern and southern Indochina, but they also split the Annamese people into three separate states. The Dutch combined a large number of ethnic groups into the Netherlands East Indies, and since that area's independence there have arisen strong centrifugal forces (see page 410). In Malaya the British governed part of the area indirectly, by means of protectorates, and the rest directly through a crown colony. The protectorates comprised a total of nine states. The crown colony, known as the Straits Settlements, consisted of Singapore (together with Cocos Islands and Christmas Island in the Indian Ocean), Penang Island (including Province Wellesley on the main-

---

[3] The major exception to this generalization is rice, which moves from surplus areas in Indochina, Thailand, and Burma to Indonesia and Malaya.

Figure 85. The Mainland Nations of Southeast Asia.

land), Malacca, a port to the northwest of Singapore, and Labuan Island, off the coast of British Borneo. This political grouping was actually a legacy of the East India Company, which had organized the area largely for the sake of expediency; not until 1946 were the Straits Settlements broken up.

In the political partitioning of southeast Asia international boundaries were in some instances so delimited as to divide ethnic groups (Thais, Shans, Cambodians, Malays) among two or more countries. These superimposed boundaries later caused considerable conflict between some of the countries of the area. In many of the more isolated parts the exact location of boundaries has never been clearly determined, and to local peoples the existence of these dividing lines probably means very little. An increase of economic and political development and the possibility of future friction between communist and noncommunist states will lead eventually to more exact boundary demarcations than now exist.

Centrifugal and centripetal forces within the individual countries of southeast Asia are included in the regional discussions later in this chapter. Distance, mountain barriers, poorly-developed circulatory systems, and diverse ethnic groups represent powerful divisive forces in some of these areas, within which the people have only begun to develop a strong sense of nationhood. Associated with the internal aspects of unity and disunity are those of an external nature. With the rise of the independence movements many of the peoples of southeast Asia were drawn together by the common bond of anticolonialism. This bond is still strong, and serves also to link this area with India, Ceylon, and other states in southwestern Asia and Africa. Most of these states have been reluctant to align themselves militarily with the Western nations in any alliance against the Soviet bloc, for fear of bringing on a return of foreign control in one form or another.

The state of Thailand is somewhat of a divisive factor among the countries of southeast Asia, for the Thais have not come under direct Western control and thus they do not share the anticolonial feelings of their neighbors. Thailand, for example, is a member of the Southeast Asian Treaty Organization (SEATO), and is thus allied militarily with the United States, Britain, and France. The country was involved in considerable territorial expansion at the expense of its neighbors during World War II and, although at the end of the war these areas were returned to their former owners, some of them continue to represent regions of potential Thai irredentism.

Another force for international diversity has been the creation of a communist-type government in North Vietnam, and the possibility of the extension of communism into other parts of southeast Asia. Because of past antagonisms, the noncommunist states of Indochina (South Vietnam, Cambodia, Laos) have made no efforts for united action in the face of this communist threat. Here, as in other parts of southeast Asia, the opportunity exists for the communists to emphasize the tensions existing between the various countries and thus to forestall future international action in this area against the expansion of communist power.

BACKGROUND TO THE INDEPENDENCE MOVEMENTS

The Era of Colonial Expansion. Southeast Asia is separated from both India and China by such physical obstacles as mountain ranges, forested hills, and difficult limestone terrain. Despite these handicaps, a great number and variety of peoples from Asia have migrated south and east into what are now Burma, Thailand, and Indochina, settling in the lowland areas or moving down through Malaya and the island archipelago stretching to the southeast.

During and after the thirteenth century Moslem traders came to southeast Asia by sea and propagated the Mohammedan faith in the area. By 1500 the Portuguese, the first of the European colonial groups, had reached the Indies and a century later the Dutch appeared. The Portuguese gradually established their control over islands and coastal points. In time they came in conflict with Dutch ambitions in the area, and since Holland was the stronger maritime power the Portuguese empire was eventually eliminated, except for a part of Timor Island. By the mid-seventeenth century Holland had become the dominant power here. At this time Britain and France were concerned primarily with India, and not until after 1800 did these countries begin to expand in southeast Asia.

The acquisition of territory in southeast Asia, first by Portugal and Holland and later by Britain and France, was motivated primarily by the desire for trade and the development of the area's resources. The British were also interested in protecting sea routes to China and the eastern approaches to India, while the French came to Indochina in the late nineteenth century partly in hopes of establishing overland routes to China and thus by-passing British-controlled Hong Kong. Prior to the nineteenth century there was little desire on the part of any of the European states to gain large territorial holdings, and for a time only a few strategically located ports were actually occupied.

In 1819 Singapore was founded, and two years later parts of southern Burma passed into the hands of the British East India Company. Subsequent British expansion in Malaya and Burma was countered by French conquests in the Mekong delta of southern Indochina. Throughout the remainder of the nineteenth century Britain and France expanded their territorial holdings in southeast Asia, partly by military campaigns and partly by concluding treaties with local rulers which established protectorates over the small, individual states. Thailand was permitted to remain an independent kingdom as a buffer between British and French possessions. Independence, however, could not protect Thailand from territorial encroachments on both the east and the west. The British, expanding their holdings in Burma, eventually annexed the Shan States in northwestern Thailand, while in the south four small Thai border states—Kelantan, Trengganu, Kedah, and Perlis—with a predominantly Moslem Malay population, were later added to British Malaya. Likewise, the French, moving inland from the coast of Indochina, acquired from Thailand the Laotian states east of the Mekong as well as the Battambang area west of Cambodia. In 1896 the Mekong River, north of Thailand, was taken to mark the border between Burma and Indochina.

The political organizations of the several colonial areas varied considerably. The principal concern the colonial powers had in these areas was in their trade potential, particularly with the mother country. The tendency of the European powers to lump together differing ethnic groups within one national unit in order to serve their particular economic interest often led to considerable antagonism on the part of the people of southeast Asia. In addition to unification, the Europeans also brought about in some countries a reorientation from the interior lowlands to the coast. In Burma, for example, Mandalay, 450 miles north of the Irrawaddy mouth, was the historical capital, but after the arrival of the British, Rangoon, located within the Irrawaddy delta, became the political and commercial center of the country.

The Effects of Commercial Development. Agricultural and mineral exploitation by the Europeans gradually expanded in line with the discovery of new resources, methods of development, and additional markets in other parts of the world. Eventually southeast Asia became a major producer of a variety of valuable commodities, most of which were exported to Europe or North America. Among the most important of these were tin, rubber, spices, tea, sugar, palm oil, cinchona (for quinine), copra, abaca (Manila hemp), petroleum, and tungsten. In terms of investments and foreign trade the southeast Asian colonies came to play significant roles in the economies of Holland, Britain, France, the United States, and, to a less extent, Portugal. As the most important rice surplus area of the world, southeast Asia has been, and still is, an extremely significant source of food for its own urban centers as well as such major countries as Japan, China, and India.

Although small numbers of both Indians and Chinese had been in contact with southeast Asia for hundreds of years prior to the nineteenth century, a great influx of people from India and China came after 1850 in response to the demand for cheap labor by European agricultural and mining enterprises, as well as to population pressures existing within India and China. The Indians came mostly to Burma and Malaya: in Burma many of them are in business, while in Malaya they have been important as laborers on the rubber plantations. Their political influence in these two countries has not been as great as their numbers might indicate, for a majority of them are temporary residents, who return home as soon as they can afford to do so.

In contrast with the Indians, the Chinese are for the most part perma-nent inhabitants (Table 15). Like the Indians, they came as laborers for

Table 15

ETHNIC CHINESE IN SOUTHEAST ASIA, 1947

Nation	Chinese Population	Total Population	Per Cent of Chinese
Burma	300,000	17,000,000	2
Thailand	2,500,000	17,359,000	14
Indochina	850,000	27,000,000	3
Malaya	2,615,000*	5,849,000	45
British Borneo	220,000	878,000	25
Indonesia	1,900,000	69,000,000	3
Total	8,385,000	137,086,000	

*Federation of Malaya: 1,885,000 out of a total of 4,908,000 (39 per cent). Singapore: 730,000 out of total of 940,824 (78 per cent).

Source: Victor Purcell, *The Chinese in Southeast Asia*, Oxford University Press, 1951, p. 2. Used by permission.

the European enterprises, but they also congregated in many of the new commercial cities—Singapore, Rangoon, Bangkok, Saigon, and Hanoi—where they performed many of the menial tasks necessary in these urban areas (Figure 86). The Chinese began to dominate the merchant class in much of southeast Asia, and soon held monopolies in a number of retail and wholesale establishments. They also developed importance as craftsmen and skilled laborers. Like the Indians of east Africa, many of them came to occupy a middle position between the indigenous peoples and the Europeans.

The First Demands for Self-Rule. The development of the independence movements in southeast Asia did not begin until after World War I. By that time the European powers had begun to train and educate certain Asians to play greater roles in the economic and political activities of their countries. Along with this went a gradual liberalization of administrative policies (par-ticularly in the British and Dutch territories), so that local political organi-zations began to assume responsibilities of self-government. Eventually some of the Asians—particularly those who had received education in Europe—grew restive under the restrictions of foreign control and became leaders in the movements for independence.

The Repercussions of World War II. World War II had been in prog-ress for two years in Europe before it spread to southeast Asia. In September, 1941, the Japanese, with the consent of the pro-Nazi government of Vichy France, occupied Indochina. After the attack on Pearl Harbor in December of that year, Japanese forces began to move south and west into Malaya, Indonesia, and Burma. By late 1942 Japanese-controlled territory extended

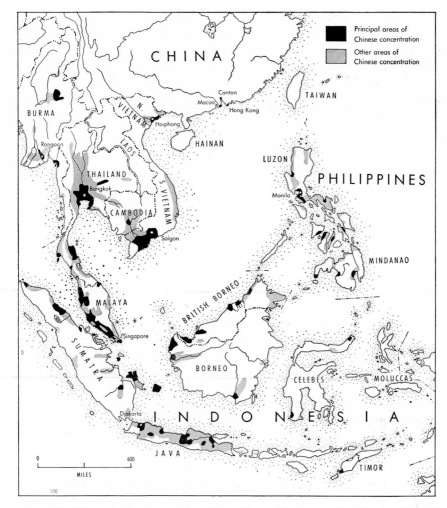

Figure 86. Chinese in Southeast Asia. (After Unger, *The Geographical Review*, XXXIV (April, 1944). Courtesy of American Geographical Society.)

westward to the mountains separating Burma from India and southward through Indonesia to southern New Guinea and the Solomon Islands.

During the three years of Japanese occupation, several significant developments took place in southeast Asia. For the first time in history the entire region was united under a single political authority, and through their "Greater East Asia Co-Prosperity Plan" the Japanese aimed at a regional economic development of the area. They played on the theme of Thai nationalism by permitting Thailand to expand its borders and reoccupy some of the lands lost to its neighbors during the late nineteenth and early twentieth centuries. They also combined the three easternmost Indochinese states into the new state of Vietnam, and they administered Cambodia, Laos, and Vietnam as separate political units, thereby destroying the myth of Indochinese unity. Finally, before their withdrawal the Japanese supported local independence movements, particularly in Indonesia and Indochina, so that by the time the European powers reoccupied their former colonies the seeds of revolt were already well sown.

POLITICAL UNITS AFTER WORLD WAR II

Burma

The independent state of Burma is an example of a political area in which centrifugal forces have constituted serious threats to national unity. With an area of about 262,000 square miles, Burma consists of a central lowland enclosed on all sides but the south by uplands. The central lowland is drained by the southward-flowing Irrawaddy, Chindwin, and Sittang rivers, and is subdivided into a northern dry zone, containing the city of Mandalay, and a southern wet zone, centered on Rangoon, the capital and largest city. The upland areas of Burma are for the most part wet and forested, and transportation facilities here are generally poor. These uplands have helped to isolate Burma from land contacts with neighboring countries, and as a consequence Burma's communications with other areas have been carried on largely by sea. Burma's territory extends northward along the borders of China's Yunnan province into the inaccessible mountains of the Kachin area; a narrow projection also extends south for nearly 400 miles along the Tenasserim coast. Thus distance, in addition to climate, surface configuration, and ethnic and economic diversity, is a centrifugal force in the country.

Within Burma's central lowland the diversity, which results from climatic differences and from the presence of two urban areas, is matched by differing economic and political conditions as well. In the dry northern zone tobacco, peanuts, and cotton predominate, whereas in southern Burma rice is the chief crop. Many farmers in the north own their own land and are considerably more prosperous than the debt-ridden tenant farmers in the Rangoon area. Such differences are reflected in the political parties and platforms existing within the country.

Less than two-thirds of the population of approximately 19 million persons are Burmese, and these are concentrated for the most part in the Irrawaddy lowlands and along the coast. Minority groups include over a million Karens east and northeast of Rangoon, another million Shans living north of the Thai border, plus several hundred thousand Kachins in the extreme north and Nagas and Chins along the Indian border. These groups are differentiated from the Burmese and from one another by language, customs, and religion, and their incorporation within the Burmese state was a result largely of administrative expediency on the part of the British. The Chinese in Burma form about two per cent of the total population, and as such are not a significant political force. Many of them are in retail and wholesale businesses, but as an important economic and political minority group they are outweighed by the more than one million Indians, who handle much of the nation's business and make up a large proportion of the craftsmen and skilled laborers.

The people of Burma emerged from World War II determined to obtain independence. The British government drew up plans for the development of Burma as a dominion at the end of a three-year preparatory period, but the proposal was met by strong protests and violence. Rather than face armed rebellion, the British acceded to Burmese demands. In January, 1948, the independent Union of Burma came into being, completely separate from the British Commonwealth.

Provisions were made for the principal minority groups by the creation of three semiautonomous states—Shan, Kachin, and Karenni. Within a few months of Burma's independence the Karens were in open revolt, seeking to expand the borders of their area and obtain a greater degree of political autonomy. Local communist groups also staged armed revolts, and for a time the country was threatened with internal collapse. Some political analysts suggested that Burma received its independence before it was actually ready to cope with the problems of self-rule. Although by 1954 the warring elements in Burma had been driven into the more inaccessible areas and had been split up into small groups, guerrilla warfare has continued in various parts of the country, thereby limiting the areas in which the government exercises effective control and hindering the development of Burma's resources. Thus one of the country's principal needs is for a well-developed circulatory system, although this can come about only as a result of large expenditures of capital and the successful conclusion of a nation-wide military campaign against the rebel forces.

Burma is important for its rice exports, as well as for teak, petroleum, lead, zinc, and tungsten. The average population density is far lower than that of many areas in eastern China. With the removal of British power from Burma in 1948, a situation has been created which might lead to Chinese expansion into all or parts of Burma in the guise of international communism. In 1956 Chinese Communist troops moved across the northeastern borders of Burma in two places and occupied parts of the Kachin and Wa areas. Both are extremely isolated and inhabited largely by mountain tribes. A British-Chinese convention at the end of the nineteenth century recognized Burma's sovereignty over the Wa area, but the legal status of the Kachin area was never clearly defined. By utilizing the theme of historic rights in these areas, China may be able gradually to encroach on Burmese territory and to further local Burmese communist movements.

Thailand

In Thailand, as in Burma, physical and ethnic differences create strong divisive forces. Unlike Burma, however, Thailand has not been a European colonial possession, and both its power status and its degree of internal unity have been greater than that of the new Burmese state.

Thailand consists of a central lowland surrounded on three sides by hills and mountains. The lowland is drained by the Menam River (Chao Phraya), within the delta of which lies Bangkok, the nation's political and commercial center. In the northern and eastern parts of the country are plateau areas which are inhabited not only by Thais but also by Cambodians, Laotians, and Shans. In these areas there are no clear-cut physical or ethnic dividing lines, and boundaries have shifted several times since the latter part of the nineteenth century. Thai territory extends over 600 miles southward onto the Malay Peninsula. In southern Thailand, adjoining Malaya, are over half a million people whose economic and cultural interests lie more with the Federation of Malaya to the south than with the Thai nation, whose major core areas lie several hundred miles to the north.

Over three-quarters of the approximately 20 million people in the country are Thais, and, except for the Chinese and Malays in the southern part of the nation, most of the non-Thai minority groups have close cultural links with the Thais. In the northwest the border with Burma cuts through territory inhabited by Shan peoples; in the northeast that with Indochina leaves many Laotians in Thailand; and in the east Cambodians live within the Thai nation. About fourteen per cent of Thailand's population is Chinese, many of whom live in and about Bangkok. These people control most of Thailand's retail trade, and practically all of its rice distribution and milling. An economically powerful minority group, they have often been the victims of discrimination by the Thai government.

The history of the Chinese in Thailand contains many features which are common to Chinese minorities in other parts of southeast Asia (Figure 86). The influx of Chinese into Thailand began about the middle of the nineteenth century, when they migrated to the area to work in the cities, on European-owned plantations, and in the mines. Practically all of the immigrants were men; many of them married Thai women, and they and their offspring gradually became assimilated into the Thai nation. By 1909 approximately ten per cent of the country's population was estimated to be Chinese, many of whom were already in powerful economic positions.

The end of Chinese assimilation began about the time of World War I, when the Chinese influx increased substantially, Chinese women began to arrive in Thailand in large numbers, and the status of China itself was enhanced by changes in political regime and increased resistance to foreign encroachments. From then on the Chinese began to adhere more closely to their own cultural characteristics, sending their children to Chinese schools and regarding themselves as a non-Thai national group. In recent years there has been more and more resentment of the Chinese in Thailand because of their habit of sending money back to China ("draining off" Thailand's wealth), their apparent willingness to undergo all manner of privations for the sake of money, their economic strength, and their associations (both real and imagined) with communism.

Thailand, like Burma, is normally a major rice-exporting area, and since World War II the nation has gradually revived this export trade. Its average population density is about the same as Burma's, with the result that Thailand is not a "crowded" nation. With its surplus food production and available land for settlement, this country, again like Burma, is a rich prize in the path of Chinese expansion. Since World War II Thailand, under a firm dictatorship, has become one of the key anticommunist nations of southeast Asia. Although the per-capita income here, as in other parts of Asia, is still very low, Thailand is an area of relative economic and political stability, in contrast with the turbulent conditions existing in the countries which border it.

Indochina

The former French possession of Indochina was an area in which strong centrifugal forces existed and in which both nationalism and communism contributed to the postwar political turmoil. Three major ethnic groups lived within the Indochinese borders—the Laotians, the Cambodians, and the Annamese. Prior to World War II the Laotians and Cambodians each had their own separate political region, while the Annamese were divided into three areas—Cochin China, Tonkin, and Annam. During the war the ethnic unity of the Annamese was recognized in the formation of the country of Vietnam; in 1954 conflicting ideologies led to a partition of Vietnam into North and South.

Geographically, as well as administratively, Indochina consisted of five regions. The lowlands of the Red and Mekong rivers are important agricultural areas, particularly the Mekong lowland, where the bulk of Indochina's rice exports was produced. Cochin China, located at the delta of the Mekong, contained Saigon, Indochina's capital, and included most of Indochina's 850,000 Chinese. Concentrated in and about Saigon, the Chinese never played as important a part in the French territory's economic development as they did in Indonesia, Thailand, and Malaya. In the Red River delta of northern Indochina was Tonkin, with its major city of Hanoi and its dense population concentration. This region was one of the poorest areas in southeast Asia. Between these two areas was Annam, consisting of sparsely-settled mountains and a narrow coastal plain interrupted by mountain spurs which come down to the sea. Cambodia, to the west of the Mekong delta, is principally an inland basin centering on a lake—Tonlé Sap. Much of the region contains good agricultural land. Cambodia also extends west to the Korat Plateau, which it shares with Thailand. The fifth geographic and administrative unit, Laos, is a dissected plateau area bordering the upper Mekong River. One of its principal drawbacks is its inaccessibility, which has been intensified by its quarrels with Thailand and by the communization of North Vietnam, which borders it on the east.

The Japanese occupied Indochina in 1941 and remained there for nearly four years. Toward the end of the war Japan combined Cochin China, Tonkin, and Annam into a new political unit—Vietnam—containing eighty per cent of Indochina's population and most of its potential wealth. Prior to the arrival of Allied occupation troops the Japanese also encouraged independence movements here and in Laos and Cambodia as part of their general policy of hindering the return of European power to southeast Asia. Economic motives were important in the Japanese efforts here and in Indonesia, for if the Europeans were forced to give up their colonies (and thus end various commercial restrictions in these areas), Japan might enjoy greater trade and investment advantages after peace had been established. For six months after Japan's surrender Chinese troops occupied Vietnam north of the 16th parallel. Like the Japanese, they did little to put down nationalist activities, and by the time the French forces returned a widespread independence movement was under way in northern Vietnam.

The Battle for Independence. In the struggle for self-government in Vietnam two trends were of particular importance: the increasing communist nature of the conflict and the eventual involvement of Chinese and American interests. The French attempted to re-establish the political unity of Indochina and incorporate Laos, Cambodia, and Vietnam as Associated States within the French Union, but these efforts were blocked, both by the refusal of the Laotians and Cambodians to join in a new Indochinese state and by the growing independence movement in Vietnam. A *de facto* Viet Minh government was set up in Vietnam by the independence fighters under Ho Chi Minh, a Moscow-trained communist, and in December, 1946, widespread fighting broke out between French troops and the guerrilla forces of the new independence group.

The military struggle for independence lasted for seven and a half years and imposed a severe strain on France's economy. The French could never bring themselves to grant complete independence to Vietnam, and many noncommunist patriots supported Ho Chi Minh out of their desire for self-government for the area. As time went on, however, the Viet Minh government became more openly communist in character. Eventually it was recognized by the Soviet Union and Communist China, and military supplies began to move across the border from China for the Viet Minh forces. Despite considerable military aid from the United States, the French were unable to stem the expanding power of the Viet Minh, and by the spring of 1954 France was forced to ask for a truce.

The Partition of Vietnam. In the ensuing peace treaty at Geneva in July, 1954, Vietnam was divided roughly along the 17th parallel: North Vietnam, with an area of 77,000 square miles and a population of 12 million, passed under the control of the communist Viet Minh government, while South Vietnam (with 50,000 square miles and 10 million population) remained under the administration of the noncommunist Vietnam government. The communists agreed to recognize the French-sponsored governments of Laos and Cambodia, but with the provision that these states be neutralized, that is, that they enter into no military alliances with other nations nor maintain more than the minimum number of troops necessary for national security. Communist forces, which had penetrated across the Vietnam border into Laos, were not required to evacuate Laotian territory but established themselves in two provinces adjoining the North Vietnam border. It was also decided that elections would be held in both North and South Vietnam during or before July, 1956, in order to select a national government for a united Vietnam state which would then come into existence.

Since the summer of 1954 France's control in Indochina has practically disappeared. North Vietnam (the Democratic Republic of Vietnam) has strengthened its association with Communist China, Cambodia has virtually severed all ties with the French Union, and Laos, although still a member of the Union, is now independent. Late in 1954 the independent Republic of South Vietnam was officially proclaimed. Like Cambodia, South Vietnam made no agreement with France regarding membership in the French Union. Since its independence it has turned more to the United States than to France for support (see also page 412).

The tragedy of French policy in Indochina—and of Dutch policy in Indonesia—illustrates the principle of "too little and too late." The French failure to adopt a liberal colonial outlook toward Indochina at a time when it could have been effective was disastrous both to France and to the people of North Vietnam, who exchanged control by France for that by the communists. The other units of Indochina now face the threat of communist control, but they also fear the return of French control and, in Laos and Cambodia, the power of Thailand as well. Under such pressure newly-independent states are hard put to achieve lasting political and economic stability.

The Federation of Malaya

The changing pattern of sovereignty in southeast Asia has not only affected Burma, Indochina, and the border areas of Thailand, but also the

British territory of Malaya, which received dominion status in August, 1957. With its exports of tin and rubber, as well as iron ore, coconuts, pineapples, and palm oil, Malaya has been one of the most valuable economic assets in the British Empire. The achievement of self-rule here has been an important step in the gradual evolution of the British Commonwealth from an area of colonialism to one of free association among independent countries.

The Federation of Malaya consists of nine states and the two former British territories of Penang and Malacca on the west coast of the Malayan Peninsula. It has an area of about 51,000 square miles, and comprises a number of mountain regions and extensive coastal lowlands. The upland topography was in part responsible for the country's historical division into the small Malay states, which during the period of British rule managed to retain considerable local autonomy. The city of Kuala Lumpur, located a short distance inland from the west coast, is the capital of the federation. It is the leading city of the peninsula and is connected by rail and highway to other population centers of the country. Because of the forests and mountains, however, there are many isolated parts of Malaya, the significance of which was evident after World War II, when British and Malayan forces here waged an all-out war against communist guerrillas. Each of the Malay states has its own local core area, but the only urban center approaching Kuala Lumpur in size is the port of Penang, situated on an island off the northwest coast.

Of the federation's population total of about 6 million some forty-nine per cent are Malays, thirty-nine per cent are Chinese, and over ten per cent are Indians. Despite the divided character of the population, there was little racial friction in Malaya before 1942. The Chinese provided most of the labor for the tin mines, were engaged in the shipping industry and the processing of pineapples and rice, and controlled much of Malaya's retail businesses.

Ethnic and Political Problems.   In February, 1942, the Japanese conquered Malaya, and during the years of enemy occupation strong antagonisms developed between the Chinese and the Malays. Chinese resistance fighters operated against the Japanese from the Malayan jungles, while the Malays and the Indians took relatively little part in the underground movements. In their efforts to end Chinese resistance activities, the Japanese resorted to the use of Malay police units against the guerrilla fighters. When British forces returned to Malaya in 1945, they found that the conflicting wartime roles played by the Chinese and Malays had resulted in widespread bitterness between the two groups. Associated with this friction was the beginning of a communist movement among the Chinese in Malaya.

Friction between the Chinese and the Malays was increased in 1948, when the various Malay states, Penang, and Malacca were organized as the

Federation of Malaya. Within the new country citizenship was so defined as to make a Chinese voting majority impossible. In 1948 Chinese communist guerrillas, many of them members of the wartime resistance groups, began a campaign of terror throughout Malaya. Operating from jungle bases, they raided isolated settlements, murdered plantation workers, and slashed rubber trees. Although the British dispatched thousands of troops against the guerrillas, nonmilitary measures eventually proved to be more effective. Restrictions on Chinese citizenship in the Malayan federation were eased, and many Chinese farmers, suspected of giving food and supplies to the guerrillas, were moved from isolated areas in or close to the jungle and resettled in other parts of the country. By 1954 the terrorism had largely subsided and the hard core of communist fighters were forced to move their base of operations into remote mountain areas along the Thai border. Two years later the British government announced that the Federation of Malaya would receive independence in 1957 as a member of the British Commonwealth. Despite its strong economic base, independent Malaya faces difficult problems in its development as a cohesive national unit.

Singapore. Although it is not politically a part of Malaya, Singapore has close ties with the mainland country and is therefore included here in the discussion of Malaya. Located on Singapore Island (217 square miles) just off the Malayan coast are Singapore city, which has been developed into one of the great commercial centers of the world, and the major British naval base in the Far East. Prior to World War II Singapore was administered as a part of the Straits Settlements (see page 393), but in 1946 it was constituted as an individual crown colony. Over three-quarters of its approximately 1,200,000 people are Chinese. With other areas of southeast Asia achieving, or scheduled to achieve, self-rule, local leaders in Singapore strongly urged Britain—particularly by 1955—to end its control and to grant the area dominion status. However, because of the city's predominance of Chinese and because of its economic structure, the British have been reluctant to agree to complete self-rule.

Singapore's wealth is based primarily upon its role as a transshipment point for goods en route to and from southeast Asia. Much of its food and raw materials, as well as its manufactured goods, must be imported. As a result, its economic viability is dependent upon the continuation of the normal pattern of commerce in this part of the world through Singapore harbor.

In order to broaden Singapore's economic base, some Singapore officials suggested that the area be combined with the Federation of Malaya into one political unit. Such a move, however, was opposed by many non-Chinese in the federation. Another proposal was to join Singapore, and possibly Malaya as well, with British Borneo. This area consists of (1) the crown colony of North Borneo, including the island of Labuan six miles off the coast, (2) Sarawak, a crown colony on the northwest coast adjoining North

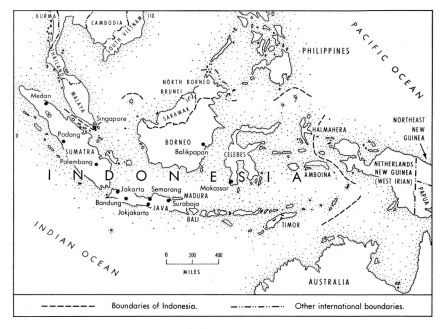

Figure 87. Indonesia and Netherlands New Guinea.

Borneo, and (3) Brunei, a small protectorate, which is split by a projection of Sarawak territory. Much of the land of British Borneo is undeveloped forest, and of a total population of about a million nearly half are members of pagan tribes. Political unification might have succeeded in balancing the ethnic compositions of the various areas, and diversifying the economies by adding the petroleum and timber of North Borneo to the tin and rubber of Malaya and the commercial activities of Singapore. However, as in other parts of the world where attempts have been made to unify two or more political units, both these proposals were defeated because of violent opposition from groups within each of the areas concerned.

The Republic of Indonesia

The Republic of Indonesia consists of four large islands—Java, Sumatra, Borneo, and Celebes—some fifteen medium-size islands, and hundreds of smaller ones (Figure 87). Although the sea acts as a unifying element for the area, there is great physical, cultural, and economic diversity in Indonesia, with the result that it has been difficult to maintain uniform political control over the region. The distribution and types of population in Indonesia indicate the area's historic role as both passageway and settlement area for migrating peoples.

About 52 million persons, nearly two-thirds of the Indonesians, are found on the island of Java, which comprises less than ten per cent of the republic's area. There are also important population concentrations on Sumatra, Madura, Bali, southern Borneo, and southern Celebes, but Java has been the political, and to some extent commercial, focus of Indonesia. One of the major problems of the new Indonesian country has been the resentment by peoples of other islands (and by the Sundanese minority on Java itself) against Javanese domination of national affairs.

Cultural diversity stands out in the various languages spoken throughout Indonesia, of which Javanese, Sundanese, and Madurese are the most important. Dutch is still widely used by well-educated Indonesians and Chinese, and the younger generation is learning English in high school. Most of the Chinese speak the dialect of their home districts. A majority of the population is Moslem, but there are about three million Christians, a million Buddhists (among the Chinese), and another million Hindus (on Bali and adjacent Lombok), while in the isolated interiors of the islands primitive religions still exist.

The Chinese in Indonesia number just under 2 million and comprise about three per cent of the total population. Nearly half the Chinese are concentrated on Java and the nearby island of Madura, but there is a large number engaged in tin mining at Bangka and Billiton, east of Sumatra. Many Chinese merchants are scattered throughout the other islands of Indonesia. Under the Dutch the Chinese were little affected by discrimination, but they suffered during the Japanese occupation of Indonesia and again during the subsequent fighting for independence, when they received protection from neither the Indonesians nor the Dutch. Within the independent state of Indonesia the Chinese are resented for their hold on trade and industry, and are the victims of various types of discrimination.

Before World War II Indonesia (then the Netherlands East Indies) was one of the richest colonial holdings in the world, producing cinchona, pepper, rubber, tin, tea, sugar, tobacco, bauxite, and petroleum. Dutch investments in the area totalled over one billion dollars, and more than 200,000 Dutch citizens lived in the Netherlands East Indies. Japanese forces seized the area in 1942, and for over three years it remained under enemy control.

The Achievement of Independence. The postwar independence movement in Indonesia began in August, 1945, when Indonesian nationalist leaders (with the approval of the Japanese) proclaimed an independent Republic of Indonesia. British forces, which occupied the Netherlands Indies after Japan's surrender, did little to block the independence drive. By the spring of 1946, when the Dutch resumed control of their dependency, the movement (like that in Indochina) had assumed major proportions, and Dutch forces were soon in open warfare against Indonesian nationalists for control of the area. Realizing the necessity for liberalizing their colonial policy, the Dutch offered the Indonesians partnership in a new Netherlands-Indonesian Union, to consist of the Netherlands on the one hand and the United States of Indonesia (embracing all of the former Netherlands East Indies) on the other. The new political organization, which was to have come into effect in January, 1949, would have been under the sovereignty of the Netherlands Crown, with joint control of defense, foreign affairs, and various economic and financial matters. Although both countries signed an agreement in 1946 providing for the establishment of such a Union, negotiations on details soon broke down, and fighting again began between Dutch and Indonesian forces. After nearly two and a half years of intermittent warfare, the United States of Indonesia finally came into existence in January, 1950, as a sovereign, independent state. The status of Netherlands New Guinea (West Irian), with a non-Indonesian population of about 700,000, was to be decided later by negotiations, and the area has continued to be controlled by the Dutch. The prolonged warfare and bitterness meant that the vague Netherlands-Indonesian Union was reduced to a mere formality, and in 1956 it was completely dissolved. Later in the same year the Indonesian government repudiated the more than one billion dollars in debts which had been owed by the former East Indies administration to the Netherlands, and which had been assumed by the new Indonesian regime.

Internal Political Problems. The Indonesian republic has had to meet a number of problems that have challenged the internal structure of the country. Among these are the economic dislocation caused by World War II and the independence struggle, the shortage of trained personnel for governing the large population, and the lack of available capital. Political immaturity is also a handicap in a nation with no past history of democracy. The number of conflicting interests is reflected by the existence of some nineteen national political parties.

At the time of Indonesia's independence the country was constituted as a sixteen-state federation in order to permit as much regional autonomy as possible. Later, however, the federal system was abolished, and a unitary government was set up, centered on Java. This move has caused considerable resentment in provincial areas.

Since 1949 the Indonesian government has been challenged by armed resistance in several parts of the country. In various parts of southwestern Java, northern Sumatra, and southern Celebes, antigovernment guerrilla forces carry on sporadic raids and terrorist acts against the settled areas. In 1948 a Darul Islam movement was started in southwestern Java for the purpose of turning secular Indonesia into a Moslem state. Since that time the movement has spread to Sumatra and Celebes as well. On Amboina, in the southern Moluccas (in eastern Indonesia), a Republic of the South Moluccas was proclaimed in 1951, embracing Amboina, Ceram, and others of the once-famous Spice Islands. Many of the natives here are Christians, and they differ from the peoples of western and central Indonesia in race and language. The proposed republic has caused the Indonesian government considerable anxiety, not only because of the continued military operations, but also because its leaders are pro-Dutch and the area in question lies close to Dutch-controlled western New Guinea.

Indonesia's National Status. The problems of Indonesia well illustrate the functioning of centrifugal and centripetal forces within a nation. The common desire for independence from European colonial control, the relative ease of communication by coastwise shipping, the overwhelming predominance of the Moslem religion, and the concentration of population and wealth in the central core area of Java represent major centripetal forces. Against these are ranged the centrifugal elements of geographic diversity, the general lack of complementary economies among the various islands, fanatical religious and political organizations, distrust of Java's political power, and a general discontent over prevailing economic conditions. One factor in Indonesia's favor is the absence of nearby nations which could exert pressures attracting units of Indonesia away from the capital's control. The influence which the Dutch in New Guinea have on the South Moluccas is the one exception. It is hard to conceive of a division of Indonesia into two or three independent nations, for there exist few other important foci of political and economic power outside of Java. On the other hand, political fragmentation into a dozen or more small groups would appear a possibility, should the control of Jakarta be sufficiently weakened.

In external affairs the Cold War and Netherlands New Guinea constitute Indonesia's major problems. The Indonesian government has sought to follow India's neutral policy toward the communists, thereby denying Western powers the use of Indonesia as a site for naval and air bases between the Philippines and Australia. Despite repeated claims by the Jakarta government for control of Netherlands New Guinea, the area remains under Dutch sovereignty (see below).

Problem Areas

1. Netherlands New Guinea (West Irian)

The problem of Netherlands New Guinea,[4] unresolved at the time of Indonesia's independence, still plagues Dutch-Indonesian relations. Indonesian nationalists claim that the new nation became heir to all the former Dutch possessions in southeast Asia, and that a majority of the natives in Netherlands New Guinea, if given the chance to express their preference, would choose Indonesian control rather than that of the Netherlands. The

---

[4] The island of New Guinea is divided politically into Netherlands New Guinea, in the west; the Territory of New Guinea, a United Nations trusteeship territory under Australian administration, in the northeast; and the Territory of Papua, an Australian possession, in the southeast.

Dutch contend that most of the native peoples of Netherlands New Guinea are Papuans, with no cultural ties to the peoples of Indonesia; that their level of cultural and political development is still extremely low; and that no significant results could be achieved from a formal plebiscite, even if the details for one could be worked out. The Netherlands has invested considerable sums of money in the development of the area, particularly in oil fields in the Vogelkop Peninsula. In the hope of reviving interest in the now-defunct Netherlands-Indonesian Union, the Dutch have stated their willingness to relinquish their sovereignty over Netherlands New Guinea to such a Union. In fact, there is a Dutch undercurrent of opinion which would be willing to sacrifice the area entirely to improve relations with Indonesia.

Although Netherlands New Guinea was once considered of little value in terms of the over-all Dutch empire, the area now constitutes an asset in the much-reduced Netherlands Empire, particularly from the point of view of prestige. It would seem that the local inhabitants would benefit more, at least under existing conditions, from Dutch rather than from Indonesian control, because of Dutch administrative efficiency and the greater availability of capital in the Netherlands. From the point of view of anticommunist defense moves in the southwest Pacific, Netherlands New Guinea in Dutch hands would be far more preferable than in Indonesian hands. Australia, in particular, has been concerned over the possibility of Indonesian sovereignty in this area, which is so vital to Australian defense plans. On the other hand, the Indonesians are unwilling to permit the retention of this colonial toe hold by the Dutch, for it represents a potential centrifugal force which might in time lead to a political division of the Indonesian state. Some Indonesians have charged that from Netherlands New Guinea encouragement and material aid are rendered to the insurgents in the nearby South Moluccas, who are seeking an autonomous republic within the Indonesian nation. Actually, much of the Indonesian propaganda about this problem is designed to divert attention from certain unsatisfactory conditions at home.

2. *Vietnam*

The division of Vietnam into communist and noncommunist areas during the summer of 1954 and the call for nationwide elections to determine a government for all of Vietnam posed serious problems for the peoples of South Vietnam, for the future of French power in southeast Asia, and for the inhabitants of all the noncommunist countries in this part of the world. In possession of North Vietnam the communists can exert pressure on Laos (because of their military control of two mountainous provinces within that country), and they can infiltrate across the border into South Vietnam in order to foment disorders.

A difficult problem for South Vietnam has been the establishment of a strong central government, capable of gaining the confidence of the people. Over a million refugees from North Vietnam have added to the economic and political problems of the South. Within this truncated country are strong political pressures: (1) local nationalism, which seeks the perpetuation of an independent state here; (2) continued colonialism, as France strives to salvage what it can from the Indochina defeat; (3) centrifugal forces in the form of private armies and political figures who resist control by the Saigon regime; (4) anticommunist pressure, particularly from the United States, attempting to strengthen the economic and military position of South Vietnam as rapidly as possible. The South Vietnam administration refused to participate in any nationwide elections in July, 1956, on the grounds that it was not a party to the Geneva treaty providing for them. However, as a result of strong political and military measures by President Ngo Dinh Diem and the receipt of considerable American aid (amounting to about 65% of South Vietnam's total budget), the country has gained strength since 1954, so that the chances of internal collapse or communization have, at least for the present, been largely removed.

3. Singapore

The city of Singapore became the scene of violent strikes and riots early in 1955, as the problems of both independence and communism in this area grew increasingly severe. The successes of the communists in China itself affected racial and national loyalties among many of the Chinese in Singapore, and a hard core of communist organizers infiltrated schools, labor unions, and other groups of the Chinese community. The communists demanded immediate independence for Singapore rather than the gradual process of self-rule envisioned by the British authorities.

In 1958 Singapore is scheduled to receive full internal self-government, and is to be known as the state, rather than the colony, of Singapore. The British government will continue to be responsible for defense and foreign affairs, and will maintain its bases in the area. Since this step falls short of complete independence, there is a danger of future trouble, particularly among the Singapore communists. In order to prepare for the possibility that the island, with its Chinese majority, might eventually become untenable, the British may develop Labuan, off the coast of British Borneo, as a naval base to replace Singapore.

BIBLIOGRAPHY

Broek, Jan O. M. "Diversity and Unity in Southeast Asia," *The Geographical Review*, XXXIV, No. 2 (April, 1944), 175–96.

An outstanding summation of basic geographic elements in southeast Asia before World War II.

CHRISTIAN, JOHN L. "Anglo-French Rivalry in Southeast Asia: its Historical Geography and Diplomatic Climate," *The Geographical Review*, XXXI, No. 2 (April, 1941), 272–83.

An interesting combination of geography and history as background elements in this area.

"Communism in Malaya: Background to the Fighting," *The World Today*, V, No. 8 (August, 1949), 346–54.

This discussion of the background of Malayan communism is important to an understanding of present political problems in that area.

KING, JOHN KERRY. "Rice Politics," *Foreign Affairs*, XXXI, No. 3 (April, 1953), 453–61.

A description of the political implications of rice surpluses and shortages in eastern Asia.

SPENCER, JOSEPH E. *Asia, East by South*. New York: John Wiley & Sons, Inc., 1954.

An up-to-date regional geography of southern and eastern Asia.

UNGER, LEONARD. "The Chinese in Southeast Asia," *The Geographical Review*, XXXIV, No. 2 (April, 1944), 196–218.

A detailed survey of the Chinese minorities in southeast Asia. Statistics are pre-World War II. but much of the material is still relevant.

16

THE TWO CHINAS

● The political pattern of eastern Asia has been one of frequent conflict and change, particularly since the latter part of the nineteenth century. The geographic diversity and the conflicting power interests in this part of the world have been important aspects of the changing nature of territorial control here. So also has been China's weakness—a situation which only since 1950 has begun to be remedied. The efforts of modern Chinese governments to win and maintain control over the various parts of China's territory are evidenced in the complex history of Far Eastern wars and treaties, particularly since the mid-nineteenth century. Even with the communization of mainland China, the task of uniting the area under Peking's control was not completed; centrifugal forces—in the form of local resistance to Peking and of foreign-controlled enclaves—still remained on the mainland itself, while off the east coast a competing Chinese government retained control of Taiwan (Formosa) and many smaller islands. In this chapter forces of unity and diversity, both on the mainland and on the offshore islands of China, will be considered in the light of the changing patterns of sovereignty in eastern Asia.

The two Chinas are mainland China, controlled by the Communist government at Peking, and the island of Taiwan, under the jurisdiction of the Nationalist government at Taipei. Despite Communist China's preponderance of size and population, the Nationalist administration has committed itself to an eventual return of its control over the mainland; conversely, the Peking regime is committed to the conquest of Taiwan. Only the Taiwan Strait, eighty miles wide at its narrowest point, separates the two Chinas from one another.

Under its communist regime mainland China has become an area of growing economic strength and nationalistic ambitions, determined to assert its power over peripheral areas—particularly Tibet, Sinkiang, Taiwan and the other offshore islands—and to become the dominant nation of eastern Asia. Allied militarily with the U.S.S.R., it forms the eastern wing of a Eurasian communist bloc which stretches from the Elbe River to the Pacific, and any major military or political moves which Communist China undertakes involve Soviet interests and possible participation as well.

Taiwan and the nearby islands, on the other hand, are the last areas under the control of the Chinese Nationalist government, which suffered military defeat at the hands of the Communists in 1949 on the mainland. The island also forms a link in the chain of offshore bases stretching from northern Japan to the southern Philippines, which have been established since World War II as part of a rimland defense system against the expansion of communist power outward from the Eurasian heartland. It was largely because of Taiwan's strategic value that the United States in 1950 stationed naval units in the Taiwan Strait and proclaimed its intention of using military force if necessary to prevent mainland China's conquest of Taiwan. Two territorial problems then are associated with this region: first, the power of Communist China[1] and its relation to its peripheral areas on the mainland; second, the contest for control of Taiwan.

Mainland China

The Chinese nation is potentially one of the great power areas of the world. Among its elements of strength are its population (amounting to nearly one-quarter of the world's total), its great area, its natural resources, and its central location in eastern Asia. Although for centuries China was subjected to foreign pressure and control, the country's position has been greatly strengthened by the recent concentration of administration in the hands of the Chinese Communists, and by the changing power pattern in other parts of the Far East since World War II. The result has been the gradual emergence of a strong national unit in an area of traditional division and weakness.

Physical Elements

The territory of China consists of several units—China proper (the former eighteen provinces south of the Great Wall), Manchuria, Inner Mongolia, Sinkiang, and Tibet. Outer Mongolia and Tannu Tuva, once units of the Chinese empire, have been separated from China within recent dec-

---

[1] The term China will henceforth be used in this chapter to refer to the mainland nation.

ades, the former area becoming a separate state under Soviet influence and the latter an integral part of the Soviet Union. The total area of China is about 3,745,000 square miles, of which approximately thirty-five per cent comprises China proper.

Location. China's location in eastern Asia has in past centuries tended to isolate the country from contacts with other nations. North of Manchuria are the coniferous forests of Siberia, northwest of China proper is the semi-arid plateau of Mongolia and the Gobi Desert, to the west is the great mountain complex of Tibet, and to the southwest rugged, forested high plateau and mountain country separates China from the populated areas of southeast Asia. To the east China faces the sea, and it was from the east and southeast that the Europeans came, particularly after 1800, in order to exploit China's market potential. It was also by sea that the Japanese attacked China during the 1930's.

Despite the physical barriers which tend to separate China from other areas, the nation's vicinal location has been of great importance to its political development. To the east and northeast Korea, Japan, the Ryukyus, and Taiwan have played significant roles in China's changing patterns of control. Both Korea and Taiwan, for example, have been historic areas of conflicting Chinese and Japanese sovereignty; both have been utilized by the Japanese in military operations against China, and since World War II the possibility of Chinese control of these areas has posed a threat to non-communist Japan. In the north and northwest China borders the Soviet Union, and here again a broad belt of conflicting sovereignty has long existed. As in the case of China's eastern frontiers, political control in this central Asian belt has reflected the relative power positions of China and its neighbors. To the south China's territory adjoins that of Indochina, Burma, and the several states of the Indian subcontinent. In the past British and French power in these areas (together with the weakness of China itself) resulted in a relative stabilization of borders. Since World War II European control has ended, while within China itself new ideologies and a new spirit of nationalism have come into being, with the result that Chinese control has gradually been pushed southward across its generally poorly-defined southern boundaries into the territories occupied by neighboring states.

Surface Configuration. Only extremely broad generalizations concerning China's topography are possible here (Figure 88). Tibet occupies part of the greatest upland region in the world, a plateau averaging over 10,000 feet in elevation, from which mountain chains extend south and east into China proper. North of Tibet is the arid Tarim basin of southern Sinkiang, with the east-west Tien Shan chain along its northern border, Northeast of the Tien Shan are the deserts and grasslands of Dzungaria (northern Sinkiang), and of Outer and Inner Mongolia. The Great Wall, separating Inner Mongolia from China proper, approximates a climatic as well as an

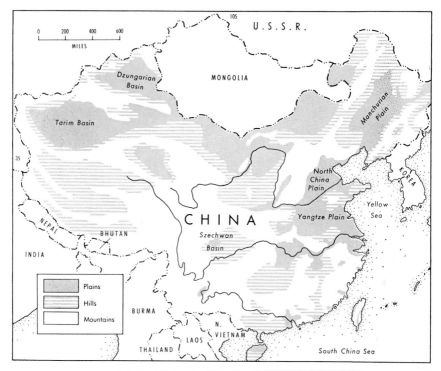

Figure 88. China: Physical Features.

ancient political boundary, for to the south and east of this wall precipitation is generally adequate for agriculture, while in Inner Mongolia it is less abundant and more erratic.

Manchuria consists of a rolling, well-drained lowland about 600 miles north to south and 200–300 miles east to west, surrounded on all sides by rough terrain. This lowland "compartment" is the most important area in China for the production of crop surpluses, primarily because of its larger farm units. South of Manchuria mountains and hills extend eastward from the Tibetan highlands; as they approach the coast the mountains become lower and divide into sub-ranges. Southern China is predominantly hilly with exceedingly rough terrain and only a few areas of level land. Three major rivers—the Hwang Ho (Yellow) in the north, the Yangtze in central China, and the Si (West) of the south—rise in the western highlands and flow south and east to the sea, forming alluvial lowlands in their lower courses. The North China Plain—more than 150,000 square miles in area—is the most extensive of these lowlands.

Surface configuration in China, as in other parts of the world, is important politically because of its effects on population distribution and on transportation routes. Some of the lowland areas have a rural population density of over 2,000 persons per square mile, indicating the intensive land utilization which is carried on here. The hill country, which is typical of much of China proper, has often contained the strongholds of local rebels, thus making difficult the task of uniting the country. The majority of China's population is concentrated near the coast. The Szechwan basin of the upper Yangtze and the Wei valley, northeast of Szechwan, are also heavily populated; both of these in the past have been important as defense areas.

Climate. China's climate reflects the nation's position on the eastern portion of a great land mass. During the summer monsoon eastern China experiences warm, moist winds from the southeast; throughout the rest of the year most of the country is influenced by dry air masses from the Asian interior. Eastern China, including the Manchurian lowland, generally receives adequate precipitation for agriculture, but in the central and western portion of China proper, as well as in most of Tibet, Sinkiang, and Inner and Outer Mongolia, steep slopes, aridity, and cold weather place severe limitations on agriculture. Crop land is estimated to be about twelve per cent of the total area.[2]

Differences in climate and surface configuration have created centrifugal forces within the Chinese state. Southern China, with its semitropical climate, is predominantly an area of rice cultivation, with tea and silk as secondary products, and the farmers here are generally more prosperous than those in the north. The regional distinctiveness of the south is further evidenced by the importance of fishing along its indented coast, as well as by its contacts with other countries, because of commercial ties and because most Chinese emigrants have come from this part of the nation. Northern China, with its cooler climate and uncertain rainfall, produces wheat, millet, and other grains, as well as cotton and tobacco. Widespread floods and famines are more common here than in the south, and the region is more oriented toward central Asia than toward overseas areas.

Within the framework of this over-all division there are a great number of local variations, such as in the Yangtze basin in central China, the Manchurian plains in the northeast, and the highland areas along China's southern and southwestern borders. In this nation of 3¾ million square miles, distance, surface configuration, soils, and other physical elements have posed serious obstacles to political unification under China's central government.

Mineral and Power Resources. Mineral and power resources in China are not extensive, considering the nation's size and population and its apparent objective of becoming one of the great industrial powers of the world. China ranks third in the world in coal resources, but there is relatively little

---

[2] George B. Cressey, *Asia's Lands and Peoples* (New York: McGraw-Hill Book Co., Inc., copyright 1952), p. 89. Used by permission. This figure includes China proper, Tibet, Sinkiang, Inner and Outer Mongolia, and Manchuria.

petroleum, and many of the major sites for hydroelectric-power development are located in the western and southwestern mountains, away from
the main population centers. Although rich in tin, tungsten, and antimony,
China has only moderate amounts of iron ore, copper, bauxite, lead, and zinc.
One of the favorable locations for industrialization is southern Manchuria,
where deposits of low-grade iron ore are situated close to reserves of coking
coal; here again, however, the known reserves of both commodities are not
great enough to sustain large-scale industrialization—measured in terms of
the German Ruhr or the Soviet Ukraine.

Much of China has not been adequately explored for mineral resources,
but there are indications that important new reserves will be found. One
of the most hopeful developments has been the successful oil drillings in
northern Sinkiang, northern Tibet, and Inner Mongolia. The development
of iron-ore reserves in Inner Mongolia and the expansion of copper, lead,
and zinc production are also predicted by the Peking government, and will
be important assets to the nation in its industrial growth.

Population Features

China has more inhabitants than any other nation on earth. The
Chinese government released a figure of nearly 583,000,000 for the 1953
census, an increase of 120,000,000 over the Nationalist figure for 1948.
Because of this difference, many experts have suggested that the true figure
for 1953 was probably closer to 500,000,000. According to the 1953 census,
Manchuria had a population of 43,000,000; Sinkiang, 4,900,000; Tibet,
3,000,000; and Inner Mongolia, 7,000,000. There would thus be about
ninety per cent of the population within China proper—an important centripetal factor for the nation.

Birth and death rates in 1953 were estimated at 37 and 17 per thousand respectively, giving China an annual population increase of 20 per
thousand, or close to 12 million persons per year. Forty-one per cent of the
population was listed as under eighteen years of age, indicating both the
high birth rate and the relatively short life span.[3] In 1957 the Peking government estimated that the annual population increase in China had risen
to about 15 million persons per year.

China's population is highly concentrated, with three-quarters of the
people in about one-sixth of the area. The major areas of settlement are
the middle and lower Yangtze valley, the North China Plain, the Canton
delta in the south, the Manchurian plain, and the Szechwan basin of central
China. There are also important population concentrations along the southeast China coast. The 1953 census listed ten cities of over one million people.

---

[3] The source for these population figures is Theodore Shabad, *China's Changing Map* (New York:
Frederick A. Praeger, Inc., 1956).

Of these Shanghai had over six million, and Peking and Tientsin (in the North China Plain) and Mukden (in Manchuria) each had over two million persons. Thus there is not one but several core areas in China; even under the highly-centralized Communist administration the presence of several core areas represents an important element of diversity in the country.

Throughout China there is a single written language, and although over forty dialects exist probably two-thirds of the population, most of them living in China proper north of the Yangtze, speak Mandarin, the "national language." Most of the Europeans and Japanese have left the country, and the 1953 census listed ninety-four per cent of the population as "Chinese." Among the minority ethnic groups are the Chinese Moslems, the Tibetans, the Mongols, and the Koreans; many of these groups have been granted local autonomy, but because of their small numbers in comparison with the Chinese themselves they do not form serious centrifugal elements.

The enormous size of China's population is both an asset and a definite liability to the nation's development. If the population can be organized for the service of the state, and trained in technical or military skills, it can constitute a strong factor of national strength. In past centuries, however, millions of Chinese have spent their entire lives without adequate food, clothing, and shelter: starvation and disease have long been two great checks to China's population growth. Despite their glowing promises of material benefits, the Chinese Communists—like the Nationalists and other governments before them—face a tremendous problem in providing food, clothing, and other necessities of life to hundreds of millions of Chinese.

Economic Features

Two major elements of power in any nation are agricultural and industrial production, both dependent in part upon the physical resources of the area. Professor Cressey estimates that the figure of twelve per cent for China's crop land represents "nearly the maximum that is profitable under present economic conditions."[4] Under the Communists various steps are being taken to increase agricultural production: extensive irrigation projects, flood control, redistribution of land, and the training of farmers in modern agricultural techniques. The Yangtze, Hwang Ho, and other rivers are undergoing important flood control development, and the Five Year Plan, announced in 1952, aims at increasing the area of irrigated land by about one-sixth over the 1952 figure. Even the Chinese government, however, admits that substantial increases in the acreage of cultivated land will be difficult, for after centuries of an agricultural economy here most of the available crop land is already in use. With its rapidly-expanding population, the nation will thus continue to be handicapped by food short-

---

[4] Cressey, *op. cit.*, p. 89.

ages for many years to come. Recurrent food deficits have already caused peasant opposition in parts of the nation to Communist policies. In China there is no important industrial class (as exists in the Soviet Union) to form a supporting base for the communist movement, and the Peking regime must depend largely on the loyalty of the Chinese peasants for the continued success of its plans. The Communists must expand production of food and other basic requirements of life for the present mass of Chinese peasants, for the growing millions of urban dwellers, and for the coming increase in the nation's population; otherwise, they will have failed in a major objective of their program, and will eventually stand to lose much of the support they have received from the Chinese people.

The industrialization of China has been hampered by three major factors: (1) the destruction and removal of industrial facilities during World War II, (2) the shortage of capital and trained personnel, and (3) inadequate transportation and power facilities. Before World War II manufacturing in China consisted largely of textiles, food processing, and related industries. Manchuria, then under Japanese control, had the only important iron and steel industry in the area of what is now China. Following World War II the Soviets dismantled much of the industrial facilities in Manchuria, and sent them to Russia as war reparations. Consequently, industrialization in this area had to start almost from the beginning after 1945, and it was further handicapped by losses sustained in the subsequent civil war and by the Nationalists' neglect of industrial equipment.

One important shortage in Communist China is investment capital. China has always been forced to depend to a large extent on foreign capital for major economic developments. Since World War II the principal sources of investment capital have been the United States and the British Commonwealth, but because of Cold War pressures no capital has moved from these areas to China since 1949. The funds which can be "squeezed" from domestic sources and capital advanced by the Soviet Union represent the only supplies available to the Chinese.

The acquisition of trained personnel and of transportation and power facilities in China will be a relatively slow process, particularly in view of the Western ban on "strategic" exports to the Chinese. Yet large-scale industrialization is important to the task of providing employment and a higher standard of living for China's rapidly increasing population. The 1952 Five Year Plan follows in principle the Soviet Five Year Plans. Under this plan industrial production was to be increased ninety-eight per cent by the end of 1957, electric power doubled, and steel output tripled. Considering the low stage of industrial development before the plan's inauguration, however, these goals are not great in terms of Western industrialized power. Steel production by the beginning of 1958 is scheduled to be about $4\frac{1}{4}$ million tons, less than four per cent that of the United States.

Clearly, China has far to go before it becomes a major industrial power.

A third facet of China's economy is transportation and trade. As in the Soviet Union, economic growth must depend primarily upon rail transport, since highway transportation is not well-developed, and only the Yangtze River, the Si Kiang in the south, and the Sungari River in northern Manchuria are navigable by medium- or large-size ships. The Chinese Communists inherited a fairly extensive rail system in China proper and in Manchuria, although much of the network had been destroyed during the course of the civil war. In addition to repairing this and building new lines to service the eastern areas, the government has embarked on a large-scale program of constructing both railroads and highways to link China proper with the peripheral areas of the country and with neighboring states. A railroad has been built northward between Peking and the Soviet Union through Ulan Bator, the capital of the Mongolian People's Republic (Outer Mongolia), and another line runs from Kweilin in south China to Hanoi in North Vietnam. A railroad is also under construction to the northwest of China proper, which will eventually link the Chinese rail system with the Soviet's through Urumchi, capital of Sinkiang. The truck road to Siberia through Sinkiang, built as a supply line during World War II, has been improved, and connections between China proper and Tibet have been increased by the construction of two highways from Chinese railheads to Lhasa, Tibet's capital. By building these transportation systems through outlying areas, China is finally beginning to overcome the centrifugal effects which distance and inaccessibility have had on the political and cultural conditions within these areas.

China has historically been an important area for foreign trade. In the nineteenth century the European powers pressed for the opening of China to commerce because of its potential value as a market, as an area for investments, and to a less extent as a source for raw materials. In 1950, however, many of the noncommunist nations imposed embargoes on the shipments of various commodities to China, in retaliation against that country's aggression in North Korea. The nation has needed petroleum, rubber, machinery, and transportation equipment, and the difficulties encountered in acquiring these have been another factor delaying China's economic development. Although by 1957 restrictions were gradually being lifted on many of the Western exports to China, the embargoes have been important in the establishment of new trade patterns between China and the states of the communist bloc.

Political Features

Since the advent of Communist power at the end of 1949, China's administrative structure has been changed several times. The old division

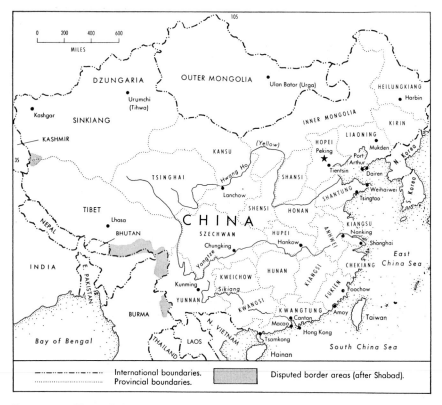

Figure 89. China: Political Divisions. (After Shabad, *China's Changing Map*, Frederick A. Praeger, 1956. Used by permission.)

of China into the eighteen provinces of China proper, Inner and Outer Mongolia, Tibet, Sinkiang, and Manchuria has been abolished. For a time China proper, Inner Mongolia, and Manchuria were grouped together into six administrative areas, within which were thirty-two provinces and thirteen regionally-administered cities. The administrative areas were eventually abolished, thereby strengthening Communist control at the provincial level. Provincial boundary adjustments were also made, and by July, 1955, China's internal political system consisted of twenty-five provinces and three centrally administered cities—Peking, Tientsin, and Shanghai (Figure 89). Of the twenty-five provinces, three are autonomous areas (Inner Mongolia, Sinkiang, and Tibet), which are inhabited largely by non-Chinese peoples (Mongols, Uigurs and Kazakhs, and Tibetans, respectively).

Although the Chinese political structure has certain aspects in common with that of the Soviet Union, there are also important differences. Because of the relatively small non-Chinese minority, the Peking government did not establish its provincial units along the lines of cultural autonomy (except in the case of the three autonomous areas mentioned above), and in the Chinese constitution the provinces, unlike those in the U.S.S.R., are not given the right of secession. The shifting pattern of internal political units is also characteristic of the U.S.S.R., as the Chinese seek to achieve more balanced economic and political functioning. Below the provincial level is the autonomous *chou,* which is somewhat analogous to the Soviet's autonomous oblast, in that it exists for non-Chinese groups whose numbers are not sufficiently great to justify the creation of a more important autonomous province (autonomous *ch'ü*). At a still lower administrative level is the autonomous *hsien,* for small concentrations of minority peoples. The changing political conditions in China are reflected in the shifts in the location of its capital. From the fifteenth century down to 1928 Peking (meaning "northern capital") was the seat of government, but in 1928 the Nationalists shifted the site to Nanking ("southern capital") in the Yangtze valley, where it was more centrally located with respect to China's population centers. Ten years later the Japanese captured Nanking, and the capital was moved inland to the Szechwan basin, where it was established at Chungking. Following the end of hostilities it was returned to Nanking, and in 1949 the Communists moved it back to Peking, thus emphasizing the city's traditional position of authority and the reorientation of China away from the Western influences which had once been strong in the lower Yangtze valley.

Of the peripheral mainland areas, China no longer exercises political control over Outer Mongolia, Tibet has a status which might be termed semiautonomous, and in Sinkiang *de jure* Chinese sovereignty exists, although the *de facto* control of Peking in some parts of this area is not strong (see page 433). Only British-controlled Hong Kong and Portuguese Macao remain of the former European possessions along the China coast, and the various foreign economic concessions within the Chinese cities have been abolished since World War II.

Since 1949 the Chinese Communist government has been engaged in a large-scale program to unite the various sectors of the nation, both within China proper and in the more distant areas. A greatly increased circulatory system, closer political organization, and improved training and education are the methods being employed to strengthen centripetal forces centered on Peking. Particular attention has been given to Manchuria, economically the most valuable of the areas outside China proper. At the same time the establishment of Peking's sovereignty has been blocked by conditions in three areas: (1) Nationalist control of Taiwan and the smaller islands off the China coast, (2) Soviet power in the Mongolian People's Republic and Sinkiang, and (3) the continued existence of European control at Hong Kong and Macao. Of these, the first is by far the most important to the Chinese Communists, since it represents a conspicuous failure on their part to unify all Chinese territory—as it existed after World War II—under Peking's authority.

THE CHANGING PATTERN OF TERRITORIAL CONTROL

The recorded history of China dates back over three thousand years, and over two thousand years ago the nation was unified under a single dynasty. As a result, the record of China's territorial expansions and contractions, and of political unification and division, is one of the longest and most complicated of any nation of the world. In this chapter only the major changes since the late nineteenth century will be considered.

The Period of Territorial Encroachment. During the nineteenth and early twentieth centuries China suffered territorial losses at the hands of the European powers, the Soviet Union, and Japan. The Europeans, who came primarily for commercial profit, won concessions from the Chinese government for the establishment of "treaty ports," amounting to enclaves of foreign territory along China's coast and in certain cities.[5] European countries also received extraterritorial rights, whereby European laws and European court and police systems exercised control over specific areas of China.

During the nineteenth century considerable land along China's north and northwest borders was ceded to Russia, as that country's expanding power began moving into Siberia. Toward the end of the century Russian influence also penetrated Manchuria, but this drive was terminated by Russia's defeat at the hands of Japan in 1905. Following World War I Russian power in Tannu Tuva and Outer Mongolia became more strongly entrenched, and these areas began to move away from the political control of China. In 1921 Tannu Tuva, formerly part of Outer Mongolia, became a virtual Russian protectorate, and Outer Mongolia itself was constituted as an autonomous area with strong ties to Moscow. The Chinese were never able to counteract these strong centrifugal pulls, and in 1946 Outer Mongolia became an independent state.

The gradual expansion of Japan's control over Chinese territory began in 1895, when Taiwan and the Pescadores passed from China to Japan after the Sino-Japanese War. Ten years later the Japanese acquired Russian leases on territories on the Liaotung Peninsula of southern Manchuria. In 1931 Japan invaded and conquered Manchuria and detached it from China's control. Japanese territorial expansion southward from this region into Jehol province in 1935 was followed in 1937 by the launching of an all-

[5] In addition to British Hong Kong and Portuguese Macao, which had been acquired early in the nineteenth century, the treaty ports included Kwangchowan (French), now Chankiang, in south China, the New Territories (British), added to Hong Kong colony, and Kiaochow (German) and Weihaiwei (British) on the Shantung Peninsula.

out attempt to conquer China. For eight years Japanese forces occupied areas in eastern China, but they were never able to destroy the Nationalist government in its refuge capital at Chungking, nor to eliminate Chinese military resistance. The eventual liberation of China came in 1945, when Japan was conquered, largely by United States and British Commonwealth forces operating in the Pacific.

During this era of territorial encroachment China itself was undergoing a series of internal political upheavals, as the old political systems were abandoned and new ideologies were tested. In 1911 the Manchu dynasty, which had been in power for over two and a half centuries, was overthrown. Subsequently, for more than a quarter of a century the administrations of Dr. Sun Yat-sen and (after 1925) Chiang Kai-shek sought to establish the central government's authority over the entire nation. In 1926–27 Chiang Kai-shek succeeded in gaining control over much of China, although he was opposed by local war lords, who controlled large stretches of territory, and, after 1927, by the outlawed Chinese Communist Army, which waged intermittent warfare against him. With the Japanese invasion of 1937 the Nationalists were gradually forced back into the interior of the country, from where they continued their attacks against the invaders until Japan was defeated.

The Communist Victory. At the end of World War II Taiwan and the Pescadores were returned by Japan to China, and, with the exception of Hong Kong and Macao, the foreign-held coastal territories gradually passed under Chinese sovereignty. Japanese power was removed from Manchuria, but control over areas on the Liaotung Peninsula reverted to the Russians. Captured Japanese military equipment in Manchuria was turned over by the Russians to the Chinese Communists, who emerged from the war as a powerful political and military group.

Between 1945 and the end of 1949 there was a series of attempted reconciliations between Nationalist and Communist political leaders in an effort to avert civil war in China, but each group was determined to be the dominant power in the nation. By 1947 open warfare was in progress in northern China, and in spite of American military and economic assistance the Nationalists suffered repeated military reverses at the hands of the Communists. The bitter civil war demonstrated the weaknesses of the Nationalist government, particularly the lack of popular support and the widespread graft and inefficiency among its officials. In contrast was the well-disciplined Communist group, with its dedicated followers. Over a two and one-half-year period Communist armies gradually won control of northern and central China. By December, 1949, practically all of mainland China was in the hands of the Communists, the People's Republic of China had been proclaimed, and the Nationalist government, with what was left of the national treasury, had fled to the island of Taiwan, where it gathered the remnants of its armies together for a final defense. In 1950 a thirty-year treaty of friendship and mutual aid was signed between China and the Soviet Union, thereby inaugurating a new era in power relationships, not only among the countries of Eurasia, but also of the entire world.

Since the end of 1949 the Chinese Communists have worked to strengthen Peking's authority over Sinkiang and Tibet through diplomatic and military action, as well as by the improvement of transportation facilities to these areas. With the construction of a railroad through Outer Mongolia, the Chinese have sought to counter Soviet pressure in that sector of the former Chinese empire. Late in 1950 the Chinese Communists moved into Korea and drove United Nations forces south of the 38th parallel; they also increased their supplies to the forces of Ho Chi Minh, fighting the French in neighboring Indochina. In 1951 Chinese forces occupied Tibet, and ended the region's semi-independent status. In 1954 the Soviets agreed to relinquish their share of ownership of the Manchurian railroad and to evacuate the base at Port Arthur, so that for the first time in half a century China obtained complete control over Manchuria. As a result of these developments, China has proved itself to be a dynamic and gradually-expanding power in eastern Asia—one which has far to go in solving its economic problems, but which has become nevertheless a potent force in the power complex in this part of the world.

Taiwan

The island of Taiwan[6] is a major objective of the expanding power-drive of Communist China. It symbolizes the unfulfilled task of extending Peking's control over all Chinese territory, and as such it also represents a rallying point for the opposition to Communist rule, both within and without China itself. Taiwan is also a base for United States air and naval power just off the Chinese coast: in this respect it constitutes a source of danger to the mainland, for the conflict of Chinese and American interests in the Far East have more than once led to potentially-explosive situations since 1949. Finally, Taiwan, like the Philippines, is something of a "showcase" in eastern Asia, inasmuch as a substantial increase in the standard of living here would suggest to other Asiatic peoples the advantages of a Western-oriented political and economic system.

Taiwan has an area of about 13,900 square miles and a population estimated at nearly 10 million, including over 1 million refugees from China. Over three-quarters of the island is mountainous, and the inaccessibility of some of the upland areas is pointed up by the fact that there are some

---

[6] Since the end of World War II the name Taiwan has been used with increasing frequency, replacing Formosa, the European name also used quite often by the Japanese.

100,000 aborigines who continue to live in an uncivilized state in the mountains. There is a wide variety of minerals, but none exists in large quantities. Power resources include a large hydroelectric potential, as well as some coal and a small amount of petroleum.

Taiwan, like southern China, has a moist, subtropical climate, except in the higher parts of the mountains. Approximately one-quarter of the land is arable, and most of this is intensively cultivated. The island has been important for the export of agricultural goods, particularly rice and sugar, as well as fruits, camphor, and tea. Since most of the arable land is already in agriculture, Taiwan faces a difficult future with respect to its food supply, if its population continues to increase. The island has the basis to expand its light industries, providing foreign capital is made available. The United States since 1949 has advanced many millions of dollars to the area, and as a result there have been important developments in the economic and social structure. Nevertheless, Taiwan, as a separate political unit, has definite limitations to its economic development, while less than 100 miles away China possesses a large potential for expanding its economic strength.

The population of Taiwan is predominantly Chinese, since the island was under Chinese control from the late seventeenth century to 1895, when Japan acquired it. Taipei, in the northern part of the island, is the capital and leading city. Transportation routes through the settled western parts of Taiwan are well-developed, and there is little basis for the growth of strong divisive forces here. The Japanese developed Taiwan into a major military base, guarding the Chinese coast and posing a threat to the Philippines. Later it became a key area amid the Cold War tensions in the Far East.

In June, 1950, at the time of the North Korean attack on South Korea, the President of the United States ordered the United States Seventh Fleet to the Taiwan Strait to protect the island against Communist invasion, and since that time Taiwan and the Pescadores, which are about thirty miles west of Taiwan in the Strait, have remained under United States protection. The Pescadores are a group of flat, windswept islands, which lie 110 miles from Amoy on the Chinese mainland, and which have been fortified to serve as advance bases for the defense of Taiwan. With a population of over 80,000 crowded on less than seventy-eight square miles of land, the islands must depend on Taiwan for over two-thirds of their food supply.

In addition to Taiwan and the Pescadores, the Nationalists also retained control of some thirty-five smaller islands immediately off the China coast, stretching about 300 miles from the Amoy area north to the vicinity of Hangchow, south of Shanghai (Figure 90). These islands—of which Matsu and Quemoy are the most important—have served the Nationalists as points of contact with loyalist groups on the mainland, as bases for local attacks on China proper, as control points over the ports of Foochow and Amoy, and as observation posts.

Figure 90. Taiwan and the Offshore Islands.

Political Problems

The existence of two Chinese governments, each one committed to the overthrow of the other, represents an extremely unstable political situation, for neither government has been willing to accept an indefinite continuation of the status quo in this area. The Nationalists have sought to win the loyalty of the overseas Chinese (including over 2 million in Hong Kong), of the local people on Taiwan, and of anti-Communist groups within China itself. Taiwan's principal hope of providing an alternative to communism would seem to depend on the creation of a truly democratic government (with an end to the abuse of civil liberties) and a sound economic program. Chiang Kai-shek's administration, however, has failed to win anything approaching universal support, because of its pre-1949 autocratic nature and the many holdovers in the present regime, and because of the obvious impossibility, without strong American backing, of a Nationalist reconquest of the mainland. "The essential question for all Chinese [mainland as well as overseas], whose illusions of the 'New Democracy' have been shattered by the harsh realities of Communist rule, is whether Formosa holds any promise for the future of their race. It is already apparent that the determining factor will be, not the international legal status of Formosa and its Chinese Nationalist Government, but the opportunity available on the island for ordinary Chinese to express and realize their hopes. The first need of the Chinese today is for an acceptable ideal that offers a demonstrable alternative to their present inadequate experience."[7]

Peripheral Areas of China

To the west and northwest of China proper are approximately 2 million square miles of territory, in which Chinese political control has varied in relation to that of Japan, Russia, Britain, or local groups themselves. This peripheral belt has in the past served to isolate, and often protect, the majority of China's land boundaries, but with the coming of twentieth-century communications these outlying areas have become the scene of power struggles between China and its neighbors. Three areas—Tibet, Sinkiang, and Outer Mongolia—will be considered here as separate units. Manchuria and Inner Mongolia, also lying outside China proper, have been integrated within China to the point where they may no longer be regarded as peripheral. In addition, the former Chinese-controlled territory of Tannu Tuva will be treated here because of its historical associations with China and Outer Mongolia.

Tibet

Tibet lies for the most part at elevations of from 10,000 to 16,000 feet, and is one of the most isolated regions of the world. On the south it borders India and the states of Nepal, Bhutan, and Sikkim; on the west it adjoins Kashmir; on the north, Sinkiang; and on the east it borders the provinces of China proper. Its strategic location is enhanced by its control of important passes leading through some of the highest mountain areas of the world into adjoining countries.

Tibet actually consists of several physical regions. Much of the northern and central parts are occupied by the Tibetan (or Chang Tang) Plateau, consisting of basins and low mountain ranges at an average elevation of over 15,000 feet. The region is dry and cold and practically uninhabited. In eastern Tibet are the great canyons formed by the upper courses of the Mekong, Salween, and other rivers of southeast Asia. The obstacles these canyons present to transportation have helped to preserve Tibet's isolated position for many centuries. In southern Tibet is an east-west valley, occupied by the Brahmaputra River (which flows to India) in the eastern portion and by the upper Indus River in the west. This valley forms the populated area of Tibet; here is located Lhasa, the capital and leading city. Although transportation facilities throughout the country are not well-developed, the concentration of population in the southern areas has been a centripetal factor.

---

[7] Albert Ravenholt, "Formosa Today," *Foreign Affairs*, XXX, No. 4 (July, 1952), 622–23.

Few important mineral resources have been discovered within Tibet, and most of the approximately 3 million people here have only recently come in contact with twentieth-century economic and political ideas. The construction of new motor roads from China to Tibet's core area and improvements to the route through Bhutan to India have diminished the area's isolation, although attempts to impose the centralized authority of communism upon the traditionally independent Tibetans have met with considerable opposition. Here, as in Sinkiang, is an example of the difficulties involved in attempting to consolidate Peking's control over the physically and culturally remote areas of China.

Chinese claims to sovereignty in Tibet date back to the early eighteenth century, when China conquered the area. These claims have been complicated, however, by the position of the Dalai Lama, spiritual ruler of this deeply religious Buddhist country, and the priesthood, whose power has been very great. Government has been largely a monopoly of the church, and religious leaders have sought to isolate Tibet from outside influence for as long as possible. The British, operating from India, became interested in establishing Tibet as a buffer area against Russian power to the north in the nineteenth century. After 1914 Britain recognized the area embracing most of the Tibetan highlands as a virtually independent state, with which foreign missions were exchanged and in which British India, with its trade and communication links, had considerable economic and political influence.

Tibet's relative independence lasted until 1951, when Chinese Communist forces occupied the area and announced the establishment of Tibet as an autonomous province of China. Since that time the British policy of maintaining Tibet as a buffer area along India's northern border has been superseded by China's plans to integrate the region as closely as possible within the Chinese nation. Territorial difficulties with India prompted the Indian government in 1956 to suggest that the 1,800-mile Tibet-Indian border be officially demarcated. Among the propaganda claims of the Chinese Communists is the assertion that Tibet should regain sovereignty over Nepal, Bhutan, and Sikkim, which at times in the past have been under its control or protection.

Sinkiang

To the north of Tibet is an area of historic conflict between China and Russia. Sinkiang, separated by distance, mountains and deserts, and ethnic differences from China proper, has been under varying degrees of Chinese control for some 2,000 years. With Soviet development of its central Asian republics close to the Sinkiang borders during the late nineteenth and the twentieth centuries, powerful centrifugal forces have been formed, which have tended to diminish China's power in this remote sector of the continent.

Sinkiang has an area of about 660,000 square miles and a population of slightly less than 5 million persons, of whom less than ten per cent are Chinese. The majority are Moslems—Uigurs in the south and Kazakhs in Dzungaria to the north. Geographically, as well as ethnically, the region is divided into two parts. In the south is the Tarim basin, a desert area surrounded on all sides but the east by mountains. In the foothills surrounding the basin are many oases, of which Kashgar in the west is the most important. The Tarim basin is separated from the Soviet Union by extremely high and difficult mountain regions, while over 1,000 miles of desert and semiarid plateau country lies between the basin and China proper, although across this area stretches the historic Kansu Corridor, a chain of oasis settlements which serve as supply points for overland traffic. To the south are the Kunlun Mountains and the Tibetan Plateau.

The Tien Shan range, forming both the western and northern borders of the Tarim area, separates it from the basin of Dzungaria. Dzungaria, which is smaller than the Tarim area, also consists of a dry interior and a string of oases in the surrounding foothills. Of these, Urumchi in southern Dzungaria, is the largest; it is also the capital for all of Sinkiang. It lies on the truck route which extends eastward to China proper, and westward through the low Dzungaria Pass (elevation 1,000 feet) to Siberia. The Turk-Sib branch of Russia's Trans-Siberian Railroad passes within about 100 miles of the Sinkiang border in the neighborhood of this pass, thus making Soviet contacts with Dzungaria relatively easy to maintain.

In the early part of the twentieth century Sinkiang was administered by a local Chinese governor as a practically independent state. The governor's assassination in 1928 opened the way for almost continuous violence and civil war in the area, affording the Soviet Communists an opportunity to extend both economic and political influence into Sinkiang. The Russians were particularly interested in the resources of the area—petroleum, tungsten, tin, gold, and, more recently, uranium. Military aid was dispatched to warring groups in Sinkiang, and at times Soviet troops and aircraft took part in local campaigns. While the Chinese government was engaged in politically unifying its own area and in fighting the Japanese, the Soviets increased their efforts to establish power in this region.

During World War II the Soviet government shipped military supplies to the hard-pressed Chinese Nationalist government through Dzungaria. In order to protect the military supply lines, the Russians stationed troops in Dzungaria, enabling them to further influence affairs in that region. In 1944 a revolt was launched by a group of Kazakhs. Supplied by arms and troops from Soviet-controlled Outer Mongolia, they succeeded in destroying the local Chinese Nationalist garrison and establishing temporarily the Republic of East Turkestan, a Soviet puppet regime in western Dzungaria. Following the war tribal revolts broke out, often supported from Outer Mongolia or the

U.S.S.R. Moreover, Soviet companies secretly exploited the minerals of western Sinkiang, and efforts by the Nationalist government to work out an agreement with Moscow for the economic development of the region were largely ignored.

The contest between the Soviet Union and China for economic and military control of Sinkiang (and of Outer Mongolia as well) entered a new phase with the communization of China itself, and information on the course of developments in the area since 1949 has been extremely meager. The Soviets have reportedly been given control of uranium-bearing areas, and are to receive half the minerals and petroleum extracted in the region. With its strongly nationalistic policies, it seems unlikely that the Peking government will abandon Sinkiang to the Russians. Actually, the Chinese are engaged in developing the area economically and in planning large-scale transfers of population from the crowded areas of China proper to Sinkiang, thereby strengthening China's hold upon the territory.

Outer Mongolia

One of the more remote areas of the world is Outer Mongolia, or the Mongolian People's Republic, a semiarid plateau region of about 600,000 square miles, located between Siberia and Chinese-controlled Inner Mongolia. Mountains in the northwest separate Outer Mongolia from Tannu Tuva, which up to 1921 was generally considered a province of Outer Mongolia. The Mongolians, numbering less than one million, are distinct in language and culture from both the Russians and the Chinese, and for centuries have struggled to maintain independence, or at least autonomy, from China and Russia, and to prevent the colonization of their country by either nation. Within Outer Mongolia food production is barely sufficient to satisfy local needs, and mineral and power resources have not proved to be of much value. The country has primarily a pastoral economy, and is extremely undeveloped commercially and politically, with few roads or railroads, and only one city—Ulan Bator (formerly Urga), the capital—with over 100,000 persons.

The processes of political control in central Asia are often less clear cut than in most other parts of the world. Many boundaries remain vague and unmarked, and the actual political status of various areas is often difficult, if not impossible, to ascertain. Terms such as "suzerainty," "autonomy," and "sovereignty" have frequently been applied to Outer Mongolia's political status by local political leaders, as well as by the Russians, Chinese, and Japanese, quite often with different interpretations by the respective parties. From 1913 to 1917, for example, the Russians continued to assure China that its sovereignty was recognized over the autonomous area of Outer Mongolia, while at the same time Moscow dealt with Outer Mongolia itself as an independent state. Under such conditions it was impossible to delimit boundaries separating Russian, Chinese, and Outer Mongolian control. Even today Outer Mongolia is something of a transition zone between Russian and Chinese power spheres.

During the nineteenth century, Outer Mongolia was technically a part of China, and the Chinese, interested in the area as a buffer against Russia, generally left it alone. However, Russian activities in southeastern Siberia in the late nineteenth and early twentieth centuries prompted the Chinese to strengthen their hold on Outer Mongolia, and they began to settle a considerable number of Chinese in southern Outer Mongolia—a process which greatly antagonized many of the Mongolians. Anti-Chinese riots broke out, and in 1911, at the time of the Chinese Revolution, an independent Outer Mongolian state was proclaimed.

The political maneuverings in this area between 1911 and 1946 illustrate the unstable nature of territorial control in central Asia. In 1912 Russia recognized Outer Mongolia's autonomy, and thereby received special economic privileges. Five years later, at the time of its Revolution, Russia's power began to wane in Outer Mongolia and was largely replaced by Chinese, but in 1921 a Soviet-styled "people's government" was established at Ulan Bator. Thus, after 1921 Outer Mongolia was again a Russian-oriented autonomous region. Although the U.S.S.R. continued officially to recognize Chinese sovereignty over Outer Monoglia, in 1936, under the pressure of Japanese expansion in Manchuria and Inner Mongolia, the Soviets concluded a treaty of mutual assistance with Outer Mongolia, after which Soviet troops occupied the country. In 1945 China was forced by the Russians to accept the independence of Outer Mongolia, providing a plebiscite indicated that the Mongolians were in favor of this move. With Soviet troops occupying the country, a plebiscite was held, resulting in virtually unanimous approval of independence, and in January, 1946, China recognized the independence of the Mongolian People's Republic with its Soviet-styled form of government.

Tannu Tuva

In the mountains of what used to be northwestern Outer Mongolia is situated the territory of Tannu Tuva, centered on the upper basin of the Yenisey River, which breaks through the mountains in the northwestern part of the area and flows northward through Siberia to the Arctic Ocean. Much of Tannu Tuva's 64,000 square miles is mountainous. The Sayan Mountains separate the Yenisey basin from Siberia, while the Tannu Ola Mountains form a natural barrier to the south. The strategic advantage of Russian control of this area was recognized as far back as the late seventeenth century. In addition, Tannu Tuva has mineral resources, including gold, coal, asbestos, and copper. Prior to World War I Tannu Tuva was at least nominally a part of the Chinese Empire, and was included within Outer Mongolia. The original inhabitants are largely Turkic, rather than Mongol. China's hold on this remote province weakened as Russian expansion increased in south central Siberia in the late nineteenth and early twentieth centuries.

Although Tannu Tuva has close physical ties with Siberia, the Soviets hesitated to incorporate it formally with Russia, for fear of arousing both the Mongolians and the Chinese. Many Russians moved up the Yenisey valley during the late nineteenth and early twentieth centuries and settled in the area; eventually Russians came to constitute about one-quarter of the area's 65,000 people. In 1921 a Congress of the People of Tannu Tuva announced the region's independence. China was unable to resist this move effectively, and the "people's government" in Outer Mongolia offered no objections. As a result, Tannu Tuva moved within the Soviet orbit, with a status which might best be termed a protectorate. After Outer Mongolia achieved independence in 1946 Tannu Tuva was formally incorporated within the U.S.S.R., since when it has been known officially as Tuva Autonomous Oblast.

Problem Areas

1. The Offshore Islands

The question of territorial control in the two Chinas is complicated by the existence of Nationalist-held islands off the Chinese coast. Two of these, Quemoy and Little Quemoy, are in the Taiwan Strait; the rest are situated to the north in the East China Sea. Although the islands are a military asset to the Nationalists, particularly in their efforts to blockade the China coast, their advantage is primarily a psychological one. Like the Pescadores and Taiwan itself, they stand as enemy-held areas, and therefore challenges to the success of communism in China.

Foreign-controlled offshore islands have frequently constituted politico-geographic problem areas, for example, the Italian-held Adriatic islands off the Yugoslav coast and Hong Kong Island in south China. In the case of the Nationalist-held islands, a state of war (albeit undeclared) still exists between the government in control of the islands and that on the mainland, which at some points is only several miles away. Quemoy Island, for example, at the entrance to the port of Amoy, is but five miles from the mainland.

To Communist China, with its claims to world power status, the existence of these hostile offshore islands represents a severe "loss of face." To the Nationalists, however, the loss of these islands would endanger one of the main objectives of their military build-up, for it would make even more unlikely the possibility of a Nationalist reconquest of mainland China. As potential Communist bases against Taiwan, the offshore islands do not offer particular strategic advantages. From Nationalist-held Paichuan Island it is about 95 miles to Taiwan, from Matsu 105 miles, from Quemoy 120 miles, while there are parts of the Chinese mainland (as well as Communist-held islands) which are within approximately 80 miles of Taiwan (Figure 90).

The primary reason for the reluctance of the Chinese Communists to attempt an invasion of the offshore islands is the uncertainty of what steps the United States Seventh Fleet, which patrols Taiwan Strait, would take in their defense. Thus American power in the Pacific extends to within sight of the Chinese mainland.

2. Hong Kong and Macao

The two remaining vestiges of European control along the China coast are British-controlled Hong Kong and Portuguese Macao, both of which are located in southern China not far from the port of Canton. At a time when the Chinese Communists are fiercely asserting their anti-Western nationalism, it seems paradoxical that these two enclaves should continue to exist, particularly since Hong Kong has been a place of refuge for over one million anti-Communist Chinese who have fled across its borders since 1949.

Hong Kong. The crown colony of Hong Kong was acquired by the British in 1841, following the Anglo-Chinese War, and was the first European enclave in China (Figure 91). It has an area of 391 square miles and a population of 2,300,000, of which about 10,000 are British. It consists of the island of Hong Kong, on which the city of Victoria is located, and the nearby Kowloon Peninsula, with the city of Kowloon. The inhabitants of

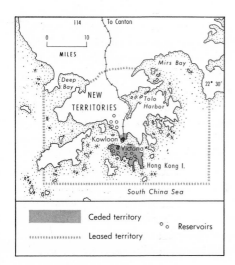

Figure 91. Hong Kong. (After map in *Focus*, IV (Nov., 1953). Courtesy of American Geographical Society.)

these two cities comprise more than nine-tenths of the enclave's population. In addition to the urban sectors, the British-controlled area also includes the mainland territory behind Kowloon as well as a number of coastal islands, which, taken together, comprise the New Territories. The colony includes two airfields and an excellent harbor. It is one of the major free ports of the Far East, and handles more of China's overseas trade than any other port along the China coast. Because of Western embargoes placed on exports to Communist China, Hong Kong plays a strategic role in the Chinese economy, for through it comes most of the licensed imports from Western nations, as well as much of the unlicensed trade.

The colony is of economic significance as a retail and wholesale center, but the volume of foreign trade handled here has dropped considerably since 1949. Hong Kong is also important as a listening post for Western nations, and as a place of safety for refugees from Communist China. With its large population, it is partly dependent upon China for food, and much of its water supply comes from reservoirs in the New Territories, over which Britain's lease expires in 1997.

Hong Kong's continued existence as a British-controlled enclave depends largely upon its future value to China in terms of foreign trade. With a lifting of the Western embargo on trade with China, other ports, particularly Shanghai, might strip Hong Kong of much of its present importance. By imposing a commercial and food blockade on the colony the Chinese could then create serious problems for the Hong Kong authorities. The British, nevertheless, have continued to invest large sums in local industries and public works. Despite the wave of anti-Western nationalism in southern and eastern Asia they give every indication of planning to remain in Hong Kong for a long time to come.

Macao. Macao, located about sixty miles southwest of Hong Kong, has an area of six square miles and a population of about 200,000, of which less than 3,000 are Europeans. The Portuguese possession consists of a peninsula and three small islands at the entrance to the Canton River. Macao is far less important commercially than Hong Kong, although it has figured prominently in the illicit trade of embargoed goods into Communist China. It is almost completely dependent on China for food, and thus would be vulnerable to any food blockade the Chinese might impose, in order to force the Portuguese from the area. Macao is a relic of bygone European power in the Far East. As with Goa, however, Portugal is unwilling to abandon its colonial possession. But if the Chinese refuse to trade through Macao— thereby ending its economic *raison d'être*—and clamp a food blockade on the enclave, economic measures might succeed in accomplishing what political pressure has been unable to do. Here, as in Hong Kong, the pressure of Chinese nationalism may eventually outweigh any actual advantage the enclave has for China, thereby precipitating a move to annex the area.

BIBLIOGRAPHY

ALEXANDROWICZ, C. H. "India and the Tibetan Tragedy," *Foreign Affairs,* XXXI, No 3 (April, 1953), 495–501.

Despite its title, this article is essentially a short, concise political history of Tibet in the twentieth century.

CHANG, LI. "The Soviet Grip on Sinkiang," *Foreign Affairs,* XXXII, No. 3 (April, 1954), 491–504.

A history of political developments in Sinkiang since 1928 and of Soviet attempts to establish control in this area.

CRESSEY, GEORGE B. *Land of the 500 Million.* New York: McGraw-Hill Book Co., Inc., 1955.

A basic, up-to-date regional geography of China.

GINSBURG, NORTON S. "China's Changing Political Geography," *The Geographical Review,* XLII, No. 1 (January, 1952), 102–18.

Well-documented article, illustrating the internal political structure of China.

LATTIMORE, OWEN. "Chinese Colonization in Manchuria," *The Geographical Review,* XXII, No. 2 (April, 1932), 177–96.

Summarizes the nature of pioneer settlement in Manchuria by the Chinese prior to the Japanese invasion of 1931.

MANSVETOV, FEDOR S. "Russia and China in Outer Mongolia," *Foreign Affairs,* XXIV, No. 1 (October, 1945), 143–53.

A political history of Outer Mongolia through its establishment as an independent state.

SHABAD, THEODORE. *China's Changing Map.* New York: Frederick A. Praeger, Inc., 1956.

Extremely valuable source of up-to-date information on China.

17

JAPAN AND KOREA

● On the eastern margin of the Asiatic land mass are located two areas—one a group of islands and the other a peninsula—whose political development strongly reflects the interaction of continental and maritime forces in the Far East. Japan, a chain of islands off the Asiatic coast, was once the major maritime power of east Asia as well as a dominant force on the Asiatic mainland, but in 1945 it was defeated by military strength which struck from across the Pacific. The peninsular state of Korea, a Japanese colony prior to World War II, was divided politically after the war's end, its northern portion eventually passing within the military and political orbit of China and its southern part coming under the protection of the United States. As a point of conflict between maritime and continental powers, the Japan-Korea area has come to occupy a strategic position in the over-all border zone between the communist and noncommunist worlds.

The histories of the two countries have been closely interwoven with one another. The modern period of this interrelationship began in the late nineteenth century, when Japanese power, under the impetus of population growth and industrialization, began to expand outwards to neighboring areas, including Korea. From 1910 to 1945 Korea was a Japanese colony. Since the end of World War II Japan has been used as a supply base for the military occupation of South Korea and for the defense of that area against communist aggression. In terms of world power alignments, Japan and South Korea have since 1950 represented strongholds of Western ideologies in a part of Asia which has otherwise been overrun by communism.

JAPAN

Japan is a striking example of an area in which territorial expansion was motivated primarily by economic pressure. With an area about the size of the state of Montana—and with four-fifths of the land surface covered by mountains—Japan has a population of close to 90 million. Mineral resources are not extensive, and Japan has been hard put to earn sufficient foreign credits for the importation of needed commodities. The economic and political repercussions of the nation's population-to-resources ratio can help to explain much of Japan's history of aggression since the latter part of the nineteenth century.

The Japanese nation consists of four large islands—Hokkaido, Honshu, Shikoku, and Kyushu—as well as hundreds of small ones, with a total area of nearly 142,000 square miles. The nation stretches northeast-southwest off the coasts of southeastern Siberia, Korea, and China north of Shanghai. Prior to 1945 Japan also controlled the Kuril and Ryukyu islands, as well as Taiwan (Formosa), and was thus in a highly strategic position with regard to the Asiatic mainland. The development of a strong navy and merchant fleet, as well as of an effective army, permitted the Japanese to utilize the strategic advantages of the island chain in establishing their power on the Asiatic mainland between 1905 and 1945.

Physical Elements

Location. Japan's maritime and vicinal locations have both been of great importance to the nation's capacity to produce food and other raw materials. Although the islands lie off the east coast of Asia and are subject to cold air masses from that area, the central and southern portions benefit throughout much of the year from the moderating influences of surrounding water bodies. Thus on central and northern Hokkaido rice cannot be grown, but in much of the nation there is double cropping (often rice and barley or wheat), permitting high agricultural production totals.

In order to supplement their national diet, the Japanese have turned to the sea; here again they have profited by location, for to the north and northeast are some of the richest fishing grounds in the world. Japanese fishing vessels, ranging thousands of miles from their home ports, have often come in conflict with Soviet, Canadian, and American fishermen. Fishing regulations and the resultant disputes of ocean sovereignty have been important to the political geography of the Pacific. Since the end of World War II Japan and the Soviet Union have frequently been at odds over the rights of Japanese fishermen off the Soviet-controlled Kuril Islands.

Under normal conditions Japan produces about three-fourths of its food requirements. Eastern Asia and the island groups to the south of Japan have in the past furnished supplementary sources of food and other raw materials. From the former colonies of Taiwan and Korea between one-fifth and one-fourth of Japan's rice requirements were normally imported in the years before 1945. Sugar and fruit were also obtained from Taiwan. Coal and iron ore came from Manchukuo,[1] and iron ore was also supplied by Korea and Malaya. China exported raw cotton and raw wool to Japan, and rubber was obtained from Malaya and the Netherlands East Indies.

Vicinal location was also important to Japan's territorial expansion, for with the defeat of Russia in 1905 the major rival to Japan's power in the Far East was removed. China was weakened by internal problems, and the United States and the European powers were too far away and too pre-occupied with other developments to offer serious resistance to most of Japan's aggressive moves. The existence of island groups and peninsulas in the eastern Asia-western Pacific area contributed to the gradual expansion of Japanese sovereignty, and the various sea lanes facilitated the maintenance of Japanese control over its far-flung empire.

Surface Configuration and Climate. The mountainous nature of Japan has already been mentioned. The upland areas offer considerable hydro-electric-power potential, a large amount of which has already been developed. Lowland areas occur only in the valleys and coastal plains, and are separated from one another by highlands. This diversity in surface configuration has been reflected in the historical contest between political unity and diversity. During many periods of its history Japan has been split up into small political units; countering these divisive forces, however, have been the centripetal effects of limited size and of the presence of the sea boundaries. Since the late sixteenth century political control in Japan has been consolidated in the central government.

Three lowlands, all located along the southern coast of Honshu, form the principal core areas of the nation: the Kwanto Plain, containing the cities of Tokyo and Yokohama; the Kinai Plain, with Osaka, Kyoto, and Kobe; and the Nobi Plain, centered on Nagoya. Since the three are strung out over a distance of less than 300 miles, this concentration of population constitutes a significant unifying element in Japan.

Climatically there is considerable difference between the northern and southern parts of Japan. Heavy snowfalls are characteristic of the western mountain slopes of Hokkaido and northern Honshu, while in southern Japan winters are short and mild. Throughout the entire country precipitation is generally sufficient for agriculture. The relatively mild winters throughout most of Japan permit the use of its seaways for transportation during the entire year.

---

[1] Between 1932 and 1945 Manchuria, under Japanese control, was officially named Manchukuo. After 1935 it also included the province of Jehol in what had been Inner Mongolia.

Natural Resources. Japan has become the leading industrial nation of Asia, despite the fact that it does not possess a rich mineral and power base. Copper, sulphur, gold, and water power are among its principal resources; manganese and chromium are found in small quantities, and there is low-grade coal and small amounts of petroleum. One of the principal sources of Japan's petroleum was lost, however, when the southern part of Sakhalin Island was ceded to Russia in 1945. Fifteen to twenty per cent of the nation's coal needs are normally imported, as well as about eighty per cent of its iron ore.

Agriculturally, Japan suffers mostly from lack of level land. Approximately one-sixth of the nation is in agriculture, and the rural densities here, as in parts of China and southeast Asia, are extremely high. Over sixty per cent of Japan is in forests, and both the government and private individuals are active in forest preservation.

Because of the proximity of most population centers to the sea, the indented coast line with numerous harbor sites, and the many small islands which exist within the archipelago, the Japanese have had close contact with the sea. It is of great importance as a source for food and as a means of transportation, both within Japan itself and to overseas areas. An indication of Japan's use of the sea is illustrated by the fact that in 1939 Japan's merchant marine ranked third in the world in tonnage.[2]

Population

The population of Japan has increased rapidly since the end of the nation's isolation. In 1868 the population was approximately 33,000,000. By the early 1930's this figure had doubled, and in 1940 the total was over 73,000,000. Although the average rate of increase has been dropping since the end of World War I, the nation faced a serious problem of population pressure even during the interwar years. Japan's territorial ambitions were often cited as an effort to relieve this population pressure by acquiring new lands for settlement. Large-scale emigration from the Japanese homeland to the colonies, however, did not occur; in 1938 approximately 1,665,000 Japanese resided in the colonial territories, or just over two per cent of the total national population. The empire was of value as a source for raw materials, markets, and investment opportunities, but it did not serve as a major settlement area for the Japanese.

The annual population increase amounts to approximately one million per year. Although the birth rate has been gradually declining in recent years, Japan's population pressure has become increasingly serious. Since World War II there has been little emigration to foreign areas, because of

---

[2] Wartime losses reduced this tonnage by eighty-eight per cent, and by 1946 the nation had dropped to eighth place. Since that time Japan's merchant fleet has gradually been rebuilt.

discriminatory immigration laws in many countries and because relatively few Japanese have been interested in leaving the homeland. In terms of national power the large population is an important asset to Japan, since it provides a large supply of cheap labor and since the great majority are sufficiently trained and organized to constitute a pool for military service and for defense industries in time of war.

The people of Japan are closely integrated by language, religion, customs, and national sentiment. Within the island-nation the only instance where the cultural attributes of one large group differ from those of another occurs between the urban and rural population. In modern times there have been no efforts for political separation of a part of the homeland from Tokyo's control. The geographic unity and compactness of the islands, together with an absence of cultural groups similar to the Japanese on the Asiatic mainland, are factors contributing to this national cohesiveness. The major non-Japanese group in Japan proper are the Koreans, of whom there are over half a million.[3]

Population distribution, of course, is influenced by surface configuration. The principal core areas were mentioned on page 442. Approximately seventy-three per cent of the population is concentrated on Honshu, and here also are the six cities of over one million population. Tokyo, with a population of over 7 million, is by far the largest city of Japan, and has been the national capital for over three and one-half centuries. It is located within the zone of core areas, and is well served by transportation lines which connect it with other parts of the nation.

Economic Factors

Japan's industrial development has been based largely upon the fabrication of imported raw materials and the export of finished goods throughout the world. Its textile production was formerly one of the largest in the world, and shipbuilding, metallurgy, and chemicals were also important manufactures. The low-income domestic market was not a particularly large one for the nation's finished goods; however, because of low production costs Japanese products—such as machinery, textiles, pottery, glassware, and toys—were often able to undersell those of their competitors in foreign markets. The combination of "trade and the flag" was important in Japan's development, as many of the areas of Japanese political and military activity (for example, Manchuria, China, the Netherlands East Indies) served as export markets and areas for investments. The nation has also built up an important structure of heavy industry. In 1955 Japan produced over $10\frac{1}{2}$ million tons of

---

[3] On Hokkaido there are about 1,000 full-blooded Ainus, descendants of the original natives of the islands. These people continue to observe their own language and customs, but because of their small number do not represent an important centrifugal force.

steel, placing it sixth among the nations of the world behind the United States, West Germany, Russia, Great Britain, and France. Here again imported raw materials have been necessary for this development.

Among the factors of economic power in Japan are the virile, energetic population and the ability of the people to adapt foreign tools and techniques to their own needs. Moreover, the national government has furthered industrial development through various forms of assistance to private organizations. As a result Japan was able to build up its economic strength rapidly in the years before World War II.

Japanese agriculture is characterized by very intensive utilization of the land. As mentioned above most of Japan's food requirements are normally met by domestic production. The principal food crop is rice, which is produced on about half the cultivated area. Supplementary items include grains, fruits, and vegetables. Silk, tea, and tobacco are important cash crops, and Japan is the principal silk exporter of the world. There is only a small livestock industry, but the deficiency in meat is partly compensated by the extensive fishing industry here.

Railroads and waterways constitute Japan's chief transportation systems. The rail lines are largely electrified, utilizing the country's hydroelectric power. Highways, on the other hand, are not as well developed, but with newspapers, radio, and other communication media, Japan has an extensive circulatory system.

In foreign commerce Japan, like Britain, has been faced with the necessity of large-scale overseas commercial ties. Inexpensive Japanese manufactured goods flooded the world markets up to the time of World War II, and resulted in the imposition of various restrictions on Japanese imports in many nations. Prior to the war Japan ranked fifth among the nations of the world in value of foreign trade (see page 444). Since the war the pattern of Japanese foreign commerce has been changed, due to the loss of the empire and the communization of China. The nation also has been troubled by a recurrent unfavorable trade balance, which has been partly met by aid from the United States (see also page 455).

KOREA

Because of its peninsular character, the mountain region separating it from Manchuria, and the cultural homogeneity of its people, Korea forms a distinct geographic unit, which throughout much of its history has been subjected to foreign interference and control. The total area is over 85,000 square miles. Because of conflicting international interests, this area has been divided since World War II into the two separate states of North Korea and South Korea, with competing ideologies and with all contacts between them completely severed.

Physical Elements

Location. The Korean Peninsula adjoins Manchuria along its land border, except for a distance of eleven miles in the extreme northeast where it touches the Soviet Union. To the west Korea faces China's Shantung Peninsula and the Liaotung Peninsula of Manchuria. To the southeast Japan lies less than 100 miles across the Korea Strait. Throughout much of its history Korea has been under varying degrees of Chinese political control. During the twentieth century, however, Japanese and Soviet power—as well as Chinese—have been extended into this area. Here, as in other historic buffer regions, independence appears to be possible only in the event of a power stalemate among the nearby countries, or if Korea's sovereignty is guaranteed by some distant state.

Surface Configuration and Climate. Despite the physical and ethnic distinctiveness of the Korean Peninsula, there are many differences between its northern and southern portions. Less than one-fifth of Korea is comprised of lowlands, and most of these are in the south central and southern areas. As in Japan, these lowlands contain important population centers which figure prominently in Korea's economic and political life. A chain of mountains borders Korea's east coast, and elevations drop sharply to the Sea of Japan; thus much of the nation's population and economic development are concentrated in the western portions of the country, facing the Yellow Sea.

Korea's climate reflects the area's transitional location between the Asian mainland and the Pacific. Winters are long and cold in the northern areas and summers short and warm; in contrast, the southern part of the peninsula has hot, humid summers and mild winters. The warmer climate of the south permits double cropping and a wider use of the land, while in parts of North Korea the growing season is too short to permit even one crop of rice.

Natural Resources. Many of Korea's mineral and power resources are concentrated in the north, a factor which facilitated the industrial development of this area by the Japanese prior to World War II. Because of the presence of mountains and of the Yalu River along the Korean-Manchurian border, the area is well supplied with hydroelectric potential. Northern Korea also has coal and iron ore, and is an important producer of graphite. Southern Korea is important for its tungsten, and in addition it has small supplies of copper, gold, manganese, and silver. Because of the mountainous character of much of its land, it also has considerable hydroelectric potential, although this has not been as well developed as in the north.

About twenty per cent of Korea is in agriculture, the majority of farms being in the south. As in Japan, the land is intensively cultivated, and the rural density of population is very high. Korea possesses rich forest lands, particularly in the north, but a great proportion of these are in inaccessible locations. Many Koreans have turned to the sea as a supplementary source of food, and disputes have arisen since World War II between the Koreans and the Japanese over areas of fishing rights in the waters between these two countries (see page 456).

Population

The Koreans form a distinct Oriental ethnic group, differing from both the Chinese and Japanese in language and culture. Despite the peninsula's historic cultural unity, internal differences have often been reflected in factional struggles for power. It was in response to internal revolts in the early 1880's that the Korean government turned to China for protection, thereby ending Korea's two and a half centuries of isolation.

Between 1913 and 1950 the population of Korea doubled in size, and the rate of increase is still high. A majority of the people is concentrated in the southern part of Korea. Even before 1945 there were strong regional differences between the people of North Korea, with its predominantly upland rural character, and the people of South Korea, with its greater number of urban areas and densely-populated lowland districts.

Of the approximately 30 million people on the Korean Peninsula, about 20 million inhabit South Korea, whose capital is Seoul, the leading city and, until 1945, the capital of all Korea. Seoul is located just south of the 38th parallel in the principal core area of Korea. Of the other four principal cities, Pyongyang is the capital of North Korea, while Pusan, Taegu, and Inchon are in the south. Before World War II Pyongyang (Heijo), in the western lowlands, was the second city of the country, and an industrial and transportation center. Pusan (Fusan) is a port on the southeast coast, facing Japan; Taegu (Taikyu) is a commercial center in southeastern Korea; while Inchon or Chemulpo (Jinsen) is the port for Seoul. Despite the scattered urban areas, Seoul remained the undisputed political and commercial center of Korea until the 1945 partition and the development of Pyongyang as the principal core area of North Korea.

Economy

The political division of Korea is paralleled somewhat by an economic division between north and south (Table 16). The north was the more industrialized area in prewar Korea, while in the south agriculture predominated. The complementary nature of the two portions of the peninsula resulted in considerable interregional trade. Since 1945, however, trade between the north and the south has ceased.

During their period of occupation the Japanese undertook to develop

Table 16

FACTS ABOUT KOREA

	NORTH	SOUTH
Area in square miles	48,000	37,700
Total population, 1949	9,170,000	20,400,000
Farm households, 1943	1,005,587	2,040,414
Farmer-owner operated	251,345	284,837
Agricultural production, 1944, in koku (1 koku = 5.12 bushels) .		
Rice	5,791,952	10,259,927
Barley and naked barley . . .	699,733	10,103,399
Millet	3,198,577	1,178,147
Soybeans	2,264,840	1,036,255
Wheat	1,118,444	790,736
Corn	1,048,256	96,050
Cultivated area by acres, 1944		
Paddy	1,097,600	3,072,300
Dry field	5,343,450	2,695,000
Total	6,441,050	5,767,300
Mineral production, 1944 (in tons)		
Anthracite coal	3,240,749	1,526,513
Lignite coal	2,821,659	29,945
Iron ore	3,221,057	110,757
Limestone	822,148	15,128
Magnesite	388,187	—
Manganese	—	32,377
Tungsten	5,292	6,217
Estimated electric power capacity installed kw, 1944		
Hydroelectric	1,528,000	67,000
Thermal power	95,000	218,000

Source: "Korean Backdrop," *Focus*, I, No. 1 (October 15, 1950). Used by permission of American Geographical Society.

Korea's agricultural and industrial resources. Agricultural production was increased, and in time rice exports to Japan (representing about forty per cent of Korea's annual production) came to constitute about ten per cent of Japan's total consumption. The Japanese constructed several large power installations in the northern part of Korea, as well as steel and textile mills, and food processing plants in both the north and the south. The benefits from these developments accrued almost exclusively to the Japanese, who controlled the investments and profited from the finished products. In 1939 trade between Korea and Japan amounted to about twenty-five per cent of Japan's total foreign and colonial trade. In addition to rice and finished products from Korea, Japan also imported tungsten, graphite, coal, and iron ore. Despite the poverty of the Korean people, the area, nevertheless, was a large market for Japanese exports and a source for investments. Thus of all of Japan's colonies, Korea was the most valuable one economically, but because of the ruthless exploitation of its physical and human resources the Koreans developed a profound hatred for the Japanese—a factor of importance in present-day political alignments.

Since the establishment of an "iron curtain" across the Korean Peninsula there has been little information as to economic development in North Korea. Even before World War II there had been a tendency on the part of the Japanese to strengthen ties between that area and Manchuria; railroads, for example, linked the two regions with one another, and on the Yalu River an important hydroelectric-power station was constructed to serve both countries. Since the communization of North Korea its economic ties with the Chinese territory which adjoins it on the north have continued to be strong.

The economic position of South Korea is described on page 455. The country has suffered heavily from the partition of the peninsula and from the war of 1950–53, as well as from the dislocation of its former trade relations with Japan. As a result large-scale assistance from the United States has been necessary in order for it to maintain economic stability.

JAPANESE EXPANSION AND KOREA'S DECLINE

The rapid growth of the Japanese empire between 1871 and World War II is one of the outstanding territorial developments of modern times. Utilizing its large and steadily-increasing population, Japan was able to capitalize on the weaknesses and divided policies of other powers and to extend its control over much of the Far East and the western Pacific (Figure 92). The eventual involvement of Japan in a global war as a result of its aggressions brought on the downfall of the Nipponese empire, for although it was the dominant power of eastern Asia, Japan could not stand up against the combined strength of Anglo-America and Europe.

Between the early seventeenth and the late nineteenth centuries both Japan and Korea attempted to isolate themselves from foreign influences. The Tokugawa shoguns in Japan forbade the people to leave the country or to build ships of more than fifty tons, while in Korea the Yi dynasty, in the interests of national protection, followed a somewhat similar course. In 1853 Commodore Perry and his naval squadron entered the harbor of Tokyo, and succeeded in opening up Japan to foreign trade and in securing guarantees for the safety of shipwrecked American sailors who landed on Japanese islands. Thirty-one years later the government of Korea, threatened by internal revolts, received the protection of the Chinese government. Trade agreements were already being concluded between Korea and various foreign powers, and, like Japan, the Koreans gradually emerged from seclusion. Once

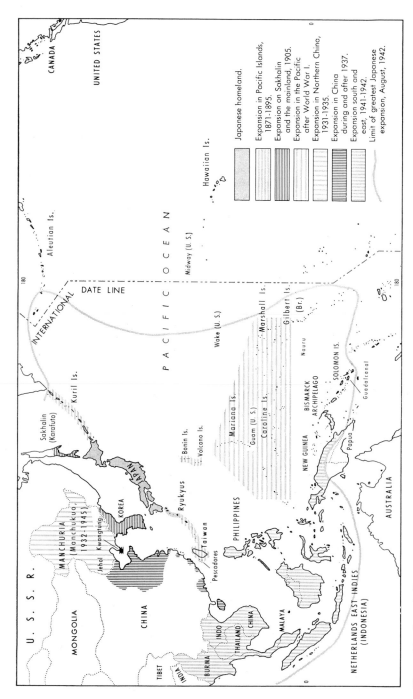

The legend reads:

Japanese homeland.

Expansion in Pacific Islands, 1871-1895.

Expansion on Sakhalin and the mainland, 1905.

Expansion in the Pacific after World War I.

Expansion in Northern China, 1931-1935.

Expansion in China during and after 1937.

Expansion south and east, 1941-1942.

Limit of greatest Japanese expansion, August, 1942.

Figure 92. Japan's Territorial Expansion, 1871-1945.

the isolation was ended, one country became a world power, while the other entered into a period of foreign control and exploitation.

Japanese Empire-Building in the Western Pacific and Yellow Sea Areas. In the early years of its empire-building Japan concentrated on the island areas in the vicinity of the homeland. In 1871 Japan annexed the southern Ryukyus,[4] and four years later the Russians agreed to recognize Japanese sovereignty in the Kuril Islands, in exchange for Japanese recognition of Russian control in Sakhalin Island to the north of Japan. The Bonin and Volcano islands, lying to the southeast of Japan, were annexed next, and after victory over China in 1895 the Japanese received Taiwan and the Pescadores. In possession of an island chain stretching through nearly 30 degrees of latitude from the Kamchatka Peninsula to the South China Sea, Japan was in a position after 1895 to turn westward to the Asian mainland.

As a result of its defeat by Japan, China was forced to relinquish its protectorate of Korea, and for a decade Korea struggled to build up its independence in the face of mounting pressure from Japan. Early in the twentieth century Japan instigated a successful war with Russia; by the Treaty of Portsmouth (1905) Russian abandoned its drive for power in Manchuria, ceded to Japan the southern half of Sakhalin Island, and transferred its rights in the Liaotung Peninsula of southern Manchuria. Thus because of its location in a part of the world from which other major power centers were considerably removed, Japan was able to establish its position of dominance in the Yellow Sea area. Korea, lying between the Yellow Sea and Japan, became a Japanese protectorate in 1905, and five years later it was annexed as a Japanese colony.

In the three decades following the Treaty of Portsmouth, Japan's two chief antagonists in the Far East—Russia and China—passed through periods of internal disorder, thereby enabling Japan to continue its course of territorial growth. The Japanese wisely supported the Allies against Germany during World War I, and helped to eliminate Germany's growing power in the Far East and the Pacific. Japan subsequently gained control of German territories in the Pacific north of the equator.

Territorial Expansion in China. In 1931 Japan turned again to the Asian mainland, and in a short conflict succeeded in conquering Manchuria, with its agricultural, mineral, and power resources and its population of over 35 million. This area in the following years was constituted as the independent country of Manchukuo, but in reality it became a Japanese puppet state. As in Korea, Japanese capital and labor were invested in the development of Manchukuo's resources for Japan's benefit; by the beginning of World War II over 1,000,000 tons each of steel and pig iron were being

[4] The northern Ryukyus (known as the Amami-Gunto group) were Japanese-controlled after 1609. The southern Ryukyus, although retaining a large measure of local autonomy, were a Japanese protectorate—and at the same time paid tribute to China—until 1871, when they were formally annexed by Japan.

produced from Japanese-constructed mills in this area. Although Manchuria contains rich agricultural lands, only about 100,000 Japanese farmers emigrated to the area between 1931 and World War II. The Japanese disliked the cold weather of Manchuria, and were generally unwilling to compete economically with the farmers here, because these people accepted lower living standards than the Japanese. Operating from Manchuria, in 1935 the Japanese invaded and occupied the Chinese province of Jehol, thereby extending Japanese territory along the eastern border of Outer Mongolia (see page 435).

An all-out invasion of China proper was launched by Japan in 1937, in a bid for uncontested supremacy in the Far East. The Japanese soon conquered the major population centers of eastern China, but the Chinese government retreated to Chungking, 1,000 miles up the Yangtze River, and from here directed military operations against the invaders. Japan's inability to destroy effective resistance in China represented the first phase in the eventual destruction of the Empire. The great size of China, its rugged topography, and the stubborn resistance of its people were obstacles which the Japanese could not overcome. Although by 1941 the military lines in China had become relatively stabilized, the Japanese were continually subjected to a war of attrition, carried on by guerrilla forces and by sporadic attacks from military units operating from the Chinese interior.

Conquest in Southern Asia and the Pacific. The final phase of Japan's territorial expansion began in September, 1941, when the nation carried out a military occupation of French Indochina. France itself had been conquered by Nazi Germany in the previous year and was in no position to resist this occupation. Three months later the Japanese military leaders launched a supreme effort to achieve Japan's "place in the sun" by eliminating American power from the Pacific and European power from southeast Asia. Japanese forces swept southeast across the Philippines, Indonesia, and areas to the east until they were finally stopped in the Solomon Islands and in the mountains of southeastern New Guinea. They moved across Thailand, Malaya, and Burma to the borders of India, and within a matter of months in 1941–42 over 135 million people, together with the riches of southeast Asia, were under Japanese control.

In the history of Japan's territorial conquests, particularly after the Pearl Harbor attack of December, 1941, there runs a sort of fatalistic thread, for although the Japanese drew up large-scale plans for their Greater East Asia Co-Prosperity Sphere embracing both the older empire and the newly-won territories, it is hard to imagine the ultimate defeat of the United States, which possessed twice the population of Japan, ten times its industrial production, and a tremendous resource base for waging a long and costly war, should one prove necessary. Those resources of the British Commonwealth which could be spared from the war in Europe were also thrown against

Japan, and the threat of Soviet attack was always present as a further strain on Japanese wartime activities. By the time of Germany's surrender in May, 1945, some Japanese officials were actively seeking an armistice. In August of that year Japan capitulated.

THE LOSS OF JAPAN'S EMPIRE
AND THE PARTITIONING OF KOREA

The Consequences of Defeat. At the end of World War II Japan's territory was reduced to the former island area from which it had launched its course of expansion in 1871. Actually, the Japan of 1945 was smaller than that of 1871, for then the nation controlled the Amami Gunto group of the northern Ryukyus, but after the war even these were taken from it. Russia annexed southern Sakhalin and the Kurils; Manchuria, Taiwan, and the Pescadores were joined to China; Korea was freed from Japanese rule and partitioned into communist and noncommunist sectors; and the Ryukyus, together with the Bonin-Volcano islands and Marcus Island in the Pacific passed under the control of the United States. The Japanese mandated islands in the Pacific were eventually constituted as United Nations trusteeship territories under United States administration. The other areas occupied by Japan between 1935 and 1942 were returned to their former status. In September, 1951, a Japanese peace treaty was concluded at San Francisco, confirming the loss of Japan's empire, although the future status of the American-held island groups remained undetermined (see page 458). Thus in a period of seventy-five years Japan's East Asian Empire passed through a complete cycle.

Power Struggle in Korea. The division of the Korean peninsula greatly changed the economic and political structure of that area. It had been agreed by the major Allied powers in 1943 that the country was to receive independence "in due course" after Japan's defeat, although the details had not been worked out. At the time of Japan's surrender Soviet forces rushed across Manchuria and into northern Korea to occupy the area, while United States troops, transported to the area by sea, occupied southern Korea. The dividing line between American and Soviet occupation zones was put at the 38th parallel, cutting the peninsula in two. In December, 1945, it was decided by the Allied powers that Korea was to be administered under the joint trusteeship of the United States, the U.S.S.R., Britain, and China for a period not to exceed five years, at the end of which time full independence would be granted.

As in the case of other postwar agreements, the Russians refused to compromise on the implementation of the Korean trusteeship. The United States was determined to create in Korea a Western-style (and presumably Western-oriented) democratic government, while the Soviets were equally determined to create a communist, Soviet-oriented regime. The political impasse was further complicated by the fact that in any unified state the south, with its greater population, would always be able to out-vote the north. While a democratic government was being developed in South Korea, under the leadership of Syngman Rhee, a repatriate from the United States, North Korea became a communist-dominated state, in which the military forces were built up rapidly under Soviet supervision. United Nations efforts in 1948 to supervise elections for a national government to control all of Korea were blocked by the Soviets, and in August of that year the democratic Republic of Korea was proclaimed at Seoul, with jurisdiction over the area south of the 38th parallel. Two months later a communist-dominated People's Democratic Republic was established at Pyongyang, with jurisdiction over North Korea. Soviet troops were withdrawn from North Korea at the end of 1948, and by June, 1949, all American forces had evacuated South Korea, leaving the peninsula divided into a heavily-armed communist state in the north, and a weakly-defended democratic state in the south.

North Korean forces invaded South Korea without warning on June 25, 1950, in an effort to unify forcibly the peninsula into a communist state. The United Nations, which had supervised the elections in South Korea two years earlier, voted for prompt retaliatory action, and a United Nations army was organized, largely under United States leadership, to go to the assistance of South Korea. By November the North Koreans had not only been driven back across the 38th parallel, but in some areas United Nations forces had reached the Yalu River bordering Manchuria. Communist China then came to the aid of North Korea, and after seven months of additional warfare the

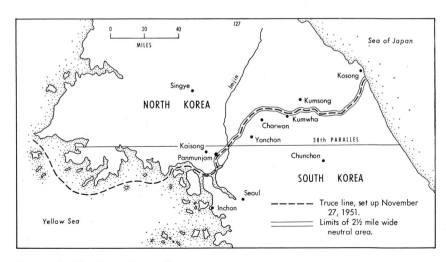

Figure 93. The Truce Line in Korea.

military front was stabilized approximately along the 38th parallel. In 1953 a Korean armistice agreement provided for the permanent cessation of hostilities, an exchange of prisoners, and an enforcement of the political and military border along the cease-fire line in the vicinity of the 38th parallel (Figure 93).

THE ECONOMIC AND POLITICAL PROBLEMS OF
SOUTH KOREA AND JAPAN

The economic and political developments within and between Japan and South Korea are important to the containment of communism in eastern Asia. Internal disorders in either area, resulting from economic difficulties, might cause the overthrow of the democratic governments and their replacement by communist administrations. Moreover, hostile relations between Japan and South Korea have helped to weaken the solidarity of the anti-communist countries in the Far East.

South Korean Economy. The economic difficulties of South Korea result from the partition of the peninsula, from the tremendous devastation wrought by the 1950–51 fighting, from the influx of refugees, and from the lack of available capital with which to rebuild the country. With a population of over 21,000,000 and an area of 36,152 square miles, South Korea is one of the most densely-populated states of the world. Although before World War II this was a food-exporting area, the dislocations caused by the Korean conflict and the expanded population of South Korea have led to difficulties in procuring domestic food requirements. In time South Korea, with its agricultural resources, its proximity to fishing areas, its hydroelectric-power potential, and its minerals, should be able to attain a reasonably sound economic position, providing it remains free from warfare and receives extensive economic assistance. If it fails to achieve economic strength, however, South Korea, like many other countries of the world, may eventually be faced with popular discontent, internal disorders, and the possible overthrow of its present government.

Japanese Economy. Japan's economic problem is primarily that of a densely-populated nation in need of trade partners and a balanced budget. As an indication of its future population growth, estimates for the 1975 figure range from 110 to 135 million (or an average density of 750–900 persons per square mile). Japan's prewar markets, foreign investments, and sources for raw materials are largely gone, and heavy damage was inflicted on the homeland itself in the final months of World War II. The Japanese have worked diligently to restore production and to secure markets for their exports, but the foreign trade deficit has continued to exist. Between 1948 and 1951 the United States granted aid to Japan totalling nearly $1.3 billion; during the Korean war the United States spent an additional $800 million annually in Japan, largely in connection with its military establishments here.

The economic situation in Japan has certain elements in common with that in Great Britain shortly after World War II. Britain also received aid from the United States, but, in addition, the British inaugurated an austerity program, cutting down imports of consumer items and resorting to strict rationing. This policy was never seriously followed by the Japanese, with the result that imports rose steadily during the postwar years. The increase in the volume of exports, meanwhile, has been held down (1) by the resentment of former conquered countries over continued Japanese refusal to pay reparations, (2) by friction with South Korea, a potential trade partner, (3) by high-priced and inferior products, resulting from low labor productivity and poor business practices in Japan, (4) by the protectionist policies of other nations, and (5) by competition, particularly from West Germany, for markets in southeast Asia and Latin America.

The continued economic instability in Japan has posed a serious situation to the United States, which has looked to the Japanese as a firm anticommunist nation in the western Pacific. The Japanese have been attracted by the great market potential in Communist China (prior to World War II about one-quarter of Japan's foreign trade was with China), and the volume of trade between the two areas has been slowly increasing since the end of the Korean war. Either new trade channels must be opened up or Japan must continue to be dependent on large-scale aid from the United States. Widespread unemployment and economic depression in Japan would give encouragement to the Japanese Communist Party, which stands ready to capitalize on popular discontent.

Political Problems. In Japan and South Korea the development of anticommunist policies have been complicated by a growing nationalist spirit in both countries. The Japanese are anxious to realize some benefits from their heavy prewar investments in Korea, a factor which has contributed to ill feeling between Japan and South Korea. On the other hand, South Korea's quarrels with the Japanese over fishing rights have resulted in breakdowns in trade discussions, despite United States appeals to both countries that such disputes weaken their economies and thereby play into the hands of the communists. Since 1952 Japan has claimed the right to fish within twelve miles of the South Korean coast, while the South Koreans claim that restrictions imposed on Japanese fishing in 1945 (in some cases prohibiting them from coming within 100 miles of Korea) are still in effect (Figure 94). The South Koreans have garrisoned Take (or Tokto) Island in the Sea of Japan between Japan and Korea, a previously uninhabited area of disputed sovereignty, and have interned Japanese ships and crews fishing in the vicinity of Take.

Many Japanese have also become increasingly resentful of their nation's role as an American-manned outpost against communism. Having suffered

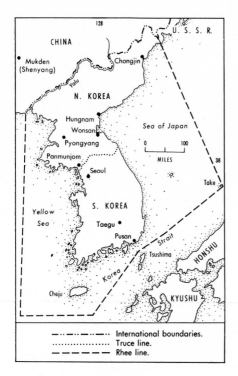

Figure 94. The Limits of Sovereignty Claimed by South Korea. The Rhee Line, laid down in January, 1952, delimits the sea areas in which South Korea claims exclusive fishing rights.

through atomic bombardments, they have little desire to serve as a base for the possible launching of American air attacks against the U.S.S.R. They also wish the return of the Ryukyu Islands from the United States and of the Kurils from Russia, since both island groups are looked upon by the Japanese as part of the homeland territory.

Problem Areas

1. Okinawa and the Ryukyus

Japan and the United States are involved in a territorial dispute concerning the Ryukyu Islands, which extend in an arc 500 miles to the southwest of Japan (Figure 95). The islands have an area of about 1,290 square miles and a population of over 900,000. The Ryukyuans are closely allied to the Japanese in language and physical characteristics and have strong sentimental ties with Japan. Before World War II the standard of living in the Ryukyus was lower than in Japan. The average population density is high, and during the past fifty years thousands of Ryukyuans have emigrated to other Japanese-controlled islands or to Hawaii.

In the spring of 1945, after some of the most costly fighting of the Pacific War, American forces captured Okinawa and began to develop it as

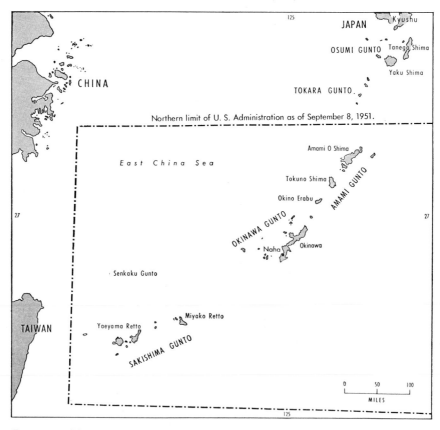

Figure 95. The Ryukyu Islands.

a major base for what was to be the final assault on Japan. After Japan's surrender the Ryukyus south of the 29th parallel were placed under the administration of the United States commander-in-chief in Toyko. Article 3 of the Japanese Peace Treaty states: "Japan will concur in any proposal of the United States to the United Nations to place under its trusteeship system, with the United States as the sole administering authority . . . the Ryukyu . . . Bonin . . . and Volcano Islands. . . . Pending the making of such a proposal and affirmative action thereof, the United States will have the right to exercise all and any powers of administration . . . over the territory and inhabitants of these islands, including their territorial waters." This paragraph also mentions the former Japanese-controlled Daito Islands, Rosario Island, Parece Vela, and Marcus Island as falling within the same category.

The future status of the Ryukyus, as well as of the Bonin-Volcano group, has remained a subject of controversy between Tokyo and Washington. The

United States has constructed a half-billion-dollar air base on Okinawa (sometimes described as the "Gibraltar of the East"), and is naturally reluctant to lose control of the island, even if continued American sovereignty means that the approximately 400,000 inhabitants are denied reunion with Japan. In 1953 the United States returned the Amami Gunto group in the northern Ryukyus, with approximately 200,000 population, to Japanese control, but indicated that for the foreseeable future American control would continue over the remainder of the Ryukyus as well as the Bonin-Volcano group. Anti-American feeling on Okinawa has been heightened by the expropriation of agricultural land for military installations.

The United States, long a champion of self-determination, may find its moral position weakened by continued control in the Ryukyus, for through their elective body the people have expressed a desire for reunion with Japan. If the Ryukyus were returned to Japan agreements could be worked out between the American and Japanese governments for continued American control over air and radar installations.[5] The Japanese would be in a stronger position to demand the return of the Kurils from Russia if America first relinquished control of the Ryukyus. Another possible solution would be the establishment of a United Nations trusteeship over the Ryukyus, with the United States as the sole administering power, although many people—including the Ryukyuans themselves—might consider this merely a continuation of the present situation. Finally, all the islands, except for Okinawa, could be returned to Japan. Such a solution would in the end satisfy no one, for Okinawa is by far the most important island in the group in terms of population and the economic value of its sugar exports, and few Ryukyuans would favor the separation of their leading territory from the remainder of the area.

2. The Kuril Islands

A second postwar territorial problem facing the Japanese is that of the Kuril Islands, a chain extending nearly 700 miles northeast from Hokkaido to the Kamchatka Peninsula (Figure 96). The Kurils have a total area of nearly 4,000 square miles and a population of less than 20,000. The inhabitants prior to World War II were entirely Japanese. Over ninety per cent of them inhabited the southern Kurils, within about 200 miles of Hokkaido. The only economic value of the Kurils area is fishing, most of which is done in the northern part of the chain, not far from Kamchatka. Shimushir Island in the central Kurils is an excellent site for a naval base. Before and during World War II the Japanese established a number of naval and air

---

[5] American reluctance to give up control of Okinawa might be compared to Britain's desire (for similar reasons) to maintain control of Cyprus. In either case a hostile government on the island might at some future time seriously interfere with the operations of the military base.

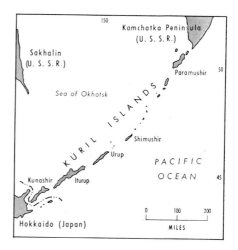

Figure 96. The Kuril Islands.

bases in the islands, from which they could dominate the southeastern part of the Sea of Okhotsk, as well as strike eastward toward the Aleutians.

The southern part of the Kurils has been Japanese-controlled since the beginning of the nineteenth century, and in 1875 Russian claims to the islands were withdrawn in exchange for control of Sakhalin. They were subsequently administered by the Japanese as part of Japan proper. At the Yalta Conference in 1945 the Soviets demanded possession of the Kurils as a price for their entry into the war against Japan, and to this American officials agreed. After Japan's surrender they were annexed by the U.S.S.R., although the United States has never officially recognized Soviet sovereignty.

Soviet control of the Kurils has had several results. The island chain lies close to the great-circle route from Alaska to Japan, used by American commercial and military aircraft. Several incidents have occurred in which American craft have been attacked by Soviet fighters off the Kuril chain. The southernmost of the islands lies less than ten miles from the Japanese island of Hokkaido. The Soviets are fortifying the Kuril chain, and thereby pose a military threat both to northern Japan and to the whole area of the northwestern Pacific. The Japanese inhabitants on the Kurils have passed under Soviet control, and Japanese fishing vessels operating in the area have been seized and their crews interned by the Russians.

The Japanese have requested that the Soviets return to them sovereignty over the Kurils, or at least the southern, most heavily-populated part, but the Russians have consistently refused to do this. Control of the Kurils gives the Russians a weapon to hold over Japan in the fishing-rights dispute. It also prevents any hostile screen being imposed across the entrance to the Sea of Okhotsk, and it makes possible Soviet air dominance over the shortest sea and air routes between the United States and Japan. By the terms of the

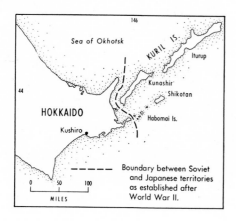

Figure 97. The Hokkaido-Southern Kurils Area. In 1956 the Soviet Union agreed to return Habomai and Shikotan islands to Japan.

peace treaty concluded between the Soviet Union and Japan in 1956, tiny Habomai and Shikotan islands in the southernmost Kurils were handed back to the Japanese, but the nearby larger islands of Kunashir and Iturup remained under Soviet control (Figure 97).

BIBLIOGRAPHY

BALLANTINE, JOSEPH W. "The Future of the Ryukyus," *Foreign Affairs,* XXXI, No. 4 (July, 1953), 663–75.

A short description of the history and geography of the islands and of alternative solutions to the problem of future control.

HOPPER, BRUCE. "The Perennial Kamchatka Discord," *Foreign Affairs,* XV, No. 3 (April, 1937), 564–68.

A brief history of the fisheries dispute between Japan and Russia up to 1937 and its relation to offshore claims by these nations.

McCUNE, GEORGE. *Korea Today.* Cambridge: Harvard University Press, 1950.

The outstanding text on problems in Korea from 1945 to the North Korean invasion.

McCUNE, SHANNON. "The Thirty-Eighth Parallel in Korea," *World Politics,* I, No. 2 (January, 1949), 223–33.

General discussion of the origin and character of the 38th-parallel boundary prior to the North Korean invasion.

PELZER, KARL J. "Japanese Migration and Colonization," in *Limits of Land Settlement,* ed. ISAIAH BOWMAN. New York: American Geographical Society, 1937, pp. 155–95.

A description of Japanese settlement prior to World War II.

TREWARTHA, GLENN T. *Japan: A Physical, Cultural and Regional Geography.* Madison: University of Wisconsin Press, 1945.

A basic regional geography of the area.

"The War in Korea: A Chronology of Events, 25 June, 1950–25 June, 1951," *The World Today,* VII, No. 8 (August, 1951), 317–29.

A detailed summary of events between the North Korean invasion and the preparations for cease-fire negotiations.

18

CONFLICT IN THE PACIFIC

● The Pacific Ocean, covering just under one-third of the earth's surface, is one of the great regions of power conflict in the modern world. Within this vast area there is a large number of islands and island groups, although in size, population, and economic value only a few are particularly significant. Many of the smaller islands, however, because of their location, possess considerable military importance, and have figured prominently in territorial disputes between colonial nations. The resultant political pattern is a complex one, reflecting the existence of the many colonial possessions here, the conflicting interests of countries which border on or lie within the Pacific, and the desires of the island peoples for greater economic and political advancement.

Several of the islands and island groups in the Pacific Basin have already been discussed in other chapters. Thus the western island chain, including the Kurils, Japan, the Ryukyus, and Taiwan, will be excluded from the area to be covered in this chapter, as will also Indonesia. The rest of the Pacific region will be considered here first as a unit, then in terms of four areas—Oceania, the Philippines, Australia, and New Zealand—each of which will be treated separately.

Islands and Power Spheres. The eastern and northern portions of the Pacific have relatively few islands, and those which are present are generally small in size (Figure 98). In contrast, the southwestern Pacific has a great number and variety of islands, ranging in size from the continental land mass of Australia and the island of New Guinea down to those which comprise less than one acre. The islands are generally classified in three groups—

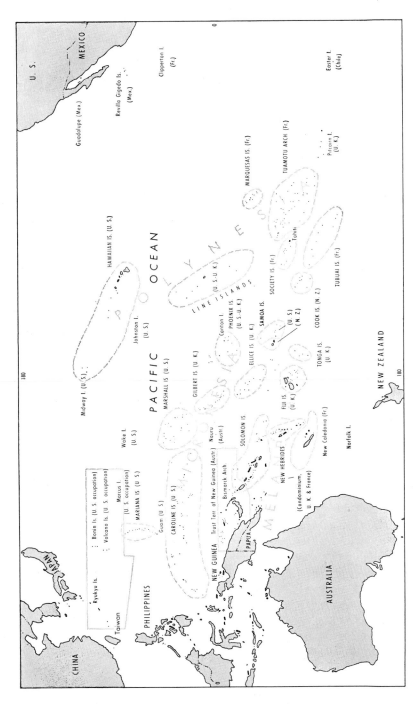

Figure 98. The Pacific Basin.

Micronesia, including the Marshalls, Gilberts, Carolines, and Marianas, in the west central Pacific; Melanesia, to the south, extending from New Guinea eastward to include the New Hebrides, New Caledonia, and Fiji; and Polynesia, comprising a triangular-shaped area, extending from Hawaii south to include Easter Island and west to New Zealand. Australia and the Philippines are not included in these three groups, but some classifications place New Zealand within the limits of Polynesia.

This three-way division reflects the cultural differences among the island areas, but patterns of political control have not corresponded with those of ethnic characteristics. Most of the colonial powers have territories in two or more of the major divisions (Table 17). This complex distribution has hindered colonial development here, for the territories of a particular nation are often separated from one another both by great distances and by island areas belonging to some other power.

Rimming the Pacific, or located within it, are several important countries—the United States, Canada, the Soviet Union, China, Japan, Indonesia, and Australia—as well as such other states as Taiwan, the Philippines, and New Zealand. In addition British and French interests are represented in colonial territories here. The interaction of power spheres in the Pacific Basin is one of the major features of the Cold War, for across this water body Anglo-America and communist Asia face one another, while within the ocean area lie many noncommunist islands and bases. This distribution of power areas is particularly significant in the light of Haushofer's prediction that a future struggle for world power would eventually take place within the Pacific Basin.

Most of the islands north of the equator are under United States control. From Hawaii an American lifeline extends westward via Midway, Wake, and Guam to United States bases in the Philippines and on Okinawa. This route also serves the United States trusteeship territories of the Mariana, Marshall, and Caroline islands. American power in the northern Pacific is further augmented by the presence of Alaska and the Aleutians near the apex of the great triangular-shaped Pacific Basin. This power position, however, is limited by Soviet control of Siberia and the Kurils, possible "neutralism" in Japan, and the vulnerability of extended sea and air lanes.

South of the equator Britain, Australia, New Zealand, and France share in the control of most of the islands. Despite the unifying effects of climate and the sea in the southern Pacific, diversity of control has represented an important centrifugal force among the island areas, and has served to delay economic and social development (see also page 473). The conflicting forces here are reflected by the political division of island groups, such as the Solomons; by politically divided individual islands, as New Guinea; and by the joint control of an island by two or more powers, as in the case of Nauru (Britain, Australia, New Zealand).

Table 17

ISLANDS AND ISLAND GROUPS OF THE PACIFIC

	Area (sq. mi.)	Population (1955 estimates)
Australia	2,974,581	9,138,000
Possessions		
Papua	90,540	500,000
Territory of New Guinea (trusteeship territory; incl. Northeast New Guinea, Bismarck Archipelago, and northern Solomon Islands)	93,000	1,215,000
Nauru (trusteeship territory; joint administration with New Zealand and Great Britain)	8	3,400
Norfolk Island	13	950
New Zealand	103,736	2,122,000
Possessions		
Cook Islands	99	16,000
Niue	100	4,700
Tokelau	4	1,800
Western Samoa (trusteeship territory) .	1,133	94,000
Philippines	115,600	21,650,000
British Possessions		
Tonga	269	53,000
British Solomon Islands	11,500	104,000
Fiji	7,040	333,000
Gilbert and Ellice Islands (incl. Phoenix and Line isls. and Ocean Island) . .	369	37,000
Pitcairn Island	2	150
New Hebrides (condominium with France)	5,700	50,000
French Possessions		
New Caledonia and dependencies (incl. Isle of Pines, Wallis Archipelago, and Loyalty, Futuna, Huon, Belep, Chesterfield, and Walpole islands)	7,202	64,000
French Oceania (Society Isls. (incl. Tahiti), Marquesas Isls., Tuamotu Isls., Gambier Isls., Tubuai Isls., Clipperton)	1,544	65,000
New Hebrides (condominium with Britain)	5,700	50,000
Netherlands Possessions		
Netherlands New Guinea	159,375	700,000
United States Possessions		
Hawaii	6,423	540,000
Guam	206	75,000
Wake	3	400
Midway	2	400

Table 17 (continued)

ISLANDS AND ISLAND GROUPS OF THE PACIFIC

	Area (sq. mi.)	Population (1955 estimates)
United States Possessions (*continued*)		
Johnston	—	50
Howland, Jarvis, Baker	3	—
American Samoa	76	21,000
Canton and Enderbury (condominum with Great Britain)	27	300
Trust Territory of the Pacific Islands (Mariana Isls., Marshall Isls., and Caroline Isls.)	685	62,000
Bonin, Volcano, and Marcus islands (former Japanese isls. now under U. S. administration)	40	210
Chilean Possessions		
Easter Island	46	600
Juan Fernández Islands	70	450
San Félix and San Ambrosio islands . .	2	—
Sala y Gómez Island	—	—
Ecuadorian Possessions		
Galápagos Islands	3,042	1,400
Costa Rican Possessions		
Cocos Island	10	—
Colombian Possessions		
Malpelo Island	—	—
Mexican Possessions		
Revilla Gigedo Islands	320	—
Guadalupe Island	102	20
Soviet Possessions		
Commander (Komandorski) Islands . .	600	—

THE DEVELOPMENT OF THE POLITICAL PATTERN

Six nations have played active roles in the contest for control of territory in the Pacific: Spain, Britain, France, Germany, Japan, and the United States. In addition, Australia and New Zealand have received island areas since the start of the twentieth century, Russia owns the Commander Islands in the northern Pacific, and Chile, Ecuador, Mexico, Colombia, and Costa Rica all control islands off their respective coasts. In the gradual establishment of sovereignty over the land areas in the Pacific, two factors in particular stand out—first, the belated recognition by most countries of the value of the Pacific areas and, second, the eventual development of conflicting power interests in the region.

The Era of Spanish Dominance. The first European explorer to cross the Pacific was Magellan, on an expedition from Spain, who discovered the Philippines in 1521. Forty-four years later the Spanish established a permanent settlement in the Philippines, and in the following century they also occupied the Mariana Islands, primarily to serve the sea lanes between Mexico and the Philippine Islands. Although Spain was the first power to win possessions in the Pacific, it did little to follow up its early gains. Defeat in the Spanish-American War at the end of the nineteenth century led Spain to sell the Philippines and cede Guam to the United States and sell the recently acquired Caroline and the Mariana islands (excluding Guam) to Germany. Thus by 1900 Spain had disappeared entirely as a Pacific power.

Britain's Territorial Expansion. Britain's early contacts in the Pacific were made largely by pirates. The great era of British exploration and mapping in that area did not come until the voyages of Captain Cook, between 1768 and 1780. The first permanent settlement in Australia was made in 1788 and in New Zealand in 1840, but it was only in the mid-nineteenth century that Britain began to annex formally the Pacific islands. By this time the activities of whalers, missionaries, and traders, as well as the prospects of economic gain from such products as sandalwood and copra, had interested several European governments in establishing sovereignty over Pacific island groups. Thus the British soon found themselves in competition with other powers, particularly France and Germany. In 1874 Britain formally annexed Fiji, and eighteen years later the Gilbert and Ellice islands. Other acquisitions followed, practically all of them to the south of the equator.

French Gains in the Southern Pacific. French pirates and adventurers were also exploring this region during the seventeenth and eighteenth centuries. The first formal French annexation was the protectorate over Tahiti in 1842, followed shortly by the acquisition of New Caledonia. As the scramble for territories accelerated during the latter part of the 1800's, French-British rivalry here became increasingly strong. France annexed the remaining Society Islands and the Loyalty group, but disputed sovereignty over the New Hebrides, lying about 1,000 miles east of Australia, led to the establishment in 1887 of dual French-British control over this area.

The Rise and Decline of German Control. Germany came late to the Pacific, as it did also to central and southern Africa. During the 1880's Germany annexed northeast New Guinea, the Bismarck Archipelago, and the northernmost Solomons, and protectorates were established over the Marshall Islands and Nauru Island. At the end of the century Germany purchased from Spain the Caroline and Mariana islands and divided Samoa with the United States.

By 1900 Germany had become an important power in the western Pacific, and the Germans energetically sought to develop the economic wealth of their possessions. Following World War I, however, Germany's Pacific possessions were apportioned out as mandates, Japan receiving the territories north of the equator, while Britain, Australia, and New Zealand divided among themselves those islands which lay to the south of the equator. Thus Germany, like Spain, was eventually eliminated as a Pacific power.

Japanese Power in the Northern Pacific. A fifth nation to establish control in the Pacific was Japan. Prior to 1896 the Japanese restricted their territorial interests primarily to the Kuril-Ryukyu-Taiwan chain, after which they turned westward to the Asiatic mainland, with its large population and potential resources. The only annexations by Japan east of the homeland were the Bonin Islands (1875) and the Volcano group (1891). At the end of World War I, however, Japan's alliance with the Allies against Germany enabled Japan to occupy the German-held Marshall, Caroline, and Mariana island groups.

Between the two World Wars the economic development of most of the Pacific islands took precedence over military activities. About 80,000 Japanese emigrated to their mandated territories, and built up exports of sugar, processed fish, and copra. In the mandated areas the administering powers were directed not to erect fortifications or military bases, nor to give military training to the inhabitants. In order to soothe Japanese objections to this provision, the United States agreed to refrain from increasing the fortifications on its own islands west of Hawaii. The Japanese subsequently refused to let foreigners visit their mandated islands, but despite allegations that they violated their mandate obligations and armed Truk and other bases, it has been pointed out[1] that there was no evidence of Japanese defense preparations at least until 1938, three years after Japan left the League of Nations. At the end of World War II defeated Japan was forced to surrender all its holdings in Micronesia; however, no permanent disposition of the Bonin-Volcano islands was decided upon (see page 470).

United States Interests in the Pacific. The United States was one of the last powers to acquire territory in the Pacific. Prior to the end of the nineteenth century the nation was preoccupied with cheap land within its own boundaries and with its rapidly-expanding economy. During the 1850's the United States announced its sovereignty over certain islands along the equator (such as Baker, Howland, and Jarvis) and Johnston Island, southwest of the Hawaiian group, in order to develop their guano deposits. Midway was acquired in 1867 in the interests of whaling ships operating in the mid-Pacific. The major American annexations in the Pacific did not take place, however, until 1898–99, when Hawaii was annexed upon petition of the Hawaiian government; the Philippines and Guam were received from Spain;

---

[1] Karl J. Pelzer, "Micronesia—A Changing Frontier," *World Politics,* II, No. 2 (January, 1950), 251–67.

eastern Samoa was acquired; and sovereignty was established over the pre-viously-unclaimed island of Wake. These acquisitions reflected the growing interests of the United States in the Pacific area.

During the period between 1900 and 1941 the United States made rela-tively few changes in the administration of its Pacific possessions, except for the granting of commonwealth status to the Philippines in 1936 as a first step towards independence. At the end of World War II, however, the United States was designated as administering power over the trusteeship territories of the Marshall, Caroline, and Mariana islands (again excluding Guam). Most of the Japanese who formerly inhabited these areas have since returned to Japan.

In the Charter of the newly-formed United Nations several changes were made with respect to the former League mandates, now known as United Nations trusteeship territories. Instead of the old assumption that in-dependence was the ultimate goal for all dependent areas, the Charter spoke of "progressive development towards self-government or independence as may be appropriate to the particular circumstances of each territory." This apparent recognition that in some areas independence might not be a prac-tical goal was written into the Charter over the protests of ardent "self-determinists," to whom independence was a natural law of political progress.

Another important difference between the United Nations Charter and the former League Covenant with respect to dependent areas was the article which permitted the designation of all or part of a trusteeship territory as a "strategic area," which could be fortified, and in which the natives could receive military training. The administering power may at any time tempo-rarily suspend United Nations supervision of a strategic area for security reasons. This privilege, if misused, could establish a dangerous precedent, for no limits are placed on area or length of time involved in the suspension. Since 1947 the United States has maintained fortifications on such trustee-ship islands as Saipan and Tinian, and has evacuated natives from several of the Marshall Islands in order to conduct atomic experiments in that area.

One territorial problem involving the United States which has remained unsettled is that of sovereignty over the former Japanese-controlled Bonin and Volcano islands, lying about 600 miles to the southeast of Japan. With their combined population of about 200 and the air and naval base at Iwo Jima, these islands have been administered by the United States since 1945. There would seem to be some logic in designating them as a United Nations strategic trusteeship territory, with the United States as sole administering authority. Such a move was implied in the Japanese Peace Treaty, and might place the United States in a better diplomatic position than is at present possible under the conditions of indefinite occupation.

The strategic importance of the Pacific islands has obviously become a factor of great significance to the United States and its allies, frequently out-

weighing considerations of economic development of the island areas or of
the national aspirations of the indigenous peoples. Many of the wartime bases
have been abandoned or put on a reserve basis, but in maintaining its supply
lines from west coast ports to South Korea, Japan, and the Philippines, the
United States continues to man its defense installations, air bases, and repair
and supply depots at key points (such as the Guam-Tinian-Saipan complex)
in the tremendous area which lies west of Hawaii.

Other Territorial Relationships.   Several Latin American states gained
possessions in the Pacific during the nineteenth century. In 1837 Ecuador
occupied the Galápagos Islands, which straddle the equator some 600 miles
west of Ecuador itself. Chile, Costa Rica, and Mexico also acquired sovereignty over various deep-sea islands and island groups lying within about 600
miles of the Latin American coast. In addition, since 1888 Chile has controlled Easter Island, 2,200 miles west of the Chilean mainland.

In the northern Pacific Russian explorers and fishermen were active
during the eighteenth and nineteenth centuries, and Russia controlled the
Pribilof Islands until 1867, when they were included in the sale of Alaska to
the United States. The Russians still maintain sovereignty, however, over the
Commander (Komandorski) Islands, which lie 200 miles west of the Aleutians and about 150 miles from the Kamchatka Peninsula.

On July 4, 1946, the Philippines became independent, and within a few
months the Philippine government had signed a ninety-nine year agreement
with the United States providing for American use of army, navy, and air
bases in the islands (for further details of Philippine independence see page
477). Together with Japan and Okinawa, the Philippines represent the
western anchor of the United States Pacific defense network.

Oceania

The term Oceania here includes the islands of Micronesia, Melanesia,
and Polynesia. It thus measures about 6,000 miles from north to south and
over 7,000 miles from west to east. Within this enormous region the total
land area amounts to only about 383,000 square miles, of which the island
of New Guinea alone accounts for over 300,000 square miles. Among the
other larger islands only Hawaii is not located in the southwestern Pacific.
New Britain, New Caledonia, New Ireland, Bougainville, Guadalcanal, and
the rest of those over 1,000 square miles lie relatively close to the Australian
mainland. These islands are continental in character, in that they are composed of rock types similar to those on continents themselves.

Many of the islands of the Pacific are "deep-sea" or "oceanic," rather
than continental. These islands are generally smaller, and may be subdivided
into two principal types—"high" islands, which are of volcanic origin, and

"low" islands, composed of coral. This difference is reflected in amounts of rainfall, availability of drinking water, and soil types. In the trade-wind belts to the north and south of the equator, the high islands are often able to intercept the rain-bearing winds, so the precipitation falls on the windward side of the island; many of the coral islands, however, receive little precipitation. The volcanic soils of the high islands are frequently of much greater fertility than those of the coral islands.

Population

The total population of Oceania is about 3,700,000. The population distribution shows definite concentrations, such as in the Hawaiian Islands (540,000), Fiji (333,000), and New Guinea (about 1,975,000, including Netherlands New Guinea or West Irian). Thus there is less than one million persons in the remainder of Oceania.

Most of the nonnative peoples in Oceania are located in the Hawaiian Islands (Japanese, Filipinos, Chinese, Americans) and Fiji (about 150,000 Indians). Rates of annual population increase are generally high: Guam, 49 per thousand; Fiji, 33 per thousand; the Cook Islands, 28 per thousand. But dense concentrations occur only in relatively few areas, such as parts of the Gilbert, Ellice, and Tonga groups. On the Ellice Islands, for example, over 4,700 persons live on a total of 9.6 square miles of land. The transfers of native peoples from densely-crowded islands to other areas has been a feature of colonial administration in the Pacific. Large amounts of potentially arable land remain unutilized, and even on much of the area now in crops considerably higher yields could be realized with improved farming techniques.

Warren S. Thompson estimates that there were some three and a half million people in Oceania before the white man arrived, and that contact between the whites and the natives was "a major population catastrophe to most of these people. In addition to the direct attempt to use the natives for plantation work (probably a minor factor), the white man brought whiskey, tuberculosis, syphillis, and clothes, all of which were deadly to people not accustomed to them. But, above all, he broke up the traditional modes of tribal life, and thus robbed the natives of their most precious social heritage."[2] Since 1900 the population of most Pacific islands has been steadily growing through natural increase, although in some areas, particularly in Polynesia, it is probably still declining.

Economy

Large-scale economic development has taken place only in the Hawaiian and Fiji islands. Power resources (except some water power) are virtually

[2] Warren S. Thompson, *Population and Peace in the Pacific* (Chicago: The University of Chicago Press, 1946), p. 37. Used by permission.

nonexistent in Oceania, and only in the two areas mentioned above is there extensive plantation agriculture. Sugar and pineapples are the principal agricultural exports from Hawaii, and the islands are also important as a tourist center. Sugar, gold, copra, coconut oil, and bananas head the list of exports from Fiji. New Caledonia, with its copra and coffee, as well as its nickel and chrome wealth, and New Guinea, with its gold and coconuts, are other exporting regions in Oceania.

Copra and other coconut products, sugar, and bananas are the principal products exported from the other areas of Oceania. Tahiti and Nauru Island also have phosphate, which is valuable as a fertilizer. Average per-capita incomes are low throughout the islands, except for the Hawaiians, and there are shortages of funds and trained personnel in most areas for schools, hospitals, and other social services. The small areas and populations on most of the islands and the lack of valuable resources have largely been responsible for the shortage of investment capital here. In many parts of Oceania, as in Africa, the native culture was supplanted by that of the white man during the nineteenth century, but the net effect has been to create a new way of life in which many of the basic wants cannot be satisfied. Lacking many of the resources of Africa, Oceania faces a difficult economic future in a competitive economic world.

Political Features

Most of the islands of Oceania are colonies, although a few, such as the eastern Solomons, have a protectorate status. The Tonga islands alone are an independent kingdom: a unique political situation exists here, for the Tongans, although independent, have voluntarily turned over foreign relations, defense, and finance to the British government for administration. There are also a number of trusteeship territories, divided among the United States, Britain, Australia, and New Zealand. The rise of Australia and New Zealand as important colonial powers in the South Pacific has been occasioned not only by the assignment to them in 1919 of League mandates—now trusteeship territories—but also by the transfer of various British territories to their administrations since the start of the twentieth century.

Because of the small and scattered populations and the poor economic potentials throughout most of Oceania, the dependent areas have not been in strong positions to bring pressures on far-off capitals for greater self-rule. Except for the transfer of colonial territories from one nation to another, there has been practically no change in the political status of the Oceania islands since they first became dependent areas. Even though from an economic point of view complete independence may be impractical, there is room for greater measures of autonomy and of co-operation among the island peoples. One governing nation, at least, has made a move in this direction.

In 1956 New Zealand announced that in the following year the trusteeship territory of Samoa would be granted self-rule, with control of defense, foreign policy, and the High Court maintained by New Zealand.

Combining certain island groups belonging to the same governing power into a federation is a future possibility, particularly among such groups as the British-controlled Gilbert, Ellice, Fiji, and Solomon islands. Already a move has been made toward co-operation on the economic and social levels by the creation of a South Pacific Commission, comprising Britain, France, the Netherlands, Australia, New Zealand, and the United States, whose function is to provide a regional basis for the betterment of economic, education, and health conditions in the islands south of the equator and the Gilbert Islands to the north.

It is, of course, impossible to maintain static political conditions indefinitely, even among the scattered peoples of the Pacific. Any isolation which these people possessed in past decades has been shattered by the increase in world-wide communications, the impact of World War II, and postwar efforts for military security. Increased demands for economic and political advancement cannot be ignored, particularly in the light of possible communist influence among discontented peoples of this strategic noncommunist area. Countries controlling dependent areas in the Pacific will be forced to balance the economic limitations of these regions against the political ambitions of the indigenous peoples, for any land area, no matter how insignificant it may seem, has strategic importance in this ocean basin.

The Philippines

As a young, democratic nation, at the edge of the turbulent east Asian area, the Philippines, even more than Taiwan, represent something of a proving ground for Western political, economic, and social philosophies in the Far East. In many respects the area is a transition zone between East and West in the Pacific. A majority of the Filipinos are descendants of early settlers who came to the islands from Asia, and there are significant strains of Chinese and Japanese blood among the Philippine population. On the other hand, the Philippines are the only thoroughly Christianized nation in the Far East; over eighty per cent of the people are Roman Catholic, a predominantly Western religion. Despite economic and cultural ties with other parts of eastern Asia, the Philippines have not been strongly affected by the political forces which have swept across that area in recent decades. The country fought bitterly against Japanese proposals in the 1930's for the creation of an East Asia Co-Prosperity Sphere, and was the only colonial area in World War II that throughout the enemy occupation continued unanimously to support the former colonial power. The government concluded a mutual assistance pact with the United States after World War II, and took an active part in the defense of South Korea against communist aggression. As a result, the future stability and progress of the country is of great importance to the contest of ideologies in this part of the world.

Physical Elements

The Republic of the Philippines consists of over 7,000 islands, of which the two major ones (Luzon and Mindanao) are each over 30,000 square miles in area, while nine others each encompass more than 1,000 square miles. The total area of the Philippines is approximately 115,600 square miles.

The strategic location of the Philippines exposes the country to the powerful political forces operating in the Far East. Two hundred and twenty miles to the north of Luzon is Taiwan, a key area in the struggle for the containment of Chinese communism. Approximately 300 miles to the northwest of Luzon is the Chinese mainland, where the new communist experiment is under way. Vietnam lies to the west, Indonesia to the south, and Japan to the northeast—all of these areas within a thousand miles of the Philippines.

Although there is great diversity of surface configuration on the islands, thereby tending to isolate various groups from one another, the sea, as in Japan and Indonesia, acts as a unifying element. The principal lowland areas are on central Luzon and in parts of Mindanao. Rail and road facilities are not particularly well developed throughout most of the country, and population clusters are generally separated from one another by upland regions. The result has been a tendency for strong divisive forces to develop in various sectors of the country.

The Philippines are well supplied with natural resources, including iron ore, chromite, manganese, gold, and hydroelectric-power potential, as well as small amounts of coal. In addition, there is timber and considerable agricultural land. The utilization of mineral and power resources, however, has not been extensive in the islands, and as a result the average per-capita income has continued to be low.

Population

The total population of the Philippines is approximately 21,650,000. Most of the Filipinos are united religiously, although not linguistically. About 8,000,000 persons speak English, and some 300,000 still use Spanish. Among the rest of the population there are eighty-seven native dialects, of which eight are of major importance. In 1946 Tagalog was made the official language of the nation, and its use is gradually growing, particularly among the educated Filipinos.

The two major minority groups are the Chinese and the Moros. The pure Chinese number about 300,000, and like other overseas Chinese they maintain a closely-knit unity among themselves. They represent a powerful minority in the nation because of their widespread business and commercial interests. In addition to this group there are about one million Chinese mestizos. A second major minority group are the 300,000 Moros, inhabiting the southern areas, who have resisted attempts by goverment authorities— Spanish, American, and now native Filipino—to integrate them within the political and economic life of the country. Moslem in faith, they have contributed little to economic and political development in the Philippines, and only within the past few years, through education and resettlement programs, are they beginning to be assimilated.

The settlement pattern is a widely-scattered one, with about thirty-five per cent of the people living on Luzon. Manila, with over a million and a quarter people, is by far the largest city. Quezon City, adjoining Manila on the northeast, has been the official capital since 1948, but many governmental activities are still carried on in Manila. The islands of Cebu, Mindanao, Panay, and Negros also have cities ranging from 40,000 to 100,000 in population, but none of these is a serious contender with Manila for power.

Economic Development

With their various resources, the Philippines possess the basis for a sound economic structure. Although parts of the nation have high concentrations of people, the average population density is not great (in contrast with other areas of eastern Asia), and there are opportunities to increase the production of both foodstuffs for domestic use and cash crops for export. Despite these advantages, however, the economic structure of the country is not yet in a strong position. A small, landowning group controls most of the nation's agricultural areas, and much of the commerce and industry are in the hands of the Chinese. As is true in many other areas of changing political status, investments of outside capital (particularly American) were not heavy in the Philippines after the mid-1930's, and as a result the expansion of industries, mining, transportation facilities, and power installations was somewhat curtailed in the years preceding World War II.

Economic relations between the Philippines and the United States became a matter of concern at the time of Philippine independence, since continued economic instability in the new country might eventually have endangered its democratic form of government. The Philippine Trade Act of 1946 provided for the entry duty-free of Philippine products to the United States for a period of eight years after independence, to be followed by gradually increasing tariffs, until by 1974 the full duty is to be assessed on

Philippine imports. In the same year the United States Congress appropriated $520 million for rehabilitation in the Philippines. As further aid to the new country's economy, the United States agreed in 1950 to provide an additional $250 million to be used for such purposes as hydroelectric-power developments and agrarian reforms. If the American policy of assistance to the Philippines during their difficult period of adjustment to independence were applied to other newly-created states, it could be of great importance in stabilizing governments based on popular representation.

Political Aspects

The establishment of a commonwealth status for the Philippines in 1936 has already been noted. The Japanese occupied the area at the end of 1941, and for three years the islands were under enemy occupation. After the country was liberated from the Japanese, the Philippines resumed their preparations for independence, and within ten months of Japan's final surrender to the Allies the United States terminated its political control. Although by this action the United States government fulfilled its pledge for a ten-year period of commonwealth status for the area, political and economic development among the Filipinos had been impossible during the war years. The economy of the country had been completely disrupted (total war damage was estimated at about $8 billion), and by mid-1946 the physical destruction and dislocation of production and exports had only begun to be repaired. Consequently, the Philippines began its independence in the face of major difficulties.

Although no part of the Philippines attempted to secede from Manila's control after World War II, the government faced serious trouble from communist-led guerrillas, the so-called Hukbalahaps or Huks, who operated in the mountains of Luzon and on Mindoro Island to the south. Their acts of terrorism hindered economic revival and forced the government to spend a large portion of its revenue in conducting military actions against them. For a time the Huks virtually controlled a number of areas, some of them but a few miles from Manila. Originally the Hukbalahaps had been formed as a guerrilla force against the Japanese, but during the early postwar period they managed to win popular support, particularly among the landless peasants of Luzon, because of their propaganda against outdated laws of land ownership and the depressed level of the Philippine economy. In addition to military action against the Huks, the Philippine government carried out extensive resettlement programs among the landless, moving many thousands of farm families to unused land on the island of Mindanao. Eventually these measures, together with a strengthening of the Philippine economy, succeeded in reducing the Huk menace to small proportions.

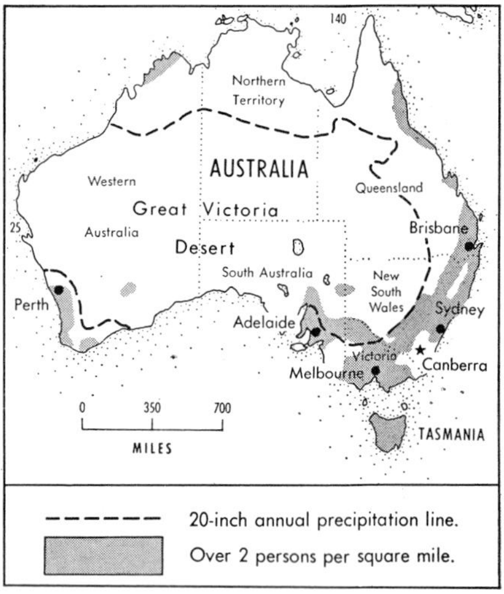

Figure 99. Australia: Precipitation and Population Patterns. Northern Australia, although receiving considerable precipitation, has few inhabitants because of the tropical conditions which exist there.

Australia

Australia is the world's only politically-unified continent. The great distances separating it from Europe resulted in its late settlement by Europeans, and this isolation has contributed to the relatively stable political conditions which have existed here since the entire area became politically organized. However, with an average population density of only three persons per square mile, Australia stands as a tempting prize to the nearby densely-crowded nations of southeastern and eastern Asia. The existence of this extremely pronounced population differential is a potential danger to the Australians. In 1942 the Japanese military drive southward was halted in the New Guinea mountains, about 300 miles from the Australian mainland, and in the Solomon Islands and Coral Sea to the northeast.

Physical Elements

The continent consists of three parts: the eastern highlands, the central lowlands, and the western plateau area. There is a narrow, well-watered coastal plain between the eastern highlands and the Pacific, and a coastal plain also lies between the western plateau and the Indian Ocean. The central lowland is a semiarid region; but along the northern coast of the continent there is heavy rainfall because of the monsoon (Figure 99). The western plateau, comprising about half the territory of Australia, is a dry, sparsely-inhabited region, except in the northernmost portions and in the southwest, where there is seasonal rainfall around Perth.

Distance and the dry areas separating many of the population centers from one another have represented important centrifugal forces in Australia's development. Not until 1901 were the various early colonies brought together into a federation. Regional differences, particularly between the western and eastern population centers, have since that time continued to be significant.

Australia is well supplied with resources, including gold, coal, iron ore, lead, zinc, silver, and bauxite. Although over eighty-five per cent of the nation has an average annual rainfall of less than thirty inches, there is hydroelectric-power potential in the eastern highlands, and Australia has a tremendous artesian basin in the northeast, which can be used for watering stock. In addition, the Murray and other rivers have been tapped for irrigation. Only about one per cent of Australia is in cultivation, but this suffices to provide important agricultural exports.

Population

Australia's population of over 9,000,000 is predominantly white and English-speaking. The principal minority are the 75,000 aborigines, who live in reserves in the northern part of the continent. The Australians have severely limited the immigration of Orientals, fearing a reduction of the general standard of living. Since the communization of China they have also been apprehensive about the political consequences of a large body of overseas Chinese in Australia. On the other hand, Australia has welcomed the immigration of Europeans, and since World War II over half a million of them (including many displaced persons) have been admitted. Some Australian officials feel that the nation could easily accommodate six to eight million more people (Europeans), thereby strengthening the white man's hold on the area. There are major obstacles to such large-scale immigration, however, including the high cost of transportation to Australia and settling there.

Over sixty per cent of Australia's population is concentrated in the two southeastern states of New South Wales and Victoria, in which are located respectively, Sydney and Melbourne, the two cities of over one million people. The rivalry between these two urban areas led to the establishment in 1927 of the Australian capital at Canberra, in the eastern highlands about midway between them. Brisbane, Adelaide, Perth, and Hobart are the capitals and leading cities of the other four Australian states, and each is an important regional center. Brisbane, Adelaide, and Perth are connected with the two principal core areas and the capital by railroad. Hobart is located on the island of Tasmania, about 100 miles to the south of Australia, and is connected with the mainland by adequate steamship and airline service. Thus, because of the transportation facilities and of the relative homogeneity of its population, Australia possesses a strong circulatory system throughout its large area.

Economy

Because of the country's great distance from western Europe and North America, the Australians have worked to develop their own industrial capacity. The nation produces normally over 2 million tons of steel a year, as well as a wide variety of manufactured goods. One of the real drawbacks to future industrial expansion lies in the relatively small domestic market.

Agriculturally Australia is perhaps more important than industrially. Wool is the most valuable export, accounting normally for nearly half the total value of exports. About two-thirds of the nation's wheat crop is generally exported. Meats, sugar, and dairy products are also shipped to other countries. Like the United States, Canada, and Argentina, Australia occupies a significant place in the world economic structure as a major exporter of foods. It has been estimated that with more intensive utilization of arable land the continent could increase its production of agricultural goods considerably. However, a small consumer market has limited economic growth.

Australia and the Pacific

Australia's interests in the southwestern Pacific are represented by its territorial possessions in the area. Australia controls southeast New Guinea (Papua), across the Torres Strait from the Australian mainland, and administers northeast New Guinea (Territory of New Guinea) and the islands to the northeast and east[3] as a United Nations trusteeship territory (Figure 100). This territory has been of little economic value, but it provides a defense screen against potential attack from the north. The Australians favor continued Dutch control of Netherlands (or West) New Guinea, since they feel that a Dutch possession would represent more of a military and political defensive force along Australia's northwest flank than would the Indonesian republic. With its small population the nation must base its security on mutual assistance pacts with other powers, particularly in view of the expansionist tendencies which in recent decades have been evidenced by countries of eastern Asia. Since 1951 Australia has maintained a military alliance with the United States.

New Zealand

New Zealand is the farthest removed from Britain of any of the Commonwealth nations, yet its ties with Britain are extremely close. Over half of its foreign trade (including 70 per cent of its exports) is normally with

---

[3] The Bismarck Archipelago (including New Britain, New Ireland, and the Admiralty Islands) and the northernmost Solomon Islands.

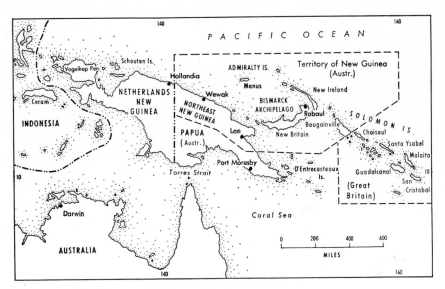

Figure 100. New Guinea and Adjacent Areas.

Britain, and its government has been a strong supporter of the Common-wealth system and of the bonds uniting New Zealand with the former mother country. One reason for this support is, of course, that here, as in Australia, the great majority of the population is of British origin and the nation must depend in part upon Britain for support in time of war in the Pacific.

Physical Elements

New Zealand consists of two large islands (North Island and South Island) as well as several smaller ones. The total area is just over 100,000 square miles. Much of the relief is mountainous, and the population is con-centrated largely in the northern and southern lowlands of North Island and in the eastern coastal plain of South Island. The isolation of New Zealand is naturally an important centripetal force, which tends to overcome the di-visive factors of surface configuration and the existence of two main islands.

New Zealand has few minerals, but there is considerable hydroelectric-power potential. Approximately two-thirds of the surface is estimated as suitable for agriculture or grazing. However, 60,000 to 65,000 square miles of agricultural land is not enough to permit extensive immigration, and, un-like Australia, New Zealand is not an area for large-scale white settlement.

Population

New Zealand's population totals about 2 million. The principal minor-ity group comprises the approximately 125,000 Maoris, descendants of the inhabitants of the islands before the arrival of the Europeans. Relations between the Maoris and the Europeans have in the past been marked by conflict and bitterness. The Maoris resisted the expropriation of their lands for European settlement, and a five-year war was waged during the 1860's between the two groups. At the present time many Maoris continue to pursue their linguistic and cultural traditions, but others have become assimilated into the white man's way of life. The land still held by Maori farmers is inadequate for the number of people who are dependent upon it for a livelihood, and the continued poverty of this ethnic group is one of New Zealand's major politico-economic problems.

About two-thirds of the people of New Zealand live on North Island. Auckland in the north central part of North Island is the largest city, followed by Christchurch in the eastern part of South Island. Wellington, the capital and third city, is located in the southern part of North Island, almost mid-way between the first two cities. Dunedin, the fourth city, is situated in the southern part of South Island. Thus New Zealand has four principal core areas, fairly evenly spaced from one another. The separation of the settlement areas originally caused strong divisive forces, but in recent decades these have largely disappeared with improved means of transportation and communication.

Economy

New Zealand's economy is primarily agricultural; dairy products, meat, and wool form the major items of export. Through the use of refrigerator ships New Zealand is able to send dairy products and fresh meat to Britain and other European markets. New Zealand suffered heavily from the worldwide depression in the 1930's, largely because of its dependence on agricultural exports to western Europe. Unlike conditions in Australia, however, there has been no great effort made to diversify New Zealand's economy and make it less dependent upon world markets. There is some gold, silver, and coal, but because of the shortages of other industrial resources and the small population, the nation has not undergone any extensive industrialization. The mild, moist climate which prevails throughout much of New Zealand and the soils which are particularly adaptable to pastures have resulted in the continued emphasis on grazing as a major aspect of the country's economic life.

New Zealand and the Southern Pacific

The overseas territories of New Zealand include the Cook and Tokelau islands in the southern Pacific, as well as the trusteeship territory of Western Samoa. None of these islands is of great commercial value. New Zealand also shares with Australia and Britain a trusteeship over the island of Nauru. Like Australia, New Zealand is concerned with the defense of the south-western Pacific against possible attack from Asia; to this end it is joined in a military alliance with Australia and the United States.

The Problem of Statehood for Hawaii

Although begun over half a century ago, the movement for statehood for the Hawaiian Islands has gained considerable momentum since the end of World War II. Unlike the case of Alaska (see page 75), there is no question but that Hawaii could afford the expense of local self-government. On the other hand, the noncontiguous location of the territory with respect to continental United States and the concern of some legislators over the inclusion of new senators and representatives in Congress have militated against Hawaii's admission as a state. Moreover, Democrats who feel the area would be a Republican stronghold have opposed statehood on the grounds of political expediency.

The Hawaiian Islands, stretching for over 2,000 miles across the Pacific, are of economic and military significance to the United States. Practically all of the area and population are concentrated on the eight principal eastern islands; Midway, at the western end of the archipelago, is the only other important island group. The islands have a total area of 6,423 square miles and an economy based on highly-commercialized agriculture (sugar and pineapples), tourism, and the military bases here, such as Pearl Harbor and Schofield Barracks. In 1952 Hawaii's total dollar earnings with the mainland through exports and services came to $645,000,000, while the islands' imports from the United States were valued at $606,000,000. The area is clearly an important component of the American economy.

One of the great objections to the inclusion of Hawaii as a state is based upon the territory's ethnic character. Approximately thirty-five per cent of the population is Japanese in origin, twelve per cent is of Filipino descent, and another six per cent is Chinese. The great majority of these, however, are United States citizens; in 1950 only fifteen per cent of Hawaii's population was foreign-born. Nevertheless, the prospect of an influx of persons of Oriental descent is alarming to certain congressmen, particularly from the Western states.

Spokesmen for Hawaii point to the area's war record as proof of the people's loyalty to the United States. Throughout the war not a single case of sabotage by a Hawaiian civilian was reported, and the Asiatic population there contributed significantly to the war effort in terms of labor and military service. The territory now has a larger population than four of the American states and contributes more to the Federal Treasury than do nine of them.

The desire of the Hawaiians for statehood was proved in 1950, when a special convention drafted a state constitution which was approved overwhelmingly, first by the territorial legislature and then by the voters of Hawaii. Political opportunism within the United States Congress would seem to be the only major obstacle to the realization of Hawaiian statehood.

BIBLIOGRAPHY

FREEMAN, O. W. (ed.). *Geography of the Pacific.* New York: John Wiley & Sons, Inc., 1951.

A basic regional text, with much material on the development and present characteristics of the area's political pattern.

JONES, STEPHEN B. "Geography and Politics in the Hawaiian Islands," *The Geographical Review,* XXVIII, No. 2 (April, 1938), 193–214.

A survey of internal political features in the Hawaiian Islands, with emphasis on boundaries and population distribution.

PELZER, KARL J. "Micronesia—a Changing Frontier," *World Politics,* II, No. 2 (January, 1950), 251–67.

Examines the development of the area under the Japanese, and its role as a U. S. trust territory.

————. *Population and Land Utilization* (I.P.R. Inquiry Series, *Economic Survey of the Pacific Area,* Part I). New York: Institute of Pacific Relations, 1941.

General survey of economic conditions in the Pacific prior to World War II.

SPENCER, JOSEPH EARLE. *Land and People in the Philippines.* Berkeley and Los Angeles: University of California Press, 1952.

A basic regional geography, with particular emphasis on rural problems.

THOMPSON, WARREN S. *Population and Peace in the Pacific.* Chicago: The University of Chicago Press, 1946.

A discussion of population problems in both the Pacific and eastern Asia in terms of resource potentials.

WEIGERT, HANS W. "Haushofer and the Pacific," *Foreign Affairs,* XX, No. 1 (October, 1942), 732–42.

A review of Haushofer's ideas as embodied in his *Geopolitics of the Pacific* (published in 1924), in the light of conditions in the Pacific at the beginning of World War II.

19

THE CHANGING NATURE OF THE
WORLD POLITICAL PATTERN

● The world political pattern has been shown to be a complex and constantly-changing phenomenon, which reacts to a great variety of forces, and which in turn influences other forces and phenomena, both political and nonpolitical in nature. In this chapter, by way of summary, several general aspects of the changing pattern are considered: basic trends in the pattern; the changing nature and function of international boundaries; and conditions of "persistent instability." Following this is a brief discussion of the position of the United States with respect to the Cold War, in order to illustrate some of these aspects of the changing pattern of political control throughout the world.

BASIC TRENDS

Out of the many types and conditions of change in the world political pattern a few basic trends may be observed. These trends, taken both singly and together, may be useful as tools for developing a general framework within which the changing nature of the pattern can be better analyzed. The four basic trends are:
1. The breakup of empires and the establishment of independent states.
2. The expansion of communist control.
3. The union or division of existing political units.
4. The political partitioning of previously-unclaimed areas.
In the following pages a brief discussion will be presented of each of these significant trends.

The Breakup of Empires and the Establishment of Independent States

The empires which have undergone the greatest territorial losses within recent years have been those of Great Britain, France, the Netherlands, Japan, and Italy. This process of change is still evident in the British and French empires (witness, for example, conditions in Cyprus, Singapore, Nigeria, and Algeria), and in 1960 Italy is scheduled to end its trusteeship over Somalia. The effects of this changing status of empires are felt in the economic, military, and political conditions within the mother countries.

The other aspect of this trend concerns the achievement of independence. Since the end of World War II over a dozen states, most of them located in the Middle East or in southern and southeastern Asia, have been granted self-rule. Many of the new governments have been faced with problems of national survival, such as economic instability, border delimitations, threats to the country's political cohesion, and the pressures of international communism. Consequently, it is in these new self-governing states that many of the current problems of territorial instability have occurred. With respect to the future, it seems very probable that the number of newly-independent states will increase—particularly in central Africa and southeastern Asia—thereby further contributing to the complexities of the world political pattern.

The Expansion of Communist Control

The expansion of communist power derives primarily from the Soviet Union and China, where the communist ideology has been a useful tool for the extension of territorial control. Soviet expansion within recent years has been of two types: direct territorial annexation, as in eastern Poland and eastern Czechoslovakia, and the establishment of friendly communist governments in eastern Europe. The net result has been the development of a large Soviet empire, stretching from the Elbe River in Germany eastward to Alaska. In only one instance, Yugoslavia, has a former Soviet satellite state succeeded in completely throwing off Moscow's control and, although still communist in ideology, followed a course of action independent of the U.S.S.R.

Communist China has established a satellite relationship over North Korea, an area once under the military and political control of Russia. Close ties exist between China and North Vietnam, although the degree of satellite relationship here is not as apparent as in North Korea. Outer Mongolia, a former Chinese territory, seems now to lie in something of a transition zone between Soviet and Chinese satellite spheres.

The future of this second trend will be determined, of course, by the ability of noncommunist states, particularly those lying on the periphery of the Soviet-Chinese area, to remain free of communist domination. One of the important methods of expanding communist influence has been the strengthening of economic bonds between the communist bloc and non-communist countries in relatively weak economic situations. Other methods are infiltration by communist agents and military occupation of a portion of a country's territory. Afghanistan, Nepal, and Laos are three countries which have experienced strong communist pressures. There are definite relationships between the trend of independence and that of communist expansion. The breakup of empires has tended to weaken the power position of some of the anticommunist countries in Europe, the new states have often been unwilling to co-operate with their former mother countries in such matters as joint defense agreements, and the instability of some of the governments in recently-independent countries has considerably strengthened local communist parties.

The Union or Division of Existing Political Units

The union or division of existing political units has taken place largely in colonial or in newly self-governing territories. The two principal cases of political union since World War II have been the Federation of Rhodesia and Nyasaland and the union of Eritrea with Ethiopia.[1] It is generally difficult to effect a political fusion of two or more countries, for in each state the forces of local nationalism will tend to obstruct such a move. The likeliest future political unions appear to be the British West Indies Federation—which will unite the various British islands in the Caribbean area into one state—and a possible East African Federation, combining Tanganyika, Kenya, and Uganda.

The division of political units may result from either internal or external causes. In India, Palestine, and Indochina the primary cause for division was largely internal, that is, the desire of groups within a country to end their association with one another. Many boundaries of colonial areas were originally laid down with little regard for indigenous ethnic groups; now the acquisition of political power by these groups has forced a revision of the old administrative borders.

The Cold War conflict represents the principal external force for political division, as evidenced in Germany, Korea, and Vietnam. In each instance the division into communist and noncommunist areas was not carried out according to the wishes of the majority of the inhabitants; rather

---

[1] Another case was the union of Newfoundland with Canada in 1949. British Togoland voted in 1956 to unite with the Gold Coast, which in 1957 became an independent state within the British Commonwealth.

there is generally a strong popular desire for reunification. The separation of Taiwan and Communist China is a variation of this "ideological" type of political partitioning. The ambitions of neighboring countries, neither of which was communist, led to the division of Kashmir. Because of the territorial problems involved in the partitioning of such areas as Palestine, India, and Germany, and because of the effects of division on the economies of political areas, this trend is an extremely important one in terms of future conflict over territorial control and the possible extension of communism into noncommunist areas.

In the future the division of political units is most likely to occur in relatively young states, where the central government's control over the entire area is subject to challenge. Ethnic differences, for example, within the borders of Nigeria, might eventually lead to a partitioning of the state. Pakistan faces the possible separation of its eastern and western portions. Indonesia, Sudan, Ghana, and Libya are other areas in which potentially strong centrifugal forces already exist to threaten internal cohesion.

The Political Partitioning of Previously-Unclaimed Areas

The last trend is one which is only beginning to have major repercussions. The two areas which are being politically partitioned are Antarctica and the high seas. In Antarctica conflicting territorial claims are already increasing in number and intensity. As far as the oceans are concerned, many countries have been asserting their rights to fishing areas, to underseas resources, and to outright sovereignty over portions of the high seas, and already many conflicting precedents and claims have come into existence. With respect to both Antarctica and the oceans, the increase in the economic and military importance of these areas may give rise to serious conflicts of control, unless the bases for claims—and the claims themselves—are carefully worked out between interested countries.

There are, certainly, other types of developments which have taken place within recent years in the world political pattern in addition to the four trends listed here. Among these have been the redistribution of Axis-controlled territory at the end of World War II, and the extension of United States sovereignty in the Pacific. Although several territorial adjustments, such as the Ryukyu Islands, still remain to be settled, the major changes in the world political pattern arising from World War II have largely become *de jure* conditions, and as a result these two other trends are no longer of major significance.

It must be remembered that this concept of trends is merely a classification system, and that its value can only be measured in terms of the insight it may provide into the complexities of change in the pattern of political areas. Students of political geography should be constantly on the alert for the appearance of new trends and for the gradual disappearance of current ones, as they affect the changes which are taking place in political areas throughout the world.

THE CHANGING NATURE AND FUNCTION
OF INTERNATIONAL BOUNDARIES

A second general feature of the world political pattern is the changing role of international boundaries. This topic has come up from time to time in the regional chapters. Some of the salient points can be summed up under the following headings: (1) the impact of technological developments, (2) national defense requirements, and (3) the role of international organizations.

(1) Technological advances have had several effects on boundaries. They have made possible the recovery of oil resources from the continental shelf, and thus influenced offshore boundary claims. They have led to a substantial increase in recent years in border violations by aircraft and by balloons. The disturbance of atmospheric phenomena by cloud seeding or thermonuclear explosions affects more than local areas, with the result that here, too, boundary questions are raised with respect to sovereignty over the air. From such examples the conclusion would seem to be that, with increased technological developments, disputes over the limits of a nation's political control are likely to increase in number and complexity.

(2) National defense requirements are a practical sequel to technological advances. With aircraft traveling at supersonic speeds at altitudes of several miles, the inviolability of national borders becomes difficult to maintain. The result has been the creation of boundary "zones" for the defense of certain major powers—zones with indefinite widths and prerogatives. Although by international law the Soviet Union claims sovereignty over a strip extending seaward twelve miles from its coast, United States planes have been shot down as much as forty miles offshore Russian territory, indicating the *de facto*, though not *de jure*, Soviet defense zone in the Baltic Sea and North Pacific. Likewise, the United States has erected a radar warning station 110 miles off its east coast in what are clearly international waters.

(3) The role of international organizations has affected the nature and function of boundaries in two respects: first, by the use of international teams in preventing violence in border areas and, second, by the reduction of certain boundary functions between states. The internationalization of the borders between North and South Korea and between Israel and the Arab states is a recent innovation in boundary supervision, which may in time be extended to other disputed areas as well. In both cases there is a United Nations-supervised cease-fire line, complete with neutral zones and

international inspection teams which seek to prevent the resumption of warfare. Such steps reflect the growing fear of modern warfare as an instrument for the settlement of territorial disputes.

Examples of the reduction of border functions as a result of international organization may be found in the Benelux area, where most commodities now pass duty-free between the member states, and in the Schuman Plan countries, between which duties on the movement of iron, steel, scrap iron, and coal have been removed. Among the NATO nations the movement of armed forces from one state to another has been facilitated. In the Soviet satellite area of eastern Europe the nature and function of boundaries has also changed, as evidenced both by the apparent absence of border disputes and by the lack of barriers to the movement of various types of goods between the communist states.

"PERSISTENT INSTABILITY"

A third aspect of the current political pattern is the appearence of what might be termed "persistent instability" with respect to certain territorial situations. Berlin, Kashmir, Korea, and the borders of Israel are examples of this instability, where at least one interested power is dissatisfied with the current pattern of control, but where little attempt has been made to force a different solution because of the general fear of a major war.

This type of situation is an extremely complicated one, about which it is difficult to draw valid generalizations. Any move by the communists to eliminate noncommunist powers from West Berlin might lead to global warfare; likewise an attempt by either North or South Korea to unify the peninsula could have world-wide repercussions. Neither the Western nations nor the Soviets try to force a permanent settlement along Israel's borders or in Kashmir, although in the past important territorial disputes of this kind would not have continued so long and with such intensity. In other areas, such as Taiwan and the islands off the China coast or Netherlands New Guinea, an attempt to change the present political pattern may also produce widespread conflict.

If the alternative to permanent instability in Berlin, Korea, Israel, and other areas is warfare on a global scale, then it would seem that, as instruments of war become increasingly destructive, there might develop more and more cases of stalemate. The results of these stalemates would be bitterness, local border incidents, and perhaps the increased use of international police forces and neutral inspection teams.

The emphasis placed here on territorial change as a source of international tension does not imply that all changes in political control should necessarily be avoided in the interests of peace. In the first place, there are many avenues for the peaceful evolution of change, such as progressive steps toward self-rule, mutual exchange of territory between states, and the sub-mission of disputes to the World Court. Even in cases where conflict may be involved it is impossible to give a blanket endorsement to the existing status quo. For the question inevitably arises: at what point in its evolution should the political pattern of a region become stabilized? If a person tries to apply value judgments to the problem of territorial revisions one point should be made clear: it is not the change itself which may be good or bad but rather the consequences of the change, both with respect to the geographic areas in-volved and to the relations which may follow between peoples and states.

The United States and the World Power Alignment

The various processes described here as responsible for the changing nature of the world political pattern can also be related to American foreign policy with respect to the communist states in Europe and Asia. This policy has had as a basic objective the unification of the countries lying outside the communist orbit in order to resist the spread of communism outward from its Eurasian stronghold. Such a policy, in effect, is directed toward the strengthening of centripetal forces within the noncommunist world[2] insofar as these forces counter the threat of international communism. Opposing these centripetal forces, however, are a great number and variety of centrif-ugal forces—both on the international and national levels—which impede the unification of the noncommunist countries in resistance to communist expansion.

The Communist Bloc

The geographic limits of the communist bloc correspond in many re-spects to those of the areas described in the writings of Mackinder and Spykman. Since World War II the stronghold of communism has come to include the Soviet-Chinese area, the east European satellite states, Outer Mongolia, North Korea, and North Vietnam. In the early part of the twentieth century Mackinder wrote of a Heartland in central Eurasia and of the strategic east European area—both of which are now largely under Soviet control (Figure 2). Thus one power in effect "rules East Europe" and "commands the Heartland." In the second part of his theory Mackinder predicted that from the Heartland-east European area a state could expand its control outward to gradually cover all of the Eastern Hemisphere. It is

---

[2] The term noncommunist world in this discussion refers to all countries outside the communist bloc, including Yugoslavia, which, although under a communist-type government, broke from Moscow's control.

this process of territorial expansion with which the second of the four basic trends—the expansion of communist control—is concerned.

Actually, the expansion of the Heartland power from its original communist nucleus in Russia has varied somewhat from the pattern envisioned by Mackinder. China, North Korea, North Vietnam, and Outer Mongolia do not appear to represent outright extensions of Moscow's sovereignty, but rather areas which are closely allied to the Soviet Union militarily, economically, and ideologically. The unity of the communist bloc is more one of policy and of purpose than of direct control by one government, as implied in Mackinder's thesis. Even though centrifugal forces have been shown to exist in the Soviet sphere—as evidenced by the 1956 uprisings in Poland and Hungary—from a global point of view the Eurasian communist stronghold may be considered as one power area which has come to represent a strong and aggressive force in world affairs.

The Noncommunist World

The noncommunist world includes (1) a belt of countries in Eurasia which is adjacent to the communist bloc on three sides; (2) Anglo-America, which faces the U.S.S.R. across the Arctic Ocean; and (3) the more distant regions of Latin America, Africa, and the Australian-Pacific realm. A world map, centered on the Soviet Union, would indicate that the Eurasian communist area is, in effect, "encircled" by the noncommunist world (Figure 101). Those noncommunist countries stretching about the periphery of the communist bloc from Scandinavia through the Arab World and the Orient form a belt of land which in many respects resembles Spykman's Rimland— an area in which much of the world's population and economic power are located (Figure 3).[3] It is within this Rimland that the most important contests between communist and anticommunist power have taken place since World War II.

Within the total noncommunist world are located over sixty per cent of the earth's population, over seventy-five per cent of its area, and the great preponderance of its food and industrial resources (petroleum, iron ore, coal, and copper). Here also is over seventy-five per cent of the world's industrial capacity, measured in terms of annual steel output. In contrast with the centralized control of the communist bloc, however, these resources are distributed among countries of widely divergent objectives and policies. Some states have had to cope with problems of territorial development, and as a result have been more concerned with their own difficulties than with the menace of communist expansion. Other states, although often more politi-

---

[3] Spykman's Rimland, of course, has been breached by the extension of communist power into eastern Europe and the Far East. Nevertheless, an encircling Eurasian ring—or rimland—of noncommunist states has continued to exist about the communist heartland.

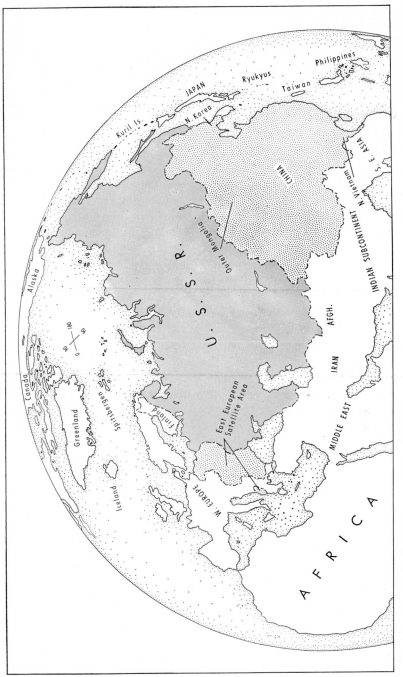

Figure 101. The Communist World and Surrounding Lands.

494 · World Political Patterns

cally mature, have for one reason or another, elected to pursue a neutralist course with regard to the Cold War, and to withhold their resources from the over-all anticommunist defense system. Consequently, the power potential of the noncommunist world is divided, and is thus only partially effective in terms of Cold War pressures.

AMERICAN EFFORTS TO UNIFY THE NONCOMMUNIST WORLD

The evolution of an American policy of commitments in the Eastern Hemisphere since the end of World War II has reflected a power situation in which there exists the ever-present danger of communist domination over all or a large part of Europe, Asia, and Africa. The unification of the Eastern Hemisphere under a hostile power or combination of powers would present a serious threat to the security of the United States and the other countries of the Western Hemisphere. Approximately seven-eighths of the world's population resides in the Eastern Hemisphere; if a power or group of powers could gain dominance over these peoples and could organize them as a source of strength, then the Eastern Hemisphere might become a considerably more powerful unit than the Western Hemisphere could ever be. In addition to population, there are, of course, other elements of potential strength in the Eastern Hemisphere, such as locational advantages, agricultural and industrial resources, and economic development. Should international communism prevail throughout the area, the United States would be faced with a situation in which (1) it might be forced to sever its close economic and cultural ties with the Eastern Hemisphere; (2) it might lose its principal sources of important raw materials (cobalt, tin, chromium, mercury, manganese, and rubber); and (3) it might be forced to undertake extensive defense preparations against possible attack from a number of directions—across the Arctic and the North Atlantic, through the North Pacific against Alaska, or via the South Atlantic from Africa to Brazil. It is largely because of the various factors cited here that the United States government has refrained from adopting a "Fortress America" policy embracing the Western Hemisphere, and instead has attempted the more expensive and more difficult task of uniting the noncommunist areas of both the Eastern and Western Hemispheres against the threat of communism.

The relationship of this process of unification to the field of world political geography may best be understood within the over-all framework of geopolitics. The achievement of unity among the noncommunist countries in resistance to communist expansion is, actually, a basic element of national self-interest on the part of the United States, and indeed of Canada, Britain, France, and many other noncommunist states as well. The process of unification represents only one aspect of political control in the noncommunist world, but in terms of the global power conflict all other aspects of control are, ideally, subordinated to this process.

The operation of this particular type of geopolitics has been characterized by American pressure for the creation of an anticommunist defense system, to take precedence over many other national and international developments. The term "containment policy" has at various times been applied to this doctrine of defense. The colonial problems of western European states, territorial disputes in Latin America, economic difficulties among the countries of southern Asia—these and other "extraneous" problems, according to the so-called containment concept, should not be permitted to interfere seriously with the basic objective, namely, the establishment of a common front against the communist menace. That the overriding fear of communism does *not* exist throughout the noncommunist world to the exclusion of other problems will be made apparent in the ensuing discussion of the containment policy.

Centripetal Forces in the Noncommunist World

There are three principal centripetal forces which have served to draw parts of the noncommunist world together: (1) fear of the communist bloc, (2) the foreign aid and alliances of the United States, and (3) existing empire associations. Many governments fear the power potential and the basic objectives of the U.S.S.R. and its allies. This fear has been based largely upon past communist aggression in eastern Europe, North Korea, and North Vietnam. It has not, however, been sufficiently strong to have affected the basic policies of many states of the Eastern Hemisphere, particularly those in northern Africa and in southern Asia.

A second unifying force has been the system of military agreements and economic pacts which the United States has concluded with other noncommunist states since the end of World War II. The military agreements have been of two general types—mutual assistance pacts between the United States and some forty other states, and those establishing U.S. military bases within the borders of over a dozen foreign countries or territories. Together with these various military agreements has been the extension of large-scale American military assistance to its allies, which amounted to over $17 billion from 1946 through 1956.

The economic pacts which the United States has signed have included its military allies as well as certain other noncommunist states, such as India and Yugoslavia, which have no military treaties with the United States. In addition to the granting of foreign aid on a vast scale, the United States in recent years has sought to promote expanded trade relations between noncommunist countries, in order to bring about a mutual strengthening of their economies. At the same time the United States has sought to limit trade between the noncommunist and communist worlds, particularly in what are termed strategic commodities—armaments, transportation equipment, petroleum, copper, and rubber.

Two economic aspects of American efforts to unify the noncommunist world are of particular importance. In the first place, much of the foreign economic assistance which the United States has rendered since World War II has been based on the proposition that communism might expand not only through territorial growth outward from its Eurasian stronghold, but also as a result of internal difficulties in the noncommunist countries. A communist victory through the medium of internal revolution, or a coup d'état by a strong local communist party, may be closely related to economic conditions. Widespread discontent as a result of depressions, unemployment, and lack of confidence in a government's ability to handle economic problems can set the stage for subversion from within. Since local communist parties are generally loyal either to Moscow or to Peking, the communization of a country would in effect represent an extension of Soviet or Chinese control.

The other aspect of these efforts to effect economic unification through greatly-expanded trade relations between noncommunist states is that these efforts often have to overcome various handicaps. Tariffs and other protectionist devices, or political difficulties (as between India and Pakistan), may interfere with normal trade relations. Nationalization moves (as in the Suez area) and the repudiation of foreign debts by new governments may result in similar difficulties. Finally, the communist countries themselves are often able to disrupt trade patterns within the noncommunist world through commercial agreements and foreign loans, and through dumping commodities—oil is one example—on the world market at prices well below those of the noncommunist countries.

The third centripetal force in the noncommunist world are the various empire associations which have continued to exist, and which serve to augment the power position of such anticommunist states as the United States, Britain, France, Portugal, and Belgium. Not only can the mother countries themselves derive economic strength from their overseas territories, but the latter may also serve as sites for military bases and as key units of the general anticommunist defense system. Although the total area of the dependent territories of Western nations has been considerably reduced in recent decades, the remaining territories still represent important military assets to the global containment of communism.

Centrifugal Forces in the Noncommunist World

The principal centrifugal forces in the noncommunist world may be considered in terms of their relationships to the four basic trends mentioned earlier in this chapter. These forces, which will be discussed here as they affect American policy, are (1) nationalism, (2) imperialism, (3) economic competition, and (4) technological advances.

1. Nationalism. The force of nationalism is reflected in the desire of groups to be independent of outside control. Such a force is associated both with the breakup of empires and the establishment of independent states, as well as with the division of political units.

Nationalism, as it affects the breakup of empires, is an important centrifugal force in the noncommunist world, for as a result of empire changes some Western states have no longer been able to utilize the economic resources and the locational advantages of overseas territories. France's withdrawal from Indochina, Britain's from Burma, Ceylon, and India, and the Netherlands from Indonesia are cases in point. A serious consequence of this is that strategic bases may no longer be available for use in the international defense system. In addition, newly-independent states may give support to causes which are inimicable to the anticommunist alliance. These causes could include disarmament moves or peace proposals which clearly favor the communist states, nationalization or other economic moves which work against the interests of certain western European states, and the adoption of neutralist policies toward the Cold War power alignment, with this neutralism directed solely toward the noncommunist countries and having no apparent effect on the basic policies of the communist bloc. In other words, the achievement of independence by noncommunist states often produces a foreign policy which tends to weaken rather than strengthen the unity of the noncommunist world with respect to communist threats.

As noted on page 486 in the discussion of the first trend, newly-independent states are often faced with a variety of internal problems. The problem of economic instability, for example, may be due to a reduction of available foreign capital or of products for export, to a shortage of economic experts, to the costs involved in the struggle for independence, or merely to the increased expenses of government as a result of self-rule. In any case the state is likely to experience economic and administrative difficulties, and in its efforts to work these out it may turn for assistance to communist as well as noncommunist sources. Thus nationalism is likely to appear in the economic, as well as political and military fields in disrupting the cohesion of the noncommunist world.

The corollation between independence and problems of territorial control was mentioned on page 488. When independence is achieved there may be serious trouble over the determination of the boundaries of the self-governing state. India and Pakistan, Israel, Korea, Vietnam, and Sudan are examples of areas in which, for one reason or another, serious problems have arisen over the determination of the limits of sovereignty. These problems obviously contribute to the general divisive tendencies in the noncommunist world.

In the division of states the centrifugal effects are almost self-evident. Because of the territorial problems involved the noncommunist states—as well as Germany, Korea, and Vietnam, which have been divided into communist and noncommunist parts—face serious problems of national development. As a result, they are often more concerned with local difficulties than with the general resistance to communism, and communist propaganda and intrigue are able to play on the fears and conflicts of the contesting groups. An analysis of the effects of the division of the Indian subcontinent will point up these centrifugal tendencies.

An important feature of nationalism is the close correlation which often exists between its political and economic aspects (see also the section on Economic Competition on page 500). Many pressures for independence for a certain group (as, for example, the Moslems of India) are based on powerful economic motives. In some dependent areas of the world, even before the forces of nationalism have succeeded in bringing about self-rule, economic differences already constitute an important centrifugal element in terms of the common resistance to communist subversion. Any assessment of nationalist drives in a particular country should take into consideration the economic interests of the people—and particularly the leading elements within the group which are working toward self-rule.

2. Imperialism. This second force is associated with both the breakup of empires and the expansion of communist control. In the first instance imperialism represents the principal counterforce to nationalism, and in the formulation of foreign policy with respect to the contest between the two the United States has often been faced with difficult decisions as to what official stand it should take. On the one hand, the United States has repeatedly emphasized its desire to help groups attain their independence and to strengthen the internal structures of sovereign states. On the other hand, the United States must take into account the interests of its European allies—particularly France, the Netherlands, and to a less extent, Portugal and Great Britain. For example, in the struggle between France and Algeria, or between Britain and France on the one hand and Egypt on the other, the United States has been in a position where it must weigh carefully its commitments to each country. Obviously, these imperial interests are a divisive force in the noncommunist world.

Imperialism, as evidenced by the expansion of communist control, has also represented a centrifugal force among the noncommunist countries, for the communists in their process of territorial expansion have often been able to confuse and to disrupt their opposition. Thus the noncommunist countries may become divided among themselves both with respect to the actual existence of the threat (as in northern Vietnam) and to the proper steps to take as countermeasures against possible expansion (as with Taiwan).

In northern Vietnam communism associated itself with the struggles of the Vietnamese against the French for self-rule. Many states, particularly some of those which recently had become independent, were sympathetic to the independence struggle, and tended to minimize or to overlook completely the communist character of the resistance movement and the close ties between its leader and Communist China. Other states, such as the United States, were deeply concerned with the menace of communist expansion in southeast Asia. France, of course, desired to retain at least some aspects of control in Indochina. The resultant divergence of policies and interests on the part of the noncommunist states toward the war in Vietnam—and toward the eventual establishment of a communist regime in the north—proved to be an important centrifugal force in the common defense against communist aggression.

In the case of Taiwan the threat of communist expansion is equally as effective as a divisive force, for, on the one hand, countries such as the United States view communist dominance of the island as a grave threat to the anticommunist defense system; to this end they are willing to render military assistance to the Nationalists in their defense of Taiwan. Other states, although taking part in anticommunist defense efforts, are greatly concerned lest conflict over control of Taiwan should eventually lead to the outbreak of global warfare. Still other noncommunist countries strongly object to any efforts to defend the island against the communist menace, first, because they feel this to be an internal Chinese matter and, second, because they are antagonistic to Chiang Kai-shek's regime. Here again, then, communist expansion—or the threat of expansion—serves the purpose of dividing the noncommunist states.

A final point should be made here. Many noncommunist states—regardless of the particulars of a given condition of communist expansion or threat of expansion—are opposed to strong counteraction, since in the event of a third world war they may stand to lose their very national existence as a result of mass destruction. The communists have shown themselves adept at playing on these fears, and thereby weakening the general resistance to their territorial advances.

One aspect of communist expansion which is particularly important is that of the conflict of political ideologies. The ideological appeal of communism has on occasion preceded the actual territorial change (as in Czechoslovakia and China), and this ideological factor can prove to be a powerful weapon for communist imperialism. The conflict of ideologies, of course, may also be an important centrifugal force within the communist orbit itself. The uprisings which took place in Hungary in 1956, for example, were directed in part against the continuation of Soviet control and in part against communism itself. One of the tasks facing the United States and its allies since World War II has been to combat the ideological appeal of communism by emphasizing the advantages of democracy to the millions of uncommitted peoples of the world, who have had little or no experience with either type of political system.

3. Economic Competition. This force, as has already been pointed out, is associated with nationalism, in that the achievement of independence or the division of states are often related to the conflicts of economic interests within the areas concerned. This competition may represent an important divisive force between a mother country and its former possession, for the latter may nationalize certain fields of its economy, thereby endangering the investments of the former controlling power, or it may repudiate the debts which it legally owes to that power. Likewise, the economic competition for foreign markets—as between Britain and the Netherlands, or West Germany and Japan—although not directly associated with territorial change, is nevertheless an important centrifugal force in the noncommunist sphere.

The problem of economic competition between the communist and noncommunist blocs has been a significant factor in American foreign policy, for the communists have waged a major trade offensive designed to undermine the joint economic policies of various noncommunist states, and to orient the trade patterns of these states more closely toward the communist world. American efforts to counter this offensive have taken several forms, such as liberalized trade policies, or attempts through foreign aid to bring about an increase in trade in the noncommunist areas, rather than between communist and noncommunist countries. The close correlation which frequently exists between economic and political phenomena points to the continuing necessity of considering the economic aspects of political areas as integral factors in the over-all processes of territorial change.

4. Technological Advances. This force has affected the development of the trends in three principal forms. First, the increase in circulatory systems throughout the world has stimulated the interchange of political ideas among people. Second, technological advances have furthered the division of unclaimed areas, as a result of the discovery of new resources in these regions and the development of new methods of resource utilization. Third, technology has altered the nature of warfare, and by so doing has increased the possibilities of mass destruction. This third aspect is treated on page 501.

The increased political awareness brought on by improved circulatory systems has often resulted in popular discontent with existing conditions; and thus it has contributed to the breakup of empires, to the division of states, and to the promulgation of communist ideologies. With respect to the political partitioning of unclaimed areas, the conflicting claims of the noncommunist states represent potential sources of trouble. The Japanese-South Korean and the United States-Mexican controversies over sovereignty in the bordering seas, and the Argentine-British dispute over control of the Palmer Peninsula in Antarctica are examples of this type of conflicting claims. Although here the controversies have not been important enough to cause serious problems, increased technological advances in the sea areas and Antarctica may in time result in serious international crises, as the utilization of resources here becomes more highly developed. It is primarily for this reason that the United States has consistently held to the principle of freedom of the high seas, and has sought to bring about universal recognition of the three-mile limit of territorial seas. Similarly, it has refused to recognize political claims in Antarctica, until a careful process of political partitioning has been evolved.

TERRITORIAL DISPUTES AND THE CONCEPT OF
LIMITED AND GLOBAL WARS

Since the anticommunist defense system, which has laboriously been formed and nurtured by the United States and several of its major allies, is directed primarily against the territorial expansion of communism, the question inevitably arises as to what should be the best form of retaliation against the communist bloc in the event that such expansion does take place through territorial aggrandizement. Earlier in this chapter the factor of "persistent instability" was briefly considered, and the point was made that, with the increased destructiveness of warfare, situations might develop in which territorial problems would remain unsettled for indefinite lengths of time, in view of the frightful alternative of global war and possible mass annihilation. This obviously has a bearing on American policy with regard to limited and global warfare as counterweapons against possible communist aggression. A great number of problems arises in this connection, of which only a few may be considered here.

For our purposes global war implies a maximum war effort by all or most of the countries of the world, and a range of military operations which would cover the entire surface of the earth. In contrast with this is limited war—as exemplified by the Korean conflict—in which military activity is confined to a relatively restricted geographic area and to a less-than-total war effort, particularly on the part of the major belligerent powers.

The United States could base its policy of military resistance to communist aggression on the use of limited wars. Thus territorial aggrandizement in such areas as South Korea, Taiwan, or South Vietnam would lead to counteraction in these areas by United States forces and possibly by those of other noncommunist countries as well. If the pattern set by the Korean War should persist, the conflict would be restricted to a relatively small geographic area. However, a policy of limited wars has these principal drawbacks. In the first place, limited wars are dangerous, since they may at any time expand into global conflicts, regardless of the plans of the various belligerents. Secondly, the preparations for limited wars are expensive, particularly if the United States must also keep itself in readiness for all-out global conflict as well. Thirdly, limited wars may "bleed" the United States, without seriously affecting the Soviet Union, and—as in Korea—may end in very inconclusive decisions, which result in further expense to the United States. There are also, of course, limited wars (such as the Suez crisis of 1956), which are not directly tied to communist expansion. Here again, however, American participation in the conflicts would carry with it the disadvantages mentioned above.

The alternative to a policy based on limited wars would, of course, be one in which communist aggression would result in global conflict. This policy embraces the concept of "instant retaliation," to which there are also several disadvantages. In the first place, the "trigger point" at which retaliation is to be unleashed may be difficult to define, both for the communists and for the United States and its allies. Under conditions of "creeping communism," aggression may take place by means of small advances, no one of which may seem worthy of total conflict. If communism, for example, should gradually engulf one after another of the provinces of Laos, what would be the reaction of the United States if it followed the policy of all-out retaliation? Might not a situation develop here in which the specter of global warfare would appear to be so threatening to the United States and its allies as to immobilize them in terms of military resistance to the communists? If this were the case, then the massive-retaliation policy would have defeated its own ends.

If, on the other hand, the United States showed itself determined to carry out its massive retaliation, the threat might well be sufficient to halt any and all forms of territorial aggression by the communists. Assuming, however, that it did not and that the United States proceeded to launch what might well be World War III, what would be the position of the other noncommunist states, particularly those on whose soil the United States maintains military bases? If attacks, for example, were launched against the Soviet Union from airfields in Britain, France, or West Germany, might not these countries be drawn into a war of great devastation (particularly to them), even if their governments were opposed to retaliation in the particular situation for which it was employed? To carry this one step further, might not these same governments begin to question the advisability of continuing American bases within their borders, in the event that the United States decided to base its military thinking primarily on the massive-retaliation concept?

This dilemma of limited versus global wars as a defense against communist expansion is a basic one to United States foreign policy, as it is to those other powers which can afford to prepare for global warfare. Again, the point must be stressed that a growing threat of thermonuclear warfare and of mass destruction may well result in important modifications in the form and processes of the political partitioning of the earth's surface.

INDEX

PRINTED IN U.S.A.